OPERATIONS RESEARCH SOCIETY
OF AMERICA

Publications in Operations Research

Number 10

PUBLICATIONS IN OPERATIONS RESEARCH

Operations Research Society of America

Editor for Publications in Operations Research
DAVID B. HERTZ

No. 1. QUEUES, INVENTORIES AND MAINTENANCE
Philip M. Morse

No. 2. FINITE QUEUING TABLES
L. G. Peck and R. N. Hazelwood

No. 3. EFFICIENCY IN GOVERNMENT THROUGH SYSTEMS ANALYSIS
Roland N. McKean

No. 4. A COMPREHENSIVE BIBLIOGRAPHY ON OPERATIONS RESEARCH
Operations Research Group, Case Institute

No. 5. PROGRESS IN OPERATIONS RESEARCH, VOLUME I
Edited by Russell L. Ackoff

No. 6. STATISTICAL MANAGEMENT OF INVENTORY SYSTEMS
Harvey M. Wagner

No. 7. PRICE, OUTPUT, AND INVENTORY POLICY
Edwin S. Mills

No. 8. A COMPREHENSIVE BIBLIOGRAPHY ON OPERATIONS RESEARCH, 1957–1958
Operations Research Group, Case Institute

No. 9. PROGRESS IN OPERATIONS RESEARCH, VOLUME II
David B. Hertz and Roger T. Eddison

No. 10. DECISION AND VALUE THEORY
Peter C. Fishburn

DECISION AND VALUE THEORY

PETER C. FISHBURN

CASE INSTITUTE OF TECHNOLOGY

JOHN WILEY & SONS, INC., NEW YORK · LONDON · SYDNEY

10 9 8 7 6 5 4 3

To Janet

PREFACE

The subject of this book* is a personalistic prescriptive theory of choice for individual decisions. Since the introductory chapter gives an outline of our studies, I shall be brief at this point.

Our first task is to say what we mean by a decision situation. In this respect I have woven my formulation from the fabrics provided by R. A. Ackoff,† writing in the vein of operations research, and from L. E. Savage,‡ whose approach to decision theory characterizes the modern subjectivistic or personalistic approach in statistics. As we shall argue in Chapter 3, there is more than one way to view the general decision structure, but the different viewpoints are equivalent.

The decision models dealt with in the book are models of the expected relative values or expected utilities of strategies, with the prescriptive criterion of choice being maximization of the decision maker's expected relative value. I have used the term "relative value" in this volume in place of "utility" (of the von Neumann-Morgenstern or Savage variety) since I feel it is more descriptive of the construct it represents. I do this, of course, at the risk of irritating those who prefer the more popular term "utility."

In our discussion of the decision maker's relative values for the various consequences which might result from the strategy he adopts and

* Written under Contract NONR-1141 (11) entered into between the Office of Naval Research and Case Institute of Technology.

† Churchman, Ackoff, and Arnoff, *Introduction to Operations Research,* John Wiley & Sons, New York, 1957.

‡ Savage, *Foundations of Statistics,* John Wiley & Sons, New York, 1954.

implements, we shall consider a variety of different value measures including ordinal rankings, metric rankings, and bounded interval measures. The reason for this is quite simple. Experience has shown that it is unrealistic to suppose that one can obtain a precise interval measure of utility or relative value in most decision situations. Therefore we will often have to make do with some less precise information about the decision maker's true relative values. The other measures considered provide less information than the interval measure but are often easier to obtain.

Similarly, when we consider the decision maker's probabilities of consequences, given strategies (or his probability distribution on the states of the world in the statistical formulation), we shall discuss rankings and other comparative probability measures as well as bounded interval measures for probability.

Having presented this array of different types of measures, we then go on to develop theorems that explain what conclusions one can or cannot make on the basis of the information about values and probabilities with respect to the expected relative values of strategies.

I have taken the liberty to include, although it might have been omitted, a discussion of the foundations of probability. This discussion, in Chapter 5, includes the extramathematical interpretations of probability offered by the classical writers, the modern school of objectivistic statisticians, the logical positivists, and the decision-oriented and nondecision-oriented subjectivistic schools. The conclusion presented on the basis of this discussion is that the only interpretation of probability that allows for nonambiguity in a prescriptive or normative theory of decision is a decision-oriented subjectivistic interpretation.

The latter part of the work is concerned with the concept of independence or additivity in value theory. There we consider independence in the value-theoretic sense in multivariate cases and its effect upon a variety of decision situations, ranging from decisions made under certainty to stochastic nonhomogeneous sequential decision processes.

In the main I have restricted our considerations to finite sets of strategies and finite sets of consequences, although Chapter 8 deals with infinite outcome spaces. Basic algebra is the only mathematical prerequisite for most of the book.

The research leading to this volume covered a 3-year period while I was on the staff of the Case Institute of Technology Operations Research Group. So that the book may be more useful if used for teaching purposes, which it was at Case, exercises have been included at the end of each chapter. These are designed to illustrate the theory and methods and, in some cases, to extend the development beyond that given in the text.

Since this book has grown out of a continuing research program in decision theory, it must be regarded as tentative. In each successive draft I have eliminated what I considered to be wrong or objectionable developments, and I have tried to clarify those that appeared desirable for presentation, if not for total acceptance.

I hope that the reader will find, in what remains, something of value in guiding his own work and decision-making activities.

McLean, Virginia   Peter C. Fishburn
July, 1964

ACKNOWLEDGMENTS

Were it not for the encouragement and guidance of my teacher, Russell L. Ackoff, this book would not have been written. I am indebted to him for planting the seeds from which this work grew, for his generous disposition of my time to permit the book to come to its tentative completion, and for his aid in securing support for the research.

I also owe a debt of gratitude to J. S. Minas, who acted as Associate Editor on behalf of the Operations Research Society of America for this volume, and to my students at Case Institute of Technology, who suffered through an earlier draft of the book, for their many and invaluable contributions to the final draft. Gad Nathan deserves special mention in this latter respect. I would also like to thank the Publications Committee of ORSA and David B. Hertz, Editor of this series, for their guidance and decision to undertake publication of this book.

For financial support I am deeply grateful to the Office of Naval Research, which under Contract NONR-1141(11) provided the majority of funds for this project, from its inception to completion. For the portion of assistance not covered by the ONR Contract, I am indebted to the generosity of the Case Institute of Technology Research Fund.

I would like to thank the following for permission to quote from their publications: Oxford University Press; The Institute of Management Sciences (*Management Science*); The Macmillan Company; Humanities Press Inc.; Charles Griffin and Co., Ltd.; University of California Press; Chelsea Publishing Company; Princeton University Press; Yale University Press; Harvard University Press; *Annals of Mathematics;* Prentice-Hall, Inc.; D. Van Nostrand Company, Inc.; The University of Chicago

Press; Dover Publications, Inc.; Stanford University Press; and John Wiley & Sons, Inc.

I also offer my sincerest thanks to Grace White for her superb supervision of the preparation of the successive drafts of the manuscript, and to Janet, my most valuable critic, for her wondrous patience during the several years this work was in progress.

P. C. F.

CONTENTS

OPERATIONS RESEARCH SOCIETY
OF AMERICA

Publications in Operations Research
Number 10

Chapter 1

INTRODUCTION

1.1 POSITION AND INTENTIONS

The basic tenet upon which this book is based has been pointed out by E. A. Singer, Jr. Ackoff (1963) has stated this clearly and concisely:

Philosophers have long searched for some one desire which all men (past, present, and even the future) have, do, or will possess: *the universal wish.* Ironically, children have long ago discovered it. Most of them observe that if they had one wish, they would wish that all their wishes come true. The recently deceased American Philosopher, E. A. Singer, put this "childish" observation into more sophisticated form and sketched a way of life based on it (1936 and 1948). His fundamental observation was that one cannot desire anything without simultaneously desiring an increased ability to attain it (even if what the person desires is to desire nothing). Thus, the ability to fulfill all desires (i.e., *power* in its nonderogatory sense) can be regarded as a universal objective, an ideal of mankind.

Hereafter anything desired by an individual will be called a *goal* or *objective.* This book is concerned with the efficient pursuit of objectives.

When doubts arise in an individual's mind and he is uncertain as to how best to pursue his objectives, then the elements of indecision and subsequent decision begin to form. This book is concerned with these elements and with the problem of transformation or transition from a state of indecision into a state of resolution or solution. In the theory there are two major steps involved in this transition. When an individual is indecisive about the most effective means for pursuing his objectives, his doubts may arise from either being uncertain as to which of a recognized set of ways is best to follow or in believing that there might be a better way which he has been unable to discover (or both). The first major step, therefore, is to recognize, discover, or construct ways in which

1

the individual may proceed (such ways are called courses of action and strategies),[1] and which *a priori* appear to provide him with efficient means for pursuing his objectives.

The second major step is to evaluate alternative strategies by means of a criterion of choice among strategies and to determine the "best" strategy for the individual to follow. The criterion of choice adopted in this theory is maximization of the individual's expected relative value. Just what is meant by "expected relative value" will be discussed briefly in Section 1.4 and developed more completely in Chapter 3. At this point let it suffice to say that the individual (or decision maker) is an integral and indispensable component in the process of evaluation, since we require his value judgments in order to help him resolve his indecision or find a solution to his problem.

This book is not primarily a book about ethics, although ethical implications are present in any theory of decision. It is postulated that an individual has objectives or goals, and that he is often required to make a choice among alternative strategies when (initially) uncertain as to which strategy is best for pursuing his objectives. We shall not speculate on what the individual's objectives ought to be: for example, whether he ought to seek Nirvana, or attempt to live the Golden Rule, or act according to Kant's categorical imperative, or seek pleasure, or live as long as he can, or make as much money as he can, or serve God, and so forth. We are concerned with the efficient pursuit of objectives and with methods of analysis which might be useful in doing this.

In the prescriptive decision model used here, measures of value, worth, or desirability (or whatever one wishes to call it) will apply to concrete consequences of decision, not to vague objectives or motivating desires. Judgments of relative values of consequences are considered relevant and useful. We reject the position that an individual's values can be revealed only through decisions already made. Needless to say, it is assumed that a more valuable consequence (to an individual) reflects a more efficient means for pursuing a set of objectives, although we are not prepared to speculate to what extent and in what way an individual's objectives determine his values.

Every decision situation is unique. Value or worth has meaning only in connection with a human agent with a purpose, and is relative to this agent within the context of a decision situation. Although we subscribe to these postulates, the reader need not do this in order to find something useful in the following pages.

---

[1] In the terms adopted in this book, a prescriptive course of action is a special kind of strategy. In general, a strategy includes several courses of action in its definition, along with other elements. This will be discussed in the next chapter.

Finally, it should also be mentioned that, in using the prescriptive criterion of maximization of expected relative value, we are asserting, in effect, that an individual ought to adopt a strategy which maximizes his expected relative value. Such a strategy is best (for the individual) or optimal, by definition. It is not assumed that the decision maker always selects an optimal strategy. If he is considering adoption and implementation of a particular strategy and wishes to test this strategy for optimality against other admissible strategies, we have provided him, by means of the theory, with recourse to a method for making this test. The main portion of this book is devoted to this theory of reflection and cognitive analysis on the part of the decision maker in an attempt to arrive at a satisfactory or perhaps even best strategy for adoption and implementation.

1.2 HISTORICAL COMMENTS AND TRADITIONAL DECISION THEORY

Since the origin of the species, men have been making decisions, and other men have been telling them how they either make or should make decisions. Numerous decision and value theories have been developed and each has had its share of proponents.[2] Within the past two decades a large body of material, written mostly by economists, mathematicians, statisticians, social scientists, and behavioral scientists, has been published on the subjects of decision theory and value theory.[3] A significant portion of this material deals with various theories of value and expected value, some of which are embedded in a decision structure. Edwards' (1954c) review article on the modern history of utility theory is recommended for readers unfamiliar with recent trends in this field. Churchman (1961b) has reviewed decision and value theory in its relation to operations research. In this he explains one meaning of decision and value theory, comments on several surveys of decision theory, presents criticism (in the form of alternative approaches) of what he calls "traditional decision theory," and discusses the problem of verifying a decision theory.

Our interpretation of Churchman's use of the phrase "traditional decision theory" runs as follows (highly simplified). Many operations research practitioners, certainly not all, believe that all relevant "cost" and "profit" data required for an operations research study should be supplied to them by the organization sponsoring the research (usually from the accounting department) and is to be taken as given in the situation.

---

[2] For a short history, see Smith (1956), Part II. Sahakian (1963) is highly recommended for a survey of ethical system and philosophies of right action.

[3] See, for example, the bibliography in Churchman (1961b, pp. 60–64), and in Savage (1954). See also Luce and Raiffa (1957, Chapters 13 and 14).

From these data, whether collected by the research worker himself or supplied to him by the organization, the practitioner constructs well-behaved cost and profit functions, combines them linearly into an effectiveness model or decision model (total expected cost model, net profit model, or similar model); then, by well-developed algorithms and mathematical techniques (differential calculus, calculus of variations, mathematical programming, etc.), he proceeds to solve the decision model for the "optimal" values of the variables appearing therein which are subject to control by the organization. Usually the decision maker plays a passive role in this situation, and there is little connection between research worker and decision maker. The latter is often far removed from the research, except that he may determine the fate of the recommendations made by the research workers.

The fundamental respect in which the theory in this book differs from the traditional theory has already been stated. The theory presented here is personalistic; the decision maker is an indispensable component in several phases of the research, including the phase of solving the decision model. Although the traditional approach is often useful, it is severely limited. It is hoped that the theory presented here (or one similar to it) will open up new horizons to the operations researcher or management scientist (or whatever one wishes to call him) which have heretofore been all but ignored in research approaches to decision problems.[4]

Operations research makes the claim that, by pitting the forces of research against large-scale problems, the decision maker (manager, president, general, etc.) will be freed to devote his time to other tasks. The scientist may be better prepared and able to deal with the analysis and synthesis of complex operations and systems than is the manager, but the manager is still the individual who must act upon the evidence and recommendations offered by the scientist. Managers have been careful to insure and protect their decision-making prerogatives, and, for the most part, management scientists have been just as careful not to infringe upon these prerogatives. Although the theory of this book is more intimately involved with the decision maker than is traditional decision theory, it should be clear that we intend no infringement on the individual's freedom to act as he sees fit. Like traditional decision theory, the aim of a more personalistic normative theory is to guide the individual toward more effective decisions.

When it is said that the scientist has freed the manager to devote some of his energies to other tasks, it is sometimes implied that these other tasks

---

[4] See Churchman and Ackoff (1954) for the outline of an approach that has certain similarities to that presented here. Their article was partly responsible for motivating the research that led to the writing of this book.

are primarily decision-making activities, often of a nature with which management scientists would rather not be concerned. Part of the reason for this is that management scientists are, for the most part, not presently equipped to deal with many aspects of decision making (particularly where the decision maker's personal values are intimately involved), and have developed certain unwritten ground rules which tend to delimit the kinds of problems which are fair game for the traditional decision theoretic approach. Another reason is that many managers simply do not want the management scientist to be a party to some of their decision-making processes, particularly those processes which are "personal" and "private."

Many persons who read this book or parts thereof may come to the conclusion that they would not particularly care to have another individual (scientist, e.g.) analyze some of their problems by the methods presented herein. To do so would constitute an invasion of their private and personal thoughts and judgments. However, they might consider employing these methods to guide their own decision making; that is, they could be both client and consultant in these more "private" matters. This, of course, is nothing new. We all make decisions we would not care to have analyzed before the fact by anyone but ourselves.[5] It is the method of analysis, not so much as who performs the analysis, that we are concerned with. When we speak of the research worker and individual or consultant and client, it is to be understood that these two may be the same person.

Along with these comments we may note that there have been good reasons why operations research (or management science, etc.) has not made more application of various decision-value theories thus far developed. Besides the problems arising from the relationship between scientist and manager, many management scientists do not understand the language of these theories since most of them have arisen in other disciplines. Perhaps more important are the restrictiveness of the assumptions of these theories and the impracticability of obtaining the data required to make use of them. We do not propose to do away with these difficulties, but believe that they may be alleviated in some cases.

The methods in this book are not recommended for all decision problems faced by an individual. That would be ridiculous. The methods discussed generally require a significant amount of the decision maker's time for their effective use. For this reason (if no other), these methods should be employed only when the decision maker feels that (1) the possible consequences which may result from his decision are of a nature critical enough to warrant the expenditure of his time and effort in employing

[5] Except, perhaps, by some implicitly trusted friend or adviser, be he minister, psychoanalyst, spouse, or someone else.

such methods and (2) that any delay or postponement in making the major decision caused by such expenditure of time and effort will more than pay for itself in the benefits to be gained by performing the analysis. In an individual's personal life, such decision situations might involve the selection of a new job, the purchase of a home, the purchase of a life insurance contract, an important marital problem, and the like. Individuals who have responsibility for making decisions in some organization, be it business, industrial, governmental, military, etc., should be able to identify the more important decision problems that they have faced in the recent past or are likely to face in the future.

1.3 MODERN UTILITY THEORY

Among the more popular decision-value theories that have been developed in recent years, two stand out as the most popular. The first of these is by von Neumann and Morgenstern (1947), the second by Wald (1950). The theory of games,[6] as developed by von Neumann and Morgenstern, has had virtually no practical application. Statistical decision theory[7] (Wald), which has recast statistics as the science of decision making under uncertainty, has fared little better. Although there are a number of reasons for lack of application by practitioners (statisticians as well as management scientists), it would be impossible to cover all of them without going into their structures in detail. We shall not attempt to do this, but do wish to make one observation concerning the difficulty. Brownlee (1960) has put it as follows:

> Statistics is frequently defined as the science of making wise decisions in the presence of uncertainty. To cite Savage's example in his review (1951) of Wald's book (1950), the decision to be made may be whether to take an umbrella on one's trip to the office. This approach requires a knowledge of the relative costs of carrying an umbrella when the day turns out to be fine and of getting wet through failing to carry an umbrella when the day turns out to be wet. The practical usefulness of this approach has been severely hindered by the rareness with which one can actually estimate with any confidence the cost functions. Whether this obstacle can be circumvented sufficiently to bring this decision-theory approach into common use remains to be seen [p. 64].

In statistical decision theory, as in the theory of games, "losses" or "profits" are measured in theory via the individual's utility function[8] (or the individuals' utility functions). By "utility function" we mean a real-valued function whose domain of definition is a specific set and

---

[6] For a more recent account and survey, see Luce and Raiffa (1957).

[7] An elementary account is given by Chernoff and Moses (1959). The most exhaustive treatment thus far known to the author has been rendered by Raiffa and Schlaifer (1961).

whose range lies in the real numbers, where the functional values are unique except for an origin and unit of measure. For example, if Ω is the set of arguments of the utility function with elements x, y, $\ldots$, and if $\phi(x)$ for all $x \in \Omega$[9] is a utility function with specified origin and unit measurement, then $a\phi(x) + b$, with $a > 0$, is also a utility function. Although the idea of a utility function unique up to an increasing linear transformation appeared in the literature (of economics, primarily) long before their book appeared, von Neumann and Morgenstern (1947) were the first to lay down a system of axioms of "rational behavior" that, if satisfied by an individual, would guarantee the existence of a utility function for that individual. Since then, other systems of axioms that yield a utility function have been presented.[10]

The von Neumann-Morgenstern Axioms

It seems advisable to pause here and take a brief look at the von Neumann-Morgenstern postulates as one basis for obtaining utilities (or relative values), since the value-theoretic development in this book relates, in part, to their postulates.

The primitive notions of the axioms are: (1) A set Ω of elements $w, x, y, \ldots$; (2) a binary relation $\gtrsim$ over Ω; (3) the set Π of all real numbers $\alpha, \beta, \ldots$ strictly between 0 and 1 ($0 < \alpha < 1$); and (4) an operation $(\alpha, x; 1 - \alpha, y)$ such that $(\alpha, x; 1 - \alpha, y) \in \Omega$ if and only if $x, y \in \Omega$ and $\alpha \in \Pi$.

With $x, y \in \Omega$, we shall use the following definitions: (1) $x > y$ if and only if $x \gtrsim y$ and not $y \gtrsim x$; (2) $y < x$ if and only if $x > y$; and (3) $x \sim y$ if and only if $x \gtrsim y$ and $y \gtrsim x$.

In the context of a decision situation, the primitives are interpreted as follows. The elements of Ω are the entities the worth of which to the individual we wish to measure. The elements of Π are interpreted as probabilities. Read:

$x \gtrsim y$ as: y is not preferred to x by the individual.

$x > y$ as: x is preferred to y by the individual.

$x \sim y$ as: The individual is indifferent between x and y; or, the individual considers x and y equally desirable (or undesirable).

$(\alpha, x; 1 - \alpha, y)$ as: The combination of x with probability α, y with probability $1 - \alpha$; or, the gamble from which x results with probability α

---

[8] In some renderings of statistical decision theory, "losses" and "profits" (negative losses) are determined in the manner of traditional decision theory. As an example, see Weiss (1961).

[9] $\in$ means "belongs to" or "is a member of the set."

[10] See, for example, Savage (1954) and Suppes and Winet (1955), and Section 5.6 in this book.

and y results with probability $1 - \alpha$ (one and only one of the two entities resulting).

With the understanding that w, x, y, $(\alpha, x; 1 - \alpha, y)$, ..., are elements of Ω, and α and β are elements of Π, the axioms are:

1. For any two x, y, one and only one of the following holds: $x > y$, $y > x$, $x \sim y$.
2. If $x > w$ and $w > y$, then $x > y$.
3. If $x > y$, then $x > (\alpha, x; 1 - \alpha, y)$ for any α.
4. If $x < y$, then $x < (\alpha, x; 1 - \alpha, y)$ for any α.
5. If $x > w > y$, then there is an α such that $(\alpha, x; 1 - \alpha, y) > w$.
6. If $x < w < y$, then there is an α such that $(\alpha, x; 1 - \alpha, y) < w$.
7. $(\alpha, x; 1 - \alpha, y) \sim (1 - \alpha, y; \alpha, x)$.
8. $(\alpha, (\beta, x; 1 - \beta, y); 1 - \alpha, y) \sim (\alpha\beta, x; 1 - \alpha\beta, y)$.
9. If $x \sim y$, then $(\alpha, x; 1 - \alpha, w) \sim (\alpha, y; 1 - \alpha, w)$ for any α and w.

These axioms are sufficient to guarantee the existence of a real-valued function ϕ defined on Ω such that

$$x > y \qquad \text{if and only if} \qquad \phi(x) > \phi(y), \qquad\qquad (1.1)$$

$$\phi(\alpha, x; 1 - \alpha, y) = \alpha\phi(x) + (1 - \alpha)\,\phi(y). \qquad\qquad (1.2)$$

These two properties are called the utility function properties. Moreover, if ϕ and ψ are two functions over Ω that satisfy (1.1) and (1.2), then they are related by

$$\psi(x) = a\phi(x) + b, \qquad a > 0 \quad \text{for all } x \in \Omega;$$

i.e., a (von Neumann-Morgenstern) utility function is unique up to a positive linear transformation.

Interpretations of the axioms follow:

1. Any two elements of Ω are directly comparable. Either one is preferred to the other or the two are equally desirable (or undesirable).
2. The preference relation ($>$) is transitive. If you prefer milk to tea and tea to coffee, then you prefer milk to coffee.
3. If x is preferred over y, then x is preferred over any gamble involving x and y. If you prefer \$10 to \$5, then you prefer the certain option of receiving \$10 to any gamble that yields \$10 or \$5 (but not both).
4. This is the dual of (3) with the obvious interpretation.
5. If x is preferable to w and w preferable to y, then there is some gamble involving x and y that is preferable to w.
6. This is the dual of (5).
7. The arrangement of alternatives in a gamble is irrelevant, or the order in which the alternatives in a gamble are presented or named is irrelevant.
8. Compound gambles can be decomposed by the rules of the probability calculus without affecting their desirability.

9. If x appears in any gamble, and if y is indifferent to x, then the gamble obtained from the original gamble by substituting y in place of x is indifferent to the original gamble.

Utility function property (1.1) states that utility is monotonically increasing with preferability or desirability. If x is preferred to y, then the utility of x exceeds the utility of y, i.e., $\phi(x) > \phi(y)$. Property (1.2) states that the utility of a gamble equals the expected utility of that gamble, or that utilities combine with probabilities according to the rules of mathematical expectations. If we were to form the composite gamble $(\alpha_1, x_1; \alpha_2, x_2; \ldots; \alpha_n, x_n)$, where $\alpha_1 + \alpha_2 + \ldots + \alpha_n = 1$, then

$$\phi(\alpha_1, x_1; \alpha_2, x_2; \ldots; \alpha_n, x_n) = \sum_{i=1}^{n} \alpha_i \phi(x_i).$$

Since the original presentation of the axioms of "rational behavior," investigators in several fields (primarily psychology and economics) have made a frontal attack on them. They have been subject to restatement in a variety of ways, and many experiments have been performed to test their credibility.[11] Some who have taken issue with the Archimedean postulate (axioms 5 and 6) have developed a theory of multidimensional utility.[12] Churchman (1961a) has given one of the most thorough (if not *the* most thorough) criticisms of these behavioral suppositions. Ackoff (1962) notes several deficiencies:

> The von Neumann-Morgenstern procedure assumes that the subject knows what the true probabilities are; that is, that the "chances" associated with the various outcomes which he believes to exist correspond exactly with the "objective" probabilities. ... There is considerable experimental evidence to indicate that this is not true in general. ...
>
> Certain practical considerations in the use of such a measuring procedure are involved. The choices presented to the decision maker are difficult for him to comprehend. In addition, the procedure is awkward to extend to more than three objectives and becomes increasingly difficult as the number of objectives increases [pp. 84–85].

If these axioms are used as guides for consistency in judgment in measuring an individual's utilities or relative values for use in a normative decision theory, it should be noted that they impute to the individual exceptionally fine powers of discriminatory judgment, a supposition which defies common sense and which behavioral experiments have been refuting for years.[13]

[11] See, for example, Preston and Baratta (1948), Mosteller and Nogee (1951), Papandreou (1953), Edwards (1953, 1954a, 1954b), and Davidson, Suppes, and Siegel (1957).

[12] A good account is given in Thrall, Coombs, and Davis (1954).

[13] von Neumann and Morgenstern were quite aware of this.

1.4 PREVIEW

As we shall see, the value-theoretic development in this book has
certain similarities to the von Neumann-Morgenstern utility theory. By
offering the limited criticism given above, we have, in a sense, begun a
criticism of the value theory presented herein. As we proceed, additional
criticisms will be raised.

Our approach to value theory begins by introducing, as a theoretic
device, the notion of a real-valued function (to be known as the value
function)[14] which assigns a number to each member of a finite set of mutually exclusive elements (to be known as consequences), where the numbers
so assigned (to be known as relative values of consequences) are unique
up to an increasing linear transformation.

As will be shown (in Chapter 3), the requirement that the relative values
of consequences be unique up to an increasing linear transformation is
necessary to have a consistent (unambiguous) theory. The reason for
not requiring complete uniqueness of relative values follows from the
position that there is no natural definition of zero value or of a unit of
value (we can pick an origin and unit measure as we please for the value
function).

Having introduced the notion of relative values of consequences
(implying that we consider it meaningful and useful to quantify the
qualitative notion of importance or desirability), we then turn to the problem
of measurement. To discuss the issues involved (and our stand with
respect to them), it will be necessary to give body to the notion "decision
situation" (in Chapter 2), so that there will be a meaningful contextual
reference as a basis for the discussion. In Chapter 4 various methods of
measuring values, and the measures so obtained will be presented. With

---

[14] "Value" will be used in four different ways in this book, as follows:

1. Numerical quantification, such as used in "real-valued function" and "the
values a real variable can take on."

2. To describe the possible realizations that a variable can assume, such as "the
values which the variable 'pet' can take on are dog, horse, and cat," "the values
which the variable X can assume are $x_1, x_2, \ldots$." Here "values of a variable" may
often be taken equivalent to "elements of a set." Usage (1) is a special case of (2)
when the values are numbers.

3. To denote a qualitative impression or expression of worth, importance, or
desirability, as used in "I value my life very highly" and "the value of a dollar."

4. To denote a quantification of the concept of worth, importance, or desirability.
When speaking of the "value function" as above, we mean "value" in the sense of
(4). It might be more proper to say "real-valued value function" instead of just
"value function," but the former phrase is too cumbersome. In addition, the term
"relative value" will always be used in the sense of (4).

If the meaning of "value" does not seem clear from the context, clarification will
be offered.

respect to the basic expected-value decision model to be developed in Chapter 3, the measures of value presented will include the ordinal measure, which provides a ranking of relative values on a "greater than or equal to" basis, several ordered metric measures which rank differences between relative values, and three bounded interval measures which give upper and lower bounds for ratios of relative value differences.   It will be shown in Chapters 6 and 7 that the measures of relative values vary in their ability to yield a complete solution to the expected-value decision model.   It will be noted that, in general, the assumptions required for the value measures considered will become stronger and less palatable (we believe) as we proceed from the least powerful measure discussed (i.e., the partial ordinal measure) to the most powerful (i.e., the interval measure). Roughly, one measure is more powerful than another if the former gives more information about the magnitudes of the relative values of consequences than the latter; that is, if the former is more likely to permit solution of the decision model than the latter.

In the theory, the decision model is used as a *prescriptive model*, as opposed to a *predictive model*.   Solving the decision model consists of finding a strategy for action the expected relative value of which is at least as great as the expected relative value of any other strategy in a specified set.   The prescriptive criterion of choice of a strategy will be maximization of the decision maker's total expected relative value. Measures of relative values to be used for the purpose of prescribing[15] a strategy for a decision maker to follow will be based upon judgments by the decision maker concerning the relative worth or desirability of the various consequences which may result from his decision (i.e., from his selection and implementation of a strategy).

To have a useful prescriptive decision theory, it is generally necessary to have in addition a usable theory of probability.   In the general theory, the consequences of decision will be structured so that they comprise an exclusive and exhaustive set; that is, one and only one consequence will result from the strategy adopted by the decision maker.   Which consequence will result if a given strategy is adopted will seldom be determinable before the strategy is carried through, the actual resultant consequence being determined in part by the occurrence of chance events.   In other words, uncertainties in the environment usually render it impossible to identify beforehand the particular consequence that will result from the decision.   To deal with such uncertainties it is useful to introduce, for a given strategy, the notion of a real-valued set function (to be called the probability function) which assigns a number to each member of a finite

---

[15] To prescribe a strategy is to advise the use of that strategy by the decision maker in pursuing his goals or objectives.   This will be considered at length in Chapter 3.

set of exclusive and exhaustive consequences, where the numbers so assigned (to be known as probabilities of consequences) are nonnegative and sum to one.

There will be a probability function for each strategy. Similar to relative values of consequences, probabilities of consequences are not observables; that is, we do not observe relative values or probabilities in nature. Hence, to obtain measures of probabilities, it is necessary to construct a theory or theories which transform statements and/or observations and/or judgments into a measure of probabilities. The extramathematical interpretation of "probability" in this book is a subjectivistic or personalistic one, similar to Savage's (1954) conception. The discussion of probability will continue in Section 3.1 and be treated in more detail in Chapter 5.

It is the purpose of the next chapter to give form to the concepts *strategy* and *consequence*. Both of these include the more basic notions of *course of action* and *outcome*, which, in turn, depend upon the notions of *action variable* and *outcome variable*. Without attempting to define all these terms at this point, it is assumed that the reader has gained enough initial insight about strategies and consequences to lend some meaning to the expected relative value of a strategy, which serves as a base for the decision model. The *expected relative value of a strategy* is simply a weighted sum of the relative values of the consequences, where the weights are the respective probabilities of the consequences occurring if the strategy is adopted and used by the decision maker. Symbolically,

$$E(S_i) = P_{i1}V_1 + P_{i2}V_2 + \ldots + P_{ir}V_r,$$

where $E(S_i)$ = expected relative value of strategy S_i,

P_{ij} = probability that the jth consequence in a set of r consequences will occur if strategy S_i is adopted by the decision maker, with $\sum_{j=1}^{r} P_{ij} = 1$,

V_j = relative value of the jth consequence to the decision maker, $j = 1, \ldots, r$.

The *decision maker's total expected relative value* is defined by

$$EV(\mathbf{I}) = \sum_{i=1}^{t} C_i E(S_i)$$

where $EV(\mathbf{I})$ = decision maker's total expected relative value,

C_i = probability that the decision maker will adopt strategy S_i, used in a prescriptive sense (to be discussed in Section 3.8), where

$$\sum_{i=1}^{t} C_i = 1, \quad C_i \geqslant 0, \quad i = 1, \ldots, t.$$

One research objective is to determine, insofar as practicable, a vector $(C_1, C_2, \ldots, C_t)$ that maximizes $EV(\mathbf{I})$. The vector $\mathbf{C} = (C_1, \ldots, C_t)$, with nonnegative components summing to one, is the *controllable variable*.

The theory discussed here applies primarily to decision situations in which the number of strategies and number of consequences are both finite. One reason for this is caused by the manner in which relative values are derived from the decision maker's preference judgments. Even when certain variables in a decision situation can take on an infinite number of values, it is possible to structure the strategies and consequences so that their number will be finite. This will be briefly discussed in Chapter 8.

Beginning with Chapter 9, we shall consider independence of variables in the relative value sense, and go on to investigate the effect that this *valuewise independence* has upon the decision model, the measurement of relative values and probabilities, and the analysis of the alternative forms of the basic decision model. Chapters 10, 11, and 12 carry out the latter program.

One of the main reasons for considering the assumption of valuewise independence among variables is that it can make many large, initially unmanageable problems capable of being analyzed economically. As an example, a problem as originally formulated that contains over one trillion (say, 2^{40}) consequences requiring value measurement may be reduced by invoking the assumption of independence to a problem that has as few as 41 entities requiring value measurement. Another very important reason is that comparative value judgments may be much easier to make under independence. This will be discussed in Section 4.3 and continued in Chapter 9.

To give the reader an idea of what is meant by independence of variables in the relative value sense, a simplified example seems appropriate at this point. It will be obvious that the example may be complicated in many ways by considering factors other than the two given.

EXAMPLE. In the state of Pennsyltucky, U.S.A., a group of citizens has succeeded in placing a certain issue on the ballot for the coming November election. This issue is opposed by a particular organization which is willing to allocate a portion of its treasury for advertising and propaganda against the issue in an effort to defeat it. The head of the organization (decision maker) has the responsibility of specifying the amount of money to put into this effort. Suppose he is concerned with this amount and with whether or not the issue is defeated in the election.

In terms to be used later, there is one *action variable*

X = amount of money allocated in the effort to defeat the issue,

and one *outcome variable*

Y = fate of the issue as decided by the election.

Suppose the decision maker plans to spend either \$100,000 or \$300,000 or \$500,000 in the campaign.   Assume further that he will use an advertising agency to run the campaign.   He therefore has three *admissible strategies*, S_1 = spend 100 G's, S_2 = spend 300 G's, and S_3 = spend 500 G's.   Depending on the strategy adopted and implemented, one of six *consequences* will occur:

$$o_1 = (\$100{,}000 \text{ spent, issue defeated}),$$
$$o_2 = (\$300{,}000 \text{ spent, issue defeated}),$$
$$o_3 = (\$500{,}000 \text{ spent, issue defeated}),$$
$$o_4 = (\$100{,}000 \text{ spent, issue passed}),$$
$$o_5 = (\$300{,}000 \text{ spent, issue passed}),$$
$$o_6 = (\$500{,}000 \text{ spent, issue passed}).$$

Each consequence is an ordered pair (x, y) with $x \in X$, $y \in Y$.   That is, o_j has the form $o_j = (x, y)$.

In this situation one might expect that

$$o_1 > o_2 > o_3 > o_4 > o_5 > o_6, \tag{1.3}$$

where "$>$" means "is preferred to" or "is more desirable than."   If V denotes the (real-valued) value function, the ordering (1.3) gives

$$V_1 > V_2 > V_3 > V_4 > V_5 > V_6, \tag{1.4}$$

where

$$V_j = V(o_j).$$

If the two variables X and Y are *valuewise independent*, then

$$V(x, y) = V_X(x) + V_Y(y) \tag{1.5}$$

where V_X is a value function defined over the three amounts 100 G's, 300 G's, and 500 G's, and V_Y is a value function defined over Y.   The origin of each value function on the right-hand side of (1.5) may be arbitrarily specified, but the two must have a common unit measure (or a common scale unit).

Supposing (1.5) to hold, we may define

$$\begin{array}{ll} V_X(\$100{,}000 \text{ spent}) = v_1, & V_Y(\text{issue defeated}) = 1, \quad (1.6) \\ V_X(\$300{,}000 \text{ spent}) = v_2, & V_Y(\text{issue passed}) = 0. \\ V_X(\$500{,}000 \text{ spent}) = 0, & \end{array}$$

In this, the two origins and unit measure have been specified. With (1.5) and (1.6),

$$\begin{aligned}
V(o_1) &= v_1 + 1, \\
V(o_2) &= v_2 + 1, \\
V(o_3) &= 1, \\
V(o_4) &= v_1, \\
V(o_5) &= v_2, \\
V(o_6) &= 0.
\end{aligned} \tag{1.7}$$

The ranking (1.4), assuming (1.5) and using (1.7), is equivalent to $1 > v_1 > v_2 > 0$. Letting

$$p_i = \text{probability (issued defeated} \mid S_i \text{ adopted)},$$

$$\begin{aligned}
E(S_1) &= p_1 V(o_1) + (1 - p_1) V(o_4), & S_1 &= \text{spend 100 G's,} \\
E(S_2) &= p_2 V(o_2) + (1 - p_2) V(o_5), & S_2 &= \text{spend 300 G's,} \\
E(S_3) &= p_3 V(o_3) + (1 - p_3) V(o_6), & S_3 &= \text{spend 500 G's.}
\end{aligned}$$

Assuming (1.5) and using (1.7), these three expected relative values of strategies become

$$\begin{aligned}
E(S_1) &= p_1 + v_1, \\
E(S_2) &= p_2 + v_2, \\
E(S_3) &= p_3.
\end{aligned}$$

Although the assumption of valuewise independence will usually result in a sacrifice of theoretical exactness (by failing to consider interdependences of values), its possibilities of economic gain in analyzing a problem may be overwhelming. Complete independence of values takes into account only "first-order components" of values and neglects "higher order interactions." Analogies to valuewise independence arise in many areas of inquiry. Consider, for example, a model of a phenomenon that takes the form $w = f(x, y, z)$ where $x, y,$ and z are "independent" variables (e.g., feed, speed, and blade angle of a carbon steel cutting tool in a turret lathe) and w is the functionally dependent variable (e.g., tool life). The "assumption of independence" would assert that the first partial derivative of f with respect to any one variable is functionally independent of the other two variables, or that one could write the differential dw as $dw = f_1(x)\,dx + f_2(y)\,dy + f_3(z)\,dz$. In analysis of variance models in statistical analysis, the "assumption of independence" would be equivalent to the hypothesis that effects due to interactions among the factors are negligible compared to the direct first-order effects due to the factors considered separately. In probability theory, the "assumption of independence" would be analogous to stochastic or statistical independence of random variables.[16]

Before going into a discussion of value measures, measures of probabilities, analysis of the decision model, and independence of variables in the relative value sense, it will be necessary to set a proper foundation for the expected-value decision model. The next two chapters are devoted to problem formulation, the structure of a decision situation, and the basic decision model.

REFERENCES

Ackoff, R. L., with S. K. Gupta and J. S. Minas, *Scientific Method: Optimizing Applied Research Decisions*, John Wiley and Sons, New York, 1962.

——, "Toward Quantitative Evaluation of Urban Services," Case Institute of Technology, 1963 (on ditto).

Brownlee, K. A., *Statistical Theory and Methodology in Science and Engineering*, John Wiley and Sons, New York, 1960.

Chernoff, H., and L. E. Moses, *Elementary Decision Theory*, John Wiley and Sons, New York, 1959.

Churchman, C. W., *Prediction and Optimal Decision*, Prentice-Hall, Englewood Cliffs, New Jersey, 1961a.

——, "Decision and Value Theory," in *Progress in Operations Research*, Vol. 1, ed. by R. L. Ackoff, John Wiley and Sons, New York, 1961b.

——, and R. L. Ackoff, "An Approximate Measure of Value," *Journal of Operations Research*, **2**, 172–187 (1954).

Davidson, D., P. Suppes, and S. Siegel, *Decision Making, An Experimental Approach*, Stanford University Press, Stanford, California, 1957.

Edwards, W., "Probability Preferences in Gambling," *American Journal of Psychology*, **66**, 349–364 (1953).

——, "Probability Preferences Among Bets with Differing Expected Values," *American Journal of Psychology*, **67**, 56–67 (1954a).

——, "The Reliability of Probability—Preferences," *American Journal of Psychology*, **67**, 68–95 (1954b).

——, "The Theory of Decision Making," *Psychological Bulletin*, **51**, 380–417 (1954c).

Luce, R. D., and H. Raiffa, *Games and Decisions: Introduction and Critical Survey*, John Wiley and Sons, New York, 1957.

Mosteller, F., and P. Nogee, "An Experimental Measure of Utility," *Journal of Political Economy*, **59**, 371–404 (1951).

Papandreou, A. G., "An Experimental Test of an Axiom in the Theory of Choice," *Econometrica*, **21**, 477 (1953).

Preston, M. G., and P. Baratta, "An Experimental Study of the Auction Value of an Uncertain Outcome," *American Journal of Psychology*, **61**, 183–193 (1948).

[16] If $x_1, x_2, \ldots, x_n$ are n random variables, valuewise independence leads to the additive form $V(x_1, x_2, \ldots, x_n) = V_1(x_1) + V_2(x_2) + \ldots + V_n(x_n)$, and statistical independence leads to the multiplicative form $P(x_1, x_2, \ldots, x_n) = P_1(x_1)P_2(x_2) \ldots P_n(x_n)$.

Raiffa, H., and R. Schlaifer, *Applied Statistical Decision Theory*, Division of Research, Harvard Business School, Boston, 1961.

Sahakian, W. S., *Systems of Ethics and Value Theory*, Philosophical Library, New York, 1963.

Savage, L. J., "The Theory of Statistical Decision," *Journal of the American Statistical Association*, **46**, 55–67 (1951).

————, *The Foundations of Statistics*, John Wiley and Sons, New York, 1954.

Singer, E. A., Jr., *On the Contented Life*, Henry Holt and Company, New York, 1936.

————, *In Search of a Way of Life*, Columbia University Press, New York, 1948.

Smith, N. M., Jr., "A Calculus for Ethics: A Theory of the Structure of Value" (in 2 parts), *Behavioral Science*, **1**, 111 and 186 (1956).

Suppes, P., and M. Winet, "An Axiomatization of Utility Based on the Notion of Utility Differences," *Management Science*, **1**, 259–270 (1955).

Thrall, R. M., C. H. Coombs, and R. L. Davis (eds.), *Decision Processes*, John Wiley and Sons, New York, 1954.

von Neumann, J., and O. Morgenstern, *Theory of Games and Economic Behavior* (Second Edition), Princeton University Press, Princeton, New Jersey, 1947.

Wald, A., *Statistical Decision Functions*, John Wiley and Sons, New York, 1950.

Weiss, L., *Statistical Decision Theory*, McGraw-Hill Book Company, New York, 1961.

Chapter 2

THE DECISION SITUATION AND PROBLEM FORMULATION

2.1 INTRODUCTION

The type of decision situation considered in this book contains an individual who in his environment must select a *strategy* from a set of strategies in order to obtain a *consequence* from a set of consequences. The probability of the jth consequence occurring if the ith strategy is adopted by the individual is assumed to be a meaningful and useful notion. In addition, it is assumed that, prior to selecting a strategy, the individual decision maker entertains doubt or indecision as to which strategy best serves his purposes, aims, goals, desires, or objectives, and he wishes to adopt a strategy that presents the best opportunity for pursuing his objectives. It is assumed that he considers his problem important enough to subject himself and his predicament to the scrutiny of analysis, reformulation, and synthesis in the hope of obtaining a satisfactory solution, and that the gain he expects to obtain from doing this more than offsets the expense involved. Whether the "scrutinizer" is the individual himself or another agency used by the individual, he will be referred to as the scientist, or research worker, or consultant.[1]

Along with strategies and consequences we shall discuss the construction of *decision trees* which often aid in obtaining a clearer picture of decision situations. After this, the notions of *descriptive courses of action* and *outcomes* are introduced as special cases of *variables* in a decision situation. The definition of a variable in a decision situation is presented in the final section.

The reader is advised to keep in mind that the interpretations of the

---

[1] Some readers will find the use of the word "scientist" in this context most unfortunate and ill chosen. If he wishes he may replace "scientist" with "management scientist" or with whatever he pleases.

emphasized terms may not be in complete agreement with the ways in which other authors use these terms.

The present development is primarily motivated by Ackoff's definition of a problem as found in Churchman, Ackoff, and Arnoff (1957, p. 107), and in Ackoff, Gupta, and Minas (1962, Chapter 2). For insight into difficulties inherent in such a formulation, see Churchman (1961a), in particular Chapters 6 through 9.

2.2 THE INDIVIDUAL—HIS ENVIRONMENT AND OBJECTIVES

The first element of a decision situation is an individual decision maker. For simplicity, the individual will usually be thought of as a single person such as the President of the United States, the manager in charge of production for a manufacturing firm, a military commander, or the reader of this book. The generalization of an individual person as decision maker would be to consider an individual decision-making unit or group, composed of two or more persons, e.g., a board of trustees, or a legislative body, or the Supreme Court, or a married couple. Here the unit selects a strategy from a set of available strategies although some members of the decision-making unit may personally prefer strategies other than the one adopted by the unit (as is often the case). The theory presented in this book essentially pertains to a single person via a theory of individual values. However, it can be extended to a general decision-making unit, provided value measures used for the unit have the same properties as those used for an individual. To date, most methods of determining group values are based on some scheme of amalgamating individual values. A discussion of several of these methods can be found in Thrall, Coombs, and Davis (1954) and in Churchman and Ackoff (1954).

It will be noted that the decision maker, in exercising his responsibility for making decisions, may be doing so as a representative of some social, political, or religious group, or industrial, business, or governmental organization, etc., or of some combination of several interested parties. He acts and reacts in the context of his internal and external worlds, and what he does will presumably have an effect on both. His internal world is a world of motivations, interpretations, and judgments. His links with his external world are in the form of sense perceptions, actions, and reactions. We shall call the union of his internal and external worlds his environment.

In considering the decision maker in his environment, we assume he has certain reasons or purposes for actually making a decision. That is, he has one or more unfulfilled desires, goals, or objectives. To pursue his objectives, he must take certain actions or make decisions. Thus a basic element of a decision situation is a set of motivating objectives $\theta = (\theta_1, \theta_2, \ldots, \theta_\alpha)$. Although the θ's are, no doubt, interrelated in some manner, it is seldom clear just how. Some objectives may complement one another and others may conflict with one another (e.g., the efficient pursuit of one implies the inefficient pursuit of another).

In making decisions, the president of a company may be concerned with and motivated by his own financial security, the stability of his position as company president, the financial security and growth of his company, the image the company presents to the public, the company's relations with its employees and their representing unions, the company's relations with its stockholders, and so forth. A congressman, voting on legislation, may be concerned with the security and health of his country, benefits to his constituents, the likelihood of being re-elected to Congress in the next election, etc. These concerns may be translated into or reformulated as objectives such as "to maintain financial security," "to be re-elected to Congress," "to prevent a strike by the union," and so forth.

In a decision situation it is of paramount importance to recognize and identify (at least some of) the decision maker's objectives. Obviously, the scientist is not in a very good position to aid the decision maker unless he knows what the decision maker wants. The theory presented here does not address itself to the question, "What should a person's objectives be?" but rather explores the question, "How can a decision maker's objectives be most effectively sought after?" We believe that the practical research worker concerned with decision making should address himself to the latter question. If he personally dislikes the objectives of the decision maker to the extent that it may bias his work, he should seriously consider disassociating himself from the research.

There seems to be no best, clear-cut method for determining a decision maker's objectives. Methods in use include direct questioning or interviewing of the decision maker[2] and those who know and have worked with him, and by observing or obtaining reports of his past behavior in related situations.

If our theory is to be concerned with the efficient pursuit of an individual's objectives, we must be aware of a complication. It seems to me that a person's motivating objectives are not immutable but rather subject to a process of evolution and change over time. In some instances this change may be gradual, with the person hardly being aware of the process, whereas in others it may be quite sudden and shocking. In the present

---

[2] The reader interested in pursuing this subject may consult Bennis, Benne, and Chin (1961), especially the abridgement of Lippitt (1959), as found therein.

theory, little account is taken of the possibility of changes in motivating objectives over future time; that is, an objective as determined in the present is assumed to continue to apply in the future, so long as the objective has not yet been attained. (If an individual's goals are realized, what new goals will replace the old?)

An even more disconcerting complication than the evolution and modification of objectives arises in the realization that an individual is not always certain just what his objectives are, regardless of what he may or may not reveal to another individual. This uncertainty of purpose creates difficulty for a decision theory which proposes to be normative or prescriptive as opposed to descriptive or predictive. (The positivistic behaviorist need not be concerned with underlying motivations because such a theorist assumes that an individual's decisions and actions are always best for him.) We shall return to these complications in discussing problems of measuring an individual's values in Chapter 4.

2.3 STRATEGIES AND CONSEQUENCES

The two sets of elements that occupy the leading position in the theory are:

1. **S**, the set of *admissible strategies*,
2. **Q**, the set of *consequences*.

In most of this book, these will be taken to be finite sets, **S** having t members $S_1, S_2, \ldots, S_t$; **Q** having r members $o_1, o_2, \ldots, o_r$. That is,

$$\mathbf{S} = \{S_i\}, \qquad i = 1, 2, \ldots, t,$$
$$\mathbf{Q} = \{o_j\}, \qquad j = 1, 2, \ldots, r.$$

Throughout the remainder of this chapter we shall develop the notions of **S** and **Q** to provide a better understanding of the decision situation before going on to the decision model structured on the relative values of consequences and the probabilities of strategies for consequences.

Strategies

In general, a strategy is a plan or program of action that may be adopted by the decision maker and implemented by him and/or by other persons working with or responsible to the decision maker. An *available strategy* is one which the decision maker believes can be implemented in full, based upon whatever information and experience he has available for making this judgment. Available strategies may be partitioned into two sets by the decision maker: (1) The set of *inadmissible strategies* and (2) the set of *admissible strategies* **S**. An available strategy is admissible if and only if the individual considers it worthy of his consideration and further evaluation, and if he feels that there is some chance that he will adopt and implement it in pursuing his objectives. An available strategy is inadmissible if it is not admissible.

These definitions are meant to be approximate. Experience indicates that in many decision situations the following events take place.

1. There is an active search for available strategies considered admissible by the decision maker. In various situations the process of discovering or constructing "good" strategies for consideration by the individual may employ not only the inherent talents of the decision maker but also the use of expert consultants or advisors, a team of scientists from different disciplines, brainstorming sessions, an "enemy" or mock competitor to devise counterstrategies, a research and development staff, and so forth. The amount of effort spent in the quest for good strategies depends, among other things, on the ingenuity of the decision maker, the responsibility he carries in his decision-making capacity, and the importance he attaches to the decision situation at hand.

2. As new strategies become available (and known) to the decision maker, he will immediately judge some of these to be inadmissible. His reasons for this may include a host of legal, social, moral, and/or physical factors. Other available strategies initially judged admissible may be relegated to an inadmissible status as time progresses and the decision maker obtains more information on which to base his decision.

3. A large number of subsidiary decisions, many implied in (1) and (2) above, will precede the major decision. Although it may be difficult to draw a clean line between a major and subsidiary decision, it appears possible to make a crude distinction between the two as follows: A minor subsidiary decision is one made for the purpose of obtaining information and/or of performing analysis to aid in the major decision.

4. The admissible strategy finally implemented will seldom if ever be carried through in the manner originally conceived. Feedback from the environment, which may offer up a variety of unforeseen and unexpected events, may indicate the necessity or desirability for changes in strategy. These changes may be effected by the decision maker or his staff. In addition, when reponsibility for implementing portions of a strategy is delegated, it is doubtful that the instructions for implementation will be followed precisely as intended by the decision maker. For this reason (among others) he may personally supervise the implementation of more critical aspects of an adopted strategy.

These comments should serve to illustrate the fluidity of a decision situation and lend credibility to the assertion that, come what may, a theory of decision can at best catch only a portion of the flavor and reality of the actual decision process.   In spite of the obvious difficulties implied by the foregoing, we shall deal with a concrete theory of decision which, although only able to approximate a very complicated state of affairs, will enable some individuals to make better decisions.

As stated before, this book is concerned with a prescriptive theory of decision making.   The tone of prescription is captured in the statement of a strategy.   Grammatically, a strategy is a set of imperative clauses, some of which may be modified by conditional phrases.   The imperative clauses are prescriptions of things to be done or actions to carry through such as: (you) buy that house; sue Mr. X for libel; vote for this amendment; do not ask your boss for a raise; sign this bill into law; send this reply to Mr. K; build a new 1,000-ton-per-year plant in Cleveland in 1972; tell your spouse to consult a marriage counselor; and so forth. A strategy must contain at least one imperative clause and will often contain a very large number of such clauses.   Conditional phrases that modify the action clauses will characteristically take the form "if such and such occurs, then."

It should be clear that a number of possible actions to be implemented at various times (modified with appropriate conditionals) may compose a single strategy.   The time or times at which these may be done should be contained (perhaps implicitly) in the statement of the strategy.

Two examples of strategies follow:

(*a*) Sue Mr. X for libel as soon as possible.   If he is willing to settle out of court initially for at least $50,000, accept the settlement; otherwise apply for a trial.   If the trial is not granted because of insufficient grounds do not pursue the matter further.

If the trial is granted and a settlement offer of at least $75,000 is made before the trial begins, accept the settlement.   Otherwise, go to trial. If you go to trial, and during the trial Mr. X is willing to settle for at least $100,000, accept the settlement.   If this does not happen and the case is thrown out of court, apply for a new trial and pursue the same course stated above as if this were the original trial.   If the trial goes to the end and the verdict is not in your favor, file an application for an appeal and pursue this through.   If the trial goes to completion and the verdict is in your favor, pursue to the end any appeals granted to Mr. X.

(*b*) Introduce product X' into market areas A, B, and C, and withdraw product X from these areas for a period of six months from May 1 to October 31 of this year and maintain the same level of advertising for X' as was used for X in these areas during this time.   If at the end of the six months the average monthly sales of X' exceed the projected sales of X (for the same period) by at least 10 percent, introduce X' into all market areas in the country and withdraw X. If the average sales of X' are at least 5 percent below the projected sales of X, drop X' from further consideration and put X back into areas A, B, and C.

If the average sales of X' are between 95 and 110 percent of the projected sales for X during the six months, leave X' in the areas A, B, and C for the next six months and, in addition, introduce X' into areas D, E, F, G, and H in place of X for these months. If on May 1 of the following year the sales of X' in these eight areas for the past six months exceed the projected sales of X, introduce X' to the whole country in place of X. Otherwise, withdraw X' completely and go back to X.

From the theoretical point of view, each strategy should be unambiguous in the sense that it prescribes an action for each future contingency upon which such actions are based. In other words, if at any point in the statement of a strategy there is a conditional imperative "if Y occurs, do X," then there should also be instruction about what to do if Y does not occur, or if any one of a set of mutually exclusive and collectively exhaustive possible contingencies including Y occurs. This was illustrated in (*a*) and (*b*) above. In (*a*) an action was prescribed for each of the two possibilities "initial settlement of at least \$50,000 offered" and "initial settlement of less than \$50,000 or no settlement offered." In (*b*) there was instruction for each of the three exclusive and exhaustive events concerning the sales of X' in relation to the projected sales of X during the initial six months of experimentation.

In formulating a set of admissible strategies, it is obviously necessary to limit ourselves to a rather small chunk of the universe. In considering a sequence of actions that may be pursued in the future, one can only go so far before becoming hopelessly mired in problems of complexity and uncertainty. The decisions of how far to go and how detailed and intricate to get in formulating explicit strategies are among the many required of the decision maker (with the aid of advisors and staff in many cases).

In connection with this, it should be noted that, for the sake of manageability, what might be conceived of as the set of all admissible strategies may be reduced in size to a set of *representative admissible strategies*, one of which the decision maker plans to adopt and implement. When an individual is planning to buy a life insurance policy he may limit his attention to policies of \$10,000 and \$20,000 coverage, not because it would be unthinkable to buy a \$12,000 policy or an \$18,000 policy, etc., but simply because he feels one of the two amounts considered will be satisfactory for his purposes and it is not worth the effort to consider a large number of other possibilities. In similar fashion, he may consider only three different life insurance companies (from the more than 1,000 in the United States) and two types of contracts, either whole life or 20-year term. In situations where a set of representative admissible strategies is considered, we shall call it **S** and make no distinction between this and the set of (all) admissible strategies.

Prescriptive Courses of Action

The phrase "course of action" is used in two senses in this book, one prescriptive, the other descriptive.

A *prescriptive course of action* is a strategy that contains no conditional phrases. It is stated in the imperative mood. Examples of prescriptive courses of action are:

(i) (You) buy a $20,000 whole-life life insurance policy next month from Mr. X representing company Z.

(ii) Buy a house this year, a new car next year, and a yacht the year after that.

Examples (*a*) and (*b*) given earlier are strategies but not prescriptive courses of action because of the conditionals. In the situation leading to the formulation of (*a*), a prescriptive course of action could be, "Don't sue Mr. X for libel." For the situation containing (*b*), two prescriptive courses of action are, "Don't introduce product X' in any market area" and "Replace product X with X' in all market areas immediately."

A *descriptive course of action* is a set of acts that may be or have been performed by the decision maker and others associated with him. It is never a strategy. We shall say more about this in the next section.

Consequences

A *consequence* is a set of things which may be done by the individual and, perhaps, by others working with or for him, and of things which may happen to the individual, or to other people, or to entities with which he is concerned in one way or another. It is relative to a given decision maker in a given decision situation. The statement of a consequence is, in the ideal, a complete description of the individual's future insofar as it is affected by or concerned with the decision situation at hand.

Because of obvious limitations, we will, in practice, try to incorporate in the formulation of consequences that may occur from the adoption and implementation of a strategy only the more important aspects of the situation. The inclusion of too many fine details in the statement of a consequence would be pointless. On the other hand, the exclusion of one or more important factors might be damaging.

If we formulate consequences beginning with admissible strategies, these will provide us with many of the terms that appear in the statements of the consequences. There may also be other factors that can be produced, at least in part, by the strategy pursued, which do not appear in the statement of a strategy but which should be included in the statement of a consequence. In many cases, these potential fruits of a strategy lead to the formulation of a set of strategies in the first place. As one example, consider the strategy, "Don't sue Mr. X for libel." From this, one consequence could be: "Mr. X is not sued for libel, no further attacks are made (on you) by Mr. X, and the potentially harmful reports of a libel trial in the newspapers are avoided." A second might be, "Mr. X is not sued for libel and he pursues his libelous attacks (on you)."

One consequence from (b) above could be: "Product X' is introduced into market areas A, B, and C. After six months, the sales of X' exceed the projected sales of X in these areas by at least 10 percent, and so X' is put into all market areas in place of X. During the next 18 months, sales of X' exceed the projected sales of X by 10 percent."

For the insurance buyer, one consequence would be: "A $20,000 whole-life life-insurance contract is purchased by the individual from Mr. X of company Z. An annual premium of $360 is paid for three years, then the individual expires under conditions which pay the beneficiary the face amount of the policy."

In the process of giving formal structure to the decision situation, Q *is to be formulated as an exclusive and exhaustive set.* In the theory, it is assumed that whatever $S_i \in S$ is adopted and implemented by the decision maker, one and only one $o_j \in Q$ will result from pursuing the strategy. Moreover, for each $o_j \in Q$, there is at least one $S_i \in S$ such that $P(o_j \mid S_i) > 0$, where $P(o_j \mid S_i)$ is the probability of o_j occurring if S_i is implemented or the probability that the individual attaches to the proposition: "o_j will result if S_i is implemented." Clearly, some consequences which may occur with one strategy cannot possibly occur with another. In many cases there will be no $o_j \in Q$ judged capable of resulting from more than one strategy. In such cases, each strategy will be associated with its own distinct subset of consequences, i.e., Q may be partitioned into t subsets in one-to-one correspondence with the t admissible strategies.

Decision Trees

A *decision tree* is a graphical representation of the alternative actions available to the decision maker and the "alternative actions available to nature" (representing things which may happen and which are not fully controllable by the decision maker), usually arranged in sequence as they appear in the statements of strategies. Possible results of strategies of concern to the decision maker but which do not arise in the statements of strategies should appear in this graph.

If the graph is properly structured, one should be able to recover the $S_i \in \mathbf{S}$ and the $o_j \in \mathbf{Q}$ from it.   In many situations it may not be feasible to draw the complete decision tree because of its potentially enormous size.

Each node of the graph that represents a point at which an action may be required by the decision maker is labeled D. The branches stemming from a D node represent alternative actions available to the decision maker if he reaches that node.   The branches stemming from any other node represent "nature's choices," should that node be reached.   "Final" nodes or points of conclusion are circled.   Each path through the tree corresponds to a consequence.

A simple example of a decision tree arises from a situation where an individual of voting age has moved to a new voting district and must register if he wishes to be eligible to vote in the upcoming presidential election.   If he registers, he can either vote Democratic or Republican, or not at all.   We suppose he is interested in the outcome of the election, the election of either a Republican or Democrat for President.   There are four strategies (don't register, register and vote Republican, register and vote Democratic, register and don't vote) which are also prescriptive courses of action, and eight consequences (e.g., the individual registers, then votes Democratic, after which a Republican is elected President) corresponding to the eight paths through the graph. The reader may feel it rather silly for an individual to "commit" himself as to voting preference before actually registering, if he does register, owing to the variety of unpredictable things that might happen in the campaigns between registration time and election day.   If so, it seems easy enough to be explicit only in the alternatives "register" and "don't register" and to delete the rest of the tree with reference to this decision.

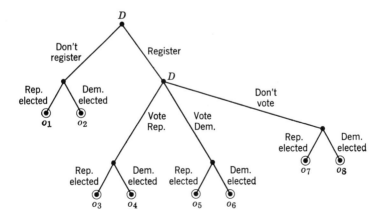

Whereas the decision maker's potential actions will be portrayed in their chronological sequence on the decision tree, this need not be true of "nature's potential actions." Suppose a judge in a state requiring the death penalty for conviction of murder is trying a case (without a jury, to make the matter simple) in which X is accused of this act. Suppose that the judge has two alternatives: (1) Set X free or (2) sentence X to death. The following table illustrates the consequences.

	X	
	Committed Murder	Did Not Commit Murder
S_1 = set X free	o_1 = set a murderer free in society	o_2 = set an innocent man free
S_2 = sentence X to death	o_3 = sentence a murderer to death	o_4 = sentence an innocent man to death

Some individuals prefer to express the decision tree for this situation as shown in the following:

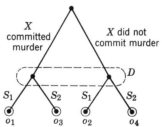

The two nodes enclosed by the dashed line constitute an *information set*,[3] the decision maker not being certain (let us suppose) at which node he is when the decision is made. This tree preserves the chronological occurrence of events. Another tree for the same situation is given by the following:

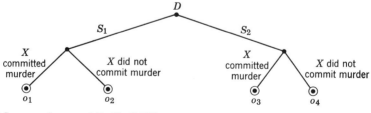

---

[3] See, e.g., Luce and Raiffa (1957).

The chronological occurrence of events is not preserved. It should be noted that whether or not X is a murderer is not affected by the judge's decision. We shall say more about similar decision situations in Section 3.6.

Suppose an individual contemplates performing one of two experiments, e_1 or e_2. If e_1 is performed, it will yield one of two results, a or b. If e_2 is performed, it will yield one of three results, 1, 2, or 3. After performing an experiment and observing the result, the decision maker will do either A or B. From this action, one of four things may occur, x, y, z, or w. The decision tree for this description is shown in Figure 2.1. From this tree we distinguish 40 consequences and 12 strategies. One strategy is: "Do e_2; if 1, then do A; if 2, then do B; if 3, then do A." This may be abbreviated as $(e_2; 1, A; 2, B; 3, A)$.

For a final example of a decision tree, consider the following simplified situation. A young man in his last year of college has applied to two graduate schools, A and B, and has been unconditionally "accepted" by both, but he is not sure that he wants to go to graduate school. If he does not enter graduate school, he plans to accept a job offer from company Z and go into their one-year training program. If he does this, at the end of the year he will receive one of three bids from the company: (1) "Get lost"; (2) "stay on as an assistant junior engineer"; (3) "stay on as a junior engineer." If either (2) or (3) happens, he must decide whether to quit and (a) enter school A, (b) enter school B, or (c) look for a job with a new company, or (d) to stay on. If (1) happens, he must choose between the two schools or (c). If in any case he enters one of the two graduate schools, he plans to work for a master's degree. If he is successful in this, he will either (i) go on for his Ph. D. at the same school or (ii) look for a job with some company. If he is not successful at the masters level, he will do (ii). If he is successful and does (i) and does not

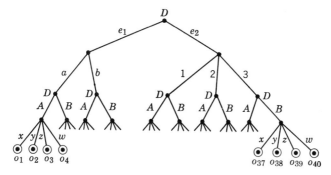

Figure 2.1   A decision tree

complete his Ph.D., he will do (ii).   If he is successful at the masters level
and does (i) and earns his Ph.D., then he will (x) go into an academic
career at a university, or (y) take a job with some company, or (w) go
into government service.

Letting M, $\sim M$, Ph. D., $\sim$Ph. D., stand for "gets master's degree,"
"doesn't get master's degree," "gets Ph. D. degree," "doesn't get Ph. D.
degree," respectively, the complete decision tree is written in Figure 2.2.
The reader is invited to verify that this tree contains 53 consequences
and 908 strategies.

2.4 VARIABLES

A consequence was identified as a possible future of the decision
maker (and other things he is concerned with) as it relates to or is influenced by the implementation of an admissible strategy.   Furthermore,
it was noted that the statement of a consequence is composed of substatements of acts performed (or that may be performed) along with the
substatements of results that occurred (or that may occur).   In this
section we shall be concerned with sets of these components of consequences, primarily sets which qualify as variables, as this term is defined
below.   The notion of variables will be employed to a limited extent in
Chapters 3 through 7 and will play a central role in Chapters 8 through 12.

Definition of a Variable

In the context of a decision situation, a *variable* is a set of elements
one and only one of which will result, or occur, or obtain whatever
admissible strategy is adopted and implemented.   Another way of
stating this is to say that a variable is a set of elements $X = \{x\}$ such that

$$\sum_{x \in X} P(x \mid S_i) = 1, \qquad \text{for each } S_i \in \mathbf{S},$$

where $P(\cdot \mid S_i)$ is a probability measure over X given S_i, with $\sum_{x \in X}$
denoting summation over all the values of the variable X (or over all the
elements of the set X).

One obvious variable in every decision situation is the set of consequences $\mathbf{Q} = \{o_j\}$.   In the remainder of this section we shall look at other
variables.   Some of these will be given special names because of the frequency with which they occur in later discussion.[4]

If X and Y are two variables in a decision situation, the product set
$X \times Y$ may or may not be a variable, according to the definition.   The
product $X \times Y$ is the set of all ordered pairs (x, y) with $x \in X$ and $y \in Y$.

----

[4] In Chapter 10 we shall introduce the phrase "performance variable" for local color
and note how this applies at that time.

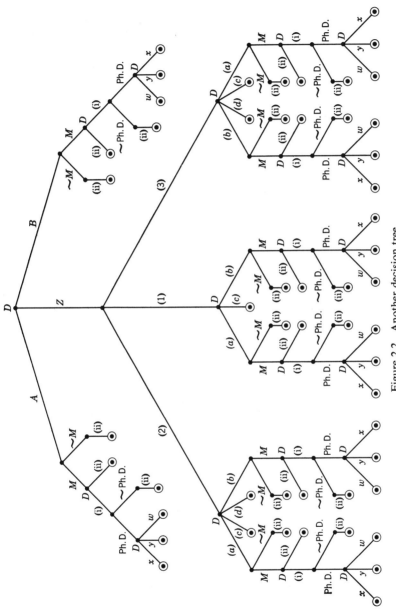

Figure 2.2 Another decision tree

If X has n elements and Y has m elements, then $X \times Y$ has nm elements. In order for $X \times Y$ to be variable, both parts of one and only one pair (x, y) must be realized with $x \neq y$. If $X \times Y$ is a variable, it does not follow that every $(x, y) \in X \times Y$ is capable of realization; that is, for some given (x, y) it may happen that, $P(x, y \mid S_i) = 0$ for each $S_i \in \mathbf{S}$.

Action, Outcome, and Mixed Variables

An *action variable* is a variable the values of which are composed entirely of things which the decision maker or those responsible to him may do in implementing an $S_i \in \mathbf{S}$. An *outcome variable* is a variable the values of which are composed entirely of things which may happen to the decision maker (and other entities he is concerned about) the occurrences of which may in part be influenced by his acts, but which are not themselves acts controlled by the decision maker. A *mixed variable* is a variable which is neither an action variable nor an outcome variable, containing both acts and other things.

Every variable in a decision situation is either an action, outcome, or mixed variable. In most situations $\mathbf{Q}$ will be a mixed variable.

Examples of variables are provided by the decision trees in the previous section. In the election situation, two variables are:

$$X_1 = \{\text{don't register, register and vote Republican,}$$
$$\text{register and vote Democratic, register and don't vote}\}, \quad (2.1)$$

$$X_2 = \{\text{Republican elected, Democrat elected}\}.$$

X_1 is an action variable; X_2 an outcome variable. Since $\mathbf{Q} \subset X_1 \times X_2,$[5] $X_1 \times X_2$ is a (mixed) variable.

In the murder situation, two variables are:

$$X_1 = \{\text{set } X \text{ free, sentence } X \text{ to death}\}, \quad (2.2)$$

$$X_2 = \{X \text{ committed murder, } X \text{ did not commit murder}\},$$

where X_1 is an action variable and X_2 is an outcome variable, although the value of X_2 that obtains is not influenced by the resultant value of X_1. In this case $\mathbf{Q} = X_1 \times X_2$.

The tree of Figure 2.1 provides four basic variables:

$$
\begin{aligned}
X_1 &= \{e_1, e_2\}, \\
X_2 &= \{a, b, 1, 2, 3\}, \\
X_3 &= \{A, B\}, \\
X_4 &= \{x, y, z, w\}.
\end{aligned} \quad (2.3)
$$

---

[5] $A \subset B$ means A is a subset of B, i.e., every element in A is also a member of the set B. $A = B$ means that $A \subset B$ and $B \subset A$.

In this situation, X_1 and X_3 are action variables; X_2 and X_4 are outcome variables; $X_1 \times X_2$ and $X_3 \times X_4$ are mixed variables; and

$$\mathbf{Q} \subset X_1 \times X_2 \times X_3 \times X_4.$$

Descriptive Courses of Action and Outcomes

Two variables that arise in most decision situations will be given special names and symbols. These are:

1. **A**, the set of *descriptive courses of action*,
2. **O**, the set of *outcomes*.

A is an action variable; **O** is an outcome variable.

A *descriptive course of action* is the set of all actions[6] occurring within a consequence, and an *outcome* is the set of all other things occurring within a consequence. By means of these notions, each consequence is partitioned into an action-outcome pair:

$$o_k = (A_i, O_j), \qquad o_k \in \mathbf{Q},$$

where A_i denotes a (descriptive) course of action and O_j an outcome. Partitioning each consequence in **Q** in this manner yields

$$\mathbf{A} = \{A_i\}, \qquad i = 1, \ldots, m,$$

$$\mathbf{O} = \{O_j\}, \qquad j = 1, \ldots, n,$$

where each $A_i \in \mathbf{A}$ corresponds to at least one $o_k \in \mathbf{Q}$ and each $O_j \in \mathbf{O}$ corresponds to at least one $o_k \in \mathbf{Q}$. Every course of action or outcome derived from **Q** appears in **A** or **O** respectively. With m courses of action, n outcomes, and r consequences, $m \leqslant r, n \leqslant r$, and $r \leqslant mn$. Obviously,[7]

$$\mathbf{Q} \subset \mathbf{A} \times \mathbf{O}. \tag{2.4}$$

In (2.1), $X_1 = \mathbf{A}$, $X_2 = \mathbf{O}$. In (2.2), $X_1 = \mathbf{A}$, $X_2 = \mathbf{O}$. In (2.3), $\mathbf{A} = X_1 \times X_3$ and $\mathbf{O} = X_2 \times X_4$. From Figure 2.2, the consequence $[Z, (2), (b), M, (i), \text{Ph. D.}, w]$ yields the course of action $[Z, (b), (i), w]$ and the outcome $((2), M, \text{Ph. D})$. The reader is invited to partition several other consequences from this figure.

The Use of S = A

In all situations **A** denotes the set of descriptive courses of action. However, in the special case where each admissible strategy in **S** contains no conditional phrases and is therefore a prescriptive course of action, **A**

---

[6] Of the decision maker or persons under his direction.

[7] In an extreme case where an entire consequence was a descriptive course of action, a null outcome would be added to **O**.

is also used to identify the strategies, i.e., prescriptive courses of action, and we will write $S = A$ (with $t = m$). In such situations A refers both to the set of prescriptive courses of action and the set of descriptive courses of action with a one-to-one correspondence between the two sets.

In any event, A_i as used in $V(o_k) = V(A_i, O_j)$, in $P(A_i, O_j \mid S_k)$, or in $P(A_i \mid S_k)$ signifies a descriptive course of action. A descriptive course of action specifies acts that may be taken by the decision maker, understood in a factual, detached sense. A prescriptive course of action carries the essence of a command or prescription for action.

n-Variable Situations

The last five chapters of this book deal with decision situations so structured that it is possible to identify n ($\geqslant 2$) variables $X_1, X_2, \ldots, X_n$ such that

$$Q \subset X_1 \times X_2 \times \ldots \times X_n. \tag{2.5}$$

In this type of situation, each consequence may be represented by an ordered n-tuple or vector of the form

$$o_k = (x_1, x_2, \ldots, x_n), \qquad x_j \in X_j, \qquad j = 1, \ldots, n.$$

A special case of (2.5) is given by (2.4) with $n = 2$. An example of a four-variable situation is provided by Figure 2.1 and (2.3).

It is important to keep in mind that in an n-variable situation each $o_j \in Q$ has the form $(x_1, x_2, \ldots, x_n)$, whereas it is not necessarily true that every $(x_1, x_2, \ldots, x_n) \in X_1 \times X_2 \times \ldots \times X_n$ is a consequence. Namely, $(x_1, \ldots, x_n)$ is not a consequence if and only if $P(x_1, \ldots, x_n \mid S_i) = 0$ for each $S_i \in S$. In (2.3), $(e_1, 1, A, z)$ is an element of $X_1 \times X_2 \times X_3 \times X_4$ but is not a consequence since result 1 cannot occur with experiment e_1.

Further comments on the formulation of n-variable situations are scattered throughout the last five chapters.

EXERCISES

1. Compare the formulation of a decision situation given in this chapter with a formulation presented by one of the following authors, and note points of similarity and differences, etc.: Ackoff (1962, Chapter 2); Schlaifer (1959, Chapters 1, 2); Weiss (1961, Chapter 5); Chernoff and Moses (1959, Chapter 1).

2. Account for the fact that there are 12 strategies distinguishable from Figure 2.1.

3. Verify that 53 consequences and 908 strategies are distinguishable from Figure 2.2, and devise a notation that can be used to represent the strategies compactly.

4. Suppose a legislator is planning to introduce three major bills into

Congress and will do this sequentially, waiting until the fate of the first has been decided before introducing the second, and so forth. He is primarily interested in the fate of each bill, either its success (passage) or failure. Call the bills A, B, and C. Let a, $\bar{a}$, b, $\bar{b}$, c, $\bar{c}$, be respectively the events "A succeeds," "A fails," "B succeeds," "B fails," "C succeeds," "C fails." Draw a decision tree for this situation, show that there are 12 strategies, and, presuming that each of these 12 are admissible, show that there are 48 consequences.

5. (*Continuation.*) In the situation of Exercise 4, show that each consequence o_j may be written as a six dimensional vector in the form $(x_1, x_2, \ldots, x_6)$. Identify the variables X_1, $X_2, \ldots$, X_6 by the values they can take on, and classify each one as an action or outcome variable. How many elements are contained in $X_1 \times X_2 \times \ldots \times X_6$? How many of these are consequences?

6. What is the difficulty in trying to draw a complete decision tree for one of the players in a game of chess? Do you think your answer provides partial reason why some individuals find chess challenging or intellectually stimulating?

7. Suppose an individual walks into a restaurant and plans to order a dinner consisting of an appetizer, salad, entree, beverage, and dessert. Let X_1 through X_5 respectively be the five action variables for these five components of the meal. For example, X_1 is the set of all appetizers. (One may include also the action value X_6, the total price of the meal including a 10 percent tip, which is a deterministic function of X_1 through X_5.) If the sizes of $X_1, \ldots, X_5$ are respectively 6, 4, 20, 5, and 10, how many different meals are available to the individual, given that he will order one and only one item from each of the five sets, the restaurant has all items on hand, and he has sufficient funds for any meal?

REFERENCES

Ackoff, R. L., with S. K. Gupta and J. S. Minas, *Scientific Method: Optimizing Applied Research Decisions*, John Wiley and Sons, New York, 1962.

Bennis, W. G., K. D. Benne, and R. Chin (eds.), *The Planning of Change*, Holt, Rinehart and Winston, New York, 1961.

Chernoff, H., and L. E. Moses, *Elementary Decision Theory*, John Wiley and Sons, New York, 1959.

Churchman, C. W., *Prediction and Optimal Decision*, Prentice-Hall, Englewood Cliffs, New Jersey, 1961*a*.

——, and R. L. Ackoff, "An Approximate Measure of Value," *Journal of Operations Research*, **2**, 172–187 (1954).

——, R. L. Ackoff, and E. L. Arnoff, *Introduction to Operations Research*, John Wiley and Sons, New York, 1957.

Lippitt, R., "Dimensions of the Consultant's Job," *Journal of Social Issues*, **15**, 5–12 (1959).

Luce, R. D., and H. Raiffa, *Games and Decisions: Introduction and Critical Survey*, John Wiley and Sons, New York, 1957.

Schlaifer, R., *Probability and Statistics for Business Decisions*, McGraw-Hill, New York, 1961.

Thrall, R. M., C. H. Coombs, and R. L. Davis (eds.), *Decision Processes*, John Wiley and Sons, New York, 1954.

Weiss, L., *Statistical Decision Theory*, McGraw-Hill, New York, 1961.

Chapter 3

THE BASIC DECISION MODEL

Having developed a framework for the setting of the type of decision situation under consideration, this chapter discusses the expected-value decision model. The model, in its basic form and in other forms that derive from the basic form, will serve as the principal subject of study in the remainder of the book. We shall be concerned with the problems of measuring the quantities used to describe the model and with analyzing various measures of these quantities with respect to obtaining a full or partial solution to the decision model.

The two sets of quantities that demand measurement before anything can be done with the model are the probabilities of strategies for consequences and the relative values of consequences. These will be discussed briefly in this chapter and will be treated more fully in the next two chapters and throughout the remainder of the book. At this time we shall also give an indication of the kinds of analysis on the decision model that will be dealt with in more detail in the sequel.

3.1 PROBABILITIES OF STRATEGIES FOR CONSEQUENCES

In the previous chapter the notions of the strategy set S, consisting of t strategies, and the consequence set Q, consisting of r consequences $o_1, o_2, \ldots, o_r$ were developed. This section briefly discusses the important relation between S and Q, namely, the probability matrix P. A typical element in P will be $P_{ij} \geqslant 0$ where

$$P_{ij} = P(o_j \mid S_i),$$

the probability that consequence o_j will result if strategy S_i is adopted by the decision maker or the probability that S_i will produce o_j.

In array form, the t-by-r probability matrix may be written as follows:

Consequences (j)

	o_1	o_2	$\ldots$	o_r	Row Sums
S_1	P_{11}	P_{12}	$\ldots$	P_{1r}	1.0
Strategies (i) S_2	P_{21}	P_{22}	$\ldots$	P_{2r}	1.0
$\vdots$	$\vdots$	$\vdots$	$\vdots$	$\vdots$	$\vdots$
S_t	P_{t1}	P_{t2}		P_{tr}	1.0

P

As noted, the probabilities in each row sum to unity. This follows the usual convention in probability theory that a probability function on a set of exclusive and exhaustive elements shall have total probability 1. That is,

$$\sum_{j=1}^{r} P_{ij} = 1 \quad \text{for each} \quad S_i, \quad i = 1, 2, \ldots, t. \tag{3.1}$$

The sum of the P_{ij} in a column of the matrix may, of course, be greater than, less than, or perhaps equal to unity—either $\sum_i P_{ij} > 1$, $\sum_i P_{ij} < 1$, or $\sum_i P_{ij} = 1$ for each o_j ($j = 1, \ldots, r$) with the obvious restriction that the sum of the column sums equal the sum of the row sums ($= t$).

Probability in and by itself is neither a desirable nor an undesirable thing. However, when related to relative values of consequences, we see it in a different perspective. For example, under a specific strategy, one would like to have a high probability (near 1) for attaining the most desirable consequence and, correspondingly, a low probability (near 0) for attaining the least desirable consequence, since there is a "fixed amount of probability," namely 1.0, that is distributed over the consequences for each strategy.

When $S = A = \{A_i\}$, $i = 1, \ldots, m$, i.e., when all strategies are simple prescriptive courses of action, an interesting thing happens to the **P** matrix. In this case,

$$P(o_j \mid S_i) = P(o_j \mid A_i) = \begin{cases} 0 & \text{if } o_j = (A_h, O_k), \quad h \neq i, \\ P(O_k \mid A_i) & \text{if } o_j = (A_h, O_k), \quad h = i, \end{cases}$$

where the consequence o_j is being written as an action-outcome pair (A_h, O_k). If **O** has n members, then each row of the **P** matrix has at most n nonzero entries. For example, with $m = 3$, $n = 2$, for $S = A$, the **P** matrix would look like

	(A_1, O_1)	(A_1, O_2)	(A_2, O_1)	(A_2, O_2)	(A_3, O_1)	(A_3, O_2)
A_1	$P(O_1 \mid A_1)$	$P(O_2 \mid A_1)$	0	0	0	0
A_2	0	0	$P(O_1 \mid A_2)$	$P(O_2 \mid A_2)$	0	0
A_3	0	0	0	0	$P(O_1 \mid A_3)$	$P(O_2 \mid A_3)$

Collapsing this gives the matrix of probabilities of courses of action for outcomes

	O_1	O_2	Row Sums
A_1	$P(O_1 \mid A_1)$	$P(O_2 \mid A_1)$	1.0
A_2	$P(O_1 \mid A_2)$	$P(O_2 \mid A_2)$	1.0
A_3	$P(O_1 \mid A_3)$	$P(O_2 \mid A_3)$	1.0

This collapsed probability matrix has essentially the same form as the **P** matrix, but it applies to probabilities of courses of action for outcomes, not strategies for consequences.

The connection between the two matrices is given by the equation

$$P(A_i, O_j \mid S_k) = P(A_i \mid S_k) P(O_j \mid A_i, S_k),$$

where $P(O_j \mid A_i, S_k)$ is defined if and only if $P(A_i \mid S_k) > 0$ in which case $P(O_j \mid A_i, S_k) = P(O_j \mid A_i)$. If S_k does not have positive probability for A_i, then $P(O_j \mid A_i, S_k)$ is not defined. When S_k has positive probability for A_i,

$$P(A_i, O_j \mid S_k) = P(A_i \mid S_k) P(O_j \mid A_i).$$

Summing both sides of this over the $O_j \in \mathbf{O}$, we obtain

$$\sum_{j=1}^{n} P(A_i, O_j \mid S_k) = P(A_i \mid S_k),$$

since $\sum_j P(O_j \mid A_i) = 1$.

Just as we can write matrices of probabilities of strategies for consequences and actions for outcomes, we can write a matrix of probabilities of strategies for courses of action:

	A_1	A_2	$\ldots$	A_m	Row Sums
S_1	$P(A_1 \mid S_1)$	$P(A_2 \mid S_1)$	$\ldots$	$P(A_m \mid S_1)$	1.0
S_2	$P(A_1 \mid S_2)$	$P(A_2 \mid S_2)$	$\ldots$	$P(A_m \mid S_2)$	1.0
$\vdots$	$\vdots$	$\vdots$		$\vdots$	$\vdots$
S_t	$P(A_1 \mid S_t)$	$P(A_2 \mid S_t)$	$\ldots$	$P(A_m \mid S_t)$	1.0

If $S = A$, with $m = t$, we have the identity matrix

	A_1	A_2	$\ldots$	A_t
S_1	1	0	$\ldots$	0
S_2	0	1	$\ldots$	0
$\vdots$	$\vdots$	$\vdots$	$\ddots$	$\vdots$
S_t	0	0	$\ldots$	1

with the appropriate subscripting of the A's and S's (i.e., $A_i = S_i$). As used in $P(A_i \mid S_k)$, A_i is a descriptive course of action.

Finally, we can write the probability matrix of strategies for outcomes:

	O_1	O_2	$\ldots$	O_n	Row Sums
S_1	$P(O_1 \mid S_1)$	$P(O_2 \mid S_1)$	$\ldots$	$P(O_n \mid S_1)$	1.0
S_2	$P(O_1 \mid S_2)$	$P(O_2 \mid S_2)$	$\ldots$	$P(O_n \mid S_2)$	1.0
$\vdots$	$\vdots$	$\vdots$		$\vdots$	$\vdots$
S_t	$P(O_1 \mid S_t)$	$P(O_2 \mid S_t)$	$\ldots$	$P(O_n \mid S_t)$	1.0

This t-by-n matrix is the product of the t-by-m strategies for actions probability matrix times the m-by-n actions for outcomes probability matrix, i.e.,

$$P(O_j \mid S_k) = \sum_{i=1} P(A_i \mid S_k) P(O_j \mid A_i).$$

For simplicity in the discussion of probabilities to this point, no attempt has been made to give an extramathematical interpretation of probability, and we shall not go into this phase until Chapter 5, where each major viewpoint or conception of probability is discussed. In Section 5.7, the role played by probability in decision theories is briefly discussed with emphasis on the formulation given herein. As noted in Chapter 1, a subjectivistic interpretation is used in this book.

3.2 RELATIVE VALUES OF CONSEQUENCES

The second important set of quantities that demand some form of measurement before we begin manipulating the decision model are the relative values of the consequences.

In considering the relative value of a consequence to the decision maker, "relative" is used in several different senses. First, it means that the value of a particular consequence o_j is relative to the set of consequences Q. Second, it means that the value or worth of a consequence is relative to the decision maker in his environment. Third, the value of a consequence is relative to the set of objectives θ held by the decision maker. Finally, in its more common usage, "relative" is used as opposed to "absolute," in the sense that absolute value is taken to mean intrinsic worth or that there is some natural definition of zero value. No object, concept, or consequence has value of and by itself, but takes on (relative) value only through a human agent with a purpose. The aspects of "relative" considered above are not, of course, independent of one another but are invariably intertwined. The important point we wish to stress is that relative value refers to the importance that the decision maker, motivated by a set of objectives θ, attaches to members of a set of consequences considered by him in a specific decision situation.

To symbolize this, consider a function V, called the value function, which assigns real numbers to the consequences. These numbers are taken to represent a measure of the relative worths of the consequences to the decision maker, where these relative values are dependent on the sets θ, Q, and, of course, upon the decision maker and his environment (Λ). Thus,

$$V(o_j) = V(o_j; Q, \theta, \Lambda).$$

Hereafter we will let the Q, θ, Λ be understood but not written.

As a requirement for nonambiguity, we specify that relative values of consequences be unique up to an increasing linear transformation. That is to say, if $\{V(o_1), \ldots, V(o_r)\}$ is one set of relative values and $\{U(o_1), \ldots, U(o_r)\}$ is another set of relative values of the same consequences in the same decision situation, then there exist real numbers a and b, with $a > 0$, such that

$$U(o_j) = aV(o_j) + b, \qquad j = 1, 2, \ldots, r.$$

According to the language of modern utility theory, we assume that V is a linear utility function.[1] (As was pointed out in Chapter 1, if an individual in a given situation satisfies a specified set of hypotheses, then there exists a linear utility function for him in that situation.)

Quite naturally, if for two consequences o_j and o_k, the decision maker considers o_j more important or valuable (or more desirable) than o_k, then we adopt the convention that $V(o_j) > V(o_k)$;[2] and if he considers o_j and o_k equally valuable (i.e., of the same relative importance), then $V(o_j) = V(o_k)$. If o_j is at least as desirable as o_k, then $V(o_j) \geqslant V(o_k)$. In this respect we may note that an increasing linear transformation of relative values is

[1] As used, for example, in von Neumann and Morgenstern (1947), Savage (1954), and Luce and Raiffa (1957).

[2] One could, instead, adopt the convention that, if o_j were more desirable than o_k, then $V(o_j) < V(o_k)$, but this would be clumsy and cause undue confusion.

order preserving. That is, if $U(o_j) = aV(o_j) + b$ and $U(o_k) = aV(o_k) + b$, with $a > 0$, then $U(o_j) \geqslant U(o_k)$ if and only if $V(o_j) \geqslant V(o_k)$.

We shall utilize the notion of relative value differences herein. Suppose $V(o_1) > V(o_2) > V(o_3) > V(o_4)$, and suppose in addition that $V(o_1) - V(o_2) \geqslant V(o_3) - V(o_4)$. This last statement says that the difference between the relative values of o_1 and o_2 is at least as great as the difference between the relative values of o_3 and o_4. Another interpretation is that the individual increases his relative value in going from o_2 to o_1 at least as much as in going from o_4 to o_3.[3] With respect to value differences, it will also be noted that an increasing linear transformation is order preserving. Thus, if $U(o_j) = aV(o_j) + b$, with $a > 0$, then $U(o_1) - U(o_2) \geqslant U(o_3) - U(o_4)$ if and only if $V(o_1) - V(o_2) \geqslant V(o_3) - V(o_4)$.

With $V_j = V(o_j)$, suppose $V_1 - V_2 = V_3 - V_4$, and $V_1 > V_2$ and $V_3 > V_4$. Let f be any transformation of the value function which preserves the equality and inequalities respectively. That is, f is an admissible transformation if and only if

$$f(V_1) - f(V_2) = f(V_3) - f(V_4), \quad f(V_1) > f(V_2), \quad f(V_3) > f(V_4).$$

With $f(V_1) > f(V_2)$ and $f(V_3) > f(V_4)$, f must be a positive transformation. In addition,

$$\frac{f(V_1) - f(V_2)}{V_1 - V_2} = \frac{f(V_3) - f(V_4)}{V_3 - V_4} = a,$$

where $a > 0$ is a constant that may be called the scale multiplier. This last equation implies that f must be a linear transformation, i.e., $f(V_j) = aV_j + b, j = 1, \ldots, 4$. Thus, to avoid ambiguities (i.e., to ensure that the relation $>$, $=$, or $<$ between relative value differences remains invariant under a transformation of the relative values), the V_j must be unique except for origin and scale unit. In the next section we shall observe the same thing in connection with the decision model.

Another way to phrase the requirement that the relative values of consequences be real numbers unique up to an increasing linear transformation is to say that the relative values exist on an interval scale,[4] meaning that the relative lengths of the intervals between the $V(o_j)$ on the real line remain unchanged with a shift of the origin or a uniform compression or stretching of the axis. Suppose $V(o_1)$, $V(o_2)$, $V(o_3)$, and $V(o_4)$ are such that

---

[3] Luce and Raiffa (1957, p. 32) point out that this reasoning is fallacious with respect to the von Neumann-Morgenstern utility function. See "Fallacy 3" on p. 32 and the example on p. 22 in their book. In the form of value theory presented by Suppes and Winet (1955) and tested by Davidson, Suppes, and Siegel (1957), the cited reasoning is not fallacious. See Section 4.9 for further comments.

[4] As designated by Stevens (1946).

$V(o_1) > V(o_2)$ or $V(o_2) > V(o_1)$. Then the ratio of lengths of value intervals or the ratio of value differences

$$\frac{V(o_3) - V(o_4)}{V(o_1) - V(o_2)}$$

remains invariant under a linear transformation, since, with $U(o_j) = aV(o_j) + b$,

$$\frac{U(o_3) - U(o_4)}{U(o_1) - U(o_2)} = \frac{aV(o_3) + b - [aV(o_4) + b]}{aV(o_1) + b - [aV(o_2) + b]} = \frac{V(o_3) - V(o_4)}{V(o_1) - V(o_2)}.$$

One set of axioms implying the existence of a value function, unique except for origin and scale unit, was presented in Section 1.3. Several other axiomatic systems leading to the same result will be discussed in Section 5.6. In this book these axioms are interpreted primarily as criteria for consistent judgment on the part of the decision maker. If an individual does not make judgments in the manner assumed by the formal theory or if he cannot make his judgments adhere to the guidelines set forth in the axioms, then our methods of analysis will be of little use to him. In Chapter 4 we shall comment further on this point (especially in Sections 4.3 and 4.5) and present an array of value measures less precise than the interval measure but, nevertheless, quite useful in comparing expected relative values of strategies.

A Special Case

When we write a consequence as an action-outcome pair (A_i, O_j), a special case of the basic decision model arises when, for each outcome O_j,

$$V(A_i, O_j) = V(A_k, O_j) \tag{3.2}$$

for all pairs of courses of action in **A** for which $\sum_{h=1}^{t} P(A_i, O_j \mid S_h) > 0$ and $\sum_{h=1}^{t} P(A_k, O_j \mid S_h) > 0$. If this is the case, we may replace $V(A_i, O_j)$ with $V(O_j)$ and speak about the relative values of the outcomes in **O**. In crude terms, (3.2) expresses the notion that the things one does have no importance *per se*, but are important only in terms of what may result from these actions. For example, if an individual involved in a parlor game were interested only in the outcomes "win" and "lose," then his actions in playing the game would have value only with respect to their ability to lead to one of these outcomes. If (3.2) were to hold, every action-outcome pair in which the outcome was "win" would be equally desirable to the person, and the same would be true for every action-outcome pair in which the outcome was "lose." This can be expressed by saying that the individual is indifferent between the two consequences in every pair of consequences containing the same outcome, i.e.,

$$(A_i, O_j) \sim (A_k, O_j) \tag{3.3}$$

for all such applicable pairs of consequences. Here "$\sim$" is the indifference relation. It should be noted that (3.2) follows from (3.3) and not vice versa. If (3.3) holds for all applicable pairs of consequences, we may also say that all consequences containing the same outcome belong to the same indifference set or equivalence class. For the parlor game illustration, there would be two equivalence classes of consequences, one consisting of "win" consequences, the other of "lose" consequences. Although it may be questionable whether (3.3) does, in fact, hold for any actual situation, in some cases it may not be unreasonable to use (3.2) as an approximation in simplifying the analysis of a decision problem. This could, for example, reduce the number of entities requiring value measurement from the order of mn to the order of n.

3.3 MODEL I—THE BASIC DECISION MODEL

The basic model is characterized by the defining equation

$$EV(\mathbf{I}) = C_1 E(S_1) + C_2 E(S_2) + \ldots + C_t E(S_t), \tag{3.4}$$

where $EV(\mathbf{I})$ = decision maker's or individual's total expected relative value,

$E(S_i)$ = expected relative value to the individual of strategy S_i,

C_i = "probability" that the individual will adopt strategy S_i, used in a prescriptive sense, with $C_i \geqslant 0$, $i = 1, \ldots, t$ and $\sum_{i=1}^{t} C_i = 1$.

Furthermore,

$$E(S_i) = \sum_{j=1}^{r} P(o_j \mid S_i) V(o_j) = \sum_{j=1}^{r} P_{ij} V_j, \tag{3.5}$$

where P_{ij} and V_j are defined in context.

We shall forgo detailed consideration of the interpretation of the controllable variable $\mathbf{C} = (C_1, C_2, \ldots, C_t)$ until Section 3.8. From previous discussion it should be clear that one of our primary objectives is to discuss ways in which a program of research can seek to find values of the C_i in $\mathbf{C}$ which maximize $EV(\mathbf{I})$, where maximization of the decision maker's total expected relative value will be used as the prescriptive criterion for strategy selection. For example, if we find that $E(S_1) > E(S_i)$ for $i = 2, 3, \ldots, t$, then $\mathbf{C} = (1, 0, 0, \ldots, 0)$ maximizes $EV(\mathbf{I})$, as is obvious from the linear form of (3.4).[5]

All models discussed herein will be models of $EV(\mathbf{I})$, their differences arising from different ways of dealing with or defining $E(S_i)$. Model I

---

[5] That is, (3.4) is linear in $\mathbf{C}$. In view of the restrictions on $\mathbf{C}$ ($C_i \geqslant 0$, $\sum C_i = 1$) we may further say that $EV(\mathbf{I})$ is a convex linear combination of the $E(S_i)$.

considers $E(S_i)$ in the form given by (3.5). Other models will be defined in the next three sections and in Chapters 10, 11, and 12.

Acceptable Value Transformations

A great deal of emphasis in this book is placed upon determining the sign of the difference of the expected relative values of two strategies, say S_1 and S_2. From (3.5),

$$E(S_1) - E(S_2) = \sum_{j=1}^{r} P_{1j}V_j - \sum_{j=1}^{r} P_{2j}V_j = \sum_{j=1}^{r} (P_{1j} - P_{2j})V_j.$$

If $E(S_1) - E(S_2) \geq 0$, then $E(S_1) \geq E(S_2)$, and we may therefore set $C_2 = 0$. If $E(S_1) - E(S_2) \leq 0$, then $E(S_2) \geq E(S_1)$, and we may set $C_1 = 0$. It should be clear that the sign of $E(S_1) - E(S_2)$ is invariant under an increasing linear transformation of the V_j (of the form $aV_j + b$, $a > 0$) on applying (3.1). What may not be clear is that we require the $V_j = V(o_j)$ to be unique up to an increasing linear transformation for the sign of $E(S_1) - E(S_2)$ to remain invariant in all cases. In other words, if we pose the question, "What class of transformations on the V_j will preserve the sign $(-, 0, +)$ of $E(S_1) - E(S_2)$ in every conceivable case?" we get the answer, "The class of increasing linear transformations." Thus, it is not simply an aribtrary convention that the relative values of consequences be unique up to an increasing linear transformation but a requirement that must be imposed to ensure invariance of conclusions. If we were to structure the decision model in some fashion other than that given above, this might not be the case, but as long as we wish to prescribe on the basis of the $\sum P_{ij}V_j$, we ought to adhere to it. [It was noted earlier that the uniqueness of relative values up to an increasing linear transformation is implied by the axioms of von Neumann and Morgenstern.[6] In this system the arguments of the value function are taken to be elements in the set of gambles $\{(\alpha_1 o_1, \alpha_2 o_2, \ldots, \alpha_r o_r)\}$, for all $\alpha = (\alpha_1, \ldots, \alpha_r)$ for which $\alpha_i \geq 0$, $\sum_1^r \alpha_i = 1$, where $(\alpha_1 o_1, \ldots, \alpha_r o_r)$ is the gamble or lottery "yielding" o_1 with probability $\alpha_1, \ldots,$ o_r with probability α_r. The degenerate gambles $(o_1), \ldots, (o_r)$ correspond to the consequences. The axioms yield $V(\alpha_1 o_1, \alpha_2 o_2, \ldots, \alpha_r o_r) = \alpha_1 V(o_1) + \alpha_2 V(o_2) + \ldots + \alpha_r V(o_r)$, the principle of mathematical expectation, which in the above notation would be rendered as $E(S_i) = V(P_{i1} o_1, P_{i2} o_2, \ldots, P_{ir} o_r) = \sum_j P_{ij}V_j.$]

We can show that any other class of transformations on the V_j besides the increasing linear transformations is unacceptable by taking $r = 3$, with

$$E(S_1) - E(S_2) = (P_{11} - P_{21})V_1 + (P_{12} - P_{22})V_2 + (P_{13} - P_{23})V_3.$$

[6] Or see Luce and Raiffa (1957) for the case of a finite set of consequences.

Since $\sum P_{1j} = \sum P_{2j} = 1$, $\sum (P_{1j} - P_{2j}) = 0$, so that this may be written as

$$E(S_1) - E(S_2) = \alpha_1 V_1 - (\alpha_1 + \alpha_3)V_2 + \alpha_3 V_3$$
$$= \alpha_1(V_1 - V_2) - \alpha_3(V_2 - V_3),$$

where $\alpha_1 = P_{11} - P_{21}$, $\alpha_3 = P_{13} - P_{23}$. Suppose then that $\alpha_1 > 0$ and $\alpha_3 > 0$, and that $V_1 > V_2 > V_3$. Dividing through by $V_1 - V_3$, we get

$$\frac{E(S_1) - E(S_2)}{V_1 - V_3} = \alpha_1 \frac{V_1 - V_2}{V_1 - V_3} - \alpha_3 \frac{V_2 - V_3}{V_1 - V_3}.$$

Since $V_1 - V_3 > 0$, $E(S_1) - E(S_2)$ has the same sign as the right-hand side.

Now let f be a function that transforms the V_j into a new set of relative values, the $f(V_j)$. It should be clear that f must be an increasing transformation, for otherwise the sign of $E(S_1) - E(S_2)$ would change in many cases. That is, if $V_1 > V_3$, we must also have $f(V_1) > f(V_3)$, and so forth. It remains to show that f must be a linear transformation. For this, suppose that under some pointwise measure of relative value, we get

$$\alpha_1 \frac{V_1 - V_2}{V_1 - V_3} - \alpha_3 \frac{V_2 - V_3}{V_1 - V_3} = 0,$$

giving $E(S_1) = E(S_2)$.

For f to preserve this sign (0), we must have

$$\alpha_1 \frac{f(V_1) - f(V_2)}{f(V_1) - f(V_3)} - \alpha_3 \frac{f(V_2) - f(V_3)}{f(V_1) - f(V_3)} = 0,$$

which is readily reduced to

$$\frac{f(V_1) - f(V_2)}{f(V_1) - f(V_3)} = \frac{\alpha_3}{\alpha_1 + \alpha_3}.$$

But $\alpha_3/(\alpha_1 + \alpha_3)$ is a constant (and equals $(V_1 - V_2)/(V_1 - V_3)$). Hence, f must satisfy

$$\frac{f(V_1) - f(V_2)}{f(V_1) - f(V_3)} = \frac{V_1 - V_2}{V_1 - V_3}.$$

Analogously f must satisfy

$$\frac{f(V_2) - f(V_3)}{f(V_1) - f(V_3)} = \frac{V_2 - V_3}{V_1 - V_3}.$$

These two together imply that

$$\frac{f(V_1) - f(V_2)}{V_1 - V_2} = \frac{f(V_2) - f(V_3)}{V_2 - V_3} = \frac{f(V_1) - f(V_3)}{V_1 - V_3}.$$

If we denote the common ratio as a, then, in general, we require that

$$\frac{f(V_i) - f(V_j)}{V_i - V_j} = a \qquad (a \neq 0), \quad i \neq j,$$

or

$$f(V_i) - f(V_j) = aV_i - aV_j.$$

But this restricts f to the linear form,

$$f(V_j) = aV_j + b, \qquad j = 1, 2, 3,$$

where a and b are arbitrary constants with $a \neq 0$. Since f must be an increasing transformation, $a > 0$.

EXAMPLE. To illustrate the type of situation to be studied later (Chapter 6, for example) suppose $r = 4$, and the four o_j have been ranked from most important to least important, giving

$$V(o_1) \geqslant V(o_2) \geqslant V(o_3) \geqslant V(o_4),$$

or

$$V_1 \geqslant V_2 \geqslant V_3 \geqslant V_4.$$

We then ask, "What must be true of the probabilities in the matrix

	o_1	o_2	o_3	o_4
S_1	P_{11}	P_{12}	P_{13}	P_{14}
S_2	P_{21}	P_{22}	P_{23}	P_{24}

in order that we can conclude $E(S_1) \geqslant E(S_2)$, given only the simple ranking of the V_j?"

To answer this, one can apply Abel's summation identity,

$$a_1 b_1 + a_2 b_2 + \ldots + a_n b_n = a_1(b_1 - b_2) + (a_1 + a_2)(b_2 - b_3) + \ldots$$
$$+ (a_1 + \ldots + a_{n-1})(b_{n-1} - b_n) + (a_1 + \ldots + a_n)b_n,$$

or

$$\sum_{j=1}^{n} a_j b_j = \sum_{k=1}^{n-1} \left(\sum_{j=1}^{k} a_j \right)(b_k - b_{k+1}) + \left(\sum_{j=1}^{n} a_j \right)b_n \qquad (3.6)$$

to

$$E(S_1) - E(S_2) = \sum_{j=1}^{r} (P_{1j} - P_{2j})V_j$$

to yield

$$E(S_1) - E(S_2) = \sum_{k=1}^{r-1} \left[\sum_{j=1}^{k} (P_{1j} - P_{2j}) \right](V_k - V_{k+1}), \qquad (3.7)$$

in which each $V_k - V_{k+1}$ is $\geqslant 0$ by virtue of $V_1 \geqslant V_2 \geqslant V_3 \geqslant V_4$. Given only this ranking of relative values, we can conclude that $E(S_1) - E(S_2) \geqslant 0$ if and only if each of the $r - 1$ terms on the right-hand side of (3.7) is $\geqslant 0$, that is, if and only if

$$P_{11} - P_{21} \geqslant 0$$
$$(P_{11} - P_{21}) + (P_{12} - P_{22}) \geqslant 0$$
$$(P_{11} - P_{21}) + (P_{12} - P_{22}) + (P_{13} - P_{23}) \geqslant 0$$

or

$$P_{11} \geqslant P_{21}$$
$$P_{11} + P_{12} \geqslant P_{21} + P_{22}$$
$$P_{11} + P_{12} + P_{13} \geqslant P_{21} + P_{22} + P_{23}.$$

3.4 MODEL I WITH S = A

When $\mathbf{S} = \mathbf{A}$, each strategy is a simple course of action, as could be the case if only one action variable were contemplated in a decision situation or if the chosen values of all action variables were implemented simultaneously or before any outcome variable's value had been observed.

In writing $E(\dot{S}_i)$ or $E(A_i)$, we can use the probability matrix of strategies (or courses of action) for outcomes:

	O_1	O_2	$\ldots$	O_n
$S_1 = A_1$	$P(O_1 \mid A_1)$	$P(O_2 \mid A_1)$	$\ldots$	$P(O_n \mid A_1)$
$S_2 = A_2$	$P(O_1 \mid A_2)$	$P(O_2 \mid A_2)$	$\ldots$	$P(O_n \mid A_2)$
$\vdots$	$\vdots$	$\vdots$		$\vdots$
$S_m = A_m$	$P(O_1 \mid A_m)$	$P(O_2 \mid A_m)$	$\ldots$	$P(O_n \mid A_m)$

and the matrix of the relative values of consequences

	O_1	O_2	$\ldots$	O_n
A_1	$V(A_1, O_1)$	$V(A_1, O_2)$	$\ldots$	$V(A_1, O_n)$
A_2	$V(A_2, O_1)$	$V(A_2, O_2)$	$\ldots$	$V(A_2, O_n)$
$\vdots$	$\vdots$	$\vdots$		$\vdots$
A_m	$V(A_m, O_1)$	$V(A_m, O_2)$	$\ldots$	$V(A_m, O_n)$

In this notation,

$$E(S_i) = E(A_i) = \sum_{j=1}^{n} P(O_j \mid A_i) V(A_i, O_j), \qquad i = 1, \ldots, m.$$

Letting $P_{ij} = P(O_j \mid A_i)$ and $V_{ij} = V(A_i, O_j)$,

$$E(A_1) - E(A_2) = \sum_{j=1}^{n} P_{1j} V_{1j} - \sum_{j=1}^{n} P_{2j} V_{2j}. \qquad (3.8)$$

TWO EXAMPLES.   For $n = 3$ and the matrices

	O_1	O_2	O_3
A_1	V_{11}	V_{12}	V_{13}
A_2	V_{21}	V_{22}	V_{23}

	O_1	O_2	O_3
A_1	P_{11}	P_{12}	P_{13}
A_2	P_{21}	P_{22}	P_{23}

suppose one obtains $V_{11} \geqslant V_{21} \geqslant V_{22} \geqslant V_{12} \geqslant V_{13} \geqslant V_{23}$, a simple ranking of the relative values of the consequences. The full **P** matrix (of strategies for *consequences*) can be written, keeping $P_{ij} = P(O_j \mid A_i)$, as

	$V_{11} \geqslant$ (A_1, O_1)	$V_{21} \geqslant$ (A_2, O_1)	$V_{22} \geqslant$ (A_2, O_2)	$V_{12} \geqslant$ (A_1, O_2)	$V_{13} \geqslant$ (A_1, O_3)	V_{23} (A_2, O_3)
A_1	P_{11}	0	0	P_{12}	P_{13}	0
A_2	0	P_{21}	P_{22}	0	0	P_{23}

with the value ranking superimposed. By applying Abel's identity ($r = 6$), it can be concluded that $E(A_1) - E(A_2) \geqslant 0$ if

(i) $P_{11} \geqslant 0$,

(ii) $P_{11} \geqslant P_{21}$,

(iii) $P_{11} \geqslant P_{21} + P_{22}$,

(iv) $P_{11} + P_{12} \geqslant P_{21} + P_{22}$,

(v) $P_{23} \geqslant 0$,

which will all be true if (iii) is true. It may be noted that in writing (i) through (v), we first form the partial sum matrix of the P_{ij} in each row (adding from left to right)

$$\begin{matrix} A_1 \\ A_2 \end{matrix} \begin{bmatrix} P_{11} & P_{11} & P_{11} & P_{11} + P_{12} & 1 & 1 \\ 0 & P_{21} & P_{21} + P_{22} & P_{21} + P_{22} & P_{21} + P_{22} & 1 \end{bmatrix}$$

and then take the difference of the entries in each column, namely, $P_{11} - 0$, $P_{11} - P_{21}$, $P_{11} - (P_{21} + P_{22}), \ldots, 1 - 1$. To determine that $E(A_1) - E(A_2) \geqslant 0$ with only the given relative value ranking, each of these differences must be nonnegative [yielding (i) through (v)]. To conclude $E(A_1) - E(A_2) \leqslant 0$ with the given information on the V_{ij}, each difference must be nonpositive ($\leqslant 0$), which is true if and only if $P_{11} = P_{23} = 0$.

Under the same circumstances, suppose we look at the other side of the coin and ask, "What must be true of the V_{ij} in order to conclude that $E(A_1) \geqslant E(A_2)$, when given the probability ranking

$$P_{11} \geqslant P_{22} \geqslant P_{23} \geqslant P_{12} \geqslant P_{13} \geqslant P_{21} \geqslant 0$$

and no additional information on the P_{ij}?" To answer this, first write

$$E(A_1) - E(A_2) = \sum_{j=1}^{3} P_{1j}(V_{1j} - U) - \sum_{j=1}^{3} P_{2j}(V_{2j} - U), \quad (3.9)$$

where U is an arbitrary constant, the changes in U causing a shift in the origin of the relative value scale (i.e., we have introduced the increasing linear transform $V_{ij} = aV_{ij} + b$, with $a = 1$, $b = -U$). In applying (3.6) to (3.9), take

$$(b_1, b_2, \ldots, b_6) = (P_{11}, P_{22}, P_{23}, P_{12}, P_{13}, P_{21}),$$

$$(a_1, a_2, \ldots, a_6) = ((V_{11} - U), -(V_{22} - U), -(V_{23} - U),$$
$$(V_{12} - U), (V_{13} - U), -(V_{21} - U)),$$

giving

$$\begin{aligned}
E(A_1) - E(A_2) = &(V_{11} - U)(P_{11} - P_{22}) + (V_{11} - V_{22})(P_{22} - P_{23}) \\
&+ (V_{11} + U - V_{22} - V_{23})(P_{23} - P_{12}) \\
&+ (V_{11} + V_{12} - V_{22} - V_{23})(P_{12} - P_{13}) \quad (3.10) \\
&+ (V_{11} + V_{12} + V_{13} - V_{22} - V_{23} - U)(P_{13} - P_{21}) \\
&+ (V_{11} + V_{12} + V_{13} - V_{21} - V_{22} - V_{23})(P_{21}).
\end{aligned}$$

Since each P term in (3.10) is $\geqslant 0$ by virtue of the probability ranking, $E(A_1) - E(A_2) \geqslant 0$ if there exists a U such that

(i) $\qquad V_{11} \geqslant U$,

(ii) $\qquad V_{11} \geqslant V_{22}$,

(iii) $\qquad V_{11} + U \geqslant V_{22} + V_{23}$,

(iv) $\qquad V_{11} + V_{12} \geqslant V_{22} + V_{23}$,

(v) $\qquad V_{11} + V_{12} + V_{13} \geqslant V_{22} + V_{23} + U$,

(vi) $\qquad V_{11} + V_{12} + V_{13} \geqslant V_{21} + V_{22} + V_{23}$.

In particular, U may be set equal to one of the V_{ij}. If the ranking $V_{11} \geqslant V_{21} \geqslant V_{22} \geqslant V_{12} \geqslant V_{13} \geqslant V_{23}$ were available, we would set $U = V_{12}$ since, with $U = V_{12}$, all inequalities excepting $V_{11} + V_{12} + V_{13} \geqslant V_{21} + V_{22} + V_{23}$ would be automatically satisfied. If it could also be shown that $\Sigma V_{1j} \geqslant \Sigma V_{2j}$, then one could conclude that $E(A_1) \geqslant E(A_2)$.

3.5 MODEL II

Model II arises when (3.2) or (3.3) holds, i.e., when all consequences containing the same outcome fall in the same indifference set of consequences, In this case, we work with the matrix of probabilities of strategies for outcomes and the relative values of the outcomes, writing

$$E(S_i) = \sum_{j=1}^{n} P(O_j \mid S_i)V(O_j). \tag{3.11}$$

The *form* of (3.11) is identical to $E(S_i)$ for Model I given by (3.5). By a semantical sleight-of-hand o_j in (3.5) has been replaced by O_j in (3.11). The connection between $P(o_j \mid S_i)$ and $P(O_j \mid S_i)$ was given earlier as

$$P(O_j \mid S_i) = \sum_{k=1}^{m} P(A_k, O_j \mid S_i) = \sum_{k=1}^{m} P(A_k \mid S_i)\, P(O_j \mid A_k).$$

Also, $V(O_j) = V(A_i, O_j)$ for all A_i for which $V(A_i, O_j)$ is defined.

3.6 THE STATISTICAL MODEL

Readers familiar with statistical literature will be quite aware that the formulation of a decision situation in the previous pages differs from the typical kind of formulation set forth by statisticians. In this section we briefly consider what, in the author's opinion, is the typical statistical formulation and compare it with Model I.[7] We begin with only part of the statistical formulation and then consider the other part (experimentation). All discussion will be held to the case of finite sets.

Formulation

Under this formulation (decision making under uncertainty), the individual is presumed to be uncertain as to which *state* of a specified *world* is the true state ("does in fact obtain"). In Savage's (1954) terminology the *world* is "the object about which the person is concerned," and a *state* of the world is "a description of the world, leaving no relevant aspect undescribed" (p. 9). The set of states of the world is assumed or taken to be mutually exclusive and collectively exhaustive, i.e., one and only one description of the world does, in fact, obtain (or "is the true description").

Let **E** denote this set with n elements $E_1, E_2, \ldots, E_n$. That is, $\mathbf{E} = \{E_j\}$, where each E_j is a state. An *act* or *terminal act* is a function which assigns a consequence to each state of the world. If we are at a point where selection of a terminal act is to be made (and no further experimentation is contemplated, e.g.), the terminal acts could correspond to what we have heretofore called courses of action or strategies. With $t\, S_i$, the *statistical consequence matrix* would look like

---

[7] See also Ackoff (1962, Chapter 9).

	E_1	E_2	$\ldots$	E_n
S_1	o_{11}	o_{12}	$\ldots$	o_{1n}
S_2	o_{21}	o_{22}	$\ldots$	o_{2n}
$\vdots$	$\vdots$	$\vdots$		$\vdots$
S_t	o_{t1}	o_{t2}	$\ldots$	o_{tn}

where o_{ij} is the resultant consequence if S_i is implemented and E_j is the true state of the world.

To illustrate these ideas, we use Savage's example (pp. 14–15). Suppose you are making an omelet, have broken five good eggs into a bowl, and contemplate a sixth, as yet unbroken, egg. The world is this sixth egg. The two states of the world are $E_1 = $ "good" and $E_2 = $ "rotten." You plan either to break the egg into the bowl with the five good eggs (A_1), or break it into a saucer for inspection (A_2), or throw it away without breaking (A_3). The statistical consequence matrix could then be

	E_1 (Good)	E_2 (Rotten)
A_1 (into bowl)	Six-egg omelet	No omelet, and five good eggs destroyed
A_2 (into saucer)	Six-egg omelet, and a saucer to wash	Five-egg omelet, and a saucer to wash
A_3 (throw away)	Five-egg omelet, and one good egg destroyed	Five-egg omelet

In this illustration it will be noted that the courses of action (or acts) have no effect on determining which state is the true state. Either the egg is rotten or is not rotten, and nothing we do can change this. In the statistical formulation this is always the case. That is, the true state among the states $E_1, E_2, \ldots, E_n$ is a factual matter and cannot be affected or altered by the contemplated strategies (used in the sense of Chapter 2).

The Model

Most modern statisticians decry the idea of assigning probabilities to the states of the world, holding that such probabilities are meaningless (or equal 0 or 1). Whether or not we do assign probabilities to the E_j depends on our interpretation of "probability." For example, under either a logical or a subjective view of probability (but not under a limiting frequency view)[8] it may be meaningful to assign probabilities $\{P(E_j)\}$ to the states $\{E_j\}$, where $P(E_j) \geqslant 0$ and

[8] These views will be discussed in Chapter 5.

$$\sum_{j=1}^{n} P(E_j) = 1.$$

We shall assume that it is meaningful to do this (rejecting the limiting frequency view of probability, at least in the present context). Letting $V(o_{ij})$ be the relative value of consequence o_{ij},

$$E(S_i) = \sum_{j=1}^{n} P(E_j) \, V(o_{ij}). \tag{3.12}$$

This may be tied in with Model I as follows. Suppose all o_{ij} are different.[9] Then write the statistical consequence matrix as

	E_1	E_2	$\ldots$	E_n
S_1	o_1	o_2	$\ldots$	o_n
S_2	o_{n+1}	o_{n+2}	$\ldots$	o_{2n}
$\vdots$	$\vdots$	$\vdots$		$\vdots$
S_t	$o_{n(t-1)+1}$	$o_{n(t-1)+2}$	$\ldots$	o_{nt}

By writing the matrix of probabilities of strategies for consequences, letting $P_j = P(E_j)$, we get

	o_1	o_2	$\ldots$	o_n	o_{n+1}	o_{n+2}	$\ldots$	o_{2n}	$\ldots$	$o_{n(t-1)+1}$	$\ldots$	o_{nt}
S_1	P_1	P_2	$\ldots$	P_n	0	0	$\ldots$	0	$\ldots$	0	$\ldots$	0
S_2	0	0	$\ldots$	0	P_1	P_2	$\ldots$	P_n	$\ldots$	0	$\ldots$	0
$\vdots$	$\vdots$	$\vdots$		$\vdots$	$\vdots$	$\vdots$		$\vdots$		$\vdots$		$\vdots$
S_t	0	0	$\ldots$	0	0	0	$\ldots$	0	$\ldots$	P_1	$\ldots$	P_n

Thus, with the omelet example, we have the following **P** matrix:

	Six-Egg Omelet	No Omelet, Five Good Eggs Destroyed	Six-Egg Omelet, Saucer to Wash	Five-Egg Omelet, Saucer to Wash	Five-Egg Omelet, One Good Egg Destroyed	Five-Egg Omelet
Break into bowl	$P(\text{good})$	$P(\text{bad})$	0	0	0	0
Break into saucer	0	0	$P(\text{good})$	$P(\text{bad})$	0	0
Throw away	0	0	0	0	$P(\text{good})$	$P(\text{bad})$

[9] This is not essential but will aid in visualization.

In this form $E(S_i)$, given by (3.12), may be written as

$$E(S_i) = \sum_{j=1}^{r} P_{ij} V(o_j), \qquad r = nt. \tag{3.13}$$

In Chapter 6 both forms for $E(S_i)$ will be employed.
With (3.12)

$$E(S_1) - E(S_2) = \sum_{j=1}^{n} P_j[V(o_{1j}) - V(o_{2j})], \qquad P_j = P(E_j) \tag{3.14}$$

and with (3.13)

$$E(S_1) - E(S_2) = \sum_{j=1}^{r} (P_{1j} - P_{2j}) V(o_j).$$

To illustrate the use of (3.14), suppose it has been determined, with $n = 5$, that $P_1 \geqslant P_2 \geqslant P_3 \geqslant P_4 \geqslant P_5 \geqslant 0$, where $P_j = P(E_j)$. Applying (3.6) to (3.14), we may write

$$E(S_1) - E(S_2) = \sum_{j=1}^{4} \left\{ \sum_{k=1}^{j} [V(o_{1k}) - V(o_{2k})] \right\} (P_j - P_{j+1})$$
$$+ P_5 \sum_{k=1}^{5} [V(o_{1k}) - V(o_{2k})],$$

from which it is possible to conclude that $E(S_1) \geqslant E(S_2)$ if

$$V(o_{11}) \geqslant V(o_{21}),$$
$$V(o_{11}) + V(o_{12}) \geqslant V(o_{21}) + V(o_{22}),$$
$$V(o_{11}) + V(o_{12}) + V(o_{13}) \geqslant V(o_{21}) + V(o_{22}) + V(o_{23}),$$
$$V(o_{11}) + V(o_{12}) + V(o_{13}) + V(o_{14})$$
$$\geqslant V(o_{21}) + V(o_{22}) + V(o_{23}) + V(o_{24}),$$
$$V(o_{11}) + V(o_{12}) + V(o_{13}) + V(o_{14}) + V(o_{15})$$
$$\geqslant V(o_{21}) + V(o_{22}) + V(o_{23}) + V(o_{24}) + V(o_{25}).$$

The hypothetical matrix of the $V(o_{ij})$ given by

	E_1	E_2	E_3	E_4	E_5
S_1	2	99	999	-5	38
S_2	0	100	1,000	-10	42

satisfies these five inequalities, and together with $P_1 \geqslant P_2 \geqslant \ldots \geqslant P_5 \geqslant 0$ it can be concluded that $E(S_1) \geqslant E(S_2)$.

Model I to the Statistical Model

By way of a simple illustration, we shall transform a decision situation structured in the language of Model I into the language of the statistical model.[10]   Suppose an individual has on hand one unit of a product. If he sells this unit, he makes \$4 profit.   If he cannot sell the unit, it must be scrapped at a \$3 loss.   These figures are independent of advertising costs.   He contemplates the two strategies "advertise" (A) and "Do not advertise" ($\overline{A}$).   Advertising costs him \$2.   For simplicity, suppose that there is only one consumer who could possibly want the item, and that, if the decision maker advertises, this consumer will see the ad. Finally, let the outcomes of interest be (1) sell the item and (2) scrap the item.   If the individual's only concern is making money, the consequence matrix from the Model I ($\mathbf{S} = \mathbf{A}$) standpoint is

	Sell	Scrap
A	\$2	$-$ \$5
$\overline{A}$	\$4	$-$ \$3

with the corresponding probability matrix

	Sell	Scrap	
A	$P(\text{sell} \mid A)$	$P(\text{scrap} \mid A)$	$= \begin{bmatrix} p_1 & 1 - p_1 \\ p_2 & 1 - p_2 \end{bmatrix}$
$\overline{A}$	$P(\text{sell} \mid \overline{A})$	$P(\text{scrap} \mid \overline{A})$	

To put this in the form of the statistical model, we must define states of a specified world.   In this case the world is the consumer (X) and the states of the world are:

E_1: X would buy in either case (with or without the ad).

E_2: X would buy without the ad and wouldn't buy with the ad.

E_3: X would not buy without the ad and would buy with the ad.

E_4: X would not buy in either case.

The statistical consequence matrix would then be given by

	E_1	E_2	E_3	E_4
A	\$2	$-$ \$5	\$2	$-$ \$5
$\overline{A}$	\$4	\$4	$-$ \$3	$-$ \$3

If one considers the $P(E_j)$ meaningful, then A and $\overline{A}$ do not affect the $P(E_j)$.   The probability matrix (under the Model I formulation) of strategies for consequences may be written

[10] The author is indebted to Professor Ackoff for this illustration.   Our discussion here is related to the process of putting a game in extensive form into a game in normal form.   See, e.g., Luce and Raiffa (1957, Chapter 3).

	$2	− $5	$4	− $3
A	$P(E_1) + P(E_3)$	$P(E_2) + P(E_4)$	0	0
$\bar{A}$	0	0	$P(E_1) + P(E_2)$	$P(E_3) + P(E_4)$

$$= \begin{bmatrix} p_1 & 1 - p_1 & 0 & 0 \\ 0 & 0 & p_2 & 1 - p_2 \end{bmatrix}$$

The reader may complicate this situation in any fashion he pleases, for example, by introducing many units of many products, any number of consumers, several levels of advertising, etc.

Experimentation

The "second-half" of the typical statistical formulation, heretofore ignored, envisions an experiment conducted for the purpose of obtaining information (or additional information) about the world. Let $\{e_j\}$ denote a set of available experiments and let $\{r_{jk}\}$, $k = 1, \ldots, w_j$, be the set of possible results of experiment e_j.

In some presentations of statistical decision theory the word "strategy" (or derived strategy or decision rule) is used to denote a function which assigns a terminal act to each possible result of a given experiment.[11] In the more comprehensive use of the word, as used herein, a strategy would first specify an experiment to be performed, and then assign a terminal act to each possible result of this experiment. Some of the strategies in the latter set of strategies would specify the same experiment but assign different terminal acts to the possible results of the experiment, and other strategies would specify different experiments, etc. For any given experiment that may be contemplated, one can often compute (under appropriate assumptions) the probabilities of getting the results $\{r_{jk}\}$ (for fixed j) given each E_α. We ask, "If, in fact, the true state of the world is E_α, what is the probability of getting the result r_{jk} if we perform experiment e_j?" Call the stated probability $P(r_{jk} \mid e_j, E_\alpha)$. For a given experiment e_j, this gives the probability matrix

	r_{j1}	r_{j2}	$\cdots$	r_{jw_j}	Row Sums
E_1	$P(r_{j1} \mid e_j, E_1)$	$P(r_{j2} \mid e_j, E_1)$	$\cdots$	$P(r_{jw_j} \mid e_j, E_1)$	1.0
E_2	$P(r_{j1} \mid e_j, E_2)$	$P(r_{j2} \mid e_j, E_2)$	$\cdots$	$P(r_{jw_j} \mid e_j, E_2)$	1.0
$\vdots$	$\vdots$			$\vdots$	$\vdots$
E_n	$P(r_{j1} \mid e_j, E_n)$	$P(r_{j2} \mid e_j, E_n)$	$\cdots$	$P(r_{jw_j} \mid e_j, E_n)$	1.0

[11] Or a function which, for each possible result of a given experiment, assigns a probability distribution over the set of terminal acts.

There will be such a matrix for each contemplated experiment. These probabilities, together with the $V(e_j, r_{jk}, o_{iv})$—which represents the relative value of performing experiment e_j, observing result r_{jk}, then having the "consequence" o_{iv} occur from the statistical consequence matrix—are combined in an appropriate fashion [along with the *a priori* probabilities $P(E_j)$, if considered meaningful, or along with a certain disposition about the world] to yield a decision model. This model, hopefully, will provide a reasonable guide in selecting an experiment and a function designating a terminal act for each possible result of this experiment. Since a full discussion of these matters can be found in Raiffa and Schlaifer (1961) and other books dealing with statistical decision theory, they will not be discussed here.

3.7 DOMINANCE AMONG STRATEGIES

Because of limited information concerning relative values and probabilities, we may not be able to identify a strategy that maximizes $EV(\mathbf{I})$, but we may be able to conclude that certain strategies have expected relative values greater than the expected values of other strategies. The term "dominance" seems appropriate to describe such situations.[12] If it can be determined that $E(S_i)$ is less than or equal to the expected value of some other strategy in the set $\mathbf{S}$, then S_i will be said to be *dominated*.

Dominance can also be defined in more refined terms. For a general definition we shall use the following.

Definition 3.1 Suppose there exists a vector of real numbers $\mathbf{a} = (a_1, a_2, \ldots, a_i, \ldots, a_t)$, with $a_i \geq 0$, $i = 1, 2, \ldots, t$, $a_s = 0$ where s is some particular value of i, and $\sum_{i=1}^{t} a_i = 1.0$, such that

$$\sum_{i=1}^{t} a_i E(S_i) \geq E(S_s),$$

or, equivalently,

$$\sum_{i \neq s} a_i E(S_i) \geq E(S_s). \tag{3.15}$$

Then S_s is dominated.

In other language, if (3.15) holds, then $E(S_s)$ is "dominated" by a convex linear combination of the other $E(S_i)$. The reader can readily

---

[12] Dominance, as used here, should not be confused with dominance in game theory or statistical decision theory.

verify that a vector **a** does exist which satisfies (3.15) if and only if $E(S_s)$ is less than or equal to the expected relative value of some other strategy in **S**.[13]

Pure and Mixed Dominance

Dominance appears in its simplest form as *pure dominance* when (3.15) holds with one $a_i = 1$ ($i \neq s$) and all other $a_i = 0$. However, because of limited information on relative values and/or probabilities, we may be able to determine an **a** in which at least two a_i are positive such that S_s is dominated, and at the same time not able to discern pure dominance. The phrase "*mixed dominance*" will be used to characterize such situations.

Mixed dominance can be illustrated by a simple example with three strategies which are courses of action and three outcomes, i.e., Model I (**S** = **A**) with $m = n = 3$. For this 3-by-3 situation, suppose the probability matrix of strategies (courses of action) for outcomes is given by

	O_1	O_2	O_3
$S_1 = A_1$	.4	.1	.5
$S_2 = A_2$	.1	.6	.3
$S_3 = A_3$	.5	.3	.2

and further suppose that the only information (thus far) obtained about the $V_{ij} = V(A_i, O_j)$ is the ordinal ranking

$$V_{11} \geqslant V_{21} \geqslant V_{31} \geqslant V_{32} \geqslant V_{22} \geqslant V_{12} \geqslant V_{13} \geqslant V_{33} \geqslant V_{23}.$$

In looking for pure dominance, we first consider the pair S_1, S_2 and write $E(S_1) - E(S_2)$ as[14]
$$E(S_1) - E(S_2) = .4(V_{11} - V_{21}) + .3(V_{21} - V_{22}) - .3(V_{22} - V_{12})$$
$$- .2(V_{12} - V_{13}) + .3(V_{13} - V_{23}),$$

from which it is clear that nothing definite can be said about the sign of $E(S_1) - E(S_2)$. Hence we can conclude neither $E(S_1) \geqslant E(S_2)$ nor $E(S_2) \geqslant E(S_1)$. Similar equations may be written for the differences $E(S_1) - E(S_3)$ and $E(S_2) - E(S_3)$ which provide us with no definite conclusion about which member of either pair has larger expected value. Hence, this analysis for pure dominance is entirely inconclusive. Now consider the three courses of action (strategies) and write the probability matrix of strategies for consequences (**P**) with attached value ranking

---

[13] If this latter statement is used as a definition, the "general definition" given in connection with (3.15) follows as a theorem and vice versa. See Exercise 15.

[14] Using methods described previously in connection with (3.8).

	$V_{11} \geqslant$	$V_{21} \geqslant$	$V_{31} \geqslant$	$V_{32} \geqslant$	$V_{22} \geqslant$	$V_{12} \geqslant$	$V_{13} \geqslant$	$V_{33} \geqslant$	V_{23}
S_1	.4	0	0	0	0	.1	.5	0	0
S_2	0	.1	0	0	.6	0	0	0	.3
S_3	0	0	.5	.3	0	0	0	.2	0

We shall show that S_2 is dominated; that is, that there exists an $\mathbf{a} = (a, 0, 1 - a)$ with $0 \leqslant a \leqslant 1$ such that $aE(S_1) + (1 - a) E(S_3) \geqslant E(S_2)$. By a slight extension of previous methods,[15] we can write

$$aE(S_1) + (1 - a)E(S_3) - E(S_2)$$
$$= .4a(V_{11} - V_{21}) + (.4a - .1)(V_{21} - V_{31})$$
$$+ (.4 - .1a)(V_{31} - V_{32}) + (.7 - .4a)(V_{32} - V_{22})$$
$$+ (.1 - .4a)(V_{22} - V_{12}) + (.1 - .3a)(V_{12} - V_{13})$$
$$+ (.1 + .2a)(V_{13} - V_{33}) + (.3)(V_{33} - V_{23}), \quad (3.16)$$

from which it is clear that all the coefficients of the adjacent value differences will be non-negative if (and only if) $a = \frac{1}{4}$ or $\mathbf{a} = (\frac{1}{4}, 0, \frac{3}{4})$. Hence we have shown

$$.25E(S_1) + .75E(S_3) \geqslant E(S_2),$$

and conclude that S_2 is dominated. Thus either S_1 or S_3 (perhaps both) has an expected relative value at least as great as the expected value of S_2. It should be cautioned that our conclusion does not permit us to say that both $E(S_1)$ and $E(S_3)$ are at least as great as $E(S_2)$, but only that one of the four orderings $E(S_1) \geqslant E(S_3) \geqslant E(S_2), E(S_3) \geqslant E(S_1) \geqslant E(S_2), E(S_1) \geqslant E(S_2) \geqslant E(S_3)$, and $E(S_3) \geqslant E(S_2) \geqslant E(S_1)$ obtains in this situation.

The Basic Theorem

The significance of dominance is expressed by the following theorem:

Theorem 3.1 If S_s is dominated, then there exists at least one vector $\mathbf{C} = (C_1, \ldots, C_s, \ldots, C_t)$ which maximizes $EV(\mathbf{I})$ such that, in $\mathbf{C}$, $C_s = 0$.

In proving this, we first establish the existence of a $\mathbf{C}$ which maximizes $EV(\mathbf{I})$, and then show that in such a $\mathbf{C}$, $C_s = 0$.

Proof Since the V_j (relative values of consequences) are essentially bounded (by the requirement that they exist as real numbers, unique up to an increasing linear transformation), there exists at least one $\mathbf{C}$, with

[15] In $\mathbf{P}$, multiply row one by a, row two by -1, row three by $1 - a$, then collect row sums from left to right. For example the coefficient of $V_{12} - V_{13}$ in (3.16) is $.4a + .1a - .1 - .6 + (1 - a) .5 + (1 - a).3 = .1 - .3a$.

$C_i \geqslant 0$, $\sum C_i = 1$, which maximizes $EV(\mathbf{I})$. To show this, let V_1 denote the relative maximum of the V_j and V_r denote the relative minimum of the V_j. Assume $V_1 > V_r$. (If $V_1 = V_r$ then all V_j are equal and the theorem is trivial.) Then,

$$EV(\mathbf{I}) = \sum_{i=1}^{t} C_i E(S_i) = \sum_{i=1}^{t} C_i \sum_{j=1}^{r} P_{ij} V_j \qquad [P_{ij} = P(o_j \mid S_i)]$$

$$EV(\mathbf{I}) - V_r = \sum_{i=1}^{t} C_i \sum_{j=1}^{r} P_{ij}(V_j - V_r)$$

since $\sum C_i \sum P_{ij} V_r = V_r$. Furthermore,

$$\frac{EV(\mathbf{I}) - V_r}{V_1 - V_r} = \sum_{i=1}^{t} C_i \sum_{j=1}^{r} P_{ij} \frac{V_j - V_r}{V_1 - V_r} = \sum_{i=1}^{t} C_i W_i,$$

where $W_i = \sum_{j=1}^{r} P_{ij}(V_j - V_r)/(V_1 - V_r)$. The W_i are invariant, since the ratios $(V_j - V_r)/(V_1 - V_r)$ are invariant on an interval scale. Hence, maximizing $EV(\mathbf{I})$ is the same as maximizing $\sum_{i=1}^{t} C_i W_i$. But to maximize this convex linear combination of the W_i, it is sufficient to choose a W_i, say W_p, such that $W_p \geqslant W_i$, $i = 1, \ldots, t$, and thus let $C_p = 1$ and $C_i = 0$ for $i \neq p$. That is,

$$\max_{\mathbf{c}} \sum_{i=1}^{t} C_i W_i = \max W_i = W_p,$$

since, for any $\mathbf{C} = (C_1, \ldots, C_t)$, $W_p = \sum C_i W_p \geqslant \sum C_i W_i$. We are assured that max W_i exists, since the W_i are invariant real numbers and there are a finite number of them.

To complete the proof, let S_s be dominated, with $\mathbf{a}$ such that

$$\sum_{i \neq s} a_i E(S_i) \geqslant E(S_s) \qquad (a_s = 0, \; a_i \geqslant 0, \; \sum a_i = 1).$$

Let $\mathbf{C} = (C_1, \ldots, C_t)$ be any vector with $C_s > 0$, $C_i \geqslant 0$ $(i \neq s)$, $\sum_{i=1}^{t} C_i = 1$, and from $\mathbf{C}$ construct the vector $\mathbf{C}' = (C_1', \ldots, C_t')$ in which $C_s' = 0$, $C_i' = C_i + a_i C_s$ for $i \neq s$, $\sum_{i=1}^{t} C_i' = \sum_{i \neq s}(C_i + a_i C_s) = \sum_{i=1}^{t} C_i = 1$. Then

$$\sum_{i \neq s} a_i E(S_i) \geqslant E(S_s)$$

implies

$$\sum_{i \neq s} C_i E(S_i) + C_s \sum_{i \neq s} a_i E(S_i) \geqslant \sum_{i \neq s} C_i E(S_i) + C_s E(S_s)$$

or

$$\sum_{i=1}^{t} C_i' E(S_i) \geqslant \sum_{i=1}^{t} C_i E(S_i).$$

Thus if S_s is dominated, we can always find a $\mathbf{C}$ in which $C_s = 0$ that yields a total expected relative value at least as large as any $\mathbf{C}$ in which $C_s > 0$. It follows that there does exist a $\mathbf{C}$ which maximizes $EV(\mathbf{I})$ in which $C_s = 0$. This completes the proof.

Among other things Chapters 6 and 7 will be concerned with analysis for dominance in the two forms of Model I, Model II, and the statistical model, the former chapter treating pure dominance, the latter dealing with the more general case of mixed dominance.

3.8   THE CONTROLLABLE VARIABLE AND CRITERIA OF CHOICE

To conclude this chapter we shall say more about the controllable variable $\mathbf{C} = (C_1, C_2, \ldots, C_t)$, $C_i \geqslant 0$, $\sum C_i = 1$, discussed at the outset of Section 3.3 and in the previous section. The discussion begins with the mathematical interpretation of $\mathbf{C}$ followed by an extramathematical interpretation of the C_i as prescriptive probabilities. After this, we shall say a brief word about descriptive or predictive decision theory and note one attempt to interpret prescription in terms of prediction. The chapter then concludes with a few remarks about decision criteria of the type proposed by holders of frequency views of probability.

Research Conclusions

Under one interpretation, $\mathbf{C}$ is simply a device used to describe conclusions of research concerning the relative magnitudes of the expected values of the admissible strategies. If we could obtain precise point values for the probabilities P_{ij} and measure the relative values of the consequences in $\mathbf{Q}$ on an interval scale, then the expected relative values of the strategies would be determined uniquely up to an increasing linear transformation. If there were then a unique $S_i \in \mathbf{S}$ such that $E(S_i) > E(S_j)$ for all $j \neq i$, we would define $C_j = 0$ for $j \neq i$. In this case $\mathbf{C} = (C_1, \ldots, C_{i-1}, C_i, C_{i+1}, \ldots, C_t) = (0, \ldots, 0, 1, 0, \ldots, 0)$ would state that S_i has an expected value greater than any other strategy. If, instead of having a unique relative maximum $E(S_i)$, there is a set $\bar{S} = \{S_i \text{ max}\}$ such that all S_i in $\bar{S}$ have the same expected relative value and any S_i not in $\bar{S}$ has an expected relative value less than some S_i in $\bar{S}$, then we may define $C_i = 0$ for S_i not in $\bar{S}$ and $C_i = 1/\alpha$ for S_i in $\bar{S}$, where α is the number of S_i in $\bar{S}$.

In an actual program of research, it will seldom, if ever, be possible to obtain such fine measurements of probabilities and relative values of consequences as supposed in the preceding paragraph. In many cases, by using whatever measures can be obtained, it will not be possible to identify an $S_i \in \mathbf{S}$ for which $E(S_i) \geqslant E(S_j)$ for all $j \neq i$, but it will be possible to show that some strategies are dominated by others or by mixtures of other strategies.

We shall consider the "partial solution" first under the case of pure dominance. To illustrate what may happen under pure dominance, suppose with $t = 10$ that given measures of probabilities and relative values allow us to conclude that:

S_1 dominates $S_2, S_3, S_4, S_7,$ and S_8;

S_2 dominates $S_4, S_7,$ and S_8;

S_4 dominates S_8;

S_5 dominates S_7;

S_6 dominates S_8;

S_9 dominates S_{10}.

In other words,

$$E(S_1) \geqslant E(S_2) \geqslant E(S_4) \geqslant E(S_8),$$
$$E(S_1) \geqslant E(S_3),$$
$$E(S_2) \geqslant E(S_7),$$
$$E(S_5) \geqslant E(S_7),$$
$$E(S_6) \geqslant E(S_8),$$
$$E(S_9) \geqslant E(S_{10}).$$

This *partial ordering* of the $E(S_i)$ can also be represented in graph form. In the following *graph* the *node* numbered i stands for $E(S_i)$ and the *directed arc* ($\rightarrowtail$) from node i to node j stands for $E(S_i) \geqslant E(S_j)$.

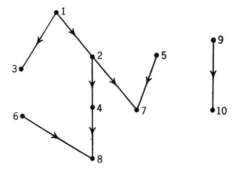

In this there are four S_i which have not been shown to be dominated by any other S_i, namely, $S_1, S_5, S_6,$ and S_9. A **C** vector which could express this would be $\mathbf{C} = (C_1, 0, 0, 0, C_5, C_6, 0, 0, C_9, 0)$. At least one such vector with $C_1 + C_5 + C_6 + C_9 = 1$ maximizes $EV(\mathbf{I})$, but it is not possible to say which one. If for some reason no additional information on probabilities and relative values can be obtained, then the best we can do in this situation,[16] under the criterion of maximization of $EV(\mathbf{I})$, is to note that either S_1 or S_5 or S_6 or S_9 is the best strategy (and that S_2, S_3, S_4, S_7, S_8, or S_{10} is not). If further distinctions among S_1, S_5, S_6, and S_9 are to be made, some secondary criterion must be used. We shall consider some of these at the end of this section.

When mixed dominance arises where pure dominance cannot be discerned, the situation is not quite as simple. Suppose, for example, that in addition to the cases of pure dominance in the foregoing illustration it can be determined that S_5 is dominated by a combination of S_1 and S_6. As noted in the last section, there is a **C** vector which maximizes $EV(\mathbf{I})$ in which $C_5 = 0$, but it is uncertain whether both $E(S_1) \geqslant E(S_5)$ and $E(S_6) \geqslant E(S_5)$ or just one of these two inequalities holds. In the situation here visualized, suppose we have been able to show that for any α such that $a \leqslant \alpha \leqslant b$ with $0 < a \leqslant b < 1$,

$$\alpha E(S_1) + (1 - \alpha)E(S_6) \geqslant E(S_5).$$

Then, by the proof of Theorem 3.1, if $\mathbf{C} = (C_1, 0, 0, 0, C_5, C_6, 0, 0, C_9, 0)$ in which $C_5 > 0$ is replaced by $\mathbf{C} = (C_1 + \alpha C_5, 0, 0, 0, 0, C_6 + (1 - \alpha) C_5, 0, 0, C_9, 0)$, the latter vector with any α in the interval $[a, b]$ will yield an $EV(\mathbf{I})$ at least as large as the $EV(\mathbf{I})$ given by the former vector. Apart from some additional interpretation of the C_i (i.e., other than to characterize conclusions of research), there is little more to say about this situation other than to point out that one may structure more interesting and complicated examples of mixed dominance.

Recommendations Based on Research Conclusions and Prescriptive Probabilities

Thus far we have been concerned with the mathematical interpretation of **C** as a manipulative variable used in maximizing $EV(\mathbf{I})$. Conclusions reached by applying the theory, such as $E(S_1) \geqslant E(S_2)$, are deductive (as opposed to inductive) conclusions. That is, beginning with a set of axioms (such as those of von Neumann and Morgenstern in Section 1.3 or of Savage in Section 5.6), we proceed to make measurements consistent with the axioms and then derive conclusions implied by the data from our measurements and the assumptions of the decision model.

As stated at the outset of this book, our concern is with a prescriptive theory of decision making, which from the present point of view leads into the extramathematical interpretation of **C** or of research conclusions.

---

[16] Neglecting the possibility of mixed dominance for the moment.

From the theory it follows that, if $E(S_1) > E(S_2)$, then strategy S_1 is preferred to or more desirable than S_2 although in causal terms $E(S_1)$ is larger than $E(S_2)$ because S_1 is preferred to S_2. Let us try to make this clearer. When we begin our investigation and arrive at a formulated decision situation, the individual is uncertain whether S_1 is a better strategy for him to adopt than S_2 (the same being true of any pair of admissible strategies). Our avowed purpose in proceeding further with the analysis is to try to remove this uncertainty. To do this, we adopt a set of rules (axioms), interpreted as criteria of consistent judgment, and proceed not to ask directly whether S_1 is preferred to S_2 (for an initial failure to provide a determinate answer to this question has led us on), but to obtain preference judgments concerned with consequences that might occur from the decision. As a result, we may be able to conclude that S_1 is, in fact, preferred to S_2 by first demonstrating that $E(S_1) > E(S_2)$ [or $V(S_1) > V(S_2)$ if we wish to define the value function over strategies as well as consequences, which is usually done in subjectivistic theories, such as the theory offered by Savage (1954)].

Based upon these considerations, we interpret $C_i = 0$ as a recommendation that the decision maker ought not to adopt S_i. Similarly, $C_i = 1$ is interpreted to mean that the decision maker ought to adopt and implement strategy S_i. If we do recommend (or prescribe) a particular $S_i \in \mathbf{S}$ to the decision maker, we say in effect: "By means of your judgments, I have measured your values for the consequences and the measures of trust (probabilities) you place in propositions of the form 'S_i if implemented will yield o_j.' Based upon these judgments, which I accept as valid, it is in your own best interests to adopt and implement strategy S_i."

Since the C_i are non-negative and add to one, they may be interpreted as subjective, prescriptive probabilities, namely,

C_i = probability with which the decision maker ought to adopt S_i.

Initially, the C_i are all undetermined. Then, as we show that certain strategies are dominated by other strategies or mixtures of other strategies, the C_i for the dominated strategies are set equal to zero as done in the example given earlier. If our measurements are fine enough, all C_i but one can eventually be set equal to zero (the remaining C_i equaling one).

In situations where a complete solution is not obtained, certain things may be done with the nonzero C_i interpreted as prescriptive probabilities. For example, if $t = 3$ and we have been able to show that $\frac{1}{2}E(S_1) + \frac{1}{2}E(S_2) \geqslant E(S_3)$ but have not been able to demonstrate pure dominance, then it is in keeping with the intended interpretation to advise the decision maker that he can do better by adopting the mixed strategy that has equal probability (to the decision maker) for S_1 and S_2 than by adopting S_3.

In other words, if he places the same measure of trust in the propositions, "This coin when flipped will show heads" and "This coin when flipped will show tails," then he can do better by flipping the coin and adopting S_1 or S_2 as the coin shows heads or tails respectively than by adopting S_3. Note that we are not asserting that this mixed strategy is the best thing available, only that it is better than something else, namely, S_3. (Also note that either S_1 or S_2 is at least as good as the mixed strategy.) If our measurements of relative values and probabilities are fine enough, there would obviously be no point in considering mixed strategies when making recommendations, except perhaps in cases where several strategies have the same maximum expected relative value.

When recommendations to a decision maker are made in the context of traditional decision theory, it is usually no surprise if the decision maker does not follow the recommendations. The primary reason for this is that traditional decision theory is only marginally concerned with measuring the decision maker's relative values, and often uses a criterion of choice which does not require the time of the decision maker for its application. In the context of the present theory, we have much greater reason to expect that the decision maker will follow the recommendations derived from the research conclusions. If he does not, there is either serious question concerning his intentions in wishing to have his problem analyzed according to this theory or else there is serious question about the methods we have used in applying the theory to his situation. By looking into cases where the individual does not follow the research recommendations, we may be able to find defects in our methodology and thus seek to improve it.

Prediction and Prescription

In recent years there has been a vast amount of research conducted for the purpose of studying human behavior in choice situations. As one might expect there is a large and growing literature on the subject [see part II of Thrall, Coombs, and Davis (1954) or various references in Churchman (1961b)].

Among the most interesting studies of human behavior in repetitive choice situations are those reported by Siegel and Fouraker (1960);[17] Scodel, Minas, Ratoosh, and Lipetz (1959);[18] and Davidson, Suppes, and Siegel (1957). The first two of these are concerned with the behavior of individuals over repeated trials in two-person nonzero-sum games[19]

---

[17] See also Fouraker, Siegel, and Harnett (1962).

[18] With the sequel Minas, Scodel, Marlowe, and Rawson (1960).

[19] For a discussion of two-person, nonzero-sum noncooperative games, see Luce and Raiffa (1957, Chapter 5).

under varying conditions of information, the former concentrating on bilateral monopoly, the latter on the "prisoner's dilemma" noncooperative game. The book by Davidson, et al., is basically concerned with experimental measurement of individuals' relative values and subjective probabilities.

Most experiments of the type recounted in these publications are designed to test specific behavioral hypotheses, and all have been concerned with gaining a better understanding of how individuals make decisions. To a very large extent they are interested in descriptive decision theory as opposed to prescriptive decision theory, i.e., their aim is to describe how individuals actually do make decisions rather than to specify how individuals ought to make decisions. This distinction is further illustrated in the interpretations of, e.g., the von Neumann-Morgenstern utility axioms. The descriptive theorist who adopts these is assuming that an individual behaves in accord with them. The prescriptive theorist may feel that an individual ought to adhere to them as criteria of rational behavior, but he does not necessarily assume that (without appropriate instruction) an individual does adhere to them.

In the scientific community it is generally felt that, in order to be able to describe adequately a phenomenon, one must first be able to predict with respect to that phenomenon. For example, a physical "law" (e.g., gravitation) may be interpreted as a prediction that, given such and such conditions, then certain results will follow. It is therefore not surprising to find that many descriptive decision theorists are concerned with constructing and testing (by behavioral experimentation) predictive models of choice behavior. Some of the more interesting examples of proposed predictive models concerned with individual choice behavior are discussed by Davidson, Suppes, and Siegel (1957, Chapter III); Royden, Suppes, and Walsh (1959); Suppes and Walsh (1959);[20] and Luce (1959).

In an extremely interesting and highly controversial book,[21] Churchman (1961a) ties together the prescriptive and predictive aspects of choice in decision situations, maintaining that prescription should emanate from prediction. In this most thorough treatise on the problems of measurement of values and probabilities for the purpose of predicting (and hence prescribing) behavior, Churchman states his basic thesis as follows:

Suppose we could agree on the standard conditions for measuring the values of outcomes. Then we would say "X values an outcome to degree k" means "X would exhibit such-and-such behavior in the standard environment for value measurements." The present suggestion is to assert that the

---

[20] See De Groot (1963) for criticism of this paper.

[21] The reader's attention is called to the reviews by Cushen (1961) and Alderson (1962), and to Smith's critique (1961) of Churchman's book.

"ought" in a recommendation can be stated as follows: "X ought to do A in *this* environment" means "X would do A in the standard environment that defines value measurements." This suggestion at present is tentative—it will take the rest of the book to defend and make its meaning approximately intelligible.

For the moment, however, the general idea can be understood. If a scientist states that an executive should follow a certain course of action, he says in effect, "I have measured the values of the executive—or his organization—for the various outcomes that may result from his decisions. These measurements predict what he would do if he were making his decision under the standard conditions of value measurements. When I say he ought to exhibit such-and-such behavior, I mean that this is the behavior he would exhibit if these standard conditions held. Of course, he may not do what he ought to do; that is, the standard conditions may not hold in this environment" [pp. 17–18].

In the present theory the predictive aspect of behavior has an important role to play, namely, in relation to decisions that other individuals may make which influence the consequence that will result from our individual's decision. If probabilities are attached to things that others may do, these would be a part of the $P(o_j \mid S_i)$. In other words, if other individuals' actions interact with our decision maker's actions (which will so often be the case) in determining the consequences of importance to our decision maker, then these ought to be accounted for in connection with the definitions of the consequences. In many cases, however, we will only have a vague notion of who these other individuals or groups of individuals may be and will find it difficult if not impossible to assess the things that they might do, let alone have any idea as to their values, intentions, and the like. The magnitude of the problems presented by these realities should not be underestimated, even though we shall do them gross injustice here by not considering them more explicitly.[22]

Secondary Criteria

From the present viewpoint it is meaningful to enquire into other prescriptive criteria only when measurements of probabilities and relative values fail to give a complete solution to the decision problem under the expected-value maximization criterion. For this reason we have previously called such other criteria *secondary criteria*.

Many secondary criteria arise in connection with the statistical model, some persons feeling that it is meaningless to speak about the $P(E_j)$, where the E_j are "states of the world," or in connection with two-person

---

[22] Game theory and discussions of conflict situations do consider these interactions more explicitly.

or n-person games.[23] In such situations some of the criteria of choice which have been proposed or discussed are the maximin utility principle, the maximax utility criteria, the Hurwicz α criterion, the minimax loss principle, and the Laplace criterion. Suppose, for example, we had measured the relative values of the consequences in the statistical consequence matrix on an interval scale and let $V_{ij} = V(o_{ij})$:

$$
\begin{array}{c|cccc}
 & \multicolumn{4}{c}{j} \\
 & E_1 & E_2 & \ldots & E_n \\
\hline
S_1 & V_{11} & V_{12} & \ldots & V_{1n} \\
S_2 & V_{21} & V_{22} & \ldots & V_{2n} \\
\vdots & \vdots & & & \\
S_t & V_{t1} & V_{t2} & \ldots & V_{tn}
\end{array}
$$

(with i labeling rows)

In the above order, without permitting mixed strategies:

1. *Maximin utility* prescribes the S_i for which min $\{V_{ij}\}$ is a maximum. This prescribes the "best of the worst": find the smallest V_{ij} in each row, then choose the row that has the largest of these smallest V_{ij}. This criterion is pessimistic.

2. *Maximax utility* prescribes the S_i for which max $\{V_{ij}\}$ is a maximum. This prescribes the "best of the best": find the largest V_{ij} in each row, then choose the row which has the largest of these largest V_{ij}. This criterion is optimistic.

3. *Hurwicz* α prescribes the S_i which maximizes $[\alpha \max_j \{V_{ij}\} + (1 - \alpha) \min_j \{V_{ij}\}]$, where α is a number between 0 and 1 reflecting the individual's "degree of optimism." $\alpha = 0$ gives the pessimistic maximin (1), and $\alpha = 1$ gives the optimistic maximax (2).

4. *Minimax loss* prescribes the S_i which minimizes $\max_j [\max_i V_{ij} - V_{ij}]$. The matrix of the $\max_i V_{ij} - V_{ij}$ is called the loss matrix after Savage (1954), each element measuring the difference in relative value that would result if E_j were the true state and S_i were adopted instead of the strategy which gives the best value under E_j. Obviously,

$$
\max_i V_{ij} - V_{ij} \geqslant 0.
$$

---

[23] In a two-person zero-sum game, an "optimal mixed strategy" for one player could take the form $\mathbf{C} = (C_1, C_2) = (\frac{1}{2}, \frac{1}{2})$ if *both* players used the maximin criterion. (See any standard text on game theory.) The "flip of a fair coin" interpretation for selecting S_1 or S_2 would apply in this type of situation.

5. *Laplace* prescribes the S_i which maximizes $\sum_{j=1}^n V_{ij}$ or $\sum_{j=1}^n V_{ij}/n$, the latter being the arithmetical average of the V_{ij} in the ith row.

From the standpoint of measuring relative values, the maximin criterion (or maximax) has an advantage over (3), (4), or (5) since it can be applied with only a quasi-ordering of consequences: for each strategy determine the least desirable consequence, then among these t consequences identify the most desirable. Maximax requires only that one identify the most desirable consequence in the statistical consequence matrix. Milnor in Thrall, et al. (1954, Chapter IV) gives a four-by-four matrix of relative values for which criteria (1), (3), (4), and (5) each prescribes a different strategy, and goes on to compare these criteria against a set of axioms (properties considered desirable for the criteria to satisfy), noting that each criterion fails on at least one axiom. He then considers the possibility of other criteria:

> It has become apparent that no possible criterion can have all of the properties that one would desire. It is therefore natural to try constructing a list of those properties which are most fundamental and important, to see if at least these can be satisfied. The following is the author's attempt to construct such a list. Others would doubtlessly have given rather different lists [p. 57].

Milnor then presents his list of eight properties (axioms) he considers to be most fundamental and important, and observes that none of the four criteria considered previously satisfies all eight axioms, but asserts that there do exist criteria which simultaneously satisfy them. He then illustrates criteria that do satisfy all eight, but comments: "In any case these criteria are probably too difficult computationally to be of practical interest" (p. 58); and he finally concludes with, "It is interesting to ask if there exist any simple, computable criteria which satisfy all of these conditions" (p. 58).[24]

Luce and Raiffa (1957, Chapters 13 and 14) go into this "problem" in a bit more detail along with related topics.[25]

If one feels that it is meaningful to consider the "probability that E_j is in fact the true state" [i.e., $P(E_j), j = 1, \ldots, n$], then with various partial measurements on the $P_j = P(E_j)$ the above criteria may still be used, but in slightly different form. The same is true in the case of Model I or Model II. We illustrate this with two examples.

---

[24] One of the difficulties which Milnor points out in his approach is that value judgments are required to obtain a list of the "most fundamental and important" properties. Thus, if different experts in the field arrive at different lists of properties, or at the same list in different orders of importance, we arrive at the unsolved problem of a best method for amalgamating individual values.

[25] Also see Ackoff (1962).

EXAMPLES. First consider the matrix of relative values of consequences

	E_1	E_2	E_3	E_4
S_1	2	7	10	8
S_2	4	3	6	7
S_3	5	3	2	6

with associated loss matrix

$$\begin{bmatrix} 3 & 0 & 0 & 0 \\ 1 & 4 & 4 & 1 \\ 0 & 4 & 8 & 2 \end{bmatrix}$$

Given no information about the $P(E_j)$, it is not possible to discern dominance among the three S_i. If the P_j are considered meaningless the five criteria in the order listed above prescribe (1) S_2; (2) S_1; (3) S_2 with $\alpha < \frac{1}{4}$, S_1 with $\alpha > \frac{1}{4}$; (4) S_1; and (5) S_1. Now suppose it has been determined that

$$P_1 \geqslant P_2 \geqslant P_3 \geqslant P_4 \geqslant 0, \qquad \sum_{j=1}^{4} P_j = 1, \qquad (3.17a)$$

where $P_j = P(E_j)$. With

$$E(S_i) = \sum P_j V_{ij}, \qquad (3.18a)$$

the reader[26] may note that it is not possible to determine either pure or mixed dominance (as defined in the previous section) among the S_i given the V_{ij} and (3.17a). Letting

$$\alpha_1 = P_1 - P_2,$$
$$\alpha_2 = 2(P_2 - P_3),$$
$$\alpha_3 = 3(P_3 - P_4),$$
$$\alpha_4 = 4P_4,$$

(3.17a) is equivalent to

$$\alpha_j \geqslant 0, \qquad j = 1, 2, 3, 4, \qquad \sum_{j=1}^{4} \alpha_j = 1. \qquad (3.17b)$$

In terms of the α_j, (3.18a) may be written as

$$E(S_i) = \sum_{j=1}^{4} \alpha_j \left\{ \frac{1}{j} \sum_{k=1}^{j} V_{ik} \right\}. \qquad (3.18b)$$

---

[26] If he considers the P_j meaningful, the reader may note quite readily the assumptions about the P_j for the different strategies that lead to the five criteria listed above when no actual measurements of the P_j have been obtained.

Given (3.17a), in view of (3.17b), (3.18b) acts in the same fashion as (3.18a) when all we know about the P_j is $P_j \geqslant 0, j = 1, 2, 3, 4, \sum P_j = 1$.[27] From the form of (3.18b), write a new "payoff" matrix whose elements are the $1/j \sum_{k=1}^{j} V_{ik}$:

	α_1	α_2	α_3	α_4
S_1	2	4.5	6.33	6.75
S_2	4	3.5	4.33	5.00
S_3	5	4.0	3.33	4.00

with the associated loss matrix

$$\begin{bmatrix} 3 & 0 & 0 & 0 \\ 1 & 1 & 2 & 1.75 \\ 0 & .5 & 3 & 2.75 \end{bmatrix}$$

The statement about dominance following (3.18a) should be clearer on inspection of the first matrix in this pair. Applying the secondary criteria to these new matrices gives, in the order listed above, (1) S_2; (2) S_1; (3) S_2 with $\alpha < {}^6/_{13}$, S_1 with $\alpha > {}^6/_{13}$; (4) S_2; and (5) S_1.

Second, suppose under Model I ($S = A$), we obtain the matrix of relative values

	O_1	O_2	O_3
A_1	5	1	10
A_2	4	6	2

Without any information about the $P(O_j \mid A_i)$, excepting that these are non-negative and sum to one for each A_i, the criteria prescribe (1) A_2; (2) A_1; (3) A_2 if $\alpha < {}^1/_5$, A_1 if $\alpha > {}^1/_5$; and (5) A_1. Minimax loss has been omitted since it does not apply under this setup.[28] (It should be noted that the other criteria are applied in a fashion similar to the above, but that the setup here is different than that for the statistical model.) Letting $P_{ij} = P(O_j \mid A_i)$, suppose that

$$P_{11} \geqslant P_{12} \geqslant P_{13} \geqslant 0, \qquad \sum P_{1j} = 1,$$
$$P_{22} \geqslant P_{21} \geqslant P_{23} \geqslant 0, \qquad \sum P_{2j} = 1,$$

---

[27] That is, under the attached conditions, both are of the form $\sum_{j=1}^{n} c_j a_{ij}$, where the a_{ij} are known but all we know about the c_j is that $c_j \geqslant 0, j = 1, 2, 3, 4$, and $\sum c_j = 1$.

[28] Minimax loss can be used in the intended fashion only if the given two-by-three matrix is made into a two-by-nine matrix where each column heading reads: "O_{j_1} occurs if A_1 is used; O_{j_2} occurs if A_2 is used," $j_1, j_2 = 1, 2, 3$.

which may be transformed into

$$\alpha_j \geqslant 0, \quad j = 1, 2, 3, \quad \sum \alpha_j = 1,$$
$$\beta_j \geqslant 0, \quad j = 1, 2, 3, \quad \sum \beta_j = 1, \tag{3.19}$$

respectively, on letting

$$\alpha_1 = P_{11} - P_{12}, \qquad \beta_1 = P_{22} - P_{21},$$
$$\alpha_2 = 2(P_{12} - P_{13}), \qquad \beta_2 = 2(P_{21} - P_{23}),$$
$$\alpha_3 = 3P_{13}, \qquad \beta_3 = 3P_{23}.$$

With these notations

$$E(A_1) = 5\alpha_1 + 3\alpha_2 + \tfrac{16}{3}\alpha_3$$
$$E(A_2) = 6\beta_1 + 5\beta_2 + 3\beta_3.$$

Subject to (3.19), these latter equations give a tie for maximin ($3 = 3$), A_2 for maximax ($6 > \frac{16}{3}$), A_2 for Hurwicz α ($\alpha > 0$), and A_2 for Laplace.

In subsequent chapters we shall focus attention on the "primary" criterion, maximization of expected relative value, and we will not go into these second criteria, perhaps to the dismay of some readers and the relief of others. Readers interested in applying the secondary criteria where the primary criterion fails should be able to tinker with these as they please after studying the foregoing examples and the references cited previously along with the mathematical methods of analysis to be discussed in Chapters 6 and 7. Before going into the analysis of dominance in these chapters, we shall consider relative values and probabilities in greater detail in the next two chapters.

EXERCISES

1. Verify (3.6).

2. Assuming the values $V_1 = 4$, $V_2 = -2$, $V_3 = -9$ are unique up to an increasing linear transformation and (U_1, U_2, U_3) is any other set of numbers which characterize these three relative values:

(a) Find U_2 when $U_1 = 8$, $U_3 = 2$.

(b) Find U_3 when $U_1 = -3$, $U_2 = -12$.

3. Suppose one has obtained the relative values $V_1 = 10$, $V_2 = 8$, $V_3 = 2$, $V_4 = 0$, $V_5 = -3$, $V_6 = -7$ and $(U_1, U_2, \ldots, U_6)$ is any other set of numbers used to represent these relative values.

(a) Find $(U_1, \ldots, U_6)$ if $U_1 = 1$, $U_6 = 0$.

(b) Find $(U_1, \ldots, U_6)$ if $U_6 = 0$, $\sum_{j=1}^{6} U_j = 1$.

4. Prove that if $V_{a1} + V_{a2} + \ldots + V_{an} \geqslant V_{b1} + V_{b2} + \ldots + V_{bn}$, with n terms on either side, then the inequality is preserved under any increasing

linear transformation of the V_j. Also show that $E(S_1) \geqslant E(S_2)$ is preserved under any increasing linear transformation of the V_j.

5. Under Model I ($S = A$), suppose with two courses of action, A_1 and A_2, there are associated five outcomes $O_1, \ldots, O_5$, and that all one knows about the relative value of the consequences is the ranking $V(A_2, O_4) \geqslant V(A_1, O_2) \geqslant V(A_2, O_3) \geqslant V(A_2, O_1) \geqslant V(A_1, O_1) \geqslant V(A_1, O_5) \geqslant V(A_2, O_5) \geqslant V(A_1, O_3) \geqslant V(A_2, O_2) \geqslant V(A_1, O_4)$. What three inequalities must the $P_{ij} = P(O_j \mid A_i)$ satisfy in order to conclude that $E(A_2) \geqslant E(A_1)$? Assuming $P_{24} > 0$, can one conclude under any conditions on the P_{ij} that $E(A_1) \geqslant E(A_2)$?

6. Under Model I ($S = A$) with two courses of action, A_1 and A_2, and four outcomes $O_1, \ldots, O_4$, suppose that all one knows about the P_{ij} is the ranking $P_{11} \geqslant P_{22} \geqslant P_{23} \geqslant P_{12} \geqslant P_{14} \geqslant P_{24} \geqslant P_{13} \geqslant P_{21} \geqslant 0$. If U is used to represent one of the V_{ij}, what inequalities must the V_{ij} satisfy in order to conclude that $E(A_1) \geqslant E(A_2)$?

7. (*Continuation.*) Suppose that in Exercise 6 above, one also has obtained the ordinal ranking $V_{14} \geqslant V_{23} \geqslant V_{11} \geqslant V_{12} \geqslant V_{22} \geqslant V_{24} \geqslant V_{13} \geqslant V_{21}$. What V_{ij} should replace U in order to obtain the weakest set of inequalities for the V_{ij} such that, if these inequalities hold, then one can conclude $E(A_1) \geqslant E(A_2)$? Then show that, if $V_{12} - V_{22} \geqslant V_{23} - V_{11}$ and $V_{14} - V_{23} \geqslant V_{24} - V_{13}$, one can conclude that $E(A_1) \geqslant E(A_2)$.

8. Given the following matrix of relative values under Model I with $S_i = A_i$

	O_1	O_2	O_3	O_4
A_1	6	2	1	12
A_2	8	4	3	14

if one makes no use of the probabilities of the A_i for the O_j, which course of action is specified by:

(a) The maximin criterion?

(b) The maximax criterion?

(c) The Hurwicz criterion for any value of α? [For this case, $H(A_i) = \alpha \max_j (V_{ij}) + (1 - \alpha) \min_j (V_{ij})$, where H is the Hurwicz function to be used in judging courses of action, and α is a constant between 0 and 1.]

(d) The Laplace criterion?

9. (*Continuation.*) Suppose in the previous exercise one also knows the probability rankings $P_{14} \geqslant P_{11} \geqslant P_{12} \geqslant P_{13} \geqslant 0$ and $P_{22} \geqslant P_{21} \geqslant P_{23} \geqslant P_{24} \geqslant 0$ which represent rankings of the probabilities of A_1 for the O_j and A_2 for O_j respectively.

(a) Show that $E(A_1) = 12\alpha_1 + 9\alpha_2 + {}^{20}/_3\alpha_3 + {}^{21}/_4\alpha_4$, subject to the restrictions $\alpha_j \geqslant 0$, $j = 1, \ldots, 4$ and $\sum \alpha_j = 1$.

(*b*) In a similar way, show $E(A_2) = 4\beta_1 + 6\beta_2 + 5\beta_3 + {}^{29}/_4\beta_4$, subject to the restrictions $\beta_j \geq 0, j = 1, \ldots, 4$ and $\sum \beta_j = 1$.

(*c*) Show then that the maximin criteria and maximax criteria both prescribe A_1 as the better course of action, and hence that, by the Hurwicz criterion for this case, any value of α between 0 and 1 will prescribe A_1.

(*d*) Specify a set of permissible values for the α_j and β_j such that, if these are in fact the true values, then $E(A_2) > E(A_1)$.

10. (*Continuation.*) Suppose in addition to the two rankings in Exercise 9, one knows the mixed ranking $P_{14} \geq P_{11} \geq P_{22} \geq P_{21} \geq P_{23} \geq P_{12} \geq P_{24} \geq P_{13} \geq 0$. Write $E(A_1) - E(A_2)$ in a form $v_1 P_1 + v_2 P_2 + \ldots + v_8 P_8$, where $(P_1, \ldots, P_8) = (P_{14}, \ldots, P_{13})$ and $v_1, \ldots, v_8$ are the corresponding value coefficients from the matrix in Exercise 8 (with appropriate signs). Then let $\sum_{i=j}^{8} \alpha_i = P_j$, so that $E(A_1) - E(A_2) = 12\alpha_1 + 18\alpha_2 + 14\alpha_3 + 6\alpha_4 + 3\alpha_5 + 5\alpha_6 - 8\alpha_7 - 7\alpha_8$, subject to $\alpha_i \geq 0, i = 1, 2, \ldots, 8, \sum i\alpha_i = 2$, and various other restrictions arising from the ranking of the P_{ij}.

(*a*) Compare this equation with (3.10), and write $E(A_1) - E(A_2)$ in a form like (3.10), introducing U and keeping $\alpha_1, \ldots, \alpha_8$ as they appear above.

(*b*) Does there exist a value of U for which every coefficient of the α_i is non-negative?

(*c*) What is the largest permissible value that α_8 can take on here? If α_8 does take on this value, what will $\alpha_1, \ldots, \alpha_7$ equal? In this case note that $E(A_1) - E(A_2) = -1.75$. On the other hand, if $P_{14} = P_{11} = P_{22} = P_{21} = {}^1/_2$, what will $E(A_1) - E(A_2)$ equal? Hence, what can one conclude about which course of action has the larger expected value?

11. Given the matrix of relative values for the statistical model,

	E_1	E_2	E_3	E_4	E_5	E_6
S_1	3	5	4	7	1	9
S_2	0	1	6	4	3	7
S_3	6	7	7	2	2	2
S_4	8	2	0	6	1	0
S_5	2	4	6	3	0	5

(*a*) Assuming no information about the $P_j = P(E_j)$, show that S_5 is dominated by a mixture of S_1, S_2, and S_3. Then, by using S_1, S_2, S_3, and S_4, find the S_i prescribed by each of the five secondary criteria discussed in Section 3.8.

(*b*) Suppose it has been determined that $P_1 \geq P_2 \geq P_3 \geq P_4 \geq P_5 \geq P_6 \geq 0$, with $\sum P_j = 1$. Under this ranking form a new 5-by-6 value matrix with columns labeled α_j, with $\alpha_j \geq 0, \sum \alpha_j = 1$ as done in connection with the example around (3.17) and (3.18). For this new matrix state which strategies are dominated by others. If at least two strategies cannot be shown to be dominated, apply the five secondary criteria to these.

(*c*) Repeat part (*b*), using the ranking $P_3 \geq P_5 \geq P_1 \geq P_4 \geq P_6 \geq P_2 \geq 0$.

12. Under the statistical model with $n = 5$ suppose it has been found that $P_1 = .08$, $P_2 = .32$, $P_3 = .20$, $P_4 = .12$, $P_5 = .28$, and that $V_{12} \geqslant V_{21} \geqslant V_{23} \geqslant V_{13} \geqslant V_{11} \geqslant V_{25} \geqslant V_{15} \geqslant V_{24} \geqslant V_{14} \geqslant V_{22}$, where V_{ij} is the relative value of the consequence associated with S_i and E_j. Show that $E(S_1) \geqslant E(S_2)$.

13. Under Model I with $t = 4$, $r = 5$, suppose $V(o_1) \geqslant V(o_2) \geqslant V(o_3) \geqslant V(o_4) \geqslant V(o_5)$ along with the probability matrix

	o_1	o_2	o_3	o_4	o_5
S_1	.14	.20	.06	.34	.26
S_2	.08	.37	.20	.22	.13
S_3	.11	.27	.13	.29	.20
S_4	.16	.19	.12	.29	.24

What conclusions can you reach concerning a $C = (C_1, C_2, C_3, C_4)$ which maximizes $EV(\mathbf{I})$?

14. Given the matrix of relative values under Model I with $S_i = A_i$,

	O_1	O_2	O_3
A_1	-6	-9	-5
A_2	-7	-5	-9

and the ranking $P_{11} \geqslant P_{21} \geqslant P_{22} \geqslant P_{13} \geqslant P_{12} \geqslant P_{23} \geqslant 0$, show that $E(A_1) \geqslant E(A_2)$, and find the set of values for the probabilities such that $E(A_1) = E(A_2)$.

15. Prove the theorem: There exists a vector of real numbers $\mathbf{a} = (a_1, \ldots, a_t)$, with $a_i \geqslant 0$, $a_s = 0$, $\sum a_i = 1$ such that $\sum a_i E(S_i) \geqslant E(S_s)$ if and only if $E(S_s)$ is less than or equal to the expected relative value of some other strategy.

16. In the example of mixed dominance in connection with (3.16), find sets of numbers satisfying the ordinal ranking of relative values such that

(a) $E(S_1) > E(S_3) > E(S_2)$.

(b) $E(S_3) > E(S_1) > E(S_2)$.

(c) $E(S_1) > E(S_2) > E(S_3)$.

(d) $E(S_3) > E(S_2) > E(S_1)$.

17. Given the probability matrix under Model I $(\mathbf{S} = \mathbf{A})$,

	O_1	O_2	O_3	O_4
A_1	.20	.35	.15	.30
A_2	.15	.35	.25	.25
A_3	.20	.50	.20	.10
A_4	.40	.35	.05	.20
A_5	.45	.35	.10	.10

and the ordinal ranking of relative values $V_{14} \geqslant V_{23} \geqslant V_{33} \geqslant V_{41} \geqslant V_{34} \geqslant V_{52} \geqslant V_{12} \geqslant V_{21} \geqslant V_{44} \geqslant V_{53} \geqslant V_{54} \geqslant V_{11} \geqslant V_{32} \geqslant V_{22} \geqslant V_{43} \geqslant V_{13} \geqslant V_{42} \geqslant V_{31} \geqslant V_{51} \geqslant V_{24}$:

(*a*) Eliminate whatever courses of action you can by analyzing for pure dominance. State then what form $C = (C_1, C_2, C_3, C_4, C_5)$ will take in maximizing $EV(I)$.

(*b*) Using only the analysis of (*a*), state which of the following orderings of the $E(A_i)$ are possible and which are impossible of realization:

(i) $E(A_1) > E(A_2) > E(A_3) > E(A_4) > E(A_5)$.

(ii) $E(A_2) > E(A_4) > E(A_5) > E(A_1) > E(A_3)$.

(iii) $E(A_4) > E(A_5) > E(A_1) > E(A_3) > E(A_2)$.

18. Given the probability matrix

	o_1	o_2	o_3
S_1	.50	.20	.30
S_2	.30	.35	.35
S_3	.10	.40	.50

and the ordinal ranking $V(o_1) \geqslant V(o_2) \geqslant V(o_3)$, what can be said about the vector $C = (C_1, C_2, C_3)$ which maximizes $EV(I)$?

19. Give an example of a decision situation that could apply to yourself in which you might suspect that $V(A_1, O_j) = V(A_2, O_j) = \ldots = V(A_m, O_j)$ for each $j, j = 1, \ldots, n$.

20. What unusual feature do the V_{ij} in the matrix of Exercise 8 possess?

21. With the probability matrix

	O_1	O_2	O_3	O_4
S_1	.3	.4	.2	.1
S_2	.1	.6	.1	.2

suppose that Model II applies and one has determined $V(O_1) \geqslant V(O_2) \geqslant V(O_3) \geqslant V(O_4)$. Show that $E(S_1) \geqslant E(S_2)$.

REFERENCES

Ackoff, R. L., with S. K. Gupta and J. S. Minas, *Scientific Method: Optimizing Applied Research Decisions*, John Wiley and Sons, New York, 1962.

Adams, E., and R. Fagot, "A Model of Riskless Choice," *Behavioral Science*, **4**, 1–9 (1959).

Alderson, W., Review of Churchman's *Prediction and Optimal Decision*, in *Management Science*, **8**, 375–380 (1962).

Churchman, C. W., *Prediction and Optimal Decision*, Prentice-Hall, Englewood Cliffs, New Jersey, 1961a.

——, "Decision and Value Theory," in *Progress in Operations Research*, Volume 1, ed. by R. L. Ackoff, John Wiley and Sons, New York, 1961b.

——, and Ackoff, R. L., *Psychologistics*, University of Pennsylvania Faculty Research Fund, Philadelphia, 1947 (mimeographed).

——, "An Approximate Measure of Value," *Journal of Operations Research*, 2, 172–187 (1954).

Cushen, W. E., Review of Churchman's *Prediction and Optimal Decision*, in *Journal of Operations Research*, 9, 914–916 (1961).

Davidson, D., P. Suppes, and S. Siegel, *Decision Making, An Experimental Approach*, Stanford University Press, Stanford, California, 1957.

De Groot, M. H., "Some Comments on the Experimental Measurement of Utility," *Behavioral Science*, 8, 146–149 (1963).

Fouraker, L. E., S. Siegel, and D. L. Harnett, "An Experimental Disposition of Alternative Bilateral Monopoly Models Under Conditions of Price Leadership," *Journal of Operations Research*, 10, 41–50 (1962).

Luce, R. D., *Individual Choice Behavior*, John Wiley and Sons, New York, 1959.

Luce, R. D., and H. Raiffa, *Games and Decisions: Introduction and Critical Survey*, John Wiley and Sons, New York, 1957.

Minas, J. S., A. Scodel, D. Marlowe, and H. Rawson, "Some Descriptive Aspects of Two-Person Non-Zero-Sum Games, II," *Conflict Resolution*, 4, 193–197 (1960).

Mosteller, F., and P. Nogee, "An Experimental Measure of Utility," *Journal of Political Economy*, 59, 371–404 (1951).

Raiffa, H., and R. Schlaifer, *Applied Statistical Decision Theory*, Division of Research, Harvard Business School, Boston, 1961.

Royden, H. L., P. Suppes, and K. Walsh, "A Model for the Experimental Measurement of the Utility of Gambling," *Behavioral Science*, 4, 11–18 (1959).

Savage, L. J., *The Foundations of Statistics*, John Wiley and Sons, New York, 1954.

Scodel, A., J. S. Minas, P. Ratoosh, and M. Lipetz, "Some Descriptive Aspects of Two-Person Non-Zero-Sum Games," *Conflict Resolution*, 3, 114–119 (1959).

Siegel, S., and L. E. Fouraker, *Bargaining and Group Decision Making*, McGraw-Hill Book Co., New York, 1960.

Smith, N. M., *A Critique of Churchman's Science of Values*, Technical Paper ORO-TP-40, Operations Research Office (now Research Analysis Corporation), McLean, Virginia, 1961.

Stevens, S. S., "On the Theory of Scales of Measurement," *Science*, 103, 677–680 (1946).

Suppes, P., and M. Winet, "An Axiomatization of Utility Based on the Notion of Utility Differences," *Management Science*, 1, 259–270 (1955).

Suppes, P., and K. Walsh, "A Non-Linear Model for the Experimental Measurement of Utility," *Behavioral Science*, 4, 204–211 (1959).

Taylor, A. E., *Advanced Calculus*, Ginn and Company, New York, 1955.

Thrall, R. M., C. H. Coombs, and R. L. Davis (eds.), *Decision Processes*, John Wiley and Sons, New York, 1954.

von Neumann, J., and O. Morgenstern, *Theory of Games and Economic Behavior*, Second Edition, Princeton University Press, Princeton, New Jersey, 1947.

Wald, A., *Statistical Decision Functions*, John Wiley and Sons, New York, 1950.

Chapter 4

MEASUREMENT OF RELATIVE VALUES

4.1 INTRODUCTION

In Section 3.2, the notion of relative values of consequences was discussed. With $\{o_j\} = \mathbf{Q}$, the set of r consequences, it was assumed meaningful to consider a set of real numbers $\{V_j\}, j = 1, \ldots, r$, to describe the relative importance of the consequences to the decision maker. This assumption is basic to the present theory and will be used throughout.

The purpose of this chapter is to discuss various measures of the V_j or $V(o_j)$ (either symbol denoting the relative value of o_j) and to explore ways in which one may attempt to obtain these measures. The measures of relative values to be considered are the following:

Partial ordinal measure;

ordinal measure;

first ordered metric measure;

nth ordered metric measure, $n = 2, 3, \ldots$;

higher ordered metric measure;

first bounded interval measure;

second bounded interval measure;

third bounded interval measure;

interval measure.

In discussing these, we shall: (1) illustrate how each measure treats the V_j; (2) consider the assumptions which are basic to the measure; (3) describe one or more ways of attempting to generate the measures; and (4) consider various criticisms of the assumptions which underlie the measurement process.

The reader may be understandably puzzled by the idea of considering such a variety of measures of relative values of consequences. There are several reasons for doing this. As will be argued, it is not at all easy from a practical standpoint to make measurements of the V_j. In different contexts, some of the above measures may be derived with less effort than others. In fact, it may be impossible or impractical (or downright foolish) to try to obtain some of these measures in certain situations.

The fundamental reason for obtaining measures of the V_j is, of course, to try to determine a strategy for action that has maximum expected value or, short of this to try to eliminate from further consideration strategies which do not maximize the decision maker's total expected value. In general, we shall find (as might be expected) that, as we pass from measures which are most imprecise in determining the V_j to the measure which is most exact (the interval measure), the assumptions of the measurement procedures become more demanding and less likely to hold in practice. It may very well be true too that, as more exacting statements concerning the V_j are "derived," the individual's confidence in the validity of the more exact statements decreases in comparison to previous (less exact) statements which serve as the basis for the more exact statements. Obviously, the more precise the measurements of the V_j are in a given situation, the greater will be our chances of being able to arrive at definite conclusions concerning the relative magnitudes of the expected values of the strategies, i.e., the $E(S_i)$. But, as just argued, a price is usually exacted for increased "precision": the assumptions become more restrictive, the effort required increases, and the individual may feel unsure as to the validity of the more precise statements (even though his judgments produce these statements).

Therefore, we consider it of paramount importance to be able to use the information contained in any measure of value to the fullest extent in seeking to derive conclusions concerning the relative magnitudes of the $E(S_i)$. Chapters 6 and 7 will be concerned with specifying when it is permissible to make conclusions such as $E(S_1) \geqslant E(S_2)$, given various measures of probabilities and relative values. As we shall see (and have seen in Chapter 3), an ordinal ranking of relative values may permit such a conclusion and thus make it unnecessary to obtain a more precise measure of value.

Before examining the measures listed above, it may be helpful to note how these are related to one another. This is done in Figure 4.1. In the diagram, an arrow from one measure to another means that the information on the V_j contained in the former measure is embedded in the latter. For example, all the information on the V_j contained in the ordinal measure is also contained in the first ordered metric measure, but not vice versa—

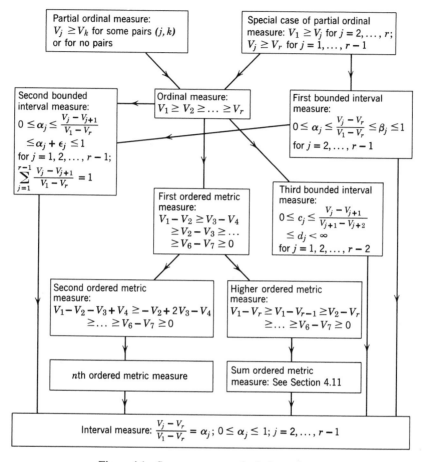

Figure 4.1 Some measures of relative values.

we might say that the ordinal measure is a prerequisite for the first ordered metric measure. Similarly, the special case of the partial ordinal measure is a prerequisite for the first bounded interval measure. If there is no arrow or directed sequence of arrows from one measure to another, this means that it is not necessarily true that the information of one is embedded in the other. Figure 4.1 also includes an indication of the way in which each measure treats the V_j. The reader may find this a handy reference and review.

At the end of this chapter we shall restate the assumption that leads to Model II, since it will be advantageous to treat Models I and II together in sequel, along with the statistical model.

4.2 THE ORDINAL MEASURE

An ordinal measure ranks the relative values of the o_j from the largest to the smallest (by decreasing magnitude) or, alternatively, from the smallest to the largest (by increasing magnitude). By subscript convention, we shall usually write an ordinal ranking as

$$V_1 \geqslant V_2 \geqslant \ldots \geqslant V_j \geqslant \ldots \geqslant V_k \geqslant \ldots \geqslant V_r. \qquad (4.1)$$

It is to be understood that we are concerned only with consequences that have a positive probability of occurrence with at least one strategy in the set of strategies under consideration. (In fact, we may say that a necessary condition for a "thing" to qualify as a consequence is that its occurrence is possible with at least one S_i.)

The assumptions for this measure and those that follow will be denoted by A1, A1(1), ..., A4(1), ... In A1(1) and A1(2) that follow, we will be concerned with a relation " $\gtrsim$," defined over pairs of consequences in **Q**, where $a \gtrsim b$ is interpreted as "a is at least as preferable as b" or "b is not more preferable than a." In different measures, $\gtrsim$ may be a different relation. For example, in the ordinal measure, $\gtrsim$ is a weak ordering, whereas for the partial ordinal measure, $\gtrsim$ is a quasi-ordering.[1] Also, $\gtrsim$ may be the same relation in several measures, but may apply to structurally different sets. In the ordinal and ordered metric measures, $\gtrsim$ is a weak ordering. For the ordinal measure, $\gtrsim$ is defined over pairs of consequences in the set of consequences. Given the ordinal measure, $\gtrsim$ then applies to pairs of pairs of consequences in defining the first ordered metric measure.

Several other relations derive from $\gtrsim$.[2] First, $b \lesssim a$ means $a \gtrsim b$. Next, $a > b$ or $b < a$ means $a \gtrsim b$ and not $b \gtrsim a$. Finally, $a \sim b$ means $a \gtrsim b$ and $b \gtrsim a$. In connection with pairs of consequences or pairs of gambles, $>$ indicates strict preference ("a is preferred to b") and $\sim$ indicates equivalence ("a and b are equally important"). Equivalence is also referred to as indifference; e.g., $o_j \sim o_k$ with $j \neq k$ means the individual is indifferent with respect to which consequence occurs, on the hypothesis that one or the other will, in fact, occur. In relational terms, $\sim$ is an equivalence relation; that is, $\sim$ is reflexive ($o_j \sim o_j$), symmetric ($o_j \sim o_k$ implies $o_k \sim o_j$), and transitive ($o_j \sim o_k$ and $o_k \sim o_t$ imply $o_j \sim o_t$). The indifference relation $\sim$ should not be confused with the identity relation $=$. $o_j = o_k$ means o_j and o_k are the same (identical) consequence. If $o_j \sim o_k$, it may be true that $o_j \neq o_k$.

---

[1] The language of relations used herein is in accordance with Suppes (1957, Chapter 10). Readers not familiar with these terms may obtain a complete account from this reference.

[2] See, for example, Savage (1954, p. 19).

For the ordinal measure, the main assumption may be stated as:

A1 The relation $\gtrsim$ is a weak ordering of the set **Q**.

This may be put in other language as:

A1(1) For every pair of consequences (o_j, o_k), $o_j \in$ **Q**, $o_k \in$ **Q**, either $o_j \gtrsim o_k$ or $o_k \gtrsim o_j$ (or possibly both).

A1(2) If $o_j \gtrsim o_k$ and $o_k \gtrsim o_l$, then $o_j \gtrsim o_l$.

A1(2) postulates that $\gtrsim$ is transitive. A1(1) is the assumption that $\gtrsim$ is strongly connected in **Q**. These two properties define the term *weak ordering*. By the definition of $\sim$, A1(1) assures that $o_j \sim o_j$. If, for $o_j \neq o_k$ it is true that $o_j \gtrsim o_k$ and $o_k \gtrsim o_j$, then $o_j \sim o_k$.

The basic statement about relative values generated by the preference relation is:

If $o_j \gtrsim o_k$, then $V(o_j) \geqslant V(o_k)$;

If not $o_j \gtrsim o_k$, then not $V(o_j) \geqslant V(o_k)$.[3]

This may be shortened to "$V(o_j) \geqslant V(o_k)$ if and only if $o_j \gtrsim o_k$," with the understanding that relative values are determined by preferences and not vice versa. That is, preference statements are the elements out of which value statements are constructed.

The statement that "$V(o_j) \geqslant V(o_k)$ if and only if $o_j \gtrsim o_k$" simply says that, if one consequence is at least as desirable or important as a second, then the relative value of the first is taken to be at least as great as the relative value of the second; and if it is not true that one consequence is at least as desirable as a second, then the relative value of the first is not as large as the relative value of the second. Obviously, if $o_j > o_k$, then $V_j > V_k$, and if $o_j \sim o_k$, then $V_j = V_k$.

It may be noted that to use "$V(o_j) \leqslant V(o_k)$ if and only if $o_j \gtrsim o_k$" would be perfectly all right except that the criterion of choice would have to be changed from maximization of expected relative value to minimization of expected relative value.

The ordinal value measure (or simple ordering) $V_1 \geqslant V_2 \geqslant \ldots \geqslant V_r$ is obtained directly from the preferential weak ordering of consequences

$$o_1 \gtrsim o_2 \gtrsim \ldots \gtrsim o_r \tag{4.2}$$

following from A1. In (4.2) the consequences have been numbered, by means of the subscript, to coincide with position in the ordering. If it is determined, along with (4.2), that $o_j > o_{j+1}$ or $o_j \sim o_{j+1}$, then the ordinal measure can be written according to these findings. For example, if

---

[3] This basic statement is not an assumption in the formal sense. It is an explication of the notion of relative value in conjunction with the preference relation $\gtrsim$.

$o_1 > o_2$, $o_2 > o_3$, $o_3 \sim o_4$, $o_4 \gtrsim o_5$, and $o_5 \sim o_6$, then we may write $V_1 > V_2 > V_3 = V_4 \geqslant V_5 = V_6$. In view of the types of analysis that we will present in Chapters 6 and 7, the knowledge that $V_j > V_k$ in addition to $V_j \geqslant V_k$ will be of almost no help in analyzing the strategies for dominance with an ordinal measure of value, but the knowledge that $V_j = V_k$ in addition to $V_j \geqslant V_k$ may prove quite useful. Although the form (4.1) will generally be used in later chapters, the effect that equality of certain V_j has in the analysis should be obvious.[4]

Some Methods of Measurement

There are several ways an ordinal measure or simple ordering of the V_j may be obtained. One is to present the individual with a sequence of pairs of o_j and have him order each pair by preference until a complete ordering has been obtained from the ordered pairs. In this it is assumed that the order in which the pairs are presented and the order of the two o_j in each pair have no effect on his judgments of importance or worth.

A second way is to give the individual the whole list of the set of consequences and have him pick one o_j he considers at least as important as any other. Call this first one o_1. Then delete o_1 from the list and have him pick an o_j from the revised list he considers at least as important as any other in the revised list. Call this second one o_2. Then delete o_2 from the list and continue in the indicated manner until a complete ordering has been obtained. Here it is assumed that the order in which the consequences are originally listed has no effect on the choices, but one might nevertheless wish to "scramble" (randomize) the order of the o_j in the list presented to the decision maker to minimize possible bias of the research worker.

A third way is to make up a deck of cards with one o_j on each card, thoroughly shuffle (randomize) this deck, and deal the cards one at a time to the decision maker. As he gets each new card, he arranges it in his hand so that at any point the o_j in his hand are ordered from most important to least important. The process continues until all cards have been dealt and ordered.

Still another way is to present the individual with a list of the consequences and ask him to assign a numerical weight to each one, assigning the largest weight to the most important, and so on. The consequences would then be ordered according to the assigned weights.

---

[4] From a formal theoretical point of view, one might wish to define equivalence classes or indifference classes of o_j, such that $o_j \sim o_k$ if and only if o_j and o_k are members of the same equivalence class. Then value measures would be defined over the equivalence classes. For an ordinal measure we would then replace the main assumption by "the relation $>$ is a strict simple ordering among equivalence classes." See Sections 4.9 and 4.13.

Which of these ways (or some other way) of ordering the consequences is "best" is very difficult to say. The answer may depend upon the particular decision maker and decision situation. Pairwise comparison offers no particular advantage over the other methods from the present point of view, although it does enable the research worker to check for consistency (i.e., transitivity). Inasmuch as we have assumed that no intransitivity will occur, some other method might serve just as well. Assigning numerical weights may help the decision maker to "think quantitatively," and allows for adjustment during the process.

In the second method, we may suppose that in choosing o_1 the decision maker is actually making a series of pairwise comparisons in arriving at o_1 as the most important, and so forth. In the third method, the decision maker has to fit each newly dealt consequence into the ordering he has established up to that point. Here, again, we may surmise that the process is composed of a series of pairwise comparisons. Adjustment during the process may also occur in this third method.

Obviously, a main objective in any measurement procedure is to measure (accurately) the thing we wish to measure, assuming we know what we wish to measure. Which procedure (if any) in the above set is "best" in this sense is, to our knowledge, an unsolved problem. For the sake of expediency and practicability, ordering a complete list of the o_j from the most desirable to least desirable may prove satisfactory. If the individual assigns numerical weights to the consequences, these weights will not only yield an ordering of the o_j but may also give an initial hint as to the relative lengths of the value intervals between adjacent V_j. In the strictest sense, however, it should be noted that the numerical weights are assumed to establish only an ordering of the o_j and that one should resist the temptation to interpret these weights literally (i.e., as giving an interval measure of value).

4.3 SOME PROBLEMS OF MEASUREMENT

The main defense offered in support of A1(1) and A1(2) generally proceeds on the notion that they embody certain principles of rational, consistent behavior, and, if an individual does not satisfy these assumptions, then he is irrational or inconsistent and there is little we can say to him except perhaps to advise him to reconsider his position. It is more relevant to the matter that we admit, for anyone who is in conflict with A1(2) (the assumption of transitivity of preference) and does not find satisfaction in altering or forcing his preference judgments into a pattern consistent with A1(2), that our theory of decision simply is not rich enough to account for his situation.

Uncertain Objectives

The potential difficulty posed by intransitivity is closely related to a more central problem of value theory and the measurement of value, which has to do with the conditions under which and the times at which value judgments (or statements of preference) are made. We may note, first of all, that in making value judgments, an individual will usually find it necessary and desirable to consider the consequences in light of his objectives. In doing this, it is not at all unlikely that he may be made aware (or more aware) of the possibility that his objectives are not particularly clear in his own mind. Thus, for example, comparing one consequence with another may require a complete re-examination of what he wishes to accomplish, not only in the context of the decision situation at hand but also with respect to an uncertain chain of future decision situations. Many persons have been faced with the question, "Just exactly what do I hope to accomplish by taking such and such an action?" or with the question, "What is valuable or important to me and why are these things valuable?" These common observations illustrate a critical fact—that uncertainty in a decision situation may arise from an individual's uncertainty as to his own objectives as well as uncertainty concerning his environment. Needless to say, one by-product of approaching decision problems by the methods presented here is to "force" an individual to reconsider his objectives and purpose. Indeed, in some situations, this may benefit the decision maker more than any fancy mathematical manipulations (of the decision model) could ever hope to do.

Changes Over Time

If we can admit to the possibility of uncertainty of objectives, then we must also accept the process of evolution of an individual's objectives over time. Humans, being endowed with the ability to reason and mature in thought and purpose, cannot very well avoid this evolution within themselves.

If an individual's objectives may change over time, then, in comparable decision situations separated by some period of time, it could easily happen that a preference between two consequences (which, for sake of illustration, we shall assume to be identical between the situations) will be reversed. Now if we consider an interval of time that applies to a particular decision situation and precedes the actual decision, then it is not altogether unlikely that, if the individual were requested to express a preference between two consequences at different times during this period, he would respond with opposite answers. This could happen because of a change in his purpose or in his objectives. Or, we might suspect the seeming inconsistency is attributable to an imperfect ability to discriminate preferentially between consequences, and that the two consequences involved are "very nearly equal in relative value." The opposite responses might also be caused by changes in the environment (occurring during the interval) which tend to alter the relative attractiveness of the consequences to him. Other explanations could also be offered. If, in fact, preferences between consequences are elicited at different times preceding the adoption of a strategy and one or more of these preferences are reversed, we would be inclined to trust the most recent statement(s) of preference.[5] Reasons for this include the facts that a later judgment (1) is made on the basis of more experience and more information than an earlier one and (2) results from additional reflection on the part of the decision maker. As far as timing is concerned, it would seem desirable to measure an individual's relative values close to the time at which the decision is made, if in fact there is sufficient time to measure values at all (and the decision maker considers it worth his while to have his problem analyzed in this way) before a decision must be made. The fact that, for many decision situations, the decision may be made at any point in a certain time interval will, of course, complicate the picture.

In taking measurements of relative values, the conditions under which these measurements are made may be as important (if not more so) as the time or times at which the process takes place. The emotional and physical states of a person may have a significant bearing on his value judgments. If the subject had just returned from a two-martini lunch with a good friend on a beautiful sunny day and underwent a session of evaluation, we might get different responses from those obtained from a session following his return from a long, tiring business trip. Partially because of difficulties of this nature, Churchman (1961a) has argued for a standard environment for value measurement (an excerpt of which appeared in Section 3.8). Ackoff (1962, Chapter 6) has also mentioned the problem of correcting measurements obtained in nonstandard conditions.

The practitioner who may want to apply this theory is advised to obtain value measurements under relatively "normal" conditions and take sufficient time (if agreeable to the decision maker) in the measurement process to allow for at least a modest degree of objectivity on the subject's part. Although the kind of value measurements we are considering are often referred to as subjective value measurements (appealing to the introspective judgment of the individual involved), objectivity on the part of the individual is of paramount importance in trying to achieve satisfactory results.

---

[5] Other possibilities have been suggested. In this respect, a body of theory called "stochastic utility theory" has been developed. Luce and Raiffa (1957, Appendix 1) were among the first (if not the first) to discuss this; see also Luce (1959).

Dishonesty

One of the greatest dangers in obtaining preference judgments from another individual is the factor of "dishonesty" on the subject's part. The subject may give perfectly consistent statements concerning his preferences but deliberately falsify his true preferences. This might happen, for example, in a situation where the subject does not wish to divulge his actual preferences to someone else. To do so might cause him great embarrassment. Or he might be a stubborn sort who resents the idea of any scientist knowing his actual preferences. He may distrust the scientist. Since the subject still has the right to make the decision, he may not really care what he tells the scientist. (From the scientist's viewpoint, it may be extremely hard to detect this sort of thing without a polygraph or sodium pentathol.) If the subject feels he cannot give honest statements to the scientist, then the scientist's conclusions are not going to do him much good, so he might as well dispense with his services (which may be costing him a good deal of money). This all goes back to the nature of the relationship between scientist and client, which has been discussed previously. If the decision maker desires to have his problem analyzed by the methods discussed in this book, and is willing to pay for the scientist's services, then, in order to get his money's worth, he would be foolish to hire someone he does not trust implicitly. If the "scientist" and "decision maker" are one and the same person, so much the better.

Practical Limitations

In the context of the types of decision situations considered in this book, there will generally be serious practical limitations in attempting to generate a weak preference ordering of the consequences. The first limitation concerns the number of consequences considered relevant. As noted previously, it is not hard to imagine decision situations with an astronomical number of possible consequences (e.g., with 10 variables, each of which can take on 10 values, there may be as many as $10^{10} = 10,000,000,000$ relevant consequences). Whereas it may not be too difficult to list the variables and their values, a listing of all the consequences could fill many volumes if anyone wanted to go to the trouble of doing this. Even if an individual were able to make pairwise preference judgments at the rate of one per second, it might take years (or a period of time longer than his expected life span) to order the consequences.

A second practical limitation, related to the first, concerns an individual's ability to state unambiguously his preference between two consequences, each of which is composed of perhaps 20 or 30 values of relevant action and outcome variables (one value for each variable). Confronted by two such consequences, he may be terribly confused in attempting to comprehend "simultaneously" the consequences and may be reduced to a shrug when requested to express a preference between them. If he really does find himself able to express a clear preference between two multidimensional consequences, one might suspect that he has gone through a process of comparing the two values of each variable, "adding up the pluses and minuses for the variables and then finding that the pluses outweigh the minuses or vice versa."

One way to alleviate the problems posed by these limitations (not only in connection with the ordinal measure of value but for the decision problem as a whole) is to assume that the variables are valuewise independent. This assumption, as noted previously, not only can cause a substantial reduction in the size of the problem but may also greatly simplify the task of measuring relative values. In Chapter 10 it will be noted how, assuming independence of variables, one can attempt to derive or "prove" a preference between two multidimensional consequences, although this will result mainly as a by-product of that chapter.

Failure to State Preferences and Incomparability

The failure of an individual to express a clear preference (or indifference) between two consequences can be interpreted several ways. At least two interpretations have been noted above: he finds the two consequences so complex as to cause confusion and a feeling of inability to discriminate clearly between the two or he is uncertain about his own objectives or purpose. A third interpretation has been alluded to—that he does have a clear preference but is unwilling to reveal this to someone else. In addition, it may happen that an important variable interacting (in the relative value sense) with other variables has been omitted from the formulation. For example, if Z is the omitted variable with values z, $z', \ldots$, and o_j and o_k are two consequences in the set of consequences as originally formulated, then the reformulated consequences (z, o_j), (z, o_k), (z', o_j), and (z', o_k) may be preferentially related as $(z, o_j) > (z, o_k)$ and $(z', o_j) < (z', o_k)$, in which case failure to specify the value of Z may make comparison of o_j and o_k rather difficult.

Related to the failure to state a preference between two consequences is a concept called "incomparability." Concerning incomparability, Davidson, Suppes, and Siegel (1957) have the following to say:

Models for decision making among alternatives involving risk generally require that the relation of preference be connected in the set of basic outcomes. This means that given any two outcomes, a and b, in the set K of basic outcomes, the subject prefers a to b or b to a. In theories which admit also a relation of indifference between outcomes, the condition of connectedness is modified to allow the third possibility that the subject is indifferent between a and b.

The question whether the theory should include indifference between basic outcomes is, from a formal point of view (though not from an empirical point of view), a relatively trivial one. The question we wish to discuss here concerns incomparable outcomes. In a theory which does not include indifference as a primitive relation, two outcomes a and b are incomparable if the subject neither prefers a to b nor b to a; in a theory admitting indifference a and b are incomparable if it is also the case that the subject is not indifferent between a and b. Thus incomparability and indifference between outcomes are entirely discrete notions: the former means that the subject does not or cannot compare the outcomes; the latter means that the outcomes are compared and are found to be equally attractive or unattractive. Indifference, like preference, represents a judgment of relative worth; incomparability represents a failure to make such a judgment [p. 104].

Although the notion of incomparability could include the reasons listed above for possible failure to express a clear preference or indifference between two consequences, something more is implied by the phrase "two consequences are incomparable." The phrase, as it is usually employed, means that it is meaningless (or nonsense) to speak about comparing two consequences with respect to the preference relation. Perhaps to the reader's dismay we are completely unable to offer an example of two consequences in an imagined decision situation which might be suspected of being incomparable. Among the supposed illustrations of incomparability that have been forwarded by others, we have not found one example that stands up under the present formulation: Either the consequences stated are not consequences at all but only fragments or parts of consequences, or the consequences are from an inadequately formulated situation, or the two "incomparable" consequences are taken from two entirely separate decision situations, or the example is stated without reference to any decision situation, and so forth. In our opinion, the notion of incomparability has not been sufficiently explained to make its further consideration worthwhile.

4.4 PARTIAL ORDINAL MEASURES

A partial ordinal measure of relative values consists of a set of inequalities among the $V(o_j)$. For example, with six consequences, the following represent partial ordinal measures (or partial orderings of the V_j):

$$(a)\ V_1 \geqslant V_2 \geqslant V_3 \geqslant V_4, \qquad (b)\ V_1 \geqslant V_2 \geqslant V_4,$$
$$V_5 \geqslant V_6, \qquad\qquad\qquad V_3 \geqslant V_4,$$
$$V_5 \geqslant V_6,$$
$$(c)\ V_1 \geqslant V_2 \geqslant V_5 \geqslant V_6,$$
$$V_3 \geqslant V_4 \geqslant V_6.$$

In (a) and (b) there is no inequality between V_5 and V_j for $j \leqslant 4$, and, similarly, no inequality between V_6 and V_j for $j \leqslant 4$. In (b), although V_1, V_2, and V_3 are all greater than or equal to V_4, no comparison is given between V_1 and V_3 or between V_2 and V_3. The partial ordinal ranking (c) has a property different than either (a) or (b) in that every other V_j has been compared to V_6. In Section 6.3 we will discuss this property further and introduce the notion of a value graph, which is another way to express a partial ordinal measure.

The formal axiom for this measure is

A2 The relation $\gtrsim$ is a quasi-ordering of the set **Q**.

A quasi-ordering is a relation which is reflexive ($o_j \gtrsim o_j$) and transitive, but is not necessarily (strongly) connected. A weak ordering is a quasi-ordering which is connected. Following are sets of pairwise preference judgments which give rise to the partial ordinal rankings shown above:

$$(a) \; o_1 \gtrsim o_2, \qquad (b) \; o_1 \gtrsim o_2, \qquad (c) \; o_1 \gtrsim o_2,$$
$$o_2 \gtrsim o_3, \qquad o_2 \gtrsim o_4, \qquad o_2 \gtrsim o_5,$$
$$o_3 \gtrsim o_4, \qquad o_3 \gtrsim o_4, \qquad o_5 \gtrsim o_6,$$
$$o_5 \gtrsim o_6, \qquad o_5 \gtrsim o_6, \qquad o_3 \gtrsim o_4,$$
$$o_4 \gtrsim o_6.$$

The two extremes of the partial ordinal measure are (1) the "null" measure which makes no comparisons whatever between (different) consequences and (2) the ordinal measure discussed in Section 4.2.

Although in the quasi-ordering of four consequences

$$o_1 \gtrsim o_3 \gtrsim o_4, \qquad o_2 \gtrsim o_3 \gtrsim o_4$$

there is no comparison between o_1 and o_2, it may be possible with some additional value measure to determine that $V_1 \geqslant V_2$ or $V_2 \geqslant V_1$. The two *preference chains* ($o_1 \gtrsim o_3 \gtrsim o_4$ and $o_2 \gtrsim o_3 \gtrsim o_4$) give $V_1 \geqslant V_3 \geqslant V_4$, $V_2 \geqslant V_3 \geqslant V_4$. Considering differences between relative values in each of these two preference chains, it may happen that

(1) $$V_1 - V_3 \geqslant V_3 - V_4,$$

(2) $$V_3 - V_4 \geqslant V_2 - V_3,$$

which together imply that $V_1 - V_3 \geqslant V_2 - V_3$ or $V_1 \geqslant V_2$. Thus, although an individual may be unable to express a clear preference between o_1 and o_2, it may nevertheless be possible to conclude that $V_1 \geqslant V_2$ (implying $o_1 \gtrsim o_2$) with the help of some additional value measure. For this illustration, the comparison of V_1 and V_2 depended on the fact that the two preference chains had two consequences in common (o_3 and o_4).

Among the partial ordinal measures, one in particular will be used in the sequel as the base of the first bounded interval measure. The first bounded interval measure depends on identifying a consequence (call it o_1) which is at least as desirable as any other consequence, and on identifying a second consequence (call it o_r) which is not preferred to any other consequence. This requires:

A3(1) There exists a consequence, say o_1, such that $o_1 \gtrsim o_j$ for all j, and there exists a consequence, say o_r, such that $o_j \gtrsim o_r$ for all j.

A3(2) It is not true that $o_r \gtrsim o_1$.

A3(2) simply insures that $o_1 > o_r$ or that $V_1 > V_r$, so that $V_1 - V_r > 0$. If it were true that $o_r \gtrsim o_1$, then $o_1 \sim o_r$, and, in fact, $o_1 \sim o_j$ for all j, giving $V_1 = V_2 = \ldots = V_r$, which renders all $E(S_i)$ equal.

4.5 INTRODUCTION TO BOUNDED INTERVAL MEASURES

In the following sections we explore three measures of relative value (the ILK measures) that bound ratios of value differences such as

$$R = \frac{V_a - V_b}{V_c - V_d}, \qquad V_c - V_d \neq 0.$$

From the measurement process, R will be bounded as $\alpha \leqslant R \leqslant \beta$. If it were possible to measure R precisely, there would obviously be no need to consider bounds. However, as argued previously, such fine measurement will seldom, if ever, be possible. Therefore it may be necessary to settle for an upper and a lower bound on R.

In obtaining bounds on R, it is desirable to get these as close together as possible, consistent with the individual's ability to make clear preference judgments, for we will use these bounds in trying to determine the sign of, say, $E(S_j) - E(S_k)$, i.e., in trying to determine dominance among strategies. Tighter bounds will give us a greater *a priori* chance of determining the sign of $E(S_j) - E(S_k)$.

4.6 THE FIRST BOUNDED INTERVAL MEASURE

The first assumptions for this measure are A3(1) and A3(2) which insure that $o_1 \gtrsim o_j \gtrsim o_r$ for each j, $j = 1, 2, \ldots, r$, and that $o_1 > o_r$. The first bounded interval measure then bounds the ratio of the two relative value intervals $(V_j - V_r)$ and $(V_1 - V_r)$, for each j. Let I_j denote the jth ratio:

$$I_j = \frac{V_j - V_r}{V_1 - V_r}.$$

Obviously $I_1 = 1$, $I_r = 0$, and $0 \leqslant I_j \leqslant 1$ for $j = 2, \ldots, r - 1$. The bounds on I_j will be denoted as α_j and β_j, $0 \leqslant \alpha_j \leqslant \beta_j \leqslant 1$:

$$I_1 = 1, \qquad I_r = 0,$$

$$\alpha_j \leqslant I_j \leqslant \beta_j, \qquad 0 \leqslant \alpha_j \leqslant \beta_j \leqslant 1 \qquad j = 2, \ldots, r - 1,$$

gives the general form of the first bounded interval measure.

We shall describe two ways in which one may attempt to determine α_j and β_j for $j = 2, \ldots, r - 1$. The first appeals directly to the individual's ability to conceptualize the notion of a preference continuum or to grasp the idea of relative value. The second uses hypothetical gambles. Both methods have their weaknesses, as will become obvious.

The Intuitive Approach

To set the stage for the first method, imagine yourself as the subject of a small experiment in which you are requested to judge the relative temperatures of three physical objects. The three objects are similar flat metal plates, the surface textures of which are identical and have the same physical appearance. Each plate is heated to a temperature which we may assume to remain constant during the experiment, the three plates having different temperatures (none of which will injure the hand). You are to feel the three plates with your hands in any manner you please and are asked to judge their relative temperatures. Suppose you do this and state that plate 1 > plate 2 > plate 3 or $P_1 > P_2 > P_3$, where > means "is warmer than" or "has a higher temperature than." You are then asked to judge where, on a relative temperature scale, the temperature of P_2 lies with respect to the temperatures of P_1 and P_3. For this purpose you are given the following "temperature scale":

T_1 $\qquad\qquad\qquad\qquad\qquad\qquad\qquad\qquad\qquad\qquad\qquad\qquad$ T_3

Letting T_i denote the temperature of P_i, the scale has been written with T_1 and T_3 at the ends (the symbols T_1 and T_3 appear on the scale instead of actual numerical values according to some scale of temperature). The interval $[T_1, T_3]$ has been marked off in 20 equal parts for your convenience and to communicate the idea of linearity. You are then asked to specify an interval between T_1 and T_3 on the "temperature scale" that you feel reasonably sure will contain T_2, but has as small a relative length as possible. This obviously requires a sort of "triplewise" comparison of P_1, P_2, and P_3: "Where does T_2 lie in relation to T_1 and T_3?" Suppose you fill in the interval which is shown by the darkened part of this scale. Then, assuming you are being honest about the whole thing, your response will be interpreted as, "You feel reasonably certain that

$$.2 \leqslant \frac{T_2 - T_3}{T_1 - T_3} \leqslant .4,"$$

where .2 is the ratio of the linear distance from the right end of the darkened interval to T_3 over the linear distance from T_1 to T_3, and .4 is the ratio of the linear distance from the left end of the darkened interval to T_3 over the linear distance from T_1 to T_3.

With this example to illustrate (crudely) the type of judgment that is envisioned, the first method of generating the first bounded interval measure proceeds as follows:

> For each o_j, designate, on a linear relative value scale with end points $V(o_1)$ and $V(o_r)$, an interval which you believe includes the relative value of o_j (to you) with respect to the positions of $V(o_1)$ and $V(o_r)$.
>
> Suppose, for a particular o_j, the interval is designated as shown in Figure 4.2 with d_1, d_2, and d_3 the indicated linear distances (with an arbitrary unit of measurement).
>
> Then

$$\frac{d_1}{d_3} \leqslant \frac{V(o_j) - V(o_r)}{V(o_1) - V(o_r)} \leqslant \frac{d_2}{d_3}.$$

For those who object to the direct appeal to relative value, an indirect approach (still highly suggestive of relative values) would replace $V(o_1)$ and $V(o_r)$ with o_1 and o_r respectively, and the first part of the above procedure would be written as:

> For each o_j, designate, on a linear "degree-of-preference" continuum with end points o_1 and o_r, an interval which you believe includes your relative degree of preference for o_j with respect to your degrees of preference for o_1 and o_r.

This method appeals directly, as mentioned, to the individual's introspective judgment of relative worth on a triple comparison basis. If it is used in practice, it might be quicker to dispense with the visual "linear

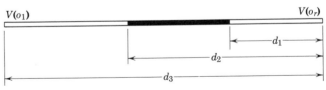

Figure 4.2

scale" and to say, for example: "Suppose we arbitrarily set $V(o_1) = 0$ and $V(o_r) = 100$. Then designate an interval between 0 and 100 which contains $V(o_j)$." However, it seems desirable to avoid the introduction of specific numerical values, since they may be suggestive of things not intended.

Besides A3(1) and A3(2), the assumption for this procedure is:

A4 For each o_j $j = 2, \ldots, r - 1$ the individual is able to designate an interval on a linear scale with end points $V(o_1)$, $V(o_r)$ such that this interval contains $V(o_j)$.

Given this interval for o_j,

$$\alpha_j \leqslant I_j \leqslant \beta_j,$$

where

$$I_j = \frac{V_j - V_r}{V_1 - V_r},$$

$$\alpha_j = \frac{d_1}{d_3}, \qquad \beta_j = \frac{d_2}{d_3},$$

with d_1, d_2, d_3 the linear distances as shown by Figure 4.2.

A4 is rather trivial because, since $o_1 \gtrsim o_j \gtrsim o_r$, the interval from $V(o_1)$ to $V(o_r)$ will always contain $V(o_j)$. That is, if no other interval between $V(o_1)$ and $V(o_r)$ seems appropriate, then the individual may designate the entire interval from $V(o_1)$ to $V(o_r)$, which would give $0 \leqslant I_j \leqslant 1$, something we already knew from $o_1 \gtrsim o_j \gtrsim o_r$ and $o_1 > o_r$. What we would hope to get from this procedure is as small a difference $\epsilon_j = \beta_j - \alpha_j$ as the individual is capable of rendering while still feeling sure that his interval contains $V(o_j)$. The ideal, of course, would be to have $\epsilon_j = 0$ or $\alpha_j = \beta_j$, arising from designation of $V(o_j)$ as a particular point (degenerate interval) on the linear scale. However, it is extremely doubtful that anyone would be able to do this and feel certain that such a point gave a reliable value of $V(o_j)$ with respect to $V(o_1)$ and $V(o_r)$. By allowing an interval rather than a point to be specified by the individual, he is permitted as much freedom in his judgment as he may desire or require.

One main criticism of the above procedure is that it appeals directly to the individual's understanding of the notion "relative value." How are we to know if his interpretation of this notion is what is intended? Indeed, it might be maintained that in measuring relative values it is not legitimate to appeal directly to the notion of relative value itself, and, therefore, the above procedure is meaningless. In the example of judging relative temperatures, we have a device for measuring "temperature" (or thermal energy of a body) which is much less subjective than the hands-on-the-plate approach, and we are able to check the subject's judgments against the readings obtained by the instrument used to measure temperature "objectively." However, in using a similar approach for value judgments, there is no "valuometer" with which to "check the reliability of his interval for $V(o_j)$ relative to $V(o_1)$ and $V(o_r)$." In the temperature example, by feeling the plates, sensory perception helps the individual in judging. For value measures (of the sort considered here), the consequences cannot be touched or visually seen in many cases, and must be imagined. Even in decision situations where the items of interest can be observed before the decision is made (as in buying a car or house), relative value does not refer to any intrinsic property of the items but to an introspective feeling of the individual concerning the relative "worths" of the items (to him) in a particular decision situation.

Many of the comments on problems of value measurement made in the previous section apply equally well here and in the sequel, and will not be repeated except for occasional clarification.

The Decision-Oriented Approach

The second method of deriving a first bounded interval measure relies on the notion of hypothetical or imaginary gambles. This method is more in line with the von Neumann-Morgenstern axioms of modern utility theory than the first (see Section 1.3), but like the first method it allows the individual a great deal of freedom in his judgment.

The primitives of the second method are the set of consequences **Q**, the set of gambles (o_1, p, o_r) for $0 \leqslant p \leqslant 1$, and a relation $\gtrsim$ between elements of the two sets. The gamble (o_1, p, o_r) is interpreted as "you get o_1 with probability p or o_r with probability $1 - p$." Comparisons in this method are between o_j and (o_1, p, o_r). As in the first method, three consequences (o_1, o_j, o_r) are involved in each judgment. In addition we now have a probability p. In a rough sense, p has been substituted in place of the notion of a linear preference continuum, that is, instead of working with the notion of a preference continuum, we now work with the notion of a probability continuum.

The statement $o_j \gtrsim (o_1, p, o_r)$ may be interpreted as "the consequence o_j is preferred or indifferent to the gamble (o_1, p, o_r)." The interpretation of $(o_1, p, o_r) \gtrsim o_j$ is similar. For this method, the assumptions we need, along with A3(1) and A3(2) are:

A5(1) For each o_j, $j = 2, \ldots, r - 1$, there is a value of p, say α_j, such that $o_j \gtrsim (o_1, p, o_r)$ for all $p \leqslant \alpha_j$.

A5(2)   There is a value of p, say β_j, such that $\beta_j \geqslant \alpha_j$ and $(o_1, p, o_r) \gtrsim o_j$ for all $p \geqslant \beta_j$.

A5(3)   If $o_j \gtrsim (o_1, p, o_r)$, then $V_j \geqslant pV_1 + (1 - p)V_r$; and if $(o_1, p, o_r) \gtrsim o_j$, then $pV_1 + (1 - p)V_r \geqslant V_j$.

Since $V_j \geqslant pV_1 + (1 - p)V_r$ implies $V_j - V_r \geqslant p(V_1 - V_r)$, we have by A3 and A5,

$$\frac{V_j - V_r}{V_1 - V_r} \geqslant p \qquad \text{for all } p \leqslant \alpha_j,$$

or

$$p \leqslant I_j \qquad \text{for all } p \leqslant \alpha_j.$$

In particular,

$$\alpha_j \leqslant I_j.$$

By similar reasoning

$$I_j \leqslant p \qquad \text{for all } p \geqslant \beta_j,$$

and, in particular,

$$I_j \leqslant \beta_j,$$

which gives

$$\alpha_j \leqslant I_j \leqslant \beta_j.$$

For this procedure we require from the individual two values of p (i.e. α_j and β_j), such that $o_j \gtrsim (o_1, p, o_r)$ for all $p \leqslant \alpha_j$, $o_j \lesssim (o_1, p, o_r)$ for all $p \geqslant \beta_j$, and $\alpha_j \leqslant \beta_j$. As in the previous method, it is desirable to have $\epsilon_j = \beta_j - \alpha_j$ as small as possible, consistent with the individual's ability to discern a clear preference or indifference between o_j and (o_1, p, o_r).

For the reader unfamiliar with the use of hypothetical gambles to elicit preference judgments, further explanation of this method is in order. It is often considered useful to introduce, in this context, the further notion of a chance event, say E, and two hypothetical courses of action, say H_1 and H_2. We suppose that the chance event E has a probability p of occurring, and its complement $\bar{E}$ has probability $1 - p$ of occurring. H_1 is imagined as a hypothetical course of action that yields the consequence o_1 if E occurs and yields the consequence o_r if $\bar{E}$ occurs. H_2 is imagined as a hypothetical course of action that yields the consequence o_j with certainty. This may be summarized by the array

	E	$\bar{E}$
H_1	o_1	o_r
H_2	o_j	o_j

where $P(E) = p$, $P(\bar{E}) = 1 - p$.

For this hypothetical choice situation (abbreviated as *h*-situation), the (hypothetical) expected relative value of the hypothetical act H_1 equals $P(E)V(o_1) + P(\bar{E})V(o_r) = pV_1 + (1 - p)V_r$; and the expected relative value of H_2 equals $P(E)V(o_j) + P(\bar{E})V(o_j) = V_j$.

In an *h*-situation of the type structured above, if the individual is requested to "choose" between H_1 and H_2, and "chooses" H_1, then it is assumed (in the present context) that $pV_1 + (1 - p)V_r \geqslant V_j$. If he "chooses" H_2, then we assume that $V_j \geqslant pV_1 + (1 - p)V_r$. That is, if an unambiguous "choice" between H_1 and H_2 is made, it is assumed that this "choice" reveals which of the two hypothetical expected relative values, $pV_1 + (1 - p)V_r$ and V_j, is greater than or equal to the other.

Now consider a set of *h*-situations for given o_1, o_j, and o_r, where each situation corresponds to a particular event from a set of events $\{E_p\}$, where $P(E_p) = p$. An *h*-situation from this set may be arrayed as:

	E_p	$\bar{E}_p$
$H_1(p)$	o_1	o_r
H_2	o_j	o_j

Here we assume that, if $H_1(p)$ is "chosen" over H_2 for an event E_p, then $H_1(p')$ will be "chosen" over H_2 for any event E_p' for which $p' \geqslant p$; and if H_2 is "chosen" over $H_1(p)$ for an event E_p, then H_2 will be "chosen" over $H_1(p')$ for any event E_p' for which $p' \leqslant p$. In other words, as p increases, we assume that the attractiveness or desirability of $H_1(p)$ to the individual increases with respect to the sure-thing act H_2.

In obtaining the bounds on I_j using *h*-situations, we may ask the individual to state the largest value of p for which H_2 is clearly at least as desirable as $H_1(p)$. This value of p is α_j. Then he is requested to state the smallest value of p for which $H_1(p)$ is clearly at least as attractive or desirable as H_2. This will give β_j. It is, of course, doubtful that the individual will be able to identify specific p values at which a "clear choice" between $H_1(p)$ and H_2 changes to indecision, so that instead of asking for *the* largest value of p . . . or *the* smallest value of p . . ., we simply ask for a value of p . . . in either case, with the understanding that it is desirable to have the two resulting values close to one another.

The device of using a visual scale can be employed in the second method as well as the first, where a linear probability scale is now used instead of a linear value scale. For example, the individual may be presented with a probability scale extending from 0 to 1 and be requested to specify two intervals, the first extending from 0 out to the right, the second extending from 1 back to the left, such that for all p in the first $o_j \gtrsim (o_1, p, o_r)$ and for all p in the second $(o_1, p, o_r) \gtrsim o_j$. He should

0 .1 p_1 .2   .3 p_2 .4   .5   .6   .7   .8   .9   1

Figure 4.3

make the two intervals come as close to meeting as possible while still being sure of his preference judgments. If in comparing o_j and (o_1, p, o_r) for $0 \leqslant p \leqslant 1$ he gives the darkened intervals shown by Figure 4.3, we take $\alpha_j = p_1, \beta_j = p_2$.

Criticism

In considering A5, A5(1) and A5(2) are rather innocuous, since the individual can always resort to selecting $\alpha_j = 0, \beta_j = 1$, which, of course, says nothing more than $o_j \gtrsim o_r$ and $o_1 \gtrsim o_j$—which was already assumed to be known by A3(1). When $\alpha_j > 0$ and/or $\beta_j < 1$, A5(3) is anything but innocuous. To discuss A5(3), assume for the sake of argument that there is a real-valued function v with arguments o_j and (o_1, p, o_r) such that, if $o_j \gtrsim (o_1, p, o_r)$, then $v(o_j) \geq v(o_1, p, o_r)$, and if $(o_1, p, o_r) \gtrsim o_j$, then $v(o_1, p, o_r) \geq v(o_j)$. We might further let $v(o_j) = V(o_j)$ so that

$$V(o_j) \geqslant v(o_1, p, o_r), \quad \text{if } o_j \gtrsim (o_1, p, o_r),$$
$$v(o_1, p, o_r) \geqslant V(o_j), \quad \text{if } (o_1, p, o_r) \gtrsim o_j.$$

Now in A5(3) we have further assumed that $v(o_1, p, o_r) = pV(o_1) + (1 - p)V(o_r)$. Although it is true that the von Neumann-Morgenstern axioms imply all that is assumed here and more (granting $o_1 > o_r$) and thus suffice for formal justification of A5(3) let us consider some cases against the hypothesis that $v(o_1, p, o_r) = pV(o_1) + (1 - p)V(o_r)$ without going any further than A3, A5(1), and A5(2). Although these cases appear to consider separate factors, it should be obvious that they may overlap and run together in some nebulous fashion.

Case 1. *The extreme optimist or pessimist.* Suppose that $o_1 > o_j > o_r$. The extreme optimist always states $(o_1, p, o_r) > o_j$ as long as p is greater than zero. So long as $p > 0$, he feels the gods will favor him with the reward of o_1 from the gamble (o_1, p, o_r). The extreme pessimist always states $o_j > (o_1, p, o_r)$, as long as $p < 1$, since he feels the gods will punish him with o_r if he "chooses" the gamble (o_1, p, o_r). This "extreme" behavior may be quite independent of the actual position of $V(o_j)$ with respect to $V(o_1)$ and $V(o_r)$. If the adjective "extreme" is deleted, we have degrees of optimism or pessimism.

Case 2. *The inveterate gambler.* This individual enjoys gambling and therefore, even in hypothetical situations, has a preference for "gambling" as such. For example, if $o_1 \sim o_j \sim o_r$, he would always state $(o_1, p, o_r) > o_j$ for any $0 < p < 1$. Or if $o_1 > o_r$ and $o_j \sim o_1$, he would state $(o_1, p, o_r) > o_j$ for some values of $p < 1$. Along with the gambler, there is the individual who detests the thought of gambling (although he does "gamble" in many situations in his everyday encounters). If the inveterate gambler is an optimist, which is likely to be the case, then things are all the worse for our measurement scheme.

Case 3. Probability preferences. Since the values of p are specific numbers, an individual may like some of the values of p more than others, independently of o_1, o_j, and o_r. Edwards (1953, 1954a, 1954b) concludes, among other things, that people have definite biases for certain probabilities (e.g., many subjects in his experiments "underestimated" the probability .75). If an individual had made a substantial bet on a certain event with quoted odds equivalent to a probability of .9 and lost a wad in the wager, he might be quite suspicious of $p = .9$ in other situations.

Case 4. Interpretation of probability. In the method described above, suppose the values of p are interpreted as objective probabilities (in the relative frequency interpretation). How do we know that the subject "knows" the p's in this sense? The experimental evidence generally indicates that the objectively interpreted probability p comes out changed after it passes through the individual's interpretative mechanism (see, e.g., the references to Edwards given in Case 3). The problem of objective versus subjective probabilities has received much attention of late,[6] and attempts (theoretical and experimental) have been made to understand the nature of subjective probabilities. Other things being equal, one may try to meet the difficulty presented by this problem by writing $v(o_1, p, o_r) = s(p)V(o_1) + (1 - s(p))V(o_r)$ instead of $v(o_1, p, o_r) = pV(o_1) + (1 - p)V(o_r)$, where $s(p)$ is the subjective interpretation of the probability p. In other cases that follow, when we confront gambles of the form (o_j, p, o_k) and may wish to write $v(o_j, p, o_k) = s(p)V(o_j) + (1 - s(p))V(o_k)$, what reason do we have for supposing that the subjective interpretation of p does not depend on o_j and o_k as well as on p? If a model of the form $v(o_1, p, o_r) = s(p)V(o_1) + (1 - s(p))V(o_r)$ is adopted, then there is the further problem of measuring $s(p)$.

Case 5. Hypothetical choice situations generate hypothetical data. In using h-situations, since the "choices" between H_1 and H_2 are imagined and not real, it may be argued that these "choices" are very poor indicators of the $V(o_j)$ or, to be more severe, that the "choices" are meaningless.

Despite this barrage of criticism against A5(3), some persons may feel that, for practical purposes, it may have some usefulness. One defense

---

[6] This is discussed at length in the next chapter.

offered in connection with A5(3) as it is used in the second method for obtaining a first bounded interval measure of relative values is that it goes only as far as the individual's judgments between o_j and (o_1, p, o_r) permit it to go. For example, if by the second method we find for a given o_j that $.2 \leqslant I_j \leqslant .5$, it may not seem unreasonable to place a high degree of confidence in this statement (even in the light of the deficiencies of the procedure). In addition, there is always the possibility of applying a "correction factor" to statements of the form $\alpha_j \leqslant I_j \leqslant \beta_j$ obtained by the second method, which serves to widen the bounds on I_j. For instance, if $\alpha_j \leqslant I_j \leqslant \beta_j$ is obtained, replace this with $\alpha_j - \delta\alpha_j \leqslant I_j \leqslant \beta_j + \delta(1 - \beta_j)$, where $0 < \delta < 1$.

It will be noted that the first method of obtaining a first bounded interval measure avoids the criticisms leveled at the second method in Cases 1 through 5, since the first method makes no reference to probabilities or to hypothetical choice situations or gambles. It will also be realized that, if both methods are used in the same situation, the two sets of results will probably be different. Just how different is difficult to guess, since there seem to be no experimental results that attempt to compare two such methods.

4.7 THE ORDINAL AND FIRST BOUNDED INTERVAL MEASURES

Suppose that, along with the first bounded interval measure

$$I_1 = 1, \quad I_r = 0, \quad \alpha_j \leqslant I_j \leqslant \beta_j \quad j = 2, \ldots, r - 1, \qquad (4.3)$$

one also obtains an ordinal measure of the V_j. We can rearrange the subscripts on the I_j, $j = 2, \ldots, r - 1$, so that the ranking

$$V_1 \geqslant V_2 \geqslant \ldots \geqslant V_{r-1} \geqslant V_r \quad (V_1 > V_r)$$

implies that

$$I_1 \geqslant I_2 \geqslant \ldots \geqslant I_{r-1} \geqslant I_r, \qquad (4.4)$$

where

$$I_j = \frac{V_j - V_r}{V_1 - V_r}.$$

In order for (4.3) and (4.4) not to contradict one another, it must be true that

$$\beta_j \geqslant \alpha_k \quad \text{for } k > j \quad (\beta_j \geqslant I_j, \ I_j \geqslant I_k, I_k \geqslant \alpha_k),$$

or that

$$\beta_j \geqslant \max \, [\alpha_{j+1}, \alpha_{j+2}, \ldots, \alpha_{r-1}], \quad j = 2, \ldots, r - 2. \qquad (4.5)$$

If $\beta_j < \alpha_k$ for $k > j$, the interval $[\alpha_j, \beta_j]$ would lie wholly to the left of $[\alpha_k, \beta_k]$, implying that $I_j < I_k$, contrary to $I_j \geqslant I_k$ $(k > j)$ as given by (4.4). If, in fact, $\beta_j < \alpha_k$ for some $k > j$, then (4.3) and (4.4) are at odds and either one or the other (or both) must be tossed out or amended. It is, of course, quite permissible to have $[\alpha_j, \beta_j]$ and $[\alpha_k, \beta_k]$ overlap or to have one lie within the other as long as (4.5) is not violated.

If (4.5) holds and it is also true that $\beta_{j+1} \leqslant \alpha_j$ for $j = 2, \ldots, r - 2$, then no overlap occurs, and the intervals $[\alpha_j, \beta_j]$ would appear as shown in Figure 4.4.

Figure 4.4

In this case, with $I_j \in [\alpha_j, \beta_j]$, we are assured that (4.4) holds, so that the first bounded interval measure contains within it the information contained in the ordinal measure.

If (4.5) holds and some of the intervals $[\alpha_j, \beta_j]$ overlap, it may be possible to refine the bounds on I_j in accordance with the ordinal ranking. The new bounds on I_j will be denoted as c_j and d_j. That is, we go from $\alpha_j \leqslant I_j \leqslant \beta_j$ to $c_j \leqslant I_j \leqslant d_j$, where

$$\alpha_j \leqslant c_j \leqslant d_j \leqslant \beta_j, \qquad j = 2, \ldots, r - 1,$$
$$c_{r-1} \leqslant c_{r-2} \leqslant \ldots \leqslant c_3 \leqslant c_2,$$
$$d_{r-1} \leqslant d_{r-2} \leqslant \ldots \leqslant d_3 \leqslant d_2.$$

Consider the α_j first. If it happens that $\alpha_{r-1} \leqslant \alpha_{r-2} \leqslant \ldots \leqslant \alpha_3 \leqslant \alpha_2$, then this causes no conflict with the ranking $I_r \leqslant I_{r-1} \leqslant \ldots \leqslant I_2 \leqslant I_1$, and we simply take $c_j = \alpha_j$ for $j = 2, \ldots, r - 1$. However, it may happen that the α_j are not so ordered. If, for example, $\alpha_2 < \alpha_3$, then, since $I_3 \leqslant I_2$ must hold, we can replace the lower bound (α_2) on I_2 with the lower bound on I_3, giving $\alpha_3 \leqslant I_2 \leqslant \beta_2$ instead of $\alpha_2 \leqslant I_2 \leqslant \beta_2$. If we had $\alpha_2 < \alpha_3 < \alpha_4$, then $\alpha_2 \leqslant I_2 \leqslant \beta_2$ could be replaced by $\alpha_4 \leqslant I_2 \leqslant \beta_2$. In general, set

$$c_j = \max [\alpha_j, \alpha_{j+1}, \ldots, \alpha_{r-1}],$$

that is, set c_j equal to the largest α_k for $k \geqslant j$.

By a similar line of reasoning for the β_j, set

$$d_j = \min [\beta_2, \beta_3, \ldots, \beta_j],$$

i.e., set d_j equal to the smallest β_k for $k \leqslant j$.

Since $\max [\alpha_j, \alpha_{j+1}, \ldots, \alpha_{r-1}] \leqslant \max [\alpha_{j-1}, \ldots, \alpha_{r-1}]$, $c_{r-1} \leqslant c_{r-2} \leqslant \ldots \leqslant c_3 \leqslant c_2$. Likewise, since $\min [\beta_2, \ldots, \beta_j] \geqslant \min [\beta_2, \ldots, \beta_{j+1}]$, $d_{r-1} \leqslant d_{r-2} \leqslant \ldots \leqslant d_3 \leqslant d_2$. In addition, we obviously have $\alpha_j \leqslant c_j$ and $d_j \leqslant \beta_j$.

To show that $c_j \leqslant d_j$, we use the restrictions (4.5). Since $\beta_j \geqslant \alpha_j$, these may be rewritten as

$$\beta_j \geqslant \max [\alpha_j, \alpha_{j+1}, \ldots, \alpha_{r-1}], \quad j = 2, \ldots, r - 1.$$

Then, since

$$\beta_2 \geqslant \max [\alpha_2, \alpha_3, \ldots, \alpha_{r-1}] \geqslant \max [\alpha_j, \alpha_{j+1}, \ldots, \alpha_{r-1}],$$
$$\beta_3 \geqslant \max [\alpha_3, \alpha_4, \ldots, \alpha_{r-1}] \geqslant \max [\alpha_j, \alpha_{j+1}, \ldots, \alpha_{r-1}],$$
$$\vdots$$
$$\beta_{j-1} \geqslant \max [\alpha_{j-1}, \alpha_j, \ldots, \alpha_{r-1}] \geqslant \max [\alpha_j, \alpha_{j+1}, \ldots, \alpha_{r-1}],$$
$$\beta_j \geqslant \max [\alpha_j, \alpha_{j+1}, \ldots, \alpha_{r-1}],$$

it must be true that

$$\min [\beta_2, \beta_3, \ldots, \beta_j] \geqslant \max [\alpha_j, \alpha_{j+1}, \ldots, \alpha_{r-1}],$$

i.e., that $d_j \geqslant c_j$.

With the new bounds on the I_j, it is still possible to have an overlapping of $[c_{j+1}, d_{j+1}]$ and $[c_j, d_j]$ of the form $c_{j+1} \leqslant c_j < d_{j+1} \leqslant d_j$. However, we have ruled out such possibilities as $c_{j+1} < c_j < d_j < d_{j+1}$ and $c_j < c_{j+1} < d_{j+1} < d_j$. That is, for each j, $j = 2, \ldots, r - 2$, either $[c_{j+1}, d_{j+1}]$ lies completely to the left of $[c_j, d_j]$, or the two intervals touch ($d_{j+1} = c_j$), or they overlap in the form $c_{j+1} \leqslant c_j < d_{j+1} \leqslant d_j$.

With this refinement, the measures in concert will read:

$$I_1 = 1, \quad I_r = 0, \quad c_j \leqslant I_j \leqslant d_j \quad j = 2, \ldots, r - 1,$$

where

$$0 \leqslant c_{r-1} \leqslant c_{r-2} \leqslant \ldots \leqslant c_3 \leqslant c_2 \leqslant 1,$$
$$0 \leqslant d_{r-1} \leqslant d_{r-2} \leqslant \ldots \leqslant d_3 \leqslant d_2 \leqslant 1,$$
$$0 \leqslant I_{r-1} \leqslant I_{r-2} \leqslant \ldots \leqslant I_3 \leqslant I_2 \leqslant 1.$$

4.8 THE SECOND BOUNDED INTERVAL MEASURE

The second bounded interval measure has, as prerequisite, the ordinal ranking

$$V_1 \geqslant V_2 \geqslant \ldots \geqslant V_r, \tag{4.1}$$

in which $V_1 > V_r$. This measure then bounds the ratio of the two relative value intervals $V_j - V_{j+1}$ and $V_1 - V_r$, for $j = 1, 2, \ldots, r - 1$. Let

$$L_j = \frac{V_j - V_{j+1}}{V_1 - V_r},$$

and let the bounds on L_j be α_j and $\alpha_j + \epsilon_j$, $0 \leqslant \alpha_j \leqslant \alpha_j + \epsilon_j \leqslant 1$, as derived from the measurement procedure. The second bounded interval measure is given by

$$\alpha_j \leqslant L_j \leqslant \alpha_j + \epsilon_j, \qquad j = 1, \ldots, r - 1, \tag{4.6}$$

in which

$$0 \leqslant \alpha_j \leqslant \alpha_j + \epsilon_j \leqslant 1, \qquad j = 1, \ldots, r - 1,$$

$$\sum_{j=1}^{r-1} \alpha_j \leqslant 1 \leqslant \sum_{j=1}^{r-1} \alpha_j + \sum_{j=1}^{r-1} \epsilon_j. \tag{4.7}$$

Restrictions (4.7) follow from

$$\sum_{j=1}^{r-1} L_j = \frac{V_1 - V_2}{V_1 - V_r} + \frac{V_2 - V_3}{V_1 - V_r} + \cdots + \frac{V_{r-1} - V_r}{V_1 - V_r} = \frac{V_1 - V_r}{V_1 - V_r} = 1$$

and from (4.6).

One way of obtaining the bounds on L_j is by employing hypothetical gambles. Now for $j = 2, \ldots, r - 2$, L_j involves four V_j, but L_1 and L_{r-1} involve only three:

$$L_1 = \frac{V_1 - V_2}{V_1 - V_r} = \frac{V_1 - V_r}{V_1 - V_r} - \frac{V_2 - V_r}{V_1 - V_r} = 1 - I_2,$$

$$L_{r-1} = \frac{V_{r-1} - V_r}{V_1 - V_r} = I_{r-1}.$$

Thus the bounds on L_1 and L_{r-1} can be obtained by the methods of the previous section.

For L_j $(2 \leqslant j \leqslant r - 2)$, the ordinal ranking gives

$$V_1 \geqslant V_j \geqslant V_{j+1} \geqslant V_r,$$

as obtained from $o_1 \gtrsim o_j \gtrsim o_{j+1} \gtrsim o_r$. With the use of these four consequences, consider the two gambles

$$(o_1, p, o_{j+1}), \qquad (o_r, p, o_j), \qquad 0 \leqslant p \leqslant 1,$$

which may be arrayed in an h-situation as

	E_p	$\bar{E}_p$
$H_1(p)$	o_1	o_{j+1}
$H_2(p)$	o_r	o_j

$\tag{4.8}$

If H_1 is "chosen" by the individual, then o_1 "occurs" with probability p, and o_{j+1} "occurs" with probability $1 - p$. If H_2 is "chosen," then o_r "occurs" with probability p, and o_j "occurs" with probability $1 - p$.

To illustrate this situation, picture the consequences as monetary prizes. For most persons it seems reasonable that the relative value of money increases with the amount, so let us imagine (4.8) in the form of

	E_p	$\bar{E}_p$
$H_1(p)$	$100	$60
$H_2(p)$	$1	$80

At the moment you are reading this passage, suppose you have a chance to participate in this situation. Which choice (between H_1 and H_2) would you make if: (a) $p = 1$; (b) $p = .5$; (c) $p = .25$; (d) $p = .15$; (e) $p = .10$; (f) $p = .05$; (g) $p = 0$? Are you uncertain as to what you would actually do with any one or more of these values of p? [For $p = 0$ the choice is between $60 or $80, so we would "choose" H_2. We would continue to pick H_2 for p up to about .1. Between .1 and .2 we feel unsure as to what we would do, but for $p \geqslant .2$ we would pick H_1.[7]] Let us examine the situation for $p = \frac{1}{2}$. For this case H_1 yields $100 or $60, each with probability $\frac{1}{2}$. H_2 yields $80 or $1, each with probability $\frac{1}{2}$. Since, with $p = \frac{1}{2}$, the two columns have the same "likelihood" of turning up [i.e., $P(E_p) = P(\bar{E}_p)$], we can, assuming the subjective interpretation of the likelihoods renders them equal, reverse the two entries in the second row to give

	$E_{1/2}$	$\bar{E}_{1/2}$			$E_{1/2}$	$\bar{E}_{1/2}$
$H_1(\frac{1}{2})$	$100	$60	$=$	$H_1(\frac{1}{2})$	$100	$60
$H_2'(\frac{1}{2})$	$80	$1		$H_2(\frac{1}{2})$	$1	$80

As rewritten for $p = \frac{1}{2}$, it would seem reasonable to expect that $H_1(\frac{1}{2})$ would be "chosen" over $H_2'(\frac{1}{2})$ or $H_2(\frac{1}{2})$. For the general h-situation shown by (4.8), the reversal in the second row gives

	$E_{1/2}$	$\bar{E}_{1/2}$			$E_{1/2}$	$\bar{E}_{1/2}$
$H_1(\frac{1}{2})$	o_1	o_{j+1}	$=$	$H_1(\frac{1}{2})$	o_1	o_{j+1}
$H_2'(\frac{1}{2})$	o_j	o_r		$H_2(\frac{1}{2})$	o_r	o_j

---

[7] By A6 and (4.9) to follow, these judgments give

$$\frac{1}{9} \leqslant \frac{V(\$80) - V(\$60)}{V(\$100) - V(\$1)} \leqslant \frac{1}{4}.$$

Since $o_1 \gtrsim o_j$ and $o_{j+1} \gtrsim o_r$ for the general situation, it also seems reasonable that $H_1(\frac{1}{2})$ would be "chosen" over $H_2(\frac{1}{2})$.

With these remarks we are in a better position to state the assumptions for the second bounded interval measure. In addition to the assumptions that give the ordinal ranking (4.1), we shall use A3(2) $(o_1 > o_r)$ and:

A6(1) For each j, $j = 1, \ldots, r - 1$, there is a value of $p \geqslant 0$, say p_j, such that $(o_r, p, o_j) \gtrsim (o_1, p, o_{j+1})$ for all $p \leqslant p_j$.

A6(2) For each j, $j = 1, \ldots, r - 1$, there is a value of p, say q_j, such that $p_j \leqslant q_j \leqslant \frac{1}{2}$ and $(o_1, p, o_{j+1}) \gtrsim (o_r, p, o_j)$ for all $p \geqslant q_j$.

A6(3) If $(o_1, p, o_{j+1}) \gtrsim (o_r, p, o_j)$, then $pV_1 + (1 - p)V_{j+1} \geqslant pV_r + (1 - p)V_j$; and if $(o_r, p, o_j) \gtrsim (o_1, p, o_{j+1})$, then $pV_r + (1 - p)V_j \geqslant pV_1 + (1 - p)V_{j+1}$.

Now if $pV_1 + (1 - p)V_{j+1} \leqslant pV_r + (1 - p)V_j$, then

$$p(V_1 - V_r) \leqslant (1 - p)(V_j - V_{j+1}),$$

or

$$\frac{p}{1 - p} \leqslant L_j.$$

In particular,

$$\frac{p_j}{1 - p_j} \leqslant L_j.$$

Likewise, if $pV_1 + (1 - p)V_{j+1} \geqslant pV_r + (1 - p)V_j$, then

$$L_j \leqslant \frac{p}{1 - p},$$

and in particular,

$$L_j \leqslant \frac{q_j}{1 - q_j}.$$

Combining these,

$$\alpha_j \leqslant L_j \leqslant \alpha_j + \epsilon_j, \qquad j = 1, \ldots, r - 1,$$

$$\alpha_j = \frac{p_j}{1 - p_j}, \tag{4.9}$$

$$\alpha_j + \epsilon_j = \frac{q_j}{1 - q_j}.$$

With $0 \leqslant p_j \leqslant q_j \leqslant \frac{1}{2}$, the reader can readily verify that $0 \leqslant \alpha_j \leqslant \alpha_j + \epsilon_j \leqslant 1$. On a plot, the transformation from p to $p/(1 - p)$ is given by Figure 4.5.

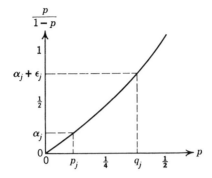

Figure 4.5

The final assumption required for this measure is:

$$A6(4) \qquad \sum_{j=1}^{r-1} \frac{p_j}{1 - p_j} \leqslant 1 \leqslant \sum_{j=1}^{r-1} \frac{q_j}{1 - q_j},$$

which guarantees that $\sum \alpha_j \leqslant 1 \leqslant \sum \alpha_j + \sum \epsilon_j$.

In applying a procedure for obtaining a second bounded interval measure, it should be understood that p_j is to be as large as the individual can make it and still feel certain that $(o_r, p_j, o_j) \gtrsim (o_1, p_j, o_{j+1})$, and that q_j is to be as small as the individual can make it and still feel certain that $(o_1, q_j, o_{j+1}) \gtrsim (o_r, q_j, o_j)$.

Criticism of the assumptions that yield this measure follow the same general line as those offered in connection with the second method of obtaining a first bounded interval measure.

4.9   THE THIRD BOUNDED INTERVAL MEASURE

Equivalence Classes

Like the second bounded interval measure, the third bounded interval measure has, as prerequisites, the ordinal assumptions A1(1) and A1(2), and A3.   In this case it will be advantageous to go one step beyond the weak ordering of **Q** and have a strict simple ordering over a set of equivalence classes.   This requires the procedural condition that for each pair of consequences $\{o_j, o_k,\}$ $j \neq k$, the individual can state whether $o_j \gtrsim o_k$ or not *and* whether $o_k \gtrsim o_j$ or not.   This will yield either $o_j > o_k$, or $o_k > o_j$, or $o_j \sim o_k$.   The consequences are then partitioned into a set of equivalence classes $\{e_i\}$, where $i = 1, \ldots, r'$ and $r' \leqslant r$.   The equivalence classes are defined by: (1) each e_i is a subset of the consequences and contains at least one o_j; (2) every o_j is in one and only one e_i; and (3) o_j and o_k are in the same equivalence class if and only if $o_j \sim o_k$. It will be assumed that there are at least three equivalence classes in the set $\{e_i\}$.

Now if $o_j \in e_i$ and $o_k \in e_i$, then, since $o_j \sim o_k$, $V_j = V_k$, and if $o_j \in e_i$, $o_k \in e_t$, $i \neq t$, then either $V_j > V_k$ or $V_k > V_j$. Moreover, if $o_j \in e_i$, $o_k \in e_t$, $i \neq t$, and $V_j > V_k$, then $V_j > V_k$ for any $o_j \in e_i$ and any $o_k \in e_t$. We define the relation $>$ between equivalence classes by $e_i > e_t$ if and only if $o_j > o_k$, with $o_j \in e_i$, $o_k \in e_t$.

This gives a strict simple ordering of the $r' \leqslant r$ equivalence classes, which, by subscript convention, will be written as

$$e_1 > e_2 > \ldots > e_{r'}. \tag{4.10}$$

The relative value of e_i is defined by

$$V(e_i) = V(o_j), \qquad o_j \in e_i.$$

$V(e_i)$ is well defined since $V(o_j) = V(o_k)$ for all $o_j, o_k \in e_i$. In accordance with (4.10),

$$V(e_1) > V(e_2) > \ldots > V(e_{r'}).$$

In obtaining additional information about the relative magnitudes of the $V(e_i)$, it suffices to work with a set of r' consequences, say $\{o_1, \ldots, o_{r'}\}$, with $o_j \in e_j$, $j = 1, \ldots, r'$. That is, select one consequence from each equivalence class, and by subscript convention for these consequences let $o_j \in e_j$. Then, for the selected subset of the o_j,

$$V(o_1) > V(o_2) > \ldots > V(o_r)$$

or

$$V_1 > V_2 > \ldots > V_j > V_{j+1} > V_{j+2} > \ldots > V_{r'}. \tag{4.11}$$

The relative value of every consequence not in the chosen subset will be equal to one of the V_j, $j = 1, \ldots, r'$.

The Measure

The third bounded interval measure is concerned with the o_j, $j = 1, \ldots, r'$ for which $o_1 > o_2 > \ldots > o_{r'}$ or with the V_j in (4.11). Its derivation is similar to the first bounded interval measure in that we work with three consequences at a time. The three consequences dealt with at any point will be o_j, o_{j+1}, and o_{j+2}, whose relative values are adjacent to one another in the ranking (4.11). Define

$$K_j = \frac{V_j - V_{j+1}}{V_{j+1} - V_{j+2}}, \qquad j = 1, 2, \ldots, r' - 2. \tag{4.12}$$

The third bounded interval measure consists of bounds on the K_j:

$$c_j \leqslant K_j \leqslant d_j, \qquad j = 1, \ldots, r' - 2,$$

$$0 \leqslant c_j \leqslant d_j < \infty, \qquad j = 1, \ldots, r' - 2.$$

For a given j, the bounds on K_j can be determined by either method presented in Section 4.6. For the first method, the subject is to indicate, on a linear scale with end points V_j and V_{j+2}, an interval which he believes contains V_{j+1} (Figure 4.6).
The bounds for K_j are given by

$$c_j = \frac{x_1}{x_3 - x_1},$$

$$d_j = \frac{x_2}{x_3 - x_2},$$

where x_1, x_2, and x_3 are the linear distances shown on Figure 4.6. For this method it is assumed that $x_2 < x_3$.

In the second method o_{j+1} is compared with (o_j, p, o_{j+2}), where (o_j, p, o_{j+2}) is the gamble "yielding" o_j with probability p or o_{j+2} with probability $1 - p$. The assumptions for this method are similar in form to A5 and are here written as:

A7(1) For each j, $j = 1, \ldots, r - 2$, there is a value of $p > 0$, say p_j, such that $o_{j+1} \gtrsim (o_j, p, o_{j+2})$ for all $p \leqslant p_j$.

A7(2) There is a value of p, say q_j, such that $q_j \geqslant p_j$ and $(o_j, p, o_{j+2}) \gtrsim o_{j+1}$ for all $p \geqslant q_j$.

A7(3) If $o_{j+1} \gtrsim (o_j, p, o_{j+2})$, then $V_{j+1} \geqslant pV_j + (1 - p)V_{j+2}$; and if $(o_j, p, o_{j+2}) \gtrsim o_{j+1}$, then $pV_j + (1 - p)V_{j+2} \geqslant V_{j+1}$.

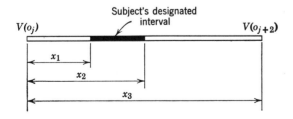

Figure 4.6

If $V_{j+1} \geqslant pV_j + (1-p)V_{j+2}$, then

$$pV_{j+1} + (1-p)V_{j+1} \geqslant pV_j + (1-p)V_{j+2},$$
$$(1-p)(V_{j+1} - V_{j+2}) \geqslant p(V_j - V_{j+1}),$$
$$\frac{1-p}{p} \geqslant \frac{V_j - V_{j+1}}{V_{j+1} - V_{j+2}} = K_j,$$
$$K_j \leqslant \frac{1-p}{p}.$$

In particular,

$$K_j \leqslant \frac{1-p_j}{p_j}.$$

Similarly, if $pV_j + (1-p)V_{j+2} \geqslant V_{j+1}$, then

$$\frac{1-p}{p} \leqslant K_j.$$

In particular,

$$\frac{1-q_j}{q_j} \leqslant K_j.$$

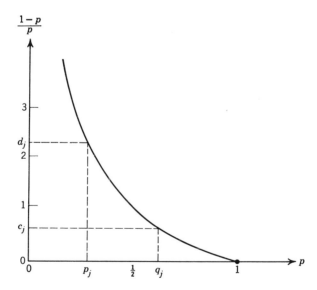

Figure 4.7

This gives

$$c_j \leqslant K_j \leqslant d_j,$$

$$c_j = \frac{1 - q_j}{q_j}, \qquad j = 1, \ldots, r' - 2$$

$$d_j = \frac{1 - p_j}{p_j}.$$

The transformation from p to $(1 - p)/p$ is plotted as shown in Figure 4.7. The criticisms of Section 4.6 and some in Section 4.3 apply equally well to this measure.

Having proceeded through the first, second, and third bounded interval measures (the ILK measures, for short) it should be apparent that the I_j, L_j, and K_j have certain relationships with one another. In addition, there is a great potential of other bounded interval measures that one could define. The reader is directed to Exercises 7 and 8 for a further look. Use of the ILK measures in connection with the decision model will be discussed in Section 6.4 and in Chapter 7.

4.10 THE ORDERED METRICS

The Forms of the Metrics

The first ordered metric measure is built upon the ordinal ranking

$$V_1 \geqslant V_2 \geqslant \ldots \geqslant V_r, \tag{4.1}$$

and the nth ordered metric measure is built upon the $(n - 1)$st ordered metric measure. The first ordered metric measure ranks the $r - 1$ adjacent differences of the V_j in (4.1) from largest to smallest. These differences are $V_1 - V_2$, $V_2 - V_3, \ldots, V_{r-1} - V_r$. With $j_1, j_2, \ldots, j_{r-1}$ a permutation of the integers $1, 2, \ldots, r - 1$, the first ordered metric ranking has the form

$$(V_{j_1} - V_{j_1 + 1}) \geqslant (V_{j_2} - V_{j_2 + 1}) \geqslant \ldots \geqslant (V_{j_{r-1}} - V_{j_{r-1} + 1}) \geqslant 0. \tag{4.13}$$

Letting

$$V_k^{(1)} = V_{j_k} - V_{j_k + 1}, \qquad k = 1, \ldots, r - 1,$$

$$V_r^{(1)} = 0,$$

(4.13) may be written as

$$V_1^{(1)} \geqslant V_2^{(1)} \geqslant \ldots \geqslant V_{r-1}^{(1)} \geqslant V_r^{(1)}. \tag{4.14}$$

The second ordered metric measure then ranks, by decreasing magnitude, the adjacent differences $V_j^{(1)} - V_{j+1}^{(1)}$, $j = 1, \ldots, r - 1$, from the first ordered metric ranking (4.14). Letting $V_k^{(2)}$ denote the kth-ranked difference $(V_j^{(1)} - V_{j+1}^{(1)})$, with $V_r^{(2)} = 0$, the second ordered metric ranking may be written as

$$V_1^{(2)} \geqslant V_2^{(2)} \geqslant \ldots \geqslant V_{r-1}^{(2)} \geqslant V_r^{(2)}.$$

Given the $(n - 1)$st ordered metric ranking

$$V_1^{(n-1)} \geqslant V_2^{(n-1)} \geqslant \ldots \geqslant V_{r-1}^{(n-1)} \geqslant V_r^{(n-1)},$$

the nth ordered metric measure ranks, by decreasing magnitude, the adjacent differences $V_1^{(n-1)} - V_2^{(n-1)}$, $V_2^{(n-1)} - V_3^{(n-1)}$, ..., $V_{r-1}^{(n-1)} - V_r^{(n-1)}$. Letting $V_k^{(n)}$ denote the kth-ranked difference $V_j^{(n-1)} - V_{j+1}^{(n-1)}$, with $V_r^{(n)} = 0$, the nth ordered metric ranking takes the form

$$V_1^{(n)} \geqslant V_2^{(n)} \geqslant \ldots \geqslant V_{r-1}^{(n)} \geqslant V_r^{(n)}.$$

By the manner in which the nth ordered metric ranking is defined, it should be apparent that it has, embedded within it, all the information about the $V(o_j)$ or V_j contained in the ordinal ranking, first ordered metric ranking, ..., $(n - 1)$st ordered metric ranking. By its construction, the nth ordered metric ranking cannot contradict the mth ordered metric ranking, $m < n$. These rankings, in order, may be thought of as giving finer and finer bounds on the V_j.

Theory

To present the assumptions of the ordered metric measures, we begin with a weak ordering of **Q**:

$$o_1 \succsim o_2 \succsim \ldots \succsim o_r.$$

Since A1 is required for this ordering, it is basic to all the ordered metric measures. The two primitives used in connection with the first ordered metric measure are the set Z_1 composed of the $r - 1$ elements (o_j, o_{j+1}), $j = 1, \ldots, r - 1$, and a relation R_1 over Z_1. The statement (o_j, o_{j+1}) $R_1(o_k, o_{k+1})$ will be interpreted as: The difference in preference or relative value between o_j and o_{j+1} is at least as great as the difference in preference or relative value between o_k and o_{k+1}. The axiom (in addition to A1) for the first ordered metric measure is:

A8(1) R_1 is a weak ordering of Z_1.

As we shall see, it will be convenient to denote the $r - 1$ elements of Z_1 as $z_1^1, z_2^1, \ldots, z_{r-1}^1$. That is, each z_j^1 is identically one and only one of the (o_k, o_{k+1}), and vice versa. We shall adopt the subscript convention

$$z_1^1 R_1 z_2^1 R_1 \ldots R_1 z_{r-1}^1. \tag{4.15}$$

For example, if with $r = 5$, A8(1) gives

$$(o_3, o_4)R_1(o_1, o_2)R_1(o_4, o_5)R_1(o_2, o_3),$$

then

$$z_1^1 = (o_3, o_4),$$
$$z_2^1 = (o_1, o_2),$$
$$z_3^1 = (o_4, o_5),$$
$$z_4^1 = (o_2, o_3).$$

For explication with respect to the value function, let

$$V^{(1)}(z_j^1) = V(o_k) - V(o_{k+1}) \qquad \text{for} \qquad z_j^1 = (o_k, o_{k+1}),$$

and define

$$V^{(1)}(z_j^1) \geqslant V^{(1)}(z_k^1) \qquad \text{if and only if } z_j^1 R_1 z_k^1.$$

For the $r = 5$ illustration,

$$V^{(1)}(z_1^1) \geqslant V^{(1)}(z_2^1) \geqslant V^{(1)}(z_3^1) \geqslant V^{(1)}(z_4^1) \geqslant 0,$$

or

$$V(o_3) - V(o_4) \geqslant V(o_1) - V(o_2) \geqslant V(o_4) - V(o_5) \geqslant V(o_2) - V(o_3) \geqslant 0,$$

or

$$V_3 - V_4 \geqslant V_1 - V_2 \geqslant V_4 - V_5 \geqslant V_2 - V_3 \geqslant 0, \qquad (4.16)$$

where $\geqslant 0$ appears since all value differences by (4.1) are nonnegative.

Starting with the ranking (4.15) as given, the primitives of discussion for the second ordered metric measure are the set Z_2 with elements $(z_1^1, z_2^1), (z_2^1, z_3^1), \ldots, (z_{r-2}^1, z_{r-1}^1), (z_{r-1}^1, z_r^1)$, where $z_r^1 = (o_r, o_r)$, and a relation R_2 over Z_2. In addition to A1 and A8(1), we require, for the second ordered metric ranking:

A8(2) R_2 is a weak ordering of Z_2.

Now redesignate the $r - 1$ elements of Z_2 as $z_1^2, z_2^2, \ldots, z_{r-1}^2$ and use the subscript convention

$$z_1^2 R_2 z_2^2 R_2 \ldots R_2 z_{r-1}^2.$$

Then, let

$$V^{(2)}(z_j^2) = V^{(1)}(z_k^1) - V^{(1)}(z_{k+1}^1) \qquad \text{for} \qquad z_j^2 = (z_k^1, z_{k+1}^1),$$

and define

$$V^{(2)}(z_j^2) \geqslant V^{(2)}(z_k^2) \qquad \text{if and only if } z_j^2 R_2 z_k^2.$$

For the going example, suppose

$$(z_1^1, z_2^1)R_2(z_4^1, z_5^1)R_2(z_3^1, z_4^1)R_2(z_2^1, z_3^1),$$

where $z_1^1, \ldots, z_4^1$ are defined above and $z_5^1 = (o_r, o_r)$. Then according to the subscripting convention,

$$z_1^2 = (z_1^1, z_2^1),$$
$$z_2^2 = (z_4^1, z_5^1),$$
$$z_3^2 = (z_3^1, z_4^1),$$
$$z_4^2 = (z_2^1, z_3^1),$$

giving

$$z_1^2 R_2 z_2^2 R_2 z_3^2 R_2 z_4^2.$$

Then

$$V^{(2)}(z_1^2) \geqslant V^{(2)}(z_2^2) \geqslant V^{(2)}(z_3^2) \geqslant V^{(2)}(z_4^2) \geqslant 0,$$

or[8]

$$V^{(1)}(z_1^1) - V^{(1)}(z_2^1) \geqslant V^{(1)}(z_4^1) - V^{(1)}(z_5^1)$$
$$\geqslant V^{(1)}(z_3^1) - V^{(1)}(z_4^1) \geqslant V^{(1)}(z_2^1) - V^{(1)}(z_3^1) \geqslant 0,$$

which, in terms of the $V(o_j)$ is the same as

$$V(o_2) + V(o_3) - V(o_1) - V(o_4)$$
$$\geqslant V(o_2) - V(o_3) \geqslant V(o_3) + V(o_4) - V(o_2) - V(o_5)$$
$$\geqslant V(o_1) + V(o_5) - V(o_2) - V(o_4) \geqslant 0. \tag{4.17}$$

Successive ordered metric rankings are defined recursively. Given the ordering (for $n > 2$),

$$z_1^{n-1} R_{n-1} z_2^{n-1} R_{n-1} \cdots R_{n-1} z_{r-1}^{n-1},$$

let $z_r^{n-1} = (z_r^{n-2}, z_r^{n-2})$. Let Z_n be the set with elements $(z_j^{n-1}, z_{j+1}^{n-1})$, $j = 1, \ldots, r - 1$, and let R_n denote a relation over Z_n. For the nth ordered metric, in addition to A1, A8(1), A8(2), $\ldots$, A8($n - 1$), we require:

A8(n) R_n is a weak ordering of Z_n.

Let $Z_n = \{z_j^n\}$, where z_j^n is identically one of the $(z_k^{n-1}, z_{k+1}^{n-1})$, and vice versa, with the subscripts on the z^n so defined that

$$z_1^n R_n z_2^n R_n z_3^n R_n \cdots R_n z_{r-1}^n. \tag{4.18}$$

With regard to the value function, let

$$V^{(n)}(z_j^n) = V^{(n-1)}(z_k^{n-1}) - V^{(n-1)}(z_{k+1}^{n-1}) \quad \text{for} \quad z_j^n = (z_k^{n-1}, z_{k+1}^{n-1}),$$

[8] $V^{(1)}(z_5^1) = V^{(1)}((o_5, o_5)) = V(o_5) - V(o_5) = 0.$

and define

$$V^{(n)}(z_j^n) \geqslant V^{(n)}(z_k^n) \qquad \text{if and only if } z_j^n R_n z_k^n,$$

giving, by (4.18),

$$V^{(n)}(z_1^n) \geqslant V^{(n)}(z_2^n) \geqslant \ldots \geqslant V^{(n)}(z_{r-1}^n) \geqslant 0. \qquad (4.19)$$

For simplicity in later work[9] let

$$V_j^{(n)} = V^{(n)}(z_j^n), \qquad j = 1, \ldots, r-1,$$
$$V_r^{(n)} = 0,$$

so that (4.19) may be written as

$$V_1^{(n)} \geqslant V_2^{(n)} \geqslant \ldots \geqslant V_{r-1}^{(n)} \geqslant V_r^{(n)}.$$

The ordered metric rankings can also be written in terms of the L_j, where

$$L_j = \frac{V_j - V_{j+1}}{V_1 - V_r}, \qquad j = 1, \ldots, r-1,$$

assuming $V_1 > V_r$. Dividing through (4.16) with $V_1 - V_r$ gives

$$L_3 \geqslant L_1 \geqslant L_4 \geqslant L_2 \geqslant 0. \qquad (4.20)$$

Then, (4.17) can be rewritten as

$$L_3 - L_1 \geqslant L_2 \geqslant L_4 - L_2 \geqslant L_1 - L_4 \geqslant 0. \qquad (4.21)$$

The third ordered metric ranking, which ranks adjacent differences in (4.21), might be (for example)

$$2L_2 - L_4 \geqslant L_3 - L_1 - L_2 \geqslant L_1 - L_4 \geqslant 2L_4 - L_1 - L_2 \geqslant 0. \qquad (4.22)$$

In each of these cases $\sum_{j=1}^{4} L_j = 1$. To give a rough indication of "change" from one ordered metric to the next, consider the "equal-increment solutions" to the last three rankings. With $\mathbf{L} = (L_1, L_2, L_3, L_4)$, each of these rankings has the form

$$f_1(\mathbf{L}) \geqslant f_2(\mathbf{L}) \geqslant f_3(\mathbf{L}) \geqslant f_4(\mathbf{L}) \geqslant 0.$$

In such a ranking, the equal-increment solution of the L_j is defined by the equations

$$f_1(\mathbf{L}) - f_2(\mathbf{L}) = f_2(\mathbf{L}) - f_3(\mathbf{L}) = f_3(\mathbf{L}) - f_4(\mathbf{L}) = f_4(\mathbf{L}),$$

$$\sum_{j=1}^{4} L_j = 1.$$

[9] See, e.g., Section 6.2.

For the rankings (4.20), (4.21), and (4.22), the equal-increment solutions are respectively,

$$(L_3, L_1, L_4, L_2) = (.400, .300, .200, .100),$$
$$(L_3, L_1, L_4, L_2) = (.417, .250, .208, .125),$$
$$(L_3, L_1, L_4, L_2) = (.431, .235, .196, .138).$$

Convergence Questions

It may be of interest to ask whether or not the successive equal-increment solutions converge as $n \to \infty$. If they do converge, say to $\mathbf{L}^0 = (L_1^0, L_2^0, \ldots, L_{r-1}^0)$, is it true that the L_j also converge to the L_j^0? Although these convergence questions may be of considerable academic interest, they are not too critical from a practical standpoint, since it is doubtful that in a particular decision situation one would attempt to go beyond the second or perhaps third ordered metric if that far.

Although we conjecture that equal-increment solutions always converge, it may be shown that the L_j do not always converge (to an interval measure). This is demonstrated by the following example. Take $r = 4$ and let

$$\alpha = \frac{V_1 - V_2}{V_1 - V_4}, \qquad \beta = \frac{V_2 - V_3}{V_1 - V_4}, \qquad \gamma = \frac{V_3 - V_4}{V_1 - V_4},$$

$$\alpha \geqslant \gamma \geqslant \beta \geqslant 0, \qquad \alpha + \beta + \gamma = 1.$$

In addition, given the nth ordered metric (in terms of α, β, γ)

$$A \geqslant B \geqslant C \geqslant 0,$$

let the $(n + 1)$st ordered metric ranking be

$$(A - B) \geqslant C \geqslant (B - C) \geqslant 0.$$

Hence we suppose:

1st ordered metric: $\alpha \geqslant \gamma \geqslant \beta \geqslant 0$;

2nd ordered metric: $(\alpha - \gamma) \geqslant \beta \geqslant (\gamma - \beta) \geqslant 0$;

3rd ordered metric: $(\alpha - \beta - \gamma) \geqslant (\gamma - \beta) \geqslant (2\beta - \gamma) \geqslant 0$;

4th ordered metric: $(\alpha - 2\gamma) \geqslant (2\beta - \gamma) \geqslant (-3\beta + 2\gamma) \geqslant 0$,

and so on *ad infinitum*.

Looking at the far right inequality in each ranking, we see that γ may be bounded in terms of β (e.g., $1.5\beta \leqslant \gamma \leqslant 2\beta$ from the 3rd and 4th metrics). Going further, the bounds on γ tighten and give $\gamma \doteq 1.62\beta$, accurate to three figures. By using $\gamma \doteq 1.62\beta$ and working with the far left inequality in each ranking, we get a succession of increasing lower bounds on α in terms of β. To three figures the successive lower bounds on α are $(1.62\beta, 2.62\beta, 3.24\beta, 3.62\beta, 3.86\beta, \ldots, 4.14\beta, \ldots)$. This sequence does not increase indefinitely but approaches a limiting value in the neighborhood of 4.24β. The reasoning behind this bald assertion depends on the fact that, with the probability matrix

$$
\begin{array}{c|cccc}
 & V_1 \geqslant V_2 \geqslant V_3 \geqslant V_4 \\
\hline
S_1 & .1 & .5 & .3 & .1 \\
S_2 & .2 & .3 & .2 & .3 \\
\text{Difference} & -.1 & +.2 & +.1 & -.2
\end{array}
$$

the given succession of ordered metric rankings is incapable of yielding a definite conclusion about the sign of $E(S_1) - E(S_2)$. (The reader should verify this after studying Section 6.2.) In other words, none of the ordered metrics given earlier yields either

$$\alpha \geqslant \beta + 2\gamma \qquad (\beta + 2\gamma \doteq 4.24\beta),$$

or

$$\alpha \leqslant \beta + 2\gamma,$$

where

$$\frac{E(S_1) - E(S_2)}{V_1 - V_4} = \frac{1}{10}(-\alpha + \beta + 2\gamma).$$

We suspect that the lower bounds on α from the rankings approach $\beta + 2\gamma$ as $n \to \infty$, i.e., that $\beta + 2\gamma$ is the greatest lower bound on α implied by the rankings. But the rankings give no clue whatever about an upper bound on α, and hence α might equal 4.6β or perhaps 100β, etc., and still be consistent with the rankings. Our conclusion in this case is that the nth ordered metric does not converge to the interval measure. [But we suspect the equal-increment solution does converge to approximately $(\alpha^0, \beta^0, \gamma^0) = (^{424}/_{686}, {}^{100}/_{686}, {}^{162}/_{686})$.]

Methods of Measurement

As in previous cases, there are several methods one may employ in trying to obtain an ordered metric measure of relative value. We shall begin by considering several of these for the first ordered metric. For this case we are interested, in general, in determining which of the two nonnegative value differences, $V(o_j) - V(o_{j+1})$ and $V(o_k) - V(o_{k+1})$, $j \neq k$, is the larger (or at least as large as the other), given the ordinal ranking (4.1).

The first method appeals directly to the individual's sense of "preference continuum," and simply asks the question: "Is the difference in preference (or relative value) between o_j and o_{j+1} at least as great as the difference in preference between o_k and o_{k+1}?" (or vice versa).

Obviously, such a question may be put in many different forms, such as, "Which 'transition' increases your relative value more—from o_{j+1} to o_j or from o_{k+1} to o_k?" but if we are going to be direct, then it seems desirable to state the question as simply as possible.

A second method uses an imaginary choice situation as follows:

> Initially, let us suppose that either o_{j+1} or o_{k+1} will result from a hypothetical course of action you are required to follow, and that they are equally likely to occur. Now without altering the equally likely supposition, you will be permitted to make one and only one of the following trades before a consequence occurs: replace o_{j+1} with o_j or replace o_{k+1} with o_k. Which trade do you make?

If o_{j+1} is "traded in" for o_j, then we assume $V(o_j) - V(o_{j+1}) \geqslant V(o_k) - V(o_{k+1})$. If o_{k+1} is "traded in" for o_k, then we assume $V(o_k) - V(o_{k+1}) \geqslant V(o_j) - V(o_{j+1})$. In this method it might be argued that the subject is actually comparing the gambles $(o_j, \frac{1}{2}, o_{k+1})$ and $(o_{j+1}, \frac{1}{2}, o_k)$. The first gamble represents the situation that results from replacing o_{j+1} with o_j; the second represents the situation that results from replacing o_{k+1} with o_k. In this form we have the h-situation:

	$E_{1/2}$	$\bar{E}_{1/2}$
H_1	o_j	o_{k+1}
H_2	o_{j+1}	o_k

where $E_{1/2}$ is an event with probability $\frac{1}{2}$.[10]

In the gambling notation we assume that $(o_j, o_{j+1})R_1(o_k, o_{k+1})$ if and only if $(o_j, \frac{1}{2}, o_{k+1}) \gtrsim (o_{j+1}, \frac{1}{2}, o_k)$, where $\gtrsim$ means "is preferred or

---

[10] It is intended that the event $E_{1/2}$ be considered as likely to occur as not to occur (and vice versa) by the individual. In their experiments to measure utility and subject probability by behavioristic methods, Davidson, Suppes, and Siegel (1957) employed actual choice situations of the type written above. In this, they report on attempts to find an event E^* with $s(E^*) = s(\bar{E}^*)$, where s denotes subjective probability. After some difficulty with several more obvious events (such as "heads" on a coin flip), they found fair agreement with $s(E^*) = s(\bar{E}^*)$ in the form of a carefully machined die with three faces marked with one symbol (e.g., ZOJ), the other three faces marked with another symbol (e.g., ZQJ). The symbols were selected on the basis of having negligible power of association and were paired to give minimal distinction between the two symbols placed on any one die. The event E^* was that a specified symbol would turn up on a roll of a given die and $\bar{E}^*$ that the other symbol would turn up.

indifferent to." The expected values of the gambles are $\frac{1}{2}V_j + \frac{1}{2}V_{k+1}$ and $\frac{1}{2}V_{j+1} + \frac{1}{2}V_k$. If $(o_j, \frac{1}{2}, o_{k+1}) \gtrsim (o_{j+1}, \frac{1}{2}, o_k)$, then

$$\frac{1}{2}V_j + \frac{1}{2}V_{k+1} \geqslant \frac{1}{2}V_{j+1} + \frac{1}{2}V_k,$$

or

$$V_j - V_{j+1} \geqslant V_k - V_{k+1}.$$

If $(o_{j+1}, \frac{1}{2}, o_k) \gtrsim (o_j, \frac{1}{2}, o_{k+1})$, then

$$\frac{1}{2}V_{j+1} + \frac{1}{2}V_k \geqslant \frac{1}{2}V_j + \frac{1}{2}V_{k+1},$$

or

$$V_k - V_{k+1} \geqslant V_j - V_{j+1}.$$

In case $k = j + 1$, only three consequences are involved, and, in the comparison of gambles method, o_{j+1} is compared with $(o_j, \frac{1}{2}, o_{j+2})$. Historically, it is interesting to note the remark made by von Neumann and Morgenstern (1947):

> ... Assume that an individual prefers the consumption of a glass of tea to that of a cup of coffee, and the cup of coffee to a glass of milk. If we now want to know whether the last preference—i.e., difference in utility—exceeds the former, it suffices to place him in a situation where he must decide this: Does he prefer a cup of coffee to a glass the content of which will be determined by a 50%–50% chance device as tea or milk [p. 18, footnote 1].

From the point of view of this book, if such a decision were actually made, then it would indeed provide some evidence of which utility difference was the larger. However, it would serve only as an item after the fact. That is, the knowledge gained about the value differences after the decision had been made may serve no useful purpose, except perhaps to satisfy someone's curiosity. The preference ranking tea > coffee > milk and the comparison of value differences apply only to the particular decision situation in which the individual is involved. If these preferences were obtained at lunch time on a particular day, it would be foolish to suppose they would remain precisely the same at supper time the same day. This serves to point out more forcefully our earlier contention that every decision situation is unique. With respect to our own decisions, many of the more common types (repetitive with respect to certain aspects) are made by force of habit without specific recourse to a cognitive analysis, for we have learned by experience that such and such a type of action generally leads to a satisfactory consequence. But the more important decisions, which might profitably be analyzed by the methods discussed here, are seldom of a repetitive nature, and it is these in which we are particularly interested. In as much as the consequences of one's own decisions may depend in part on strategies adopted by others, there may be a very real need to attempt to infer how others will act from a knowledge of their previous behavior, in which case after-the-fact observation of their past decisions may be extremely useful and important. Thus, in attempting to determine our own actions, it may be important to predict the actions of others.

Depending on the nature of the situation, any one of the methods described in Section 4.2 for obtaining a weak ordering of consequences might be used to obtain a weak ordering of differences in preference between adjacent consequences in the ordinal ranking, particularly when the direct approach is used. If the method of gambles is employed, one is pretty well limited to a succession of pairwise comparisons.

In discussing the second ordered metric, we shall begin with a specific example. Suppose with $r = 4$, the ordinal and first ordered metric rankings are

$$V_1 \geqslant V_2 \geqslant V_3 \geqslant V_4,$$
$$V_1 - V_2 \geqslant V_3 - V_4 \geqslant V_2 - V_3 \geqslant 0.$$

For the second ordered metric we wish to compare differences

$$a = (V_1 - V_2) - (V_3 - V_4) = V_1 + V_4 - V_2 - V_3,$$
$$b = (V_3 - V_4) - (V_2 - V_3) = 2V_3 - V_2 - V_4, \qquad (4.23)$$
$$c = V_2 - V_3.$$

Picturing the V_j as points along a line, Figure 4.8 illustrates a, b, and c. If hypothetical gambles are used to compare a with b, etc., then it may be necessary to go to gambles which involve probabilities other than 0, $\frac{1}{2}$, and 1. In comparing a and b

$$a \geqslant b \qquad \text{if and only if} \qquad V_1 + V_4 - V_2 - V_3 \geqslant 2V_3 - V_2 - V_4,$$

or

$$V_1 + 2V_4 \geqslant 3V_3,$$

or

$$\tfrac{1}{3}V_1 + \tfrac{2}{3}V_4 \geqslant V_3,$$

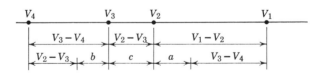

Figure 4.8

and

$$a \leqslant b \quad \text{if} \quad \tfrac{1}{3}V_1 + \tfrac{2}{3}V_4 \leqslant V_3.$$

Thus, the natural comparison for a versus b would be $(o_1, \tfrac{1}{3}, o_4)$ versus o_3. In comparing a and c,

$$a \geqslant c \quad \text{if and only if} \quad \tfrac{1}{2}V_1 + \tfrac{1}{2}V_4 \geqslant V_2,$$

so that we compare $(o_1, \tfrac{1}{2}, o_4)$ versus o_2 in this case. Finally, in comparing b and c,

$$b \geqslant c \quad \text{if and only if} \quad V_3 \geqslant \tfrac{2}{3}V_2 + \tfrac{1}{3}V_4,$$

so that o_3 will be pitted against $(o_2, \tfrac{2}{3}, o_4)$. If we get $o_3 \gtrsim (o_2, \tfrac{2}{3}, o_4)$ and $o_2 \gtrsim (o_1, \tfrac{1}{2}, o_4)$, then $b \geqslant c \geqslant a$.

In the general case for a second ordered metric, we can state all comparisons in terms of gambles involving four consequences, some of which may be identical. To set this up, let us suppose A, B, C, and D are four events (exclusive and mutually exhaustive) each with probability $\tfrac{1}{4}$. That is, the events A through D are equally likely to occur. Let

$$(o_h, o_i, o_j, o_k) \tag{4.24}$$

denote a gamble, which, if "chosen," "yields" o_h if A occurs, o_i if B occurs, o_j if C occurs, or o_k if D occurs.

Suppose, in a situation with $r = 20$, the first ordered metric begins

$$V_4 - V_5 \geqslant V_{10} - V_{11} \geqslant V_1 - V_2 \geqslant V_{19} - V_{20} \geqslant \ldots,$$

and we are interested in comparing the differences

$$d = (V_4 - V_5) - (V_{10} - V_{11}),$$
$$e = (V_1 - V_2) - (V_{19} - V_{20}).$$

Now $d \geqslant e$ if and only if

$$V_2 + V_4 + V_{11} + V_{19} \geqslant V_1 + V_5 + V_{10} + V_{20}$$

or

$$\tfrac{1}{4}V_2 + \tfrac{1}{4}V_4 + \tfrac{1}{4}V_{11} + \tfrac{1}{4}V_{19} \geqslant \tfrac{1}{4}V_1 + \tfrac{1}{4}V_5 + \tfrac{1}{4}V_{10} + \tfrac{1}{4}V_{20}.$$

Hence, we compare the gambles $(o_2, o_4, o_{11}, o_{19})$ and $(o_1, o_5, o_{10}, o_{20})$.

For a, b, and c as given by (4.23), if we rewrite c as $c = V_2 - V_3 + V_4 - V_4$, then

$$a \geqslant b \quad \text{if and only if} \quad V_1 + V_2 + V_4 + V_4 \geqslant V_2 + V_3 + V_3 + V_3,$$
$$a \geqslant c \quad \text{if and only if} \quad V_1 + V_3 + V_4 + V_4 \geqslant V_2 + V_2 + V_3 + V_4,$$
$$b \geqslant c \quad \text{if and only if} \quad V_3 + V_3 + V_3 + V_4 \geqslant V_2 + V_2 + V_4 + V_4,$$

so that the comparisons, if made by the type of gamble in (4.24), will read:

a versus b: (o_1, o_2, o_4, o_4) versus (o_2, o_3, o_3, o_3),

a versus c: (o_1, o_3, o_4, o_4) versus (o_2, o_2, o_3, o_4),

b versus c: (o_3, o_3, o_3, o_4) versus (o_2, o_2, o_4, o_4).

If the method of gambles is extended to the third ordered metric measure, then the general case will involve the comparison of two gambles, each with eight consequences (some of which may be identical), the "outcome" of the "chosen" gamble depending upon the "occurrence" of one event from a set of eight equally likely events. In trying to obtain an nth ordered metric measure using gambles, the two gambles under comparison in the general case will each contain 2^n consequences (some of which may be identical), where the "outcome" of the gamble is determined according to the occurrence of one event from a set of 2^n equally likely events. To repeat our previous remark, "It is doubtful that in a particular decision situation one would attempt to go beyond the second or perhaps third ordered metric if that far."

4.11 OTHER ORDERED METRICS

The Higher Ordered Metric Ranking

Besides the first, second, . . ., nth, . . . ordered metric measures, there are many others one could work with. We shall mention two of these—the higher ordered metric[11] measure and sum ordered metric measure.[12]

The higher ordered metric is essentially an extension of the first ordered metric in the realm of first-order value differences. This measure ranks all nonnegative value differences $V_j - V_k$, $j < k$, as obtained from the ordinal ranking

$$V_1 \geqslant V_2 \geqslant \ldots \geqslant V_r.$$

With $r = 4$, two h.o.m. (higher ordered metric) rankings are

(a) $\quad V_1 - V_4 \geqslant V_1 - V_3 \geqslant V_2 - V_4 \geqslant V_1 - V_2 \geqslant V_3 - V_4$
$$\geqslant V_2 - V_3 \geqslant 0,$$

(b) $\quad V_1 - V_4 \geqslant V_2 - V_4 \geqslant V_3 - V_4 \geqslant V_1 - V_3 \geqslant V_2 - V_3$
$$\geqslant V_1 - V_2 \geqslant 0,$$

which are illustrated by Figure 4.9.

---

[11] See Siegel (1956) for the use of this term and discussion of the (first) ordered metric and higher ordered metric scales.

[12] The name "sum ordered metric" is of the author's choosing.

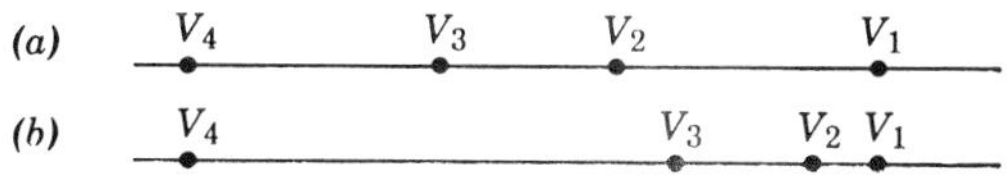

(a)

$$\underset{\bullet}{V_4} \qquad \underset{\bullet}{V_3} \quad \underset{\bullet}{V_2} \qquad \underset{\bullet}{V_1}$$

(b)

$$\underset{\bullet}{V_4} \qquad\qquad\qquad \underset{\bullet}{V_3} \quad \underset{\bullet}{V_2}\,\underset{\bullet}{V_1}$$

Figure 4.9

Given the ordinal ranking (A1), the primitives for the h.o.m. measure are the set $Z = \{(o_j, o_k)\}$ of the $r(r - 1)/2$ pairs (o_j, o_k) with $j < k$, and a relation R on Z. Our assumption is:

A9 R is a weak ordering of Z.

$(o_h, o_i)R(o_j, o_k)$ is interpreted as: The difference in preference between o_h and o_i is at least as great as the difference in preference between o_j and o_k.

With

$$o_1 \gtrsim o_2 \gtrsim \ldots \gtrsim o_r,$$

we note that, if $o_h \gtrsim o_j \gtrsim o_k \gtrsim o_i$, then $(o_h, o_i)R(o_j, o_k)$, since (o_j, o_k) is "contained within" (o_h, o_i). Thus, for example, $V_1 - V_5 \geq V_2 - V_3$, $V_5 - V_7 \geq V_6 - V_7$, $V_2 - V_{10} \geq V_2 - V_9$, and so forth.

In addition, if two relative differences $V_h - V_i$ and $V_j - V_k$ overlap (e.g., $h < j < i < k$), then to compare these two, it suffices to compare their nonoverlapping parts. Thus, comparing $V_3 - V_7$ with $V_5 - V_8$ is equivalent to comparing $V_3 - V_5$ with $V_7 - V_8$. To obtain a h.o.m. ranking, it suffices to compare relative differences which have no common part.

To illustrate the construction of a h.o.m. ranking with $r = 5$, using pairwise comparisons, let us start with the ordered metric ranking

$$V_3 - V_4 \geq V_1 - V_2 \geq V_4 - V_5 \geq V_2 - V_3 \geq 0,$$

as given. From this point:

1. Fit $V_1 - V_3$ into the ranking. Since $V_1 - V_3 \geq V_1 - V_2$, we compare $V_1 - V_3$ with $V_3 - V_4$. Suppose $(o_1, o_3)R(o_3, o_4)$, giving

$$V_1 - V_3 \geq V_3 - V_4 \geq V_1 - V_2 \geq V_4 - V_5 \geq V_2 - V_3 \geq 0.$$

2. Fit $V_2 - V_4$ into the ranking in (1) above. Since $V_3 - V_4 \geq V_1 - V_2$ gives $V_2 - V_4 \geq V_1 - V_3$, we obtain

$$V_2 - V_4 \geq V_1 - V_3 \geq V_3 - V_4 \geq V_1 - V_2 \geq V_4 - V_5 \geq V_2 - V_3 \geq 0.$$

3. Fit $V_3 - V_5$ into the ranking in (2) above. Since $V_4 - V_5 \geq V_2 - V_3$ implies $V_3 - V_5 \geq V_2 - V_4$, we get

$$V_3 - V_5 \geq V_2 - V_4 \geq V_1 - V_3 \geq V_3 - V_4$$
$$\geq V_1 - V_2 \geq V_4 - V_5 \geq V_2 - V_3 \geq 0.$$

4. In fitting $V_1 - V_4$, $V_2 - V_5$, and $V_1 - V_5$ into the ranking, steps similar to (2) and (3) reveal that no further comparisons are required and we get directly

$$V_1 - V_5 \geqslant V_1 - V_4 \geqslant V_2 - V_5 \geqslant V_3 - V_5 \geqslant \ldots$$
$$\geqslant V_4 - V_5 \geqslant V_2 - V_3 \geqslant 0. \quad (4.25)$$

In this example only one comparison, (o_1, o_3) versus (o_3, o_4), was required, given the ordered metric ranking to start with. The remainder of our labor was algebraic.

The Sum Ordered Metric Ranking

The sum ordered metric measure may be thought of as an extension of the higher ordered metric measure. An s.o.m. (sum ordered metric) measure ranks not only the relative lengths of all value intervals (and therefore has an h.o.m. ranking embedded in it) but also ranks all sums of the lengths of nonoverlapping intervals. With the h.o.m. measure, there were $r(r - 1)/2$ elements in the complete ranking. With the s.o.m. measure there are $2^{r-1} - 1$ elements in the complete ranking. Thus, the s.o.m. measure is somewhat more cumbersome than the h.o.m., and is impractical unless r is quite small.

To illustrate the s.o.m. measure, suppose $r = 5$ with the ordinal ranking $V_1 \geqslant V_2 \geqslant V_3 \geqslant V_4 \geqslant V_5$. Let

$$\alpha = V_1 - V_2,$$
$$\beta = V_2 - V_3,$$
$$\gamma = V_3 - V_4,$$
$$\epsilon = V_4 - V_5.$$

The s.o.m. measure then ranks the quantities

$\alpha, \beta, \gamma, \epsilon,$

$\alpha + \beta, \quad \alpha + \gamma, \quad \alpha + \epsilon, \quad \beta + \gamma, \quad \beta + \epsilon, \quad \gamma + \epsilon,$

$\alpha + \beta + \gamma, \quad \alpha + \beta + \epsilon, \quad \alpha + \gamma + \epsilon, \quad \beta + \gamma + \epsilon,$

$\alpha + \beta + \gamma + \epsilon.$

The h.o.m. ranking (4.25) is written in $\alpha, \beta, \gamma, \epsilon$ notation as

$$(\alpha + \beta + \gamma + \epsilon) \geqslant (\alpha + \beta + \gamma) \geqslant (\beta + \gamma + \epsilon) \geqslant (\gamma + \epsilon)$$
$$\geqslant (\beta + \gamma) \geqslant (\alpha + \beta) \geqslant \gamma \geqslant \alpha \geqslant \epsilon \geqslant \beta \geqslant 0.$$

One s.o.m. ranking that has this h.o.m. ranking embedded in it is

$$(\alpha + \beta + \gamma + \epsilon) \geqslant (\alpha + \gamma + \epsilon) \geqslant (\alpha + \beta + \gamma) \geqslant (\alpha + \gamma)$$
$$\geqslant (\beta + \gamma + \epsilon) \geqslant (\alpha + \beta + \epsilon) \geqslant (\gamma + \epsilon)$$
$$\geqslant (\alpha + \epsilon) \geqslant (\beta + \gamma) \geqslant (\alpha + \beta) \geqslant \gamma \geqslant \alpha$$
$$\geqslant (\beta + \epsilon) \geqslant \epsilon \geqslant \beta \geqslant 0. \quad (4.26)$$

Suppose in this ranking we consider the 15 adjacent nonnegative differences:
$(\alpha + \beta + \gamma + \epsilon) - (\alpha + \gamma + \epsilon)$, $(\alpha + \gamma + \epsilon) - (\alpha + \beta + \gamma)$, $(\alpha + \beta + \gamma)$
$- (\alpha + \gamma), \ldots, \epsilon - \beta, \beta - 0$. After the obvious cancellations, we find
six distinct nonnegative differences:

$$\beta \geqslant 0,$$
$$\epsilon - \beta \geqslant 0,$$
$$\gamma - \alpha \geqslant 0,$$
$$\alpha - \beta - \epsilon \geqslant 0, \tag{4.27}$$
$$\alpha + \beta - \gamma \geqslant 0,$$
$$\alpha + \epsilon - \beta - \gamma \geqslant 0.$$

The reader may verify that (4.26) can be constructed solely on the basis
of (4.27). Thus (4.26) and (4.27) contain the same information about the
V_j and the intervals between the V_j. A specific assumption which generates
the s.o.m. ranking and a method for obtaining this ranking are left as
exercises.

4.12 THE INTERVAL MEASURE

The interval measure of relative values is *the* exact value measure.
Sets of axioms which are sufficient for the existence of a utility function
unique up to a linear transformation (the same thing as that which results
from the interval measure) have been presented by von Neumann and
Morgenstern (1947), Savage (1954) and Suppes and Winet (1955). The
von Neumann-Morgenstern postulates, presented in Section 1.3, are
based on the notion of gambles or lotteries, and do not account for the
difficulty posed by subjective probabilities, among other things. Savage,
aware of this practical difficulty, interwove the notion of personal probability (or subjective probability) into his axiomatic system. Suppes and
Winet proceeded on a somewhat different foundation, using the notion of
utility differences and not explicitly employing any probabilistic notions.
We shall look at these latter two theories in Section 5.6.

Regardless of what attitude one adopts with respect to the theories of
these writers, there remain great practical difficulties in actually trying to
obtain a measure of relative value unique up to an increasing linear
transformation. One can fairly say that any measure of relative value
which assigns unique numerical values to the consequences in a decision
situation is, at best, approximate, except in the simple case where there
are just two consequences.[13] As noted in Section 4.3, it may be impossible
to obtain even an ordinal measure, which is one of the weaker measures

---

[13] Or where there is only one or at most two equivalence classes.

that have been considered.   Nevertheless, it may be noted how, in practice, one may try to obtain an (approximate) interval measure.

With a finite number of consequences, one may begin with A3(1) and A3(2), identifying the most desirable and least desirable consequences in Q, say o_1 and o_r respectively.   Following the procedure adopted by Luce and Raiffa (1957, p. 30), we then seek to determine a value of p, say p_j, such that the individual is indifferent between o_j and (o_1, p_j, o_r), and do this for each $j, j = 2, \ldots, r - 1$.   Stated formally:

A10   Given $o_1 \gtrsim o_j \gtrsim o_r$ and $o_1 > o_r$, for each j, $j = 2, \ldots, r - 1$, there exists a probability p_j, $0 \leqslant p_j \leqslant 1$, such that $o_j \gtrsim (o_1, p_j, o_r)$ and $(o_1, p_j, o_r) \gtrsim o_j$ [i.e., $o_j \sim (o_1, p_j, o_r)$].   Moreover, $o_j > (o_1, p, o_r)$ for every $p < p_j$ and $(o_1, p, o_r) > o_j$ for every $p > p_j$.   In addition, $V(o_j) \geqslant pV(o_1) + (1 - p)V(o_r)$ if and only if $o_j \gtrsim (o_1, p, o_r)$.[14]

If we set $V(o_1) = 1$, $V(o_r) = 0$, then $V(o_j) = p_j$, $j = 2, \ldots, r - 1$, or more generally

$$I_j = \frac{V_j - V_r}{V_1 - V_r} = p_j,$$

or

$$V_j = p_j(V_1 - V_r) + V_r.$$

In the discussions of Section 4.6 on the first bounded interval measure, particularly in Cases 1 through 5, arguments were presented which cast grave doubts upon this approach although it is formally justified by the von Neumann-Morgenstern or Luce and Raiffa axioms.   Our problem is a problem of measurement, not of theory.   In addition to those arguments, A10 raises the practical question of whether it is possible, in a general case, for an individual to distinguish a unique p that satisfies A10. We regard this as wishful thinking, and for this reason the bounded interval measures were introduced.

Let us suppose, however, that an individual is able to state values of p_2 through p_{r-1}.   Now consider comparisons other than o_j versus (o_1, p, o_r). Suppose, for illustrative purposes, that $o_1 \gtrsim o_2 \gtrsim \ldots \gtrsim o_r$ and that $p_1 \geqslant p_2 \geqslant \ldots \geqslant p_r$, where $p_1 = 1$, $p_r = 0$.   If the individual is able to state values of p such that $o_j \sim (o_1, p, o_r)$, then it should not be too much to expect that he could also state values of p such that $o_j \sim (o_i, p, o_k)$, for $i < j < k$.   Let q_{ijk} be the value of p for which $o_j \sim (o_i, p, o_k)$. Then $o_j \sim (o_i, q_{ijk}, o_k)$.   Hence we would expect that

$$V_j = q_{ijk}V_i + (1 - q_{ijk})V_k. \tag{4.28}$$

[14] Luce and Raiffa's axioms, like the von Neumann-Morgenstern postulates, do not introduce the utility or value function, but deal with properties of $\gtrsim$.   The last sentence of A10 follows as a theorem from their axioms.

According to the von Neumann-Morgenstern or Luce-Raiffa postulates, this must indeed be the case. Taking $V_1 = 1$, $V_r = 0$, (4.28) can be rewritten as

$$p_j = q_{ijk}p_i + (1 - q_{ijk})p_k \qquad (i < j < k). \qquad (4.29)$$

Without the availability of (4.29) as a guide, it is extremely doubtful that an individual's judgments would satisfy (4.29). However, it may be one's intention to use (4.29) as a guide, and to successively alter the p_j and q_{ijk} until (4.29) holds for all cases. On the other hand, if (4.29) is not used explicitly in the judgment process, numerical approximation of the V_j could be obtained from the q_{ijk} by some kind of "averaging" or "fitting." For example, suppose $o_1 \gtrsim o_2 \gtrsim \ldots \gtrsim o_r$ and, for each triple (i, j, k) with $1 \leqslant i < j < k \leqslant r$, let q_{ijk} be the value of p judged by the individual to render $o_j \sim (o_i, p, o_k)$. Take $V_1 = 1$, $V_r = 0$, and treat $V_2, \ldots, V_{r-1}$ as variables. Let D^2_{ijk} be the square of the difference between the two sides of (4.28), i.e.,

$$D^2_{ijk} = [V_j - q_{ijk}V_i - (1 - q_{ijk})V_k]^2 \qquad (1 \leqslant i < j < k \leqslant r)$$

and let D^2 denote the sum of the squared differences,

$$D^2 = \sum_{1 \leq i < j < k \leq r} D^2_{ijk}.$$

Then take as the approximate values of $V_2, \ldots, V_{r-1}$ those values that minimize D^2. This is, of course, an application of the least-squares technique. To find these minimizing values, set $\partial D^2 / \partial V_j = 0$ for $j = 2$, $\ldots, r - 1$, and solve the resultant set of $r - 2$ linear equations for $V_2, \ldots, V_{r-1}$. If r is large, this approach may be quite impractical.

A variation of the method which compares o_j with (o_1, p, o_r) uses an h-situation

	E	$\bar{E}$
H_1	o_1	o_r
H_2	o_j	o_j

with a set of events $\{E\}$. It is assumed that $\{E\}$ is rich enough to contain an event, say E_j, such that the individual is indifferent between H_1 and H_2 in

	E_j	$\bar{E}_j$
H_1	o_1	o_r
H_2	o_j	o_j

Letting $V_1 = 1$, $V_r = 0$, we then assume that

$$V_j = s(E_j),$$

where $s(E_j)$ denotes the subjective probability of the event E_j to the individual. This, of course, is not much good unless there is available a method for measuring $s(E_j)$.[15]

4.13 `VALUE MEASURES FOR MODEL II

It will be recalled that in most decision situations each consequence is an ordered pair (A_i, O_j), where $A_i \in \mathbf{A}$, $O_j \in \mathbf{O}$. $\mathbf{A}$ is the set of courses of action and $\mathbf{O}$ is the set of outcomes. With $o_k = (A_i, O_j)$, $V(o_k) = V(A_i, O_j)$. The condition on the value function that defines Model II is stated as follows:

Let $A(O_j)$ be the set of all $A_i \in \mathbf{A}$ for which $P(A_i, O_j \mid S_k) > 0$ for some $S_k \in \mathbf{S}$. If for each $O_j \in \mathbf{O}$ it is true that

$$V(A_i, O_j) = V(A_t, O_j)$$

for every pair (A_i, A_t) such that $A_i \in A(O_j)$, $A_t \in A(O_j)$, then Model II applies.

If the $V(A_i, O_j)$ satisfy this definition, let the common value of $V(A_i, O_j)$ for a given O_j and all $A_i \in A(O_j)$ be denoted as $V(O_j)$. That is,

$$V(A_i, O_j) = V(O_j) \qquad \text{for all } A_i \in A(O_j),$$

where $V(O_j)$ is the relative value of outcome O_j.

The defining equations for Model II simply state that the worth or importance of any given outcome is the same regardless of which course of action (with positive probability for the outcome under one or more strategies) may produce the outcome.

In terms of preference and indifference, Model II applies if and only if for each $O_j \in \mathbf{O}$ the individual is indifferent among the set of consequences (A_i, O_j) for $A_i \in A(O_j)$; that is, if and only if for each $O_j \in \mathbf{O}$,

$$(A_i, O_j) \sim (A_t, O_j)$$

for every pair (A_i, A_t) such that $A_i \in A(O_j)$ and $A_t \in A(O_j)$.[16]

If it can be ascertained that the individual satisfies these conditions for Model II, then measures of the relative values of outcomes are obtained in precisely the same fashion as measures of the relative values of conse-

---

[15] See, e.g., the latter part of Section 5.6.

[16] This can also be expressed in terms of equivalence classes defined in Section 4.9. Having obtained the equivalence classes $\{e_i\}$, Model II applies if and only if for each O_j all consequences (A_i, O_j) for which $A_i \in A(O_j)$ belong to the same equivalence class.

quences. If in the previous sections of this chapter we replace o_j with O_j, call V_j the relative value of the jth outcome, let r be the number of relevant outcomes (in **O**), replace **Q** with **O**, and substitute "outcome" for "consequence," then those sections apply in full.

EXERCISES

1. Suppose you wish to obtain a first bounded interval measure and proceed by using both methods mentioned in Section 4.6. With $r = 6$, $o_1 > o_r$, and $o_1 \gtrsim o_j \gtrsim o_r, j = 2, 3, 4, 5$, you get

	First Method			Second Method	
j	d_1	d_2	d_3	α_j	β_j
2	5	6.5	10	.40	.60
3	1	3	10	.15	.25
4	8	9	10	.70	.95
5	6	7.5	10	.65	.80

Combining the two sets of results, both of which are considered valid, state the narrowest bounds on $I_j, j = 2, 3, 4, 5$, as given by the data.

2. An ordinal measure of relative value and a first bounded interval measure have been obtained in a situation where $r = 10$. They are respectively

$$V_1 \geqslant V_2 \geqslant \ldots \geqslant V_9 \geqslant V_{10},$$

$I_1 = 1, \quad .60 \leqslant I_2 \leqslant .95, \quad .70 \leqslant I_3 \leqslant .80, \quad .65 \leqslant I_4 \leqslant .85,$

$.30 \leqslant I_5 \leqslant .46, \quad .42 \leqslant I_6 \leqslant .50, \quad .40 \leqslant I_7 \leqslant .54,$

$.26 \leqslant I_8 \leqslant .38, \quad .07 \leqslant I_9 \leqslant .12, \quad I_{10} = 0.$

Using the ordinal measure, refine the bounds on the I_j wherever possible by using the method of Section 4.7.

3. For $r = 6$, state which of the following are admissible second bounded interval measures and which are not admissible:

(a) $.15 \leqslant L_1 \leqslant .20,$ (b) $.10 \leqslant L_1 \leqslant .18,$

    $.15 \leqslant L_2 \leqslant .20,$ $.08 \leqslant L_2 \leqslant .12,$

    $.30 \leqslant L_3 \leqslant .40,$ $.24 \leqslant L_3 \leqslant .30,$

    $.06 \leqslant L_4 \leqslant .15,$ $.15 \leqslant L_4 \leqslant .20,$

    $.14 \leqslant L_5 \leqslant .25,$ $.10 \leqslant L_5 \leqslant .15,$

(c) $.13 \leqslant L_1 \leqslant .30,$ (d) $.16 \leqslant L_1 \leqslant .20,$

    $.17 \leqslant L_2 \leqslant .40,$ $.28 \leqslant L_2 \leqslant .40,$

    $.22 \leqslant L_3 \leqslant .50,$ $.18 \leqslant L_3 \leqslant .24,$

    $.09 \leqslant L_4 \leqslant .35,$ $.34 \leqslant L_4 \leqslant .46,$

    $.10 \leqslant L_5 \leqslant .28,$ $.08 \leqslant L_5 \leqslant .14.$

4. For $r = 8$, suppose the method of gambles yields the second bounded interval measure:

$$.08 \leqslant L_1 \leqslant .14, \quad .10 \leqslant L_2 \leqslant .20, \quad .06 \leqslant L_3 \leqslant .15, \quad .03 \leqslant L_4 \leqslant .09,$$
$$.20 \leqslant L_5 \leqslant .30, \quad .09 \leqslant L_6 \leqslant .15, \quad .13 \leqslant L_7 \leqslant .18.$$

For each $j, j = 1, \ldots, 7$, determine the values of p_j and q_j (see A6) that yielded the specified bounds.

5. The following two second bounded interval measures for $r = 4$ are equivalent. Why is this?

  (a) $.30 \leqslant L_1 \leqslant .50, \quad .35 \leqslant L_2 \leqslant .40, \quad .20 \leqslant L_3 \leqslant .45,$

  (b) $.30 \leqslant L_1 \leqslant .45, \quad .35 \leqslant L_2 \leqslant .40, \quad .20 \leqslant L_3 \leqslant .35.$

6. The method of hypothetical gambles was used to obtain a third bounded interval measure with $r' = 6$, yielding the (p_j, q_j) values for $j = 1, 2, 3, 4$ (p_j and q_j as used in A7):

$$(p_1, q_1) = (.2, .3),$$
$$(p_2, q_2) = (.6, .8),$$
$$(p_3, q_3) = (.4, .7),$$
$$(p_4, q_4) = (.1, .2).$$

Determine the bounds on $K_j, j = 1, \ldots, 4$, from these data.

7. For the third bounded interval measure with K_j as defined in (4.12), show that

$$K_j K_{j+1} \ldots K_{r'-2} = \frac{V_j - V_{j+1}}{V_{r'-1} - V_{r'}}, \quad j = 1, \ldots, r' - 2.$$

Let

$$R_j = \frac{V_j - V_{j+1}}{V_{r'-1} - V_{r'}}, \quad j = 1, \ldots, r' - 2,$$

and denote bounds on R_j as a_j, b_j, i.e., $a_j \leqslant R_j \leqslant b_j$. Call the set $a_j \leqslant R_j \leqslant b_j$, $j = 1, \ldots, r' - 2$, the fourth bounded interval measure. Describe a procedure for obtaining a fourth bounded interval measure by using the definition of R_j as guide, without recourse to the third bounded interval measure. In this, state your assumptions.

8. Suppose $V_1 > V_2 > \ldots > V_r$. Let

$$I_j = \frac{V_j - V_r}{V_1 - V_r}, \quad j = 1, \ldots, r,$$

$$L_j = \frac{V_j - V_{j+1}}{V_1 - V_r}, \quad j = 1, \ldots, r - 1,$$

$$K_j = \frac{V_j - V_{j+1}}{V_{j+1} - V_{j+2}}, \quad j = 1, \ldots, r - 2,$$

$$R_{jk} = \frac{V_j - V_{j+1}}{V_k - V_{k+1}}, \quad j, k = 1, \ldots, r - 1.$$

Show that

(a) $L_j = I_j - I_{j+1}$;

(b) $I_j = L_j + L_{j+1} + \ldots + L_{r-1}$;

(c) $K_j = R_{j, j+1}$;

(d) $K_j K_{j+1} \ldots K_{r-2} = R_{j, r-1}$;

(e) $K_1 K_2 \ldots K_j = R_{1, j+1}$;

(f) $I_j/L_j = R_{jj} + R_{j+1, j} + \ldots + R_{r-1, j}$;

(g) $K_j = R_{jk}/R_{j+1, k} = R_{k, j+1}/R_{k, j}$.

9. In accord with Section 4.10, let the first four ordered metric rankings with $r = 5$ be given by

(a) $L_1 \geqslant L_2 \geqslant L_3 \geqslant L_4 \geqslant 0$;

(b) $L_1 - L_2 \geqslant L_3 - L_4 \geqslant L_4 \geqslant L_2 - L_3 \geqslant 0$;

(c) $L_1 + L_4 - L_2 - L_3 \geqslant L_3 + L_4 - L_2 \geqslant L_2 - L_3 \geqslant L_3 - 2L_4 \geqslant 0$;

(d) $L_3 - 2L_4 \geqslant 2L_3 + L_4 - 2L_2 \geqslant L_1 - 2L_3 \geqslant L_2 + 2L_4 - 2L_3 \geqslant 0$.

For each of these rankings, find the equal-increment solution of the L_j.

10. For $r = 4$, let $V_1 \geqslant V_2 \geqslant V_3 \geqslant V_4$ be given and define

$$\alpha = V_1 - V_2, \qquad \beta = V_2 - V_3, \qquad \gamma = V_3 - V_4,$$

$$(\alpha \geqslant 0, \ \beta \geqslant 0, \ \gamma \geqslant 0).$$

Given $\gamma - \alpha - \beta \geqslant 0$ and $\alpha - \beta \geqslant 0$, construct a h.o.m. ranking and an s.o.m. ranking.

11. For $r = 6$, let $V_1 \geqslant V_2 \geqslant V_3 \geqslant V_4 \geqslant V_5 \geqslant V_6$ be given. Let

$$\alpha = V_1 - V_2, \qquad \beta = V_2 - V_3, \qquad \gamma = V_3 - V_4,$$

$$\delta = V_4 - V_5, \qquad \epsilon = V_5 - V_6.$$

Given

$$\delta + \epsilon \geqslant \alpha + \beta, \qquad \beta + \gamma \geqslant \alpha,$$

$$\alpha \geqslant \delta, \qquad \delta \geqslant \beta,$$

$$\gamma \geqslant \epsilon, \qquad \alpha \geqslant \gamma,$$

$$\epsilon \geqslant \delta,$$

construct a h.o.m. ranking of the V_j.

12. Formulate assumptions which "generate" a sum ordered metric ranking of the V_j, and develop a procedure for obtaining such a measure.

13. Let the h.o.m. ranking of Section 4.11 be called the first h.o.m. ranking, since it builds upon the first ordered metric ranking. Let the nth h.o.m. be a ranking which ranks, by decreasing magnitude, all differences between the

members of the $(n-1)$st ordered metric ranking. That is, given the $(n-1)$st ordered metric ranking

$$V_1^{(n-1)} \geqslant V_2^{(n-1)} \geqslant \ldots \geqslant V_{r-1}^{(n-1)} \geqslant V_r^{(n-1)},$$

the nth h.o.m. measure ranks the $V_j^{(n-1)} - V_k^{(n-1)}$, $j < k$. Formulate an assumption for the nth h.o.m. measure, given A1, A8(1), A8(2), ..., A8($n-1$).

14. Given $o_1 > o_2 > o_3 > o_4$, suppose an individual states that

$$o_2 \sim (o_1, .4, o_3),$$
$$o_2 \sim (o_1, .6, o_4),$$
$$o_3 \sim (o_1, .3, o_4),$$
$$o_3 \sim (o_2, .5, o_4).$$

Are these judgments perfectly consistent according to (4.29)? Letting $V_1 = 1$, $V_4 = 0$, find the least-squares values of V_2 and V_3.

REFERENCES

Ackoff, R. L., with S. K. Gupta and J. S. Minas, *Scientific Method: Optimizing Applied Research Decisions*, John Wiley and Sons, New York, 1962.

Churchman, C. W., *Prediction and Optimal Decision*, Prentice-Hall, Englewood Cliffs, New Jersey, 1961a.

Davidson, D., P. Suppes, and S. Siegel, *Decision Making, An Experimental Approach*, Stanford University Press, Stanford, California, 1957.

Edwards, W., "Probability Preferences in Gambling," *American Journal of Psychology*, **66**, 349–364 (1953).

———, "Probability Preferences Among Bets with Differing Expected Values," *American Journal of Psychology*, **67**, 56–67 (1954a).

———, "The Reliability of Probability-Preferences," *American Journal of Psychology*, **67**, 68–95 (1954b).

Luce, R. D., and H. Raiffa, *Games and Decisions: Introduction and Critical Survey*, John Wiley and Sons, New York, 1957.

Luce, R. D., *Individual Choice Behavior*, John Wiley and Sons, New York, 1959.

Savage, L. J., *The Foundations of Statistics*, John Wiley and Sons, New York, 1954.

Siegel, S., "A Method for Obtaining an Ordered Metric Scale," *Psychometrica*, **21**, 207–216 (1956).

Suppes, P., *Introduction to Logic*, D. van Nostrand, Princeton, New Jersey, 1957.

———, and M. Winet, "An Axiomatization of Utility Based on the Notion of Utility Differences," *Management Science*, **1**, 259–270 (1955).

von Neumann, J., and O. Morgenstern, *Theory of Games and Economic Behavior*, Second Edition, Princeton University Press, Princeton, New Jersey, 1947.

Chapter 5

PROBABILITY AND DECISION THEORY

5.1 INTRODUCTION AND APOLOGY

Our discussion of probability, begun in Section 1.4 and continued in Section 3.1, is summarized as follows. By means of the formulation presented in Chapter 2 we arrive at a set of r consequences $\mathbf{Q} = \{o_j\}$, $j = 1, \ldots, r$, and a set of t strategies $\mathbf{S} = \{S_i\}$, $i = 1, \ldots, t$. In Chapter 3, we introduced the notion of a (conditional) probability measure P given S_i such that

$$P(o_j \mid S_i) \geqslant 0, \qquad \text{for all } i, j, \tag{5.1}$$

$$\sum_{j=1}^{r} P(o_j \mid S_i) = 1, \qquad i = 1, \ldots, t. \tag{5.2}$$

By construction, the consequences in $\mathbf{Q}$ are exclusive and exhaustive for each S_i. That is, whichever $S_i \in \mathbf{S}$ is adopted by the decision maker, one and only one element (consequence) in $\mathbf{Q}$ will result. The reason for introducing the probability notion is simply that, prior to the implementation of a strategy, there is generally uncertainty about which $o_j \in \mathbf{Q}$ will result, given that strategy.

If the decision situation is formulated so that each S_i logically implies an $o_j \in \mathbf{Q}$, or if we assume that a (known) $o_j \in \mathbf{Q}$ occurs with certainty given S_i for each $S_i \in \mathbf{S}$, then the $P(o_j \mid S_i)$ (if we care to refer to them) take values from the set $\{0, 1\}$ and we are faced with a decision situation under certainty. We shall return to this case fleetingly in Section 9.2 and dwell upon it at length in Chapter 10.

In connection with the basic decision model of Section 3.3, it should be apparent that our primary interest concerning probabilities lies in obtaining measures of the $P(o_j \mid S_i) = P_{ij}$ for use in that model. This does not, of course, preclude the possible usefulness of measuring the probabilities of subsets of $\mathbf{Q}$ other than the unit sets $\{o_1\}$, $\{o_2\}$, ..., $\{o_r\}$. If we consider the Boolean field $(\mathbf{Q}, \mathbf{F})$, where $\mathbf{F}$ is the set of all of the 2^r subsets of $\mathbf{Q}$, including the null set $\emptyset$, then $(\mathbf{Q}, \mathbf{F}, P \mid S_i)$ is taken to be a (conditional) probability space such that $P(\emptyset \mid S_i) = 0$ and for any $B \in \mathbf{F}$, $B \neq \emptyset$,

$$P(B \mid S_i) = \sum_{o_j \in B} P(o_j \mid S_i). \tag{5.3}$$

That is, $P(B \mid S_i)$ is equal to the sum of the $P(o_j \mid S_i)$ corresponding to the o_j that are elements of B. In the present context, the $B \in \mathbf{F}$ or a subset of these sets will be employed in obtaining comparative probability statements, as discussed in Section 5.8.

In later sections of this chapter, we shall take a brief look at several measures of probabilities,[1] including rankings (e.g., $P_{11} \geqslant P_{12} \geqslant \ldots \geqslant P_{1r} \geqslant 0$) and bounded interval measures (e.g., $.02 \leqslant P_{11} \leqslant .08 \ldots .14 \leqslant P_{1r} \leqslant .22$), which will be used in Chapter 6 in analyzing strategies for dominance. We shall not go into a general treatment of mathematical probability in any detail, since this is well covered in a variety of texts.[2]

Besides considering measures of the $P(o_j \mid S_i)$ we shall also consider the $P(E_j)$ for the statistical model since not only has a great deal of literature concentrated on the latter but it may also be quite advantageous in some situations to formulate our problem in the statistical framework (whereas in others it will not). As noted in Section 3.6 there is a correspondence between the two basic formulations, the basic decision model and the statistical model. We shall go into this further in Sections 5.6 and 5.7.

The next several sections discuss some basic views and issues of probability. Section 5.2 will serve, in part, to set the stage for Sections 5.3 through 5.6, which deal with some of the extramathematical interpretations of probability. The major viewpoints to be considered in these four sections will be called the classical, frequency, logical, and subjective viewpoints respectively. The choice of terms used as headings is to some degree arbitrary, since modifiers of "probability" are sometimes used differently by different authors. For those familiar with Savage's book (1954), the latter three headings correspond approximately with his

[1] "Probability measure" is being used in two senses. First, in the formal measure-theoretic sense in "probability measure P" and, second, in the sense of a set of statements, such as $P_{11} \geqslant P_{12} \geqslant \ldots \geqslant P_{1r} \geqslant 0$, which contain information about relative magnitudes of the P_{ij}.

[2] See, for example, Feller (1957), Wadsworth and Bryan (1960), Loeve (1960), and Doob (1953).

objectivistic (frequency), necessary (logical), and personalistic (subjective) classification.

The discussion of interpretations of probability will be carried out with a minimum of reference to the process of decision making, although one cannot avoid it altogether for the simple reason that some probabilistic positions depend for their interpretation on the idea of decision. This is especially true of some subjective views. Our main reasons for including this discussion is first to give the reader a feeling for the way that "probability" has been kicked about and to present a summary[3] of its interpretations and, second, to enable us to be on firmer ground when probability is tied in with decision.[4] Thus, in Section 5.7, we shall consider how several decision theories make use of probability, with attention focused on the general thesis of this book. For those readers who already know a good bit about interpretations of probability, we suggest a light reading of Section 5.2 followed by Section 5.7.

Before getting on with interpretations and meanings, an apology is in order, not only to the reader but also to authors whose views on probability we have attempted to interpret. The contents of the next five sections have already been stated by numerous writers in diverse places, and we do not claim that our interpretations of various authors' views are altogether correct and unbiased. The brief space devoted to the foundations of probability cannot possibly do justice to a very complex and complicated topic, and to obtain a more thorough account the serious student will find it necessary to visit the references. The incompleteness of our account may irritate some experts on probability, but we offer it in the hope that it will benefit the majority of readers. Among the sampling of references, the most useful ones are those by John Maynard Keynes (1921, 1962),[5] Richard von Mises (1936, 1939, 1957), Ernest Nagel (1939), Rudolph Carnap (1950), and Leonard J. Savage (1954). Ramsey (1950), Good (1950) and Churchman (1948), (1961a) also make good reading in their discussion of foundations.

5.2 MATHEMATICAL PROBABILITY AND OTHER TERMS

As in a great many subjects with philosophical overtones, it is at best a rather difficult task to discover the essential meanings that other writers attribute to a word like "probability." As Carnap (1950) points out,

---

[3] Which may have some value in itself.

[4] As noted in Chapter 3, and later in this chapter, our position is essentially subjective.

[5] When giving several dates for one reference, the first refers to an early version or edition, the latter to a later edition(s) which may be a translation and may differ significantly in context from the earlier version.

the informal discourse and the formal development of a theory of probability by a single author in one book are sometimes a bit at variance with one another, so that it requires rather intense research to try to interpret his intended meaning. Moreover, it appears that, although different authors use similar adjectives to modify "probability" (e.g., objective probability, subjective probability, etc.), those who use the same modifier are not always discussing the same thing. Savage (1954, p. 2) has put the matter quite well:

> ... as to what probability is ... there has seldom been such complete disagreement and breakdown of communication since the Tower of Babel. There must be dozens of different interpretations of probability defended by living authorities, and some authorities hold that several different interpretations may be useful, that is, that the concept of probability may have different meaningful senses in different contexts. Doubtless, much of the disagreement is merely terminological and would disappear under sufficiently sharp analysis. Some believe that it would all disappear, or even that they have themselves already made the necessary analysis.

Attempts have indeed been made to reconcile the apparent differences of various interpretations of probability,[6] but vital differences still remain when all is said and done.

In view of Savage's remarks, it is not surprising to find widespread confusion as to the exact nature of probability. Readers will undoubtedly have encountered at least several of the following terms (given in alphabetical order):

Degree of confirmation	Mathematical probability
Degree of conviction	Objective probability
Degree of rational belief	Personal probability
Empirical probability	Physical probability
Geometric probability	Psychological probability
Impersonal probability	Random chance
Inductive probability	Relative frequency
Intuitive probability	Statistical probability
Judgment probability	Subjective probability
Logical probability	

Although we shall not attempt any strict classification or definition of these terms (or the modifiers), most of them will appear at one place or another in the next four sections. One term, namely, "mathematical probability," will be dispensed with quite readily.

[6] See, for example, Carnap (1950) and LeBlanc (1962).

Mathematical Probability

Savage (p. 2) notes that "... it is surprising, and certainly gratifying, to find that almost everyone is agreed on what the purely mathematical properties of probability are." We interpret *mathematical probability* to mean "the purely mathematical properties of probability" as follow from Kolmogorov's (1933) generally accepted axiomatic system or one similar to it.

Most modern writers, when using the phrase "probability theory," are speaking of mathematical probability. For example, Loeve (1963, p. 149), states:

As a branch of mathematics ... probability theory partakes of and contributes to the whole domain of mathematics and, at present, its general set-up is expressible in terms of measure spaces and measurable functions.

Doob (1953, Preface) advises his readers that:

There has been no compromise with the mathematics of probability. Probability is simply a branch of measure theory,[7] with its own special emphasis and field of application, and no attempt has been made to sugar-coat this fact.

Since there is deep-rooted and widespread agreement[8] on probability theory *per se*, we shall not pursue it here, although occasional use is made of its generally accepted results.

Some Additional Terms

In addition to the terms in the foregoing list, several other sets come to mind: (1) *a priori* (prior, initial) probability and *a posteriori* (posterior) probability and (2) comparative probability, qualitative probability, and quantitative probability. The terms in (1) are generally used to distinguish probabilities evaluated before (prior to) obtaining (additional) information, evidence, or experience and then re-evaluated on the basis of this additional data. It should be noted that *a priori* and *a posteriori* probabilities are relative to intervening data, and that *a posteriori* probabilities in one situation may become *a priori* probabilities at a later time. One

[7] *Author's note:* Doob offers a supplement on measure theory, and Loeve devotes Part One of his book to measure theory. See also, for example, Halmos (1950) and Kolmogorov and Fomin (1961).

[8] Since Kolmogorov (1933) advanced the generally accepted axiomatic system of probability theory, minor disagreements and variations have occurred, most of which are beyond the level of mathematical sophistication of this book. In connection with their experiments reported in Davidson, Suppes, and Siegel (1957), the authors present a set of axioms defining what they call a "weak subjective probability structure" which differs slightly in its consequences from the usual "probability laws" [in particular, their axioms do not imply (5.3) above].

rule of transformation from given *a priori* probabilities to *a posteriori* probabilities is called Bayes' rule,[9] which arises from conditional probability formulas.[10]

To illustrate Bayes' rule, suppose Smith opposes Jones in an election with three voters including neither Smith nor Jones. Let x denote the numbers of votes received by Smith ($x = 0, 1, 2, 3$), $3 - x$ being the number Jones gets. Before the ballots are counted, Smith, based upon his "knowledge" of Jones, the three voters, etc., arrives at the following *a priori* probabilities for the variable x:

$$P(x = 0) = 1/25,$$
$$P(x = 1) = 8/25,$$
$$P(x = 2) = 14/25,$$
$$P(x = 3) = 2/25.$$

Suppose one ballot, "drawn at random," is for Jones. Let J_1 be the event, "the first ballot opened, having been randomly selected, is for Jones." The conditional probabilities of J_1, given x, are

$$P(J_1 \mid x = 0) = 1,$$
$$P(J_1 \mid x = 1) = 2/3,$$
$$P(J_1 \mid x = 2) = 1/3,$$
$$P(J_1 \mid x = 3) = 0.$$

With the additional evidence that J_1 does, in fact, obtain (or on the hypothesis it will obtain), Smith can compute the *a posteriori* probabilities $P(x \mid J_1)$, using

$$P(x \mid J_1)P(J_1) = P(J_1 \mid x)P(x),$$

$$P(J_1) = \sum_x P(J_1 \mid x)P(x) = 1/25 + 2/3(8/25)$$
$$+ 1/3(14/25) + 0(2/25) = 33/75,$$

to yield

$$P(x = 0 \mid J_1) = 3/33,$$
$$P(x = 1 \mid J_1) = 16/33,$$
$$P(x = 2 \mid J_1) = 14/33,$$
$$P(x = 3 \mid J_1) = 0.$$

[9] Named after Thomas Bayes, an eighteenth-century mathematician and one of the early pioneers in probability. See Bayes (1940) for a special case of "Bayes' rule."

[10] See, e.g., Savage (1954, p. 47), Carnap (1950, Section 60), Feller (1957, p. 114), and Schlaifer (1959, Chapter 21).

At this point two ballots are still unopened. Suppose one of these two, selected at random, is for Smith. Let S_2 be the event, "the second of the three ballots, opened in a randomly determined order, is for Smith." Smith can now compute a new set of *a posteriori* probabilities $P(x \mid J_1, S_2)$, using either the $P(x)$ or the $P(x \mid J_1)$ as *a priori* probabilities. With $P(x)$ he uses

$$P(x \mid J_1, S_2) = \frac{P(J_1, S_2 \mid x)P(x)}{P(J_1, S_2)},$$

$$P(J_1, S_2) = \sum_x P(J_1, S_2 \mid x)P(x) = 0(1/25) + 1/3(8/25)$$
$$+ 1/3(14/25) + 0(2/25) = 22/75,$$

yielding

$$P(x = 0 \mid J_1, S_2) = 0,$$
$$P(x = 1 \mid J_1, S_2) = 8/22 = 4/11,$$
$$P(x = 2 \mid J_1, S_2) = 14/22 = 7/11,$$
$$P(x = 3 \mid J_1, S_2) = 0.$$

On the other hand, if Smith uses the $P(x \mid J_1)$ as *a priori* probabilities, he computes as follows:

$$P(x \mid J_1, S_2) = \frac{P(S_2 \mid x, J_1)P(x \mid J_1)}{P(x, S_2 \mid J_1)},$$

$$P(x, S_2 \mid J_1) = \sum_x P(S_2 \mid x, J_1)P(x \mid J_1) = 0(3/33)$$
$$+ 1/2(16/33) + 1(14/33) + 0 = 2/3;$$

$$P(x = 0 \mid J_1, S_2) = 0,$$

$$P(x = 1 \mid J_1, S_2) = \frac{8/33}{2/3} = 4/11,$$

$$P(x = 2 \mid J_1, S_2) = \frac{14/33}{2/3} = 7/11,$$

$$P(x = 3 \mid J_1, S_2) = 0.$$

If a candidate wins by a simple majority, then Smith's "probability of winning" changes from .64 (*a priori*) to .4242...(*a posteriori* after J_1 occurs) to .6363...(*a posteriori* after J_1 and S_2 occur).

In this illustration we have been rather loose in the use of "probability," and deliberately so, for we shall use it later in discussing some of the viewpoints on probability.

The terms in (2) mentioned above apply, roughly, to relations between probabilities. A comparative or qualitative probability relation is generally of the "is more probable" or "is not more probable" type. Under various viewpoints, the following could be called comparative probability statements:

(*a*) On the basis of the available evidence, the hypothesis that Mr. X is guilty of the stated crime is confirmed to a higher degree than the hypothesis that Mr. X is not guilty of the stated crime.

(*b*) I personally consider it more probable that it will snow in Cleveland on May 1, 1984, than that I will shoot a hole-in-one the next time I play golf.

(*c*) A letter chosen at random from p. 3 of Savage (1954) is more likely to be an *e* than a *t*.

(*d*) The probability of rolling an ace with this die is less than the probability of flipping a head with that coin.

As distinguished from qualitative probability, "quantitative probability" refers to the assignment of real numbers to "contingencies" (hypotheses, events, sets, propositions, pairs of sentences, etc.) and, as used by Savage (1954), is equivalent to a certain type of probability measure (in the measure-theoretic sense). Quantitative or numerical probability statements under various viewpoints would include the following:

(*a'*) On the basis of the available evidence, the hypothesis that Mr. X is guilty of the stated crime is confirmed to the degree .83.

(*b'*) I personally believe that I shall shoot a hole-in-one the next time I play golf with probability .001.

(*c'*) The probability that a letter chosen at random from p. 3 of Savage (1954) will be an *e* is equal to 289/2266.

(*d'*) The probability of rolling an ace with this die is 1/6.

(*d''*) The probability of rolling an ace on the next throw with this die equals 1/6.

Further modifiers from our original list are often used with "*a priori* probability," "comparative probability," "quantitative probability," and so forth, to yield such phrases as "subjective *a priori* probability," "comparative inductive probability," "quantitative personal probability," and the like.

These statements, and others given below, will serve as examples for the following sections.

One is often tempted to discuss probability in terms of subjective versus objective probability, taking for granted that the reader knows what the author means by these terms (if the author himself knows). It seems that this apparent dichotomy is most often taken to apply to the degree to which feelings, beliefs, or personal judgment of an individual, or perhaps a group of individuals, may enter into the determination or estimation of the magnitude of a probability (in one sense or another). Rather than to suppose a dichotomy that partitions viewpoints into those that are dependent on an individual's experience, feelings, or judgment (i.e., "subjective") and those that are free of such elements (i.e., "objective"), it seems more relevant to admit that all measurements of probability rely upon human judgment to some extent. Some writers[11] make the distinction between subjective and objective probability by use of the phrases "actual degree of belief" and "rational degree of belief." These phrases arise, for example, in discussions of logical views of probability, the former referring to a psychological disposition towards a contingency, the latter to a "logical" relation between two propositions (the evidence and the hypothesis, or the premise and the conclusion).

Summary of Conceptions of Probability

Before going on to a discussion of classical views of probability, we shall briefly indicate the nature of the other three categories since cross references to other views will occur throughout our discussion.

Frequency views are characterized by defining the magnitude of a probability as the relative frequency with which a stated property occurs among the elements of a specified set of elements, called the reference set or reference class. Some frequency views define probability in terms of the limit of a sequence of relative frequencies with respect to finite subsets of a denumerable reference set, the limit taken as the sizes of successive subsets become indefinitely large (relative frequency "in the long run"). Among the holders of frequency views we find Venn (1886, 1962), von Mises (1939, 1957), Reichenbach (1949), Cramer (1954), R. A. Fisher (1950), and others in the modern school of mathematical statistics.

According to logical views, probability is a unique logical relation between propositions or sentences. Under such views, "probability measures the extent to which one set of propositions, out of logical necessity and apart from human opinion, confirms the truth of another" (Savage, p. 3). Keynes (1921, 1962), Jeffreys (1939), and Carnap (1950), (1952) are representatives of the logical position. Both the frequency and logical viewpoints claim to be "objective."

In subjective views, "probability measures the confidence that a particular individual has in the truth of a particular proposition, for example, the proposition that it will rain tomorrow" (Savage, p. 3). In most subjective views the magnitudes of probabilities are not estimated by

---

[11] See, for example, Ramsey [1931; 1950, VII (2)] on Keynes, and Carnap (1950, p. 51).

individual whim or fancy, but rather are subject to certain rules of consistency, usually stated as axioms.

These views postulate that the individual concerned is in some ways "reasonable," but they do not deny the possibility that two reasonable individuals faced with the same evidence may have different degrees of confidence in the truth of the same proposition [Savage, p. 3].

Major exponents of subjective views are Ramsey (1931, 1950), de Finetti (1937), Koopman (1940), Good (1950), and Savage (1954).

5.3 CLASSICAL VIEWS

Although considerations of something akin to modern-day uses of probability date back to Aristotle and before, and the insurance business was a going concern long before 1700, it was not until after 1700 that a mathematical theory of probability began to emerge. The stimulus for the development of probability theory was provided by games of chance. According to Nagel (1939, p. 8):

Solutions of special problems in the division of stakes and the placing of wagers were first given by Cardan and Galileo (sixteenth century); but the general attack on the theory which was involved in their analyses began with Pascal and Fermat (seventeenth century), who showed that all the special problems under consideration could be reduced to problems in the mathematical theory of permutations and combinations. Upon this basis a convenient calculus was developed, which was subsequently applied to many different fields of inquiry. Huygens, the Bernoullis,[12] Montmort, DeMoivre, and Bayes are the prominent figures in the early history of the subject. Their work was systematized and completed in the great treatise of Laplace (early nineteenth century), and the point of view from which they conducted their analyses remained until quite recently the basis for the interpretation and extension of the mathematical theory.

The point of view to which Nagel refers has come to be known as the classical view of probability. Laplace's views are set forth in *A Philosophical Essay on Probabilities* (1951) which he attached as an introduction to later editions of his major work (1812, 1847) on probability. The epitome of his interpretation of probability, stated in the 1951 translation of the *Essay* (pp. 6, 7), is as follows:

Probability is relative, in part to . . . ignorance, in part to our knowledge. We know that of three or a greater number of events a single one ought to occur; but nothing induces us to believe that one of them will occur rather than the others. In this state of indecision it is impossible for us to announce their occurrence with certainty. It is, however, probable that one of these

---

[12] *Author's note:* We assume Nagel is referring to Jacob (James) and Daniel, and perhaps Nicholas.

events, chosen at will, will not occur because we see several cases equally possible which exclude its occurrence, while only a single one favors it.

The theory of chance consists in reducing all the events of the same kind to a certain number of cases equally possible, that is to say, to such as we may be equally undecided about in regard to their existence, and in determining the number of cases favorable to the event whose probability is sought.   The ratio of this number to that of all the cases possible is the measure of this probability, which is thus simply a fraction whose numerator is the number of favorable cases and whose denominator is the number of all the cases possible.

At best, we find it quite difficult to interpret Laplace's interpretation, since it seems rather ambiguous. If by "equally possible" he simply means "possible of realization," then, when we inspect this obviously lopsided six-faced die, we should attach probability 1/6 to the occurrence of each face on the next roll. However, in Chapter VII of the *Essay*, Laplace discusses imbalance in an object such as a coin, and believes that this may affect the probability of a "head," but he gives no guide concerning how to adjust the probability 1/2 to account for the imbalance. On the other hand, if "equally possible" is taken equivalent to "equally probable," then the definition is circular, and one must step outside this circle to get at his meaning. One clue which Laplace seems to provide for taking this step is given by his phrase, "Such as we may be equally undecided about in regard to their existence." This phrase suggests that equally probable is to be determined, in some means, by what we know (or do not know) about the cases in question.

Followers of the Laplacian school have indeed taken the step in this direction, formulating what is called the *principle of insufficient reason*, otherwise known as the principle of nonsufficient reason, the principle of indifference, the principle of equally possible cases, the principle of equal distribution of ignorance, the principle of sufficient ignorance, etc.   In one form this principle reads: If there is no known reason for assigning unequal probabilities to possible contingencies, then, relative to our knowledge, they must be assigned equal probabilities.   Another form reads: The possible events or cases are considered to be equally probable if we have not the barest knowledge of the conditions under which each may occur.

This rule, since its earliest formulation, has been criticized in many ways by numerous writers.[13]   For one thing, the principle may lead to ambiguities and contradictions, as shown by D'Alembert's folly (in tossing a coin twice the three cases "two heads," "one head and one tail," and "two tails," are equally likely), and by Betrand's paradox (in which the

---

[13] See, e.g., Keynes (1962, Chapter IV), von Mises (1957, Third Lecture), Venn (1962, p. 77), Savage (1954, pp. 63–67), and Nagel (1939, pp. 44–48).

number of cases is nondenumerable, leading some to exclude such instances from application of the principle). Because of such difficulties, Keynes attempted to reconstruct the principle of indifference to put it on a firmer footing by defining relevance and irrelevance of evidence ("There must be no *relevant* evidence relating to one alternative, unless there is *corresponding* evidence relating to the other; our relevant evidence . . . must be symmetrical with regard to the alternatives, and must be applicable to each in the same manner."), and by insisting that the alternatives or "cases" be reduced to the most basic set of mutually exclusive and collectively exhaustive entities "of the same form." (It is not entirely clear how this may be done in every situation.) In one form or another, most logical views have held to a principle of indifference, as illustrated by Keynes. Jeffreys (1939, p. 34) gives his opinions as follows:

At any stage of knowledge it is legitimate to ask about a given hypothesis that we accept "How do we know?" The answer will usually rest on some observational data. . . . but if we go far enough back we shall always reach a stage where the answer must be: "I thought the matter worth considering, but had no opinion about whether it was true." What was the probability at this stage? . . . If there is no reason to believe one hypothesis rather than another, the probabilities are equal. In terms of our fundamental notions of the nature of inductive inference, to say that the probabilities are equal is a precise way of saying that we have no ground for choosing between the alternatives. . . . The rule that we should take them equal is not a statement of any belief about the actual composition of the world, nor is it an inference from previous experience; it is merely the formal way of expressing ignorance.

As one might expect, holders of frequency views do not care much for the principle of indifference, as shown by von Mises' (1957) and Nagel's (1939) attacks. In general, they consider it flagrantly *ad hoc*, and feel that, if one is in a state of complete ignorance about which of a set of events will obtain (under a frequency definition), then one has no basis for assigning probabilities to the events. Characteristically, the principle trades upon ignorance, and the experimentalists feel that this is the worst possible basis for making inferences.

Since the classical conception of probability is the forerunner of other views (frequency, logical, and subjective), we might ask if it shows more of a likeness to one of these than to the others. On this point it seems fairly clear that the classicists (Laplace, Bayes, J. Bernoulli) did not have in mind a frequency interpretation of probability but something more akin to a logical or subjective viewpoint. Jeffreys, for example, says that, "It is often said that some frequency definition of probability is implicit in the work of Bernoulli, and even of Bayes and Laplace" (1939, p. 334), and after a long paragraph concludes with "I maintain that the work of the pioneers shows quite clearly that they were concerned with the construction of a consistent theory of reasonable degrees of belief, and in cases of Bayes and Laplace with the foundations of common sense or inductive inference" (p. 335). Carnap (1950, pp. 47–51) concurs with this judgment. It is not perfectly clear whether the pioneers were more concerned with actual (psychological) degree of belief or with rational degree of belief (arrived at by "inductive logic"), but Carnap seems convinced it is the latter.

5.4 FREQUENCY VIEWS

Beginnings

While the classical conception of probability was undergoing minor alterations and modernizations during the nineteenth century (leading, according to Carnap, to present-day logical views), a quite different interpretation of probability began to emerge in the literature. Although there is some question as to who first introduced the idea of probability in terms of a limit of relative frequencies, Keynes (1962, p. 92) gives Leslie Ellis (1843) priority. In a later paper (1854) Ellis says that, "If the probability of a given event be correctly determined, the event will on a long run of trials tend to recur with frequency proportional to their probability."

The frequency conception received its major impetus from John Venn who, in his *Logic of Chance* (1886, 1962), gave the first systematic treatment of this conception. A few excerpts from Venn (1962) follow:

Every problem of Probability, as the subject is here understood, introduces the conception of an ultimate limit, and therefore presupposes an indefinite possibility of repetition. When we have only a finite number of occurrences before us, *direct* evidence of the character of the arrangement fails us, and we have to fall back upon the nature of the agency which produces them. And as the number becomes smaller the confidence with which we can estimate the nature of the agency becomes gradually less.

Begin with an intermediate case. There is a small lawn, sprinkled over with daisies; is this a random arrangement? We feel some confidence that it is so, on mere inspection; meaning . . . that . . . no trace of any regular pattern can be discerned and . . . that if we take any moderately small area, say a square yard, we shall find . . . about the same number of plants included in it [pp. 109, 110].

. . . this question of randomness is . . . here treated as simply one of ultimate statistical fact. . . . to adopt it seems the only course open to us if we are to draw inferences such as those contemplated in Probability [p. 110].

A word or two of explanation may be added about the expression . . . "the proportion in the long run"! The run must be supposed to be very long indeed, in fact never to stop. As we keep on taking more terms of the series we shall find the proportion still fluctuating a little, but its fluctuations will grow less. The proportion, in fact, will gradually approach toward some fixed numerical value, what mathematicians term its *limit* [p. 164].

Relative Frequency in Finite Sets

Before expanding upon limit concepts and the like, we shall first consider *relative frequency* in finite sets. In simple terms, the relative frequency of a specified property (or class of properties), say z, within a specified reference set[14] R, is equal to the number of elements in R which have the property z, say $n(z)$, divided by the number of elements in R, say n. By this definition, the relative frequency of z in R, denoted $r(z, R)$, is given by

$$r(z, R) = \frac{n(z)}{n}. \tag{5.4}$$

In a practical sense, the elements in R must be capable of being identified as actually being in R (that is, we should like to be able to say whether or not a thing is an element of R), so that a second set of properties, say Z, are used to characterize the elements of R. Then everything that has the property (or properties) Z belongs to R, and anything that does not have the property Z does not belong in R.

Suppose we inquire as to the relative frequency of letters e (or E) among all letters on p. 3 of our copy of Savage (1954). z is then the property of being a letter e and Z is the property of being a letter on p. 3 of our copy of Savage (1954). R is then the set of letters on the given page, and the size of R is (by our count) equal to 2,266. Also (by our count), the number of elements in R which have the property z equals 289. We therefore submit that the relative frequency of e's among the set of letters on p. 3 of our copy of Savage (1954) equals 289/2,266. In the same fashion we claim that the relative frequency of faces that are aces on this die equals 1/6.

As long as we stay in the context of finite sets, the process of determining a relative frequency includes identification and enumeration of the reference set and those elements in the reference set that have the property z. Even if this is economically and physically feasible, such a process is not always simple or completely objective,[15] since, for example, it may require judgment on the identifier's part in deciding whether or not a member of R has the property z. More interesting considerations arise when it is not economically feasible to enumerate and inspect completely each element in R and/or when it is physically impossible to do this (part of the reference class may be no more or may only be extant far into

---

[14] Also referred to as the reference class, parent set, population, universe, etc.

[15] See, e.g., Churchman (1961a, Chapter 5) or Ackoff (1962, Chapter 5).

future time, the reference class may be infinite, etc.). Points relating to these considerations will arise toward the end of this section and occasionally in later sections.

A rather "restricted" definition of probability may be given with respect to a finite reference class R and a property z by simply equating the probability that an element in R has the property z with $r(z, R)$ as given by (5.4). Letting $P(z, R)$ denote such a "probability," we propose to define

$$P(z, R) = r(z, R). \tag{5.5}$$

This is just another way of talking about a relative frequency. To holders of frequency views who accept probability defined only in terms of a limit of a *sequence* of relative frequencies, the use of $P(z, R)$ in (5.5) is not permissible. To such persons, (5.5) is false. Others may be willing to use "probability" as defined by (5.5).

Now consider (c') above ("The probability that a letter chosen at random from p. 3 of Savage (1954) will be an e is equal to 289/2,266"). Although this may appear to be of the same form as (5.5), it is not, the distinction lying in the phrase "chosen at random." In our definition of relative frequency in (5.4), we had no occasion to refer to an act of choosing or drawing an element at random from the reference set. A common "textbook" interpretation of "drawing an element at random from R" states that such a process is equivalent to the process of "drawing an element from R in such a fashion that each element of R has the same probability of being drawn, namely $1/n$." But what is meant by equally probable in this context? Clearly we need some interpretation. Will we get something resembling the classical conception or principle of indifference or something else (say a frequency interpretation)? Since we refer to a process of "choosing" or "drawing," how do we give operational meaning to it? We shall defer further direct questions in the realm of sampling until later in this section and turn first to some frequency views of probability.

Limiting Frequency

One frequency view holds that probability is meaningful only in terms of certain types of repetitive processes, such as rolls of a die, the behavior of which can be adequately described by the purely mathematical model of identical stochastically independent random trials (or, in other terms, of the mathematical concept of a sequence of independent, identically distributed random variables). Agreement between the behavior of the repetitive process and the mathematical model is to be judged solely on the basis of empirical evidence, namely, on observation of the outcomes of a necessarily finite sequence of repetitions (trials) of the process (experiment). Similarly, estimates of the magnitudes of the probabilities that apply to various events (outcomes or sets of outcomes), in case any do, are to be obtained on the basis of such observations, and from no other source.

Consider, for example, the process of rolling a standard six-sided die on a flat, hard surface. Suppose that in n rolls n_1 aces are observed to have occurred as the "up" face, so that the relative frequency of aces in n repetitions of the process is given by n_1/n. If the process is repeated indefinitely (an idealization of course) and n_1/n approaches a limit as n approaches infinity or as n becomes large beyond all bounds, then this limit is, according to one definition, the probability of rolling an ace with the given die on the given surface. In this description we are letting our reference class, with respect to which relative frequencies are defined, increase with the number of rolls. The reference class R that will serve to define probability then becomes a denumerable reference set with cardinality $\aleph_0$.[16] If z denotes the event "ace face up on a roll of a die" (or is the property of the "up" face on a roll of a die being an ace), one may use

$$P(z, R) = \lim_{n \to \infty} \frac{n_1}{n} \qquad (5.6)$$

as a definition of $P(z, R)$. According to most frequency views, if the sequence $\{n_1/n\}$ does not approach a limit, then $P(z, R)$ is not defined.[17] In more technical terms, the assertion that the limit in (5.6) exists is equivalent to the assertion that there exists a (unique) real number p between 0 and 1 inclusive such that for each $\epsilon > 0$ there is some natural number

---

[16] $\aleph_0$ is the cardinal number of the set of all positive integers or of any set the elements of which can be placed in a one-to-one correspondence with the positive integers. A finite set of n elements has the cardinal number n or is of cardinality n.

[17] Several writers, including Popper (1935) and Copeland (1941), have proposed that probability be defined in terms of *accumulation points* (also called limit points or cluster points) of a sequence of relative frequencies instead of in terms of the limit of relative frequencies as defined above. A value p is an accumulation point of the sequence of values $x_1, x_2, x_3, \ldots$ if for every $\epsilon > 0$ and every N there is at least one $n > N$ such that $|x_n - p| < \epsilon$. We are assured by the Bolzano-Weierstrass Theorem [Taylor (1955, p. 483)] that *every* sequence of relative frequencies has an accumulation point, and therefore a probability. However, such a sequence of relative] frequencies of a property may have *more than one* accumulation point and, hence, more than one probability for the property with respect to R. This complicates the probability calculus considerably, and the accumulation point definition has therefore not been widely adopted. [If the limit in (5.6) exists, then there is just one accumulation point of the sequence $\{n_1/n\}$, and it coincides with the limit.]

$N(\epsilon)$ such that for all $n > N(\epsilon)$, $|n_1/n - p| < \epsilon$. If such a p exists, it is the limiting value. Note here that we have no simple guide for choosing $N(\epsilon)$, and that an $N(\epsilon)$ that satisfies the requirement for a given ϵ (if any does) may vary according to the choice of ϵ.

We have not required in the definition of (5.6) that the sequence of results for the succession of rolls of the die exhibit the properties of a "random sequence." The problem of defining a random sequence has not been an easy one, and many writers do not even attempt to try to define it but give heuristic illustrations that will hopefully satisfy the reader and provide him with an intuitive grasp of the idea. Consider, for example, a repetitive process where on each trial we define a (random) varia ble which takes on the value 1 if a specified event occurs ("heads' on a coin, e.g.) and the value 0 if the event does not occur.[18] A sequence of results of the trials may be conveyed by

$$1101000110100111100110110010\ldots (ad\ infinitum). \quad (5.7)$$

For this sequence the specified event occurred at the first, second, fourth, eighth, ninth, eleventh, ... trial and its complement occurred at the third, fifth, sixth, seventh, tenth, ... trial. A random sequence is often said to be one in which the results occur in a completely irregular progression, or one in which the sequence of results reveals no repetitive pattern (e.g., 01010101 ... would not qualify). One hastens to add that, although a random sequence is irregular, it also has the property of *statistical regularity* (i.e., n_1/n tends to stabilize as n increases).

Cramer (1954, Chapter 13) is characteristic of this heuristic position:

> It does not seem possible to give a precise definition of what is meant by the word "random." The sense of the word is best conveyed by some examples.
>
> If an ordinary coin is rapidly spun several times, and if we take care to keep the conditions of the experiment as uniform as possible ... we are unable to predict whether, in a particular instance, the coin will fall "heads" or "tails." ... Even if we try to build a machine throwing the coin with perfect regularity, it is not likely that we shall succeed in predicting the results of individual throws. On the contrary, the result of the experiment will always fluctuate in an uncontrollable way from one instance to another.
>
> ... it will obviously be impossible to make exact predictions with regard to the life and death of one particular person, since the causes leading to the ultimate result are far too numerous and too complicated to allow of any precise calculation.
>
> Suppose ... our observations consist in making a series of repeated measurements of some physical constant ... in spite of all precautions taken by the observer, the successive measurements will generally yield different results. This phenomenon is commonly ascribed to the action of a large number of

---

[18] This is usually called the indicator function.

small disturbing factors, which combine their effects to a certain total "error" affecting each particular measurement. The amount of this error fluctuates from one observation to another in an irregular way that makes it impossible to predict the result of an individual measurement.

In spite of the irregular behavior of individual results, the average results of long sequences of random experiments show a striking regularity.

... if we observe the frequency v/n of a fixed event E for increasing values of n, we shall generally find that it shows a marked tendency to become more or less constant for large values of n.[19]

von Mises' Irregular Collective

In contrast to the common-sense-based-upon-experience interpretation of randomness,[20] von Mises presented a controversial definition of a random sequence or an "irregular collective" which, in his (translated) words, is as follows (1957, pp. 24-25):

... A collective appropriate for the application of the theory of probability must fulfill two conditions. First, the relative frequencies of the attributes must possess limiting values. Second, these limiting values must remain the same in all partial sequences which may be selected from the original one in an arbitrary way. ... The only essential condition is that the question whether or not a certain member of the original sequence belongs to the selected partial sequence should be settled *independently of the result* of the corresponding observation, i.e., before anything is known about this result.

To back up the credibility of his definition, von Mises relies on experimental results in games of chance, pointing to the "Principle of the Impossibility of a Gambling System." What von Mises' translators call a "partial sequence" is better known as a subsequence. To form a subsequence from the original sequence, we throw out of the original sequence any number of terms we please so long as the terms that remain (i.e., the subsequence) form a denumerable set. The terms in a subsequence remain in the same order of their appearance as in the parent sequence. A subsequence appropriate under von Mises' definition, only part of which appears above, must be capable of being characterized by a well-defined rule (e.g., all odd-numbered terms shall form one subsequence, even-numbered terms a second, every term whose position number in the original sequence is the square of a positive integer a third, etc.) formulated independently of the actual results of each trial. If from the original

---

[19] *Author's note:* Compare these remarks with the quotations of Venn (1886, 1962) at the beginning of this section.

[20] von Mises (1957, pp. 81–82) says of Cramer: "Cramer omits giving a clear definition of probability and in no way explains or derives in a logical manner the elementary operations of probability calculus."

sequences of 0's and 1's in (5.7) we form a subsequence using all odd-numbered terms (i.e., the first, third, fifth, etc.), we get

$$100011011011100\ldots(ad\ infinitum). \qquad (5.8)$$

In order for the original sequence (5.7) to qualify under von Mises' definition, the relative frequencies in each subsequence such as (5.8), formed by a definite position-selection rule formulated independently of the results of the parent sequence, must converge to the same limit as do the relative frequencies in the parent sequence.[21]

One objection to von Mises' formulation arises from the fact that it is impossible to construct, by means of a mathematical formula, a sequence (of 0's and 1's) that (*a*) has a limit to the relative frequency of 1's strictly between 0 and 1 *and* (*b*) is also random or "irregular" by von Mises' definition; for if this were so, then the very same formula could be used to form a subsequence entirely of 1's whose relative frequency limit would equal 1. Since it is impossible to construct an "irregular collective" mathematically, one can never demonstrate such a collective in which the relative frequencies of 1's converge.

Now if we consider all possible subsequences of a given sequence, each subsequence is conceptually formed by specifying for each element in the original sequence, whether or not (two possibilities) that element is to be included in the subsequence. Hence there are $2^{\aleph_0}$ such subsequences, where $2^{\aleph_0}$ is the cardinality of the continuum.[22] If the original sequence contains a denumerable number of 1's and also a denumerable number of 0's, some subsequences will converge to things other than the limit of the original sequence (if it has a limit, in the relative frequency sense, of course). However, it has been shown[23] that, if we restrict ourselves to denumerably infinite sets of position-selection rules, then there exist sequences which satisfy von Mises' postulate of insensitivity to these position-selection rules.[24]

Reichenbach

Reichenbach (1949), among others, considers von Mises' definition of sequences that are acceptable for study under a frequency view of probability much too restrictive. Suppose, for simplicity, that a leap year

---

[21] The sequence of relative frequencies of occurrence of the specified event from (5.7) is 1, 2/2, 2/3, 3/4, 3/5, 3/6, 3/7, 4/8, 5/9, 5/10, ..., and from (5.8) it is 1, 1/2, 1/3, 1/4, 2/5, 3/6, 3/7, 4/8, 5/9, 5/10, ...

[22] That is, there is a nondenumerable (or continuous) infinity of subsequences. They cannot be placed in one-to-one correspondence with the positive integers.

[23] See, e.g., Wald ("Die Wiederspruchsfreiheit...").

[24] For additional discussion of this and related points, see von Mises (1957, pp. 87–93) and the references given therein.

will occur every fourth year from now on. The sequence of ordinary years (*O*) and leap years (*L*), in their natural order will then take the form

$$LOOOLOOOLOOOLOOO\ldots.\tag{5.9}$$

This is a precisely regular and predictable sequence in which the relative frequencies of *L*'s approach the limit 1/4. For Reichenbach this is a perfectly legitimate sequence for probability, and if we agree with him (as von Mises and some others do not), we may say that the probability that a year is a leap year equals 1/4. For Reichenbach, *any* sequence whose relative frequencies for the various attributes (0's and 1's, *L*'s and *O*'s, etc.) approach limits is acceptable for study under probability theory. It appears that Venn (1962, p. 164) considered regular sequences appropriate as well as "random" ones, for he says: "In the cases in which deductive reasoning is possible, this fraction may be obtained without direct appeal to statistics, from reasoning about the conditions under which the events occur."

Reichenbach (Chapter 4) considers not only regular sequences such as (5.9) and random sequences (what he calls "normal sequences," defined somewhat differently than von Mises' irregular collective) but also includes a variety of intermediate types of sequences. A necessary condition for a sequence to qualify as a normal sequence[25] is that it be free from "aftereffect," i.e., that the probability of the occurrence of a given event be independent of the results of previous trials (or "the probability of the occurrence of a specific element is independent of its predecessors"). The sequences which fall between the two extremes of regular and normal sequences are those that have a "probability aftereffect" but are not completely predictable. The simplest of these are sequences for which the result of a particular trial is dependent only on the result of the preceding trial. If $B_1, B_2, \ldots, B_n, \ldots$, represent general symbols for the results of trials $1, 2, \ldots, n, \ldots$, respectively, this type of sequence is characterized by the conditional probability equation

$$P(B_n \mid B_{n-1}, B_{n-2}, \ldots, B_2, B_1) = P(B_n \mid B_{n-1}), \quad \text{for all } n > 1.\tag{5.10}$$

Processes or sequences having property (5.10) are called Markov processes[26] (or Markov sequences) or Markov processes of the first order. If the result of a particular trial depends on the results of the previous k trials and no others, i.e., if

$$P(B_n \mid B_{n-1}, \ldots, B_1) = P(B_n \mid B_{n-1}, \ldots, B_{n-k})$$

---

[25] For a discussion of sufficient conditions, see Reichenbach (1949, Section 30).

[26] See, for example, Feller (1957), Rosenblatt (1962), and Doob (1953). In the above discussion, one may replace "trial" by "position in a sequence" and "result" by "attribute."

for all $n > k$, such a process is called (by some authors) a Markov process of order k.   A generalization of these notions leads to sequences in which the result of each trial is influenced by a specified combination of the results of previous trials.

Impossibility of Perfect Measurement

As a consequence of frequency views that define probability as the limit of a sequence of relative frequencies, it is never possible (except perhaps in the case of a sequence whose behavior is completely known, such as a regular sequence) to determine the magnitude of a probability because of obvious physical limitations.   Practically speaking, in any situation we can observe only a finite number of trials of a repetitive process and therefore obtain only a finite number of terms in a sequence of relative frequencies.   But from these initial terms as a start, we can extend the sequence by construction and make it converge to anything between 0 and 1, or make it diverge.[27]   Hence, on the basis of the attainable evidence (the result of a finite number of trials) for a nonpredictable sequence,[28] the existence of a limit for the parent relative frequency sequence can neither be proved nor disproved.   This, of course, does not prevent one from *postulating* the existence of a limit, which is usually done.   But if this limit is postulated, it is never possible (for nonpredictable sequences) to determine its value.

The problems illustrated in the foregoing for nonpredictable sequences have played a prominent role in frequency views, and one line of criticism of these views concerns these difficulties.[29]   It should be apparent that for practical application one desires to make statements about the infinite (or very lengthy finite) segment of a sequence of repetitions of a process

---

[27] A sequence which has no limit is said to diverge.   Consider the sequence of 0's and 1's which begins with 2 0's, followed in order by 2^2 1's, 2^3 0's, 2^4 1's, 2^5 0's, 2^6 1's, ...   The sequence of relative frequencies of 1's (or 0's) from this sequence diverges, oscillating between $1/3$ and $2/3$.   It can be shown that every value in the closed interval from $1/3$ to $2/3$ is an accumulation point of the sequence of relative frequencies in this example.   (Note that, although the sequence is precisely predictable, it has no limit.)

[28] Reichenbach (1949, Chapter 9) calls nonpredictable sequences "extensionally given sequences" as opposed to "intensionally given sequences," which are thoroughly predictable sequences defined by a precise mathematical rule.

[29] In order to try to overcome certain difficulties of probability defined as a limit of an infinite sequence, some authors have proposed to define probability in terms of long, finite runs of trials.   In such cases, probability is defined in terms of an interval (e.g., $x \pm \epsilon$) instead of a point.   It has been argued, however, that not only does such a view cause serious mathematical complications but also is incapable of resolving the difficulties that it proposes to do away with.   See, e.g., Nagel (1939, p. 52), Reichenbach (1949, p. 348), and von Mises (1957, pp. 82–84) for further comments.

that has not been observed. Whatever statement may be made, it has been argued *that it is not* possible in many cases either to prove or disprove the statement. Although such a statement as "this coin will never fall heads" can presumably be disproved (if the coin has a "head" side and the flipper has sufficient patience), one generally deals with statements that have a bit more import, such as "this coin will fall heads at least half the time," "the proportion of people in the United States who live to age 60 and die before age 61 lies between x and $x \pm \delta$," etc. We are concerned here with the problem of making inferences about a portion of a reference class (be it a finite one, an infinite one that is ordered as a sequence, etc.) which has not been observed, based upon a finite portion of the reference class which has been observed. The general process of making such inferences lies in the realm of induction. Statistical inferences, which usually emanate from a frequency interpretation of probability, fall under the more general topic of inductive inferences.

The Problem of Induction

Historically, the problem of induction has been closely bound to probability, in its many interpretations, and hence it seems appropriate to allow it brief space here. The great Scottish philosopher David Hume[30] [1711–1776] brought the problem of induction to the fore, and, since his time, it has been a controversial issue in philosophical thought. To indicate what is meant by "the problem of induction," consider two illustrations:

1. I have flipped this coin 1,000 times, resulting in 489 heads and 511 tails. What justification do I have for believing that in another 1,000 flips the number of heads will be approximately equal to the number of tails?

2. ... granted that the only evidence I can possibly have for my belief in any statement is past experience, what evidence do I have for believing ... that when I strike this bell with a hammer a sound will arise? [Churchman (1948, p. 98)].

The first question relates to statistical induction and the second to "classical" induction, a degenerate case of the former (where *all* previous trials have resulted in a sound). The most "obvious" answers to these questions rely on experience: (1) "Because I observed an approximately equal number of heads and tails in the first 1,000 flips," and (2) "because this bell has always rung before when I struck it with a hammer." What Hume demonstrated was that these obvious answers are also inadequate

[30] See Hume (1911) and (1955).

answers for justifying the inductive inferences in question. In Katz's (1962, p. 5) words:

> We make one prediction rather than another because we inductively extrapolate past uniformities. . . . We are tempted to say that we judge the reliability of this policy by looking at the record. But, as Hume points out, this option in not open, because we cannot legitimately justify the general policy of appealing to experience by appealing to experience. Since it is this very type of appeal to the record whose justifiability is in question, justificatory arguments based on what has been experienced merely go in a circle and beg the very question at issue.[31]

Since a rule of induction[32] cannot be justified (philosophically) by appealing to experience, on what bases can it be justified or is such justification impossible? Posed as a question, this is the problem of induction. It is not a scientific problem but rather one which arises when we reflect on science, and, correspondingly, the language used to discuss the problem is not the object language of science, but rather the metalanguage.

Without going into detail, it may be briefly noted that the problem of induction has aroused great furor among philosophers,[33] and various stands have been taken on the issue. One group[34] (the Humean skeptics) claims that it is impossible to justify the process of induction, but that we are led by force of habit into the use of induction. Another group (the "methodologists") holds that the problem of induction as usually stated is meaningless, but does take on meaning when reformulated as the problem of "the formulation of the general features of scientific method—of the method which, in short, leads to a proportionately greater number of successful terminations of inquiry than the number

[31] It is important to note the difference between inductive inference and deductive inference. The latter is concerned with formal derivations arising from the use of well-defined rules of deductive logic (as, e.g., in mathematics), beginning from certain axioms. Deductive inferences do not "add" anything to our "knowledge" (i.e., the axioms), they simply express this "knowledge" in different forms. Probability theory, as defined earlier, is concerned with deductive inferences arising from an axiomatic system and certain auxiliary definitions, and has nothing to do in its formal sense with induction.

[32] That is, a rule which extrapolates past uniformities (or statistical regularities, etc.) to future events. With respect to his frequency views of probability, Reichenbach (1949, p. 446) states his *rule of induction*: "If an initial section of n elements of a sequence x_i is given, resulting in the frequency f^n, and if, furthermore, nothing is known about the probability of the second level for the occurrence of a certain limit p, we posit that the frequency f^i $(i > n)$ will approach a limit p within $f^n \pm \delta$ when the sequence is continued."

[33] Whitehead (1927, p. 34) once called the problem of induction "the despair of philosophy," and C. D. Broad (1926, p. 67) referred to it as "the scandal of philosophy." See Katz (p. 17).

[34] See, e.g., Ramsey (1950, pp. 196–197).

which other methods may have to their credit" (Nagel, p. 73). Other writers hold that the problem of induction is meaningful and solvable—at least to some degree—even though an acceptable solution may not yet exist. Russell (1912, p. 33) argues for this position:

> I am convinced that induction must have validity of some kind to some degree, but the problem of showing how and why it is valid remains unsolved. ... Until it is solved, the rational man will doubt whether his food will nourish him, and whether the sun will rise tomorrow.

Reichenbach (1949, pp. 469–482) has presented what some others have called a "weak justification" for induction. The crux of his conclusions in his solution of the problem of induction follows:[35]

> The answer to Hume's question is thus found. Hume was right in asserting that the conclusion of the inductive inference cannot be proved to be true; and we may add that it cannot even be proved to be probable. But Hume was wrong in stating that the inductive procedure is unjustifiable. It can be justified as an instrument that realizes the necessary conditions of prediction, to which we resort because sufficient conditions of prediction are beyond our reach. The justification of induction can be summarized as follows.... *The rule of induction is justified as an instrument of positing because it is a method of which we know that if it is possible to make statements about the future we shall find them by means of this method.* [p. 475].

The practical-minded among us may find some balm among these and further remarks made by Reichenbach:

> We can devise a method that will lead to correct predictions if correct predictions can be made—that is ground enough for the application of the method, even if we never know, before the occurrence of the event, whether the prediction is true.
>
> If predictive methods cannot supply a knowledge of the future, they are, nevertheless, sufficient to justify action [p. 480]. ...
>
> The justification of induction may, therefore, be called a *pragmatic* justification: it demonstrates the usefulness of the inductive procedure for the purpose of acting. It shows that our actions need not depend on a proof that the sequences under consideration have the limit property. Actions can be made in the sense of trials, and it is sufficient to have a method that will lead to successful trials if success is attainable at all [p. 481].

Katz (1962) casts serious doubt on Reichenbach's justification. From his Preface:

> Reichenbach's pragmatic argument has by no means met with unanimous acceptance among philosophers, though it has won many strong supporters.
>
> In ... this book we examine Reichenbach's argument in great detail and show why it is inconclusive. ... What is shown is not only that Reichenbach's argument is inconclusive as it stands but that there can be no extension of it which leads to a satisfactory argument justifying induction.

[35] See footnote 32.

Whether Katz's arguments are sufficiently powerful to convert Reichenbach's "strong supporters," we do not know, but we suspect that the problem of induction will remain a controversial issue for many years to come.

Competing Hypotheses

If (d') in Section 5.2 is interpreted under a frequency view, it might assume such a form as:

(d'_1) A limit of the sequence of relative frequencies $\{n_1/n\}$ is assumed to exist, and it is hypothesized that this limit has the value $1/6$.

We have noted that it is not possible either to prove or disprove the existence of such a limit, or, under the assumption that $\{n_1/n\}$ does approach a limit, either to prove or disprove that this limit has a particular value. In practice, this has not caused much dismay with most limitists (i.e., those who define probability as a limit). The existence of a limit or limits is normally postulated without further consideration. Questions dealing with the value(s) of a limit(s) and/or the behavior of a sequence of outcomes of a repetitive process are to be dealt with on the basis of empirical evidence and the application of "accepted" statistical techniques as applied to the evidence. The general subject of statistical hypothesis testing has a vast literature[36] and we mention only some aspects here. If one is interested in the general nature of a repetitive process, it is common to set up two or more exclusive (and sometimes exhaustive) competing hypotheses, one of which is to be preferred to all others on the basis of data obtained by experiment with the process. Since the potential number of hypotheses about the nature of the process is usually if not always infinite, judgment or common sense may dictate a small number of these for testing purposes.[37] Suppose, for example, the outcome of each trial of an experiment is a random variable (which may be multidimensional). Among the alternative hypotheses concerning the nature of the process or the sequence of random variables which may be used to describe the process, we might find (1) the random variables are stochastically independent and identically distributed, (2) the random variables form a first-order Markov process, (3) the sequence of random variables describes a weakly stationary time series with spectral density function, and so forth. Each of these hypotheses presumes a mathematical model describing the process under study. The selection of a model out of the lot considered is to be

[36] See, e.g., Brownlee (1960), Wilks (1962), Wald (1950), Lehmann (1959), and Raiffa and Schlaifer (1962).

[37] More often that not, hypotheses for inclusion in a test are determined in large measure on their mathematical tractability or simplicity and, obviously, upon whatever practical consequences may attend the various hypotheses.

decided on the "amount of agreement" between the empirical data and each candidate model.[38] In many cases the statistician does not test hypotheses concerning the basic sequential nature of the process, but rather assumes a certain model for this and then goes ahead and tests alternative hypotheses about the parameters in the model. The whole subject of statistical hypotheses testing is permeated with decision making, and, as noted in previous chapters, statistical decision theory has given new status to the role of empirical statistics in decision processes. In statistical decision theory there is no necessity of accepting one hypothesis and rejecting all others. Instead, the probability of each given hypothesis (or probability distribution or mathematical model) "yielding" the observed experimental data is determined, and all such relevant probabilities are taken into account in the statistical decision model. We shall return to this in Section 5.7.

Illustrations

We now explore some further aspects and illustrations of frequency views. If in 1,000 rolls of a standard die, 183 ace faces occur, we may *estimate* the probability of rolling an ace with this die as 183/1,000. This, of course, is the straight frequency estimate. If it is *assumed* that the process of rolling this die is adequately described by the idealized mathematical model of stochastically independent and identically distributed random variables,[39] this estimate also corresponds to the maximum likelihood estimate[40] of rolling an ace, which, as estimates go, is considered by statisticians to have fairly desirable properties. If another 1,000 rolls of the die yield 168 aces, then the revised estimate 351/2,000, based on *all* 2,000 rolls, would be used.

Under frequency views it is meaningless to speak of an estimate of the probability of an ace based upon no rolls. (One might say the straight frequency estimate, given zero aces in zero rolls, "equals" the indeterminate 0/0.) This may be compared with the classical view which says the probability of rolling an ace equals 1/6, based on no rolls. If one roll results in a non-ace, the frequency estimate of the probability of rolling an ace given this datum equals 0, and so forth. If we are estimating the magnitude of a probability in this fashion, one is inclined to feel that the larger the sample size or number of repetitions of the process, the closer the estimate will be, generally speaking, to the true probability

---

[38] We shall not attempt here to define "amount of agreement," because vagueness is the best policy in avoidance of an unnecessarily lengthy discussion. Students of statistics may read into "amount of agreement" whatever they please.

[39] The credibility of this assumption may, of course, be questioned.

[40] Fisher (1922) is credited as the originator of the method of maximum likelihood. Most recent texts in mathematical statistics contain discussions of this method.

(the limit of the sequence). Many experiments have been performed to "verify" this assertion, and although they are heuristically appealing, we have noted that complete verification is impossible. We may say perhaps that we are confident that a larger sample size will in most instances yield an estimate closer to the true probability. Such a "degree of confidence" however impinges upon a different conception of "probability" (either logical or subjective), which is rejected by many limitists. The limitist is likely to try to justify the increase in accuracy of an estimate as the sample size increases on the basis of the binomial theorem or weak law of large numbers,[41] but this "justification" is based upon a mathematical idealization and will not do. The limitist may then reply that this "justification" is valid if one is willing to assume that the sequence of repetitions of the process under study agreed with the model of stochastically independent trials with the same probability of occurrence (say p) for the event in question on each trial. But what justification does he have for this assumption? He is likely to refer to experience and the experiments with repetitive processes that he or others have performed. But this brings us right back to where we started, and we find ourselves chasing our proverbial tails in a vicious circle.

If instead of being concerned with the probability of an ace resulting from a roll of a die, we are interested in the probability of getting two or more aces in 10 rolls of a die, the latter is defined by the limitist in the same manner as the former. For defining the latter, each repetition or trial consists of 10 rolls (not one) of the die, and the event in question occurs on any given trial if 2 or more of the 10 rolls result in aces. If m_1, m, and p' are respectively the number of times 2 or more aces came up in 10 rolls, the number of times the die was rolled 10 times, and P (2 or more aces in 10 rolls), then p' is defined as the limit of the sequence $\{m_1/m\}$, provided it exists.

Consider now statement (d'') in Section 5.2 ("The probability of rolling an ace on the *next* throw with this die equals 1/6"). For the true limitist this is meaningless, since he holds that probability applies only to long-run results or physical phenomena *en masse*. Modified limitists, who also subscribe to the interpretation of probability as equal to relative frequency in finite sets as defined by (5.5), would insist that the probability in question

---

[41] Under the assumption that the sequence of trials is in perfect agreement with the mathematical model of stochastically independent trials on each of which the event in question (the ace face turning up, e.g.) has the same probability, p, of occurring, the weak law of large numbers states that for any given $\epsilon > 0$ the probability that n_1/n deviates from p by less than ϵ approaches 1 as n increases. Symbolically, $P(|(n_1/n) - p| < \epsilon) \to 1$ as $n \to \infty$. Here n is the number of trials or repetitions and n_1 is the number of times the event occurs in n trials.

equals either 0 or 1 depending on whether an ace does or does not result from the throw.[42]   Comments similar to these apply, under a frequency view, to (a') and (b') in Section 5.2.

In the election of Smith versus Jones, Smith's *a priori* probabilities are meaningless for the limitist. On the other hand, some limitists would consider the conditional probabilities $P(J_1 \mid x = 0), \ldots, P(J_1 \mid x = 3)$ having the values 1, 2/3, 1/3, 0, respectively, as quite meaningful, provided the first ballot is truly "drawn at random."[43]   On the basis of first ballot, given that it is for Jones, the relative frequency or maximum likelihood estimate of $x/3$ (the true proportion of votes for Smith) equals 0.[44]

Random Sampling

In concluding this section, we return to questions on random sampling. Most readers will be quite familiar with various devices used to generate "random" samples, such as one finds at bingo games, lotteries, etc. Bingo provides an example both of sampling without replacement and sampling with replacement.   For any one game, we take the finite reference class R to be the set of balls identified as $B1$, $B2, \ldots, O1$, $O2, \ldots$, corresponding to places on all the cards. Balls are drawn "at random" without replacement until someone gets "bingo." Then all drawn balls are replaced and the process repeats. (For defining various probabilities of winning, corresponding to the bingo cards, the limitist would consider an infinite sequence of games.)   Although barrel drawings, bingo randomizers, etc., may be all right for some purposes, more efficient means for taking random samples are available for scientific purposes.[45]   Such means take shape in connection with tables of random numbers and computer routines for generating sequences of random digits.[46]

[42] In this case the reference class R has only one element, "the next roll of this die." The number of aces on this roll equals either 0 or 1, so that the probability of an ace with respect to R equals either 0 or 1.

[43] The interpretation could be as follows, considering the case where $x = 2$. Three balls, two marked S and one marked J, are placed in an urn.   On each trial of the experiment, one ball is drawn at random and replaced before the next trial. Then $P(J_1 \mid x = 2)$ would be the limit of the frequency with which the J ball is drawn. The value of $1/3$ for $P(J_1 \mid x = 2)$ presupposes a condition of randomness.   With respect to one particular draw (or one particular election), the comments of the previous paragraph apply.

[44] Here we are estimating the relative frequency in a finite reference class with three elements (the three ballots) by the relative frequence in a subclass with one element.

[45] Churchman (1961a, pp. 154–164) gives a concise critique of sampling in nonmathematical terms.   For more detailed accounts of sampling methodology and theory, see Cochran (1953), Deming (1950), (1960), Hansen, Hurwitz, and Madow (1953a), (1953b), Ackoff (1953), and Ackoff and Pritzker (1951).

[46] See Kendall (1947, Chapter 8) and Meyer (1954).

Suppose we have a finite reference class R, and it is physically and economically feasible to order this reference set by making a one-to-one correspondence between the n elements of R and the integers 1, 2, ..., n, but it is not economically feasible to inspect every element of R to determine certain properties or characteristics that it may exhibit. To take a random sample from R, we could go to a random number table and proceed through it in some arbitrary order until a suitable sample size is obtained. [Suppose R has 26,543 elements. The numbers corresponding to the elements could be the five-digit numbers 00001, 00002, ..., 26542, 26543. If a sample of size 100 is desired, we then proceed through the table in blocks of five digits until we have run across 100 different 5-digit numbers in our class from 00001 to 26543. The 100 elements corresponding to these 100 5-digit identifiers would constitute the sample.] The elements thus selected would then be inspected to determine their relevant characteristics. Obviously, with some finite accessible reference classes or populations (such as all individuals in the United States), it is not economically feasible to put the elements into one-to-one correspondence with the positive integers, but statisticians and sampling experts apparently know how to cope with this situation by using other sampling designs besides the simple random sample noted above. In many cases we do not know the exact size of the reference class (which, perhaps, is what we wish to estimate, as in wild-life surveys), or some of the reference class may be inaccessible. These and numerous other complications have been dealt with in sampling theory, and there is no need to go into them here. Unfortunately it is altogether too often that one is tempted to assert that any sample that happens along is a random sample, simply for the sake of being able to use the techniques of statistical analysis that may be applied to random samples or their closely related brethren.

For scientific purposes it is difficult to overestimate the importance of sampling methods. Sampling procedures are used in a great many ways, in practical research (to estimate the proportion of families in a large city who own their own homes, the lengths of time individuals in a population have been using product X, etc.) and in most basic and applied experimental research (in agriculture, physics, medicine, psychology, operations research, etc.). Sampling techniques, using sequences of random numbers, have been widely used in the Monte Carlo method[47] for studying the behavior of simulated systems in a wide variety of contexts, when the basic mechanisms which govern the behavior of the system are postulated or assumed to be known but when it is not feasible (economically and/or mathematically) to obtain precise analytical models

[47] See, for example, Churchman, Ackoff, and Arnoff (1957), Meyer (1954), Galliher (1959), Morgenthaler (1961), and Schlaifer (1959, Chapter 20).

for patterns of behavior that the system may exhibit under various conditions and the probabilities or frequencies with which such patterns result. As noted in the last paragraph, if the samples obtained are random samples (in one form or another), it is possible to apply various statistical techniques in making inferences about the population from which the sample was drawn and to describe the accuracy of such inferences in probabilistic terms. If the samples are not random, this is not usually possible.

Thus, the notion of randomness as it appears in connection with sampling procedures is basic to a vast body of research being carried on today. It follows that, if one is using random number generators or random number tables, there should be at least some partial verification that the finite sequences of numbers employed are in fair agreement with the mathematical model being assumed. In the case of random digits $(0, 1, \ldots, 9)$, the model would be that of stochastically independent trials with the mathematical probability of $1/10$ on each trial for each of the ten digits. If a finite sequence of digits is, in fact, "random," then we would expect about equal frequencies for each digit,[48] about equal frequencies for each pair of digits $(00, 01, \ldots, 99)$, approximately equal frequencies for each digit in the even-numbered positions in the sequence (or any other "simple" place selection), and so forth. There are, of course, some fairly standard tests used for checking digit strings for randomness, and these are frequently applied. The RAND Corporation's *A Million Random Digits and 100,000 Normal Deviates* has been elaborately tested for randomness (before publication). As Churchman (1961*a*) has pointed out, the decision as to whether a given sequence of digits qualifies as a random sequence necessarily involves judgment in several aspects—deciding what tests to perform, what criteria of acceptance or rejection to use, and so on. One might, of course, argue that, if the finite sequence of digits were doubled in length, the second half could be identical to the first half, etc., but if the original sequence has enough digits for our purpose this criticism becomes rather irrelevant. In any event, the point remains that it is not possible to verify completely that a string of digits is a random one.

5.5 LOGICAL VIEWS

A major criticism of frequency views not raised in the previous section is that such views are much too narrow in what they consider acceptable for probability, namely, various types of repetitive processes. This

---

[48] If in a string of 1,000 numbers, each digit $(0, 1, \ldots, 9)$ appeared 100 times, the sequence would be highly suspect of *not* being random.

criticism is raised both by holders of logical views and subjective views, who desire to include under "probability" many more things than are admitted under frequency views.

Since probability is interpreted in several ways, it seems unfortunate that the same word is used for these different conceptions. As we noted in Section 5.2, modifiers may help to relieve this difficulty. For example, under logical views we generally find the terms "degree of confirmation" (Carnap), "inductive probability" (LeBlanc), and "logical probability." Carnap (1950) differentiates between logical views and frequency views by using "probability$_1$" and "probability$_2$" respectively for these two schools. Whatever names are used, we should keep in mind not only the fact that these views differ but also that there are differences in the ways in which the holders of these views intend to use "probability" in applications.

In comparing and contrasting interpretations of probability, we have found a much greater qualitative degree of compatibility between logical and subjective views than between either of these and frequency views. In a word, we find it difficult to differentiate clearly in every case between what are here being called logical views and subjective views, and we have not been greatly aided by the literature since there is not complete agreement about where the division comes. For example, Koopman (1940) and Ramsey (1931) have been claimed by some writers to be expounding a primarily logical view whereas other writers have put them in the subjectivistic camp. As noted earlier, the distinction between these views seems to depend in good measure on the degree to which personal judgment and belief are permitted to enter the process of evaluation of magnitudes of probabilities, and it is difficult in some cases to determine with sufficient accuracy the intentions of an author with respect to this factor.

The Probability Relation

Under what we interpret as logical views, probability is an objective logical relation between propositions, sentences, or statements. To follow Carnap's nomenclature, probability, as a logical relation, operates in a closed system between two sentences, called the evidence (*e*) and the hypothesis (*h*), and is concerned with the degree to which *e* confirms *h*. Determination of this degree of confirmation is to be obtained independent of personal judgment, belief, etc., by the rules of inductive logic, whatever these may be. To repeat Savage (1954, p. 3), in logical views, "probability measures the extent to which one set of propositions, out of logical necessity and apart from human opinion, confirms the truth of another."

It is important to note that the probability relation says nothing about the credibility of the evidence. For example, if our evidence *e* is, "All married women have three green eyes and Mrs. Jones is a married woman," the hypothesis *h* is, "Mrs. Jones has three green eyes," then (to use Carnap's notation) $c(h, e) = 1$, where $c(h, e)$ denotes the degree of confirmation of *h* on the basis of *e*. This, of course, is an extreme example in several respects. First, the major premise is rather inane, but it does serve to illustrate that in the logical view the probability relation operates in a closed system between *e* and *h*. Secondly, our inference from premise to conclusion (or evidence to hypothesis) is a deductive inference. In logical views a deductive inference is usually thought of as a degenerate case of an inductive inference. When the former can be made, $c(h, e)$ equals either 1 or 0, depending on whether *e* logically implies *h* or *e* logically implies the contradictory of *h*. The convention of requiring $0 \leqslant c(h, e) \leqslant 1$ is adopted in all logical views that we know of.

To illustrate an inductive inference (that is not degenerate) consider the following:

e: This die has been inspected, and was found to be a symmetrical cube with no irregularities. Moreover, it appears perfectly balanced. The six faces are numbered ace through 6. No rolls with this die are known to us.

h: One violent roll of this die will result in an ace.

$$c(h, e) = 1/6.$$

The reader will recognize this as an application of the principle of in-difference, which in one form or another appears in all logical views. In the case at hand, $c(h, e)$ is based on the evidence about the symmetry of the die. In contradistinction to the limitist, the logical position finds meaning in the probability of a single roll resulting in an ace (based upon the evidence) and does not require that we have any previous rolls upon which to base this probability or degree of confirmation. If we now roll the die 100 times and observe a sequence of results, new evidence is made available (call it *e'*), and this may be used in conjunction with the original evidence *e* to attach a value, say $c(h, ee')$, to the probability that the next roll (the 101st) will result in an ace. There is no requirement here that $c(h, e)$ and $c(h, ee')$ be equal, since different evidence sentences (*e* and *e'*) apply. This again points out that the probability for a proposition or hypothesis in the logical sense cannot be spoken of meaningfully apart from the evidence.

On the basis of *ee'* as described above, most logical views would, we believe, attribute the same probability to obtaining an ace on any future roll. For example, after 100 rolls and no more, the same probability would apply to getting an ace on the 101st roll, the 102nd roll, ..., the

200th roll, ... But when the die has been rolled an additional 99 times (a total of 199 times) and the new evidence (e'') is used in conjunction with the old (ee'), the probability of getting an ace on the 200th roll based upon the total evidence to that point may very well differ from the probability of getting an ace on the 200th roll based upon e or upon ee'.

Relative Frequency

Holders of logical views often find no objection to frequency interpretations of probability, but hasten to point out that the two schools are talking about quite different things. Carnap is a representative of this position. In the case of a finite reference class R, Carnap states that, under certain conditions, the degree of (logical) probability for the proportion of a property z in R based upon the evidence obtained by inspecting a proper subset of R may be interpreted as an *estimate* of the true relative frequency of z in R. For example, if R has six elements and four of these have been sampled, two of which have the property z, then we know that the relative frequency of z in R is either $2/6$, $3/6$, or $4/6$, depending on whether 0, 1, or 2 of the two uninspected elements have the property z. Let h_0, h_1, and h_2 be the hypotheses that 0, 1, and 2 of the two elements outside the sample have the property z respectively, and let e denote the evidence about the size of R, the way the sample was drawn, the results of the sample, etc. Finally, let $c(h_i, e)$, $i = 0, 1, 2$ denote the three logical or inductive probabilities pertaining to the three hypotheses with e, with $\sum_i c(h_i, e) = 1$. Then $^2/_6 c(h_0, e) + ^3/_6 c(h_1, e) + ^4/_6 c(h_2, e)$ may be taken to be an estimate of $r(z, R)$, the relative frequency of z in R. In a situation where the sample was drawn in such a fashion (e.g., "randomly") that the principle of indifference or considerations of symmetry would apply, one assignment of the inductive degrees of confirmation would be $c(h_0, e) = 1/4$, $c(h_1, e) = 1/2$, $c(h_2, e) = 1/4$, yielding an inductive estimate for $r(z, R)$ equal to $1/2$, identical to the maximum likelihood estimate. In *The Continuum of Inductive Methods* (1952) Carnap explores this line of reasoning in great detail. The values of $c(h_i, e)$ given above follow from his "straight rule of confirmation," under which $c(h_z, e)$, with h_z the hypothesis that an element not in the sample has the property z, equals the relative frequency of the property z in the sample ($1/2$ in the present case).

An Unattained Ideal

A major problem in logical views, around which a great deal of criticism is formed, concerns the difficulty of assigning an unambiguous, universally acceptable value to the degree of confirmation of h on the basis of e. Keynes, whose views appear to be primarily logical, introduces numerical probabilities only in connection with equiprobable alternatives (under his revised principle of indifference), and hence cannot account for the use of numerical probabilities when his principle does not apply. (Keynes discussions are mostly concerned with comparative probability, which we shall look at shortly.) Carnap and other writers are more optimistic about assigning numerical probabilities to pairs of sentences or propositions, but even with their monumental efforts, no clear system of inductive logic has yet been devised for realizing this vision. Savage (1954, p. 61), writing from a subjective (personal) position, opines about logical (necessary) views as follows:

> ... from the positions of the personalistic view, there is no fundamental objection to the possibility of constructing a necessary view, but it is my impression that the possibility has not yet been realized, and, though unable to verbalize reasons, I conjecture that the possibility is not real. ... Carnap ... has begun to state what he hopes will prove a satisfactory necessary ... view of probability. Keynes ... was not fully satisfied that he had solved his problem. That these men express any doubt at all about the possibility of narrowing a personalistic view to the point where it becomes a necessary one, after such extensive and careful labor directed toward this possibility, speaks loudly for their integrity; at the same time it indicates that the task they have set themselves, if possible at all, is not a light one.

To illustrate the difficulty with an example, consider statement (a') in Section 5.2. Here the hypothesis is that Mr. X is guilty of the stated crime. The evidence pertaining to this hypothesis may include, among other things, a transcript of Mr. X's trial, which may cover several hundred or several thousand pages. Just how does one come up with a numerical degree of confirmation of h on the basis of e (or the degree to which e supports h) by the use of well-defined rules (what rules?) which permit no amount of extraevidence judgment on the part of the evaluator?[49]

Logic and Judgment

The last sentence in Savage's quote above (... "narrowing a personalistic view to the point where it becomes a necessary one"...) gives an interesting contrast between subjective and logical views. As stated before, some subjective views are concerned with rules of consistent judgment. Along this line Savage (p. 60) remarks that "... any necessary view can be regarded as an extreme personalistic view in which so many criteria of consistency have been invoked that there is no role left for the person's individual judgment." Looked at through different eyes, LeBlanc (1962, pp. 128–129), in discussing inductive (logical) probability comments:

[49] In order to avoid an ambiguity, logical views require that e be internally consistent or noncontradictory. This may make the given example a poor choice.

Though personal probabilities may differ upon occasion from inductive probabilities, those among them that commonly pass muster as fair or coherent are thus nothing but inductive probabilities of a sort.   ... personal qualitative probabilities, as Savage's assessments have come to be called, are thus nothing but inductive inequalities of a sort.

I ... conclude ... that personal probabilities, be they of the Ramsey-de Finetti sort or the Savage sort, soon turn in their sponsor's very hands into inductive probabilities or inductive inequalities of a sort.

Truth of the Evidence

Another criticism of logical views, alluded to earlier, has to do with the "truth" of the evidence.   If logical probability is used, say, in connection with decision making in one realm or another, one would like to feel that the evidence used has some validity, particularly if the degree of confirmation of a hypothesis (or hypotheses) is critical in selecting a strategy or course of action.   But if we talk about the validity of the evidence or the "probability" that the evidence or some part thereof is valid, under a logical view we require that his probability be based upon another evidence statement.   Where this regression should end, we do not know.   Perhaps the most primitive evidence, taken as valid, should be those things directly experienced through our senses (as Hume suggests). But this does not appear to clear the logical position, since individual judgment is invariably involved in the acts of perceiving and accepting what is perceived as valid or only partially valid (or only "probable" in a subjective sense).

Frequency views are not, of course, exempt from the same criticism, although it is not as serious for these views.   But then the frequency position applies to a much more restricted class of things it considers acceptable for probability.   Some subjective views are not, to our knowledge, bothered much by this problem, since in these views probability is a personal concept, and an individual's experience (or "evidence"), although bearing on his estimates of magnitudes of subjective probabilities, enters into the process in an introspective "unanalyzable" fashion. Thus, in these views, we may speculate that the individual weighs his experience and evidence in some fashion or another, but there is no need to try to analyze what this fashion may be, and some subjective views hold that it is meaningless to try to do so.   Koopman (1940) supports the latter stand.

Comparative Logical Probability

We conclude this section with a brief glance at comparative logical probability.   Statement (*a*) in Section 5.2 is an example of this.   Employing the symbol $\leqslant$ to denote a comparative probability relation, read $(h, e) \leqslant (h', e')$ as "the degree of confirmation of h on the basis of e

is not greater than the degree of confirmation of h' on the basis of e'," or "h is not more strongly confirmed by e than h' by e'." The derived relations $\geqslant$, $>$, $<$, and $=$, are defined in the usual manner. For example, $(h, e) > (h', e')$ if and only if $(h', e') \leqslant (h, e)$ and not $(h, e) \leqslant (h', e')$. In some instances, $\leqslant$ may be used with three sentences— (h, h, e') or (h, e, e')—as a triadic relation:

(i) $(h, e) \leqslant (h', e)$;

(ii) $(h, e) \leqslant (h, e')$.

In (i) the two hypotheses differ but the evidence is the same. In (ii) the evidence varies but is applied to the same hypothesis. For the general case where h and h' are not logically equivalent and the same is true of e and e', $\leqslant$ is a tetradic relation between four sentences (or a dyadic relation between two pairs of sentences). Carnap (1950) in his chapter "Comparative Inductive Logic," goes into the comparative concept in some detail, prefacing his discussion[50] (1950, p. 428) with the following:

Although we shall try in later chapters to construct a quantitative system of inductive logic, at the present time the question whether a comprehensive and adequate quantitative system is at all possible is still controversial. This fact is the chief reason for the importance of a comparative system of inductive logic. However, even if a quantitative system is possible, it is still interesting to see which results can be obtained with more restricted means.

As in the case of comparative concepts of relative value, the comparative probability relation $\leqslant$ (or $\geqslant$) is not always assumed to be a weak ordering of a given set of sentence pairs. That is, it is not always assumed that, for two given sentence pairs, say (h, e) and (h', e'), either $(h, e) \leqslant (h', e')$ or $(h', e') \leqslant (h, e)$. In some sense or another they may be incomparable. What then results is $\leqslant$ as a quasi-ordering.[51] Many writers, including Keynes and Carnap, do not require that $\leqslant$ be a weak ordering for all sets of sentence pairs. Although we have considered the comparative relation $\gtrsim$ (is at least as desirable as) as a quasi-ordering with respect to consequences in Section 4.4, and will analyze partial orderings of relative values in some detail in Section 6.3 with regard to dominance among strategies, we shall not go into the same detail with regard to partial orderings of probabilities. However, in Sections 6.5 and 6.7, several special cases of partial orderings of probabilities (under a subjective interpretation) will be encountered. In the next section and in Section 5.8, comparative probability is further considered.

---

[50] Compare with Savage's (p. 61) remarks quoted on page 164.
[51] See Section 4.4.

5.6 SUBJECTIVE VIEWS AND RELATIVE VALUES

As we have observed, the logical views (of Keynes, Jeffreys, and Carnap, e.g.,) seek to exclude the individual and his judgments from the probability relation, holding forth the hope that a system of inductive logic will be developed that will lead all reasonable persons to the correct degree of confirmation of *h* on the basis of *e*. Holders of subjective views, including Ramsey, de Finetti, Good, and Savage, put the individual back into the picture by giving him center stage in a manner closely related to our previous discussion of relative value or utility.

The main stream of modern subjective views emanate,[52] so far as we can tell, from Ramsey (1950), who in *Truth and Probability* (written in 1926) follows up a brief criticism of frequency views and Keynes' view with his own formulation, in which the concept of decision plays a central role. Savage's (1954) viewpoint is quite similar to Ramsey's: "Ramsey's concepts of probability and utility are essentially the same as those presented in this book, but his logical development of them is an interesting alternative to the one used here, his definitions of probability and utility being simultaneous and interdependent" (p. 279). We shall have more to say about this later.

Koopman's Intuitive Thesis

A second stream of subjective views, with which we associate the phrase "intuitive probability" does not hold decision central. Koopman (1940) is representative of this position:

The intuitive thesis in probability holds that ... probability derives directly from the intuition, and is prior to objective experience; it holds that it is for experience to be interpreted in terms of probability and not for probability to be interpreted in terms of experience; and it holds that all the so-called objective definitions of probability depend for their effective application to concrete cases upon their translation into the terms of intuitive probability [p. 269].
... The fundamental viewpoint of the present work is that primal intuition of probability expresses itself in a (partial) ordering of eventualities ... *a* on the presumption that *h* is true is equally or less probable than *b* on the presumption that *k* is true [p. 270].

Although Koopman's formulation seems to have a good bit in common with Keynes, Koopman's viewpoint is definitely subjective since he maintains that probability may differ from person to person, at different times, etc.[53] After presenting the axioms of his system, Koopman goes on to

---

[52] Here we are led by Savage (1954, p. 60).

[53] Although Koopman seems to feel that Keynes is pursuing the thesis of intuitive probability, this does not appear correct. Even though Keynes makes several statements (primarily in his first chapter) which have a very intuitive ring, his main

derive various theorems of comparability. Up to this point we may say that his theory is comparative rather than quantitative. He then introduces an additional assumption which, if it holds, yields numerical probabilities and the usual theorems of quantitative probability (as derivable from Kolmogorov's axioms). This additional assumption states roughly that, for any positive integer n, there exists at least one set of n propositions which are mutually exclusive, have a non-null union, and which are regarded as equiprobable by the individual, given that one of them is "true." In a subsequent paper, Koopman (1941) compares the frequency theory with his intuitive conception, achieving "a complete synthesis of the intuitive concept of probability with the objective notion of statistical weight which forms the basis of statistics and quantum mechanics—and this without the assumption of a single general principle beyond those... posited in our earlier work" (p. 169). His conclusion in the latter paper asserts that every application of frequency (in sequences) definitions of probability in "experimental science implicitly presupposes the *a priori* intuitive conception of probability."

Good

Good (1950) has also expounded what we feel to be a primarily intuitive view. He begins his "Preface" thus:

When we wish to decide whether to adopt a particular course of action, our decision clearly depends on the values to us of the possible alternative consequences. A rational decision depends also on our degrees of belief that each of the alternatives will occur. Probability, as it is understood here, is the logic (rather than the psychology) of degrees of belief and of their possible modification in the light of experience.

However, he does not effect an intimate tie between the measurement of probability and the idea of decision as do Ramsey and Savage. Further remarks in Good's "Preface" give additional insight into his position and intentions:

The aim of the present work is to provide a consistent theory of probability that is mathematically simple, logically sound and adequate as a basis for scientific induction, for statistics, and for ordinary reasoning....
Various authorities have attempted to eliminate the necessity for subjective probability judgments by employing instructions that are outside the theory adopted here. There instructions are imprecisely stated or... apply only to

---

exposition is not subjective but logical, as has been pointed out by Ramsey (1950) and Carnap (1950), among others. It is interesting to note, however, that in a later work (*Essays in Biography*, London, 1933), "Keynes admitted that he no longer adhered to an objective theory" (Good, 1950, p. 10).

ideal circumstances.... It is maintained here that judgments should be given a recognized place from the start....

The theory presented in the following pages follows precise rules, although it uses subjective judgments as its raw material.

Two Conceptions of Relative Value

In our discussion thus far we have distinguished two major forms of subjective views:[54] (1) the intuitive-oriented (Koopman, Good) and (2) the decision-oriented (Ramsey, Savage).[55] Before going into these further, particularly the latter, we shall first give a parallel to these forms with respect to relative value. Suppose an individual is comparing two consequences, say o_i and o_k. An "intuitive approach" to relative value might pose the question, "Which of these two is more desirable?" without further comment. The decision-oriented approach might request a preference statement thus: "If you could choose just one of two 'strategies,' the first leading to o_i with certainty and the second leading to o_k with certainty, which of the two would you choose?"[56] Whether the reader feels there is a real difference between these two will depend on his interpretation of "desirable" in the first interrogation. The distinction may be made clearer by considering the two approaches to obtaining a first bounded interval measure of relative value, as discussed in Section 4.6, where we worked with three o_j at a time, say $o_1 \gtrsim o_j \gtrsim o_r$, with $o_1 > o_r$. The first method presented there (give an interval on a linear preference continuum between o_1 and o_r that contains o_j) would be more in line with an intuitive approach,[57] whereas the latter [the hypothetical choice situation pitting o_j against the gambles or options (o_1, p, o_r) for $0 \leqslant p \leqslant 1$] is decision-oriented.

To illustrate the approximate way the two schools would interrogate with respect to probability in a decision situation, consider a decision situation in the form of the statistical model[58] (since this is the usual framework for such discussion). For two states of the world, say E_j and E_k, the intuitive approach might ask, "Which state do you consider more likely to be the true state?" whereas the decision-oriented might proceed as follows: "Consider two hypothetical strategies (or acts) the

[54] A third form is the behaviorally (after-the-fact) oriented, which we shall not consider.

[55] Bruno de Finetti (1937) presents two conceptions of subjective probability, one in terms of an intuitive position, the other related to betting behavior, giving him a foot in each of the above camps.

[56] The reader will recognize this as a form of an *h*-situation or hypothetical choice situation introduced in Chapter 4.

[57] It might be more appropriate to give this a different name, but we are unable to suggest a satisfactory substitute.

[58] See Section 3.6.

first yielding a relative value V_1 if E_j obtains and a value V_2 if any other state obtains, the second yielding V_1 if E_k obtains (is the true state) and V_2 if any other state obtains, with $V_1 > V_2$. If you had to choose between the two acts, which would you select?" If the first is "chosen" (or preferred), then $P(E_j) \geqslant P(E_k)$. If the second is "chosen," then $P(E_k) \geqslant P(E_j)$.

The views of Koopman and Good differ from those of Ramsey and Savage in another way. In a fashion vaguely similar to that of logical views, the former consider the probability of a first proposition given a second proposition (or on the assumption that the second proposition is true).[59] The views of Ramsey and Savage do not do this explicitly in the basic formulation, although conditional probabilities are naturally included in their theories. In these latter views, the probability of a proposition p (or the probability that p is true; Ramsey) or the probability that E_j is the true state of the world (Savage) is conditioned not upon an explicitly stated second proposition or evidence statement but upon all previous experience of the individual whose judgments are sought. Here *experience* is used in a very general sense and may be viewed as the total history of the individual. (The intuitive views also recognize this, but still include an explicit second proposition.)

The Logic of Consistency

In all subjective views discussed in this section, logic plays an important role, but these views are not logical views as conceived of in the previous section. The logic of subjective views is not some as yet incomplete system of inductive logic leaving no room for individual judgments, interpretations, and beliefs, but rather a set of criteria for consistency and reasonableness in our beliefs or judgments (or behavior). If, for example, you consider "precipitation tomorrow" more probable than "Hitler is still alive" and consider "Hitler is still alive" more probable than "the earth is flat," then one of these rules of consistency (i.e., transitivity) would require that you consider "precipitation tomorrow" more probable than "the earth is flat." As noted in Section 4.3, if such rules of consistency are violated by an individual (with respect either to relative value or, in the new context, subjective probability), and one is constructing a theory of decision upon adherence to these rules, then this theory is not capable of dealing with the individual's decision situation.[60] If, however,

---

[59] See, e.g., the excerpt from Koopman at the beginning of this section.

[60] Whatever criteria of consistency are proposed, it must be kept in mind that these are reasonable or rational criteria in the judgment of the formulator and may not be so to someone else. It is a grave oversimplification to say that, if Mr. X does not meet our criteria of rationality, then he is somehow unreasonable or unbalanced.

an individual agrees with the theorist and feels that his judgments should conform (and, in fact, can be satisfactorily made to conform) to the consistency criteria, then such a theory offers him a rational or consistent basis for making decisions.

Decision-Oriented Views, Ramsey

To obtain an idea of Ramsey's (1950) position, from which many modern decision-oriented approaches have emanated, we offer the following excerpts:

The subject of our inquiry is the logic of partial belief, . . . what partial belief is, and how, if at all, it can be measured [p. 166].

Let us then consider what is implied in the measurement of beliefs. A satisfactory system must . . . assign to any belief a magnitude or degree having a definite position in an order of magnitudes . . . we have also to assign numbers to these degrees in some intelligible manner [p. 168].

There are, I think, two ways in which we can begin. We can, in the first place, suppose that the degree of belief is something perceptible by its owner; . . . that beliefs differ in the intensity of a feeling by which they are accompanied, which might be called a . . . feeling of conviction, and that by the degree of belief we mean the intensity of this feeling. This view would be very inconvenient . . . it seems to me observably false[61] . . . .

We are driven therefore to the second supposition that the degree of a belief is a causal property of it, which we can express vaguely as the extent to which we are prepared to act on it . . . it is not asserted that a belief is an idea which does actually lead to action, but one which would lead to action in suitable circumstances . . . .

As soon as we regard belief quantitatively, this seems to me the only view we can take of it [pp. 169–170].

It will no doubt be objected that we know how strongly we believe things, and that we can only know this if we can measure our beliefs by introspection. This does not seem to me necessarily true; in many cases, I think, our judgment about the strength of our belief is really about how we should act in hypothetical circumstances [pp. 170–171].

Let us now try to find a method of measuring beliefs as bases of possible actions. It is clear that we are concerned with dispositional rather than with actualized beliefs . . . [p. 172].

At this point, Ramsey presents his axiomatic system, on which we shall comment momentarily. Some further comments by Ramsey that follow the previous excerpts are given as follows:

From his viewpoint we might be crazy. Society, however, seems to be able to determine (recognizing the possibility of Type I and Type II errors) whether someone is so "irrational" that he ought to be confined and rehabilitated (morally or mentally) if possible.

[61] *Author's note:* Here Ramsey is talking about what we have called the intuitive view, which he rejects.

We find, therefore, that a precise account of the nature of partial belief reveals that the laws of probability are laws of consistency.... They do not depend for their meaning on any degree of belief in a proposition being uniquely determined as the rational one; they merely distinguish those sets of beliefs which obey them as consistent ones [p. 182].
... The theory of probability is ... a generalization of formal logic; but in the process of generalization one of the most important aspects of formal logic is destroyed ... unlike the calculus of consistent full belief, the calculus of objective partial belief cannot be immediately interpreted as a body of objective tautology [pp. 186–187].

The basic notions underlying Ramsey's axiomatic system for measuring utility (relative value) and subjective probability are (1) an "ethically neutral proposition p believed to degree 1/2" and (2) the notion of equal utility differences. These ideas have served as the basis for Suppes and Winet's (1955) axiomatization of utility and for the experiments on measuring utility and subjective probability reported in Davidson, Suppes, and Siegel (1957). We have previously noted that the latter found propositions of the sort, "A roll of this die (with three faces marked *ZOJ*, the other three faces marked *ZEJ*, e.g.) will result in *ZOJ* on the up-face," that appear to satisfy the conditions which Ramsey terms "ethical neutrality"; that is, if x and y are any two consequences, then the individual will be indifferent to choosing (x, p, y) and (y, p, x), where (a, p, b) is the gamble[62] (or lottery or option) yielding a if the proposition p obtains, and b if p does not obtain.

Axioms of Utility Based on Utility Differences

Although Suppes and Winet's axiomatization of utility does not explicitly employ the notion of "an ethically neutral proposition p," they point out that the idea of differences in utility may be interpreted on this basis. For example, if the subjective probability of p equals 1/2 and $x > y$, $z > w$ (where x, y, z, and w are consequences, and $>$ means "is preferred to"), and if (z, p, y) is preferred to (x, p, w), we may interpret this as "the utility difference between x and y is less than the utility difference between z and w" (Suppes and Winet, p. 259).[63]

The formal axioms in their system are based upon three primitives:[64] (1) a set $\mathbf{Q}$ (of consequences x, y, z, w, u, v, ...); (2) a binary relation $\gtrsim$ on $\mathbf{Q}$ (interpret "$x \gtrsim y$" as "y is not preferred to x"); and (3) a quaternary

---

[62] Or hypothetical gamble.

[63] From Ramsey (p. 178): "We have to explain what is meant by the difference in value between α and β being equal to that between γ and δ; and we define this to mean that, if p is an ethically neutral proposition believed to degree 1/2, the subject has no preference between the options (1) α if p is true, δ if p is false, and (2) β if p is true, γ if p is false."

[64] This account is in the author's words and notation.

relation ($\leqslant$) on **Q** [interpret "$x, y (\leqslant) z, w$" as "the difference in preference between x and y is less than or equal to the difference in preference between z and w"]. From $\gtrsim$, the relations $\lesssim$, $>$, $<$, and $\sim$ are defined in the usual way. Similarly, ($\geqslant$), ($>$), ($<$), and ($=$) are defined in the obvious fashion from ($\leqslant$). Two other defined relations are used:

1. A ternary relation B, where yBx, z if and only if either $x > y$ and $y > z$ or $z > y$ and $y > x$. (Read "yBx, z" as "y is between x and z.")

2. A quaternary relation M, where x, yMz, w if and only if $y \sim z$, yBx, w, and $x, y (=) z, w$. Recursively, define

x, yM^1z, w if and only if x, yMz, w,

x, yM^nz, w if and only if there exist $u, v \in$ **Q** such that $x, yM^{n-1}u, v$ and u, vMz, w.

[If x, y, etc., are pictured as points on a line, x, yM^nz, w may be interpreted as "the intervals (x, y) and (z, w) are of equal length, and there are $n - 1$ intervals of the same length between these two."]

Suppes and Winet's axioms, which imply the existence of a real-valued utility function on **Q** (unique up to an increasing linear transformation), are:[65] For every x, y, z, w, u, and v in **Q**:

A1 $\gtrsim$ is a weak ordering of **Q**.

A2 $x, y (\leqslant) z, w$ or $z, w (\leqslant) x, y$.

A3   ($\leqslant$) is transitive.

A4 $x, y (=) y, x$.

A5   There is a $t \in$ **Q** such that $x, t (=) t, y$.

A6   If $x \sim y$ and $x, z (\leqslant) u, v$, then $y, z (\leqslant) u, v$.

A7   If yBx, z, then $x, y (<) x, z$.

A8   If yBx, z, and wBu, v, and $x, y (\leqslant) u, w$, and $y, z (\leqslant) w, v$, then $x, z (\leqslant) u, v$.

A9   If $x, y (<) u, v$, then there is a $t \in$ **Q** such that tBu, v and $x, y (\leqslant) u, t$.

A10   If $x, y (\leqslant) u, v$ and not $x \sim y$, then there are elements $s, t \in$ **Q** and a positive integer n such that u, sM^nt, v and $u, s (\leqslant) x, y$.

In the previous chapter it will be recalled that our ordered metric rankings were based on the notion of utility differences and, under a subjective view of probability in hypothetical choice situations, on an "ethically neutral proposition p." A1 gives an ordinal ranking (Section

---

[65] Here, again, we have taken some liberty with their presentation.

4.2), and A1 through A⁴ ⸱·e a higher ordered metric ranking (Section 4.11). One of the diffi ₂s in using the above axioms in this book is that, in trying to gene , an interval measure of relative value, **Q** will often not be rich enor . to satisfy A5, A9, and A10. This does not, of course, prevent one fₐ m adding to **Q**, as structured previously, a whole slew of additional hypothetical consequences, such as a continuum of monetary prizes. If this could be done (or if all consequences were stated in terms of one variable, such as dollars or hours and fractions thereof), practical application might require the determination of a finite number of values of the variable equally spaced in utility or relative value, interpolation being used between these values to approximate the relative values of other consequences.

Starting with the above axioms, it is quite possible to supplement these with additional postulates that lead to a quantitative measure of subjective probability. For example, if p were a proposition (e.g., $p = E_j$ is the true state of the world) and x, y, z were consequences with relative values $V(x)$, $V(y)$, and $V(z)$ respectively, then we might introduce the axiom (following Ramsey):

A11 Either (1) there exist x, y, $z \in$ **Q**, with yBx, z, such that $y \sim (x, p, z)$:[66] Moreover, it is true that $[V(y) - V(z)]/[V(x) - V(z)]$ is the same for every x, y, z that gives $y \sim (x, p, z)$; or (2) for every pair $x, y \in$ **Q**, $y \sim (x, p, y)$; or (3) for every pair $x, y \in$ **Q**, $y \sim (y, p, x)$.

We may then define $P(p)$, the subjective probability of p, by

1. $P(p) = \dfrac{V(y) - V(z)}{V(x) - V(z)}$,

2. $P(p) = 0$,

3. $P(p) = 1$,

respectively. Tacked onto this would be whatever other axioms are required for P to be a proper probability measure with respect to the set of propositions that apply.

A Double Application of the von Neumann-Morgenstern Axioms

As we have noted before, the axioms of von Neumann and Morgenstern[67] (Section 1.3) also imply the existence of a utility function unique except for origin and unit measurement, but that these are based on gambles in which the probabilities are "known" by the individual, criticism of this having been raised previously. Anscombe and Aumann (1963) have

---

[66] The gamble (x, p, z) must make sense, i.e., be logically consistent. The consequences $x, y, z, \ldots$ might be taken as hypothetical monetary prizes.

[67] See also Luce and Raiffa (1957, Chapter 2).

presented "A Definition of Subjective Probability" based upon a double application of the von Neumann-Morgenstern axioms. As in most statistically oriented literature, the probabilities they wish to measure subjectively are the $P(E_j)$, i.e., the probabilities of the various states of the world being the true state. In their discussion they use an illustration for which the world is a horse race, each state taking the form "horse *i* wins the race." In their scheme the first application of the axioms applies to "roulette lotteries" in which "known" probabilities are used. The utilities thus derived may be interpreted as the utilities of the consequences that may result in the actual decision situation [i.e., the $V(o_{ij})$ as used in Section 3.6]. The second application of the axioms (with several additional assumptions thrown in for completeness) is used again for roulette lotteries, but here prizes are "horse lotteries," where a horse lottery may be interpreted as an act (perhaps hypothetical) assigning a consequence to each state of the world. The second application serves to generate the utilities of the horse lotteries. Letting u denote the first utility function for the consequences $(o_{ij} \in Q)$ and u^* denote the second utility function for the acts or horse lotteries $\{[o_{i1}, o_{i2}, \ldots, o_{in}]\}$, the authors prove that for all horse lotteries (acts) of the form $[o_{i1}, \ldots, o_{in}]$ there exists a unique set of n nonnegative numbers $p_1, \ldots, p_n$, with $\Sigma p_j = 1$, such that $u^*[o_{i1}, o_{i2}, \ldots, o_{in}] = p_1u(o_{i1}) + p_2u(o_{i2}) + \ldots + p_nu(o_{in})$ under appropriate normalizations of u and u^*. The p_j are, of course, defined as the subjective probabilities for the states [i.e., $p_j = P(E_j)$]. In concluding, the authors compare their scheme to Savage's, noting that their derivation of the $P(E_j)$ is based upon the preference relation, whereas Savage's is based upon a comparative probability relation (which is derived from a preference relation). We might note that, although this is quite true, Savage nowhere makes use of "known" probabilities in his basic formulation, which might be termed "entirely subjective," or, in his own words, "personalistic." Although Ramsey's or Davidson, Suppes, and Siegel's views are also "entirely subjective," Savage differs from these in the fact that he does not base his axioms on the notions of utility differences and on an "ethically neutral proposition."

Savage's Theory

This leads us to the final axiomatic system to be considered. Savage's views, like those considered before that are decision-oriented, are built upon the statistical model outlined in Section 3.6. From our previous discussions the reader should be able, with appropriate alterations in notation, to grasp the essentials of Savage's system by referring to the end papers of his book in which he has graciously summarized his theory. In the following partial account of Savage's theory we shall follow his notation. This should make it much easier for readers who wish to refer to the source, although it may, regrettably, cause some confusion here. His primitives are:

1. S, the set of states of the world, with elements $s, s', \ldots$ and subsets $A, B, C, \ldots$. Here $s, s', \ldots$ are the states (exclusive and exhaustive, denoted before as $E_j, E_k, \ldots$) and $A, B, C, \ldots$ sets of states or events ($A \subset S, B \subset S, \ldots$). S is required (by P6 to follow) to be an infinite set.

2. F, the set of consequences, with elements $f, g, h, \ldots$ (denoted before as **Q** with elements $o_j, o_k, \ldots$ or $o_{ij}, o_{jk}, \ldots$).

3. Acts (called strategies above), which are arbitrary functions **f, g, h,** $\ldots$ from S to F. That is, each act assigns a consequence to each state of the world. $f(s) = g$ means that the consequence g is assigned to state s by **f**.

4. The binary relation $\leqslant$ ("is not preferred to").

Savage's postulates are denoted by[68] P1 through P6, and his definitions by D1, D2, ...

P1 $\leqslant$ is a weak ordering[69] of the acts.

Thus $\leqslant$ is initially applied to acts (not consequences). This relates to Anscombe and Aumann's second application of the von Neumann-Morgenstern postulates. Next, conditional preference between acts is defined thus:

D1 **f** $\leqslant$ **g** given B, if and only if **f'** $\leqslant$ **g'** for every **f'** and **g'** that agree with **f** and **g**, respectively, on B and with each other on $\sim B$ (the complement of B with respect to S).

f agrees with **f'** on B if $f(s) = f'(s)$ for each $s \in B$ (i.e., if **f** and **f'** assign the same consequence to each state in B. The consequences may of course differ for different $s \in B$). Similarly, **f'** and **g'** agree with each other on $\sim B$ if and only if $f'(s) = g'(s)$ for each $s \in \sim B$.

The next postulate, the first in the pair (P2 and P3) explicating Savage's sure-thing principle, asserts connectedness for conditional preference:

P2 For every **f, g** and B, **f** $\leqslant$ **g** given B, or **g** $\leqslant$ **f** given B.

Along with P1 this implies that each of the conditional relations "$\leqslant$ given B" is a weak ordering of the acts for each $B \subset S$. For $B = S$,

---

[68] We shall not be concerned with his P7, since it goes beyond our finite-set considerations.

[69] Savage uses "simple ordering" here.

this amounts to P1. If $f(s) = g(s)$ for all $s \in B$, then **f** and **g** are indifferent, given B (i.e., $\mathbf{f} \doteq \mathbf{g}$ given B, where $\doteq$ is used for indifference).

D2 $g \leqslant g'$, if and only if $\mathbf{f} \leqslant \mathbf{f}'$ when $f(s) = g$, $f'(s) = g'$ for every $s \in S$.

Thus preference or indifference between consequences is defined in terms of preference or indifference between constant acts (an act being constant if it assigns the same consequence to all states in S).

D3 B is null if and only if $\mathbf{f} \leqslant \mathbf{g}$ given B, for every **f**, **g**.

"B is null" is interpreted as "the individual considers B virtually impossible," i.e., he considers it virtually impossible that any state in B will obtain. Further postulates imply that $P(B) = 0$ if and only if B is null, where P is a quantitative personal probability or probability measure on S. The second half of the sure-thing principle is:

P3   If $f(s) = g$ and $f'(s) = g'$ for every $s \in B$ and B is not null, then $\mathbf{f} \leqslant \mathbf{f}'$ given B, if and only if $g \leqslant g'$.

In view of D2, this might also be rendered, "If **f** and **f**' are constant acts and B is not null, then $\mathbf{f} \leqslant \mathbf{f}'$ given B, if and only if $\mathbf{f} \leqslant \mathbf{f}'$," but its interpretation best applies to preference between consequences (g and g'), asserting that: (1) the knowledge of an event cannot affect the preference between consequences and (2) when the event is not null, knowledge of the event cannot reduce preference among consequences to indifference.

The next definition sets $\leqslant$ to the events. Read "$A \leqslant B$" as "A is not more probable than B."

D4 $A \leqslant B$ if and only if $\mathbf{f}_A \leqslant \mathbf{f}_B$ or $g' \leqslant g$ [70] for every $\mathbf{f}_A$, $\mathbf{f}_B$, g, g' such that: $f_A(s) = g$ for $s \in A$, $f_A(s) = g'$ for $s \in \sim A$, $f_B(s) = g$ for $s \in B$, and $f_B(s) = g'$ for $s \in \sim B$.

Thus "is not more probable than" is defined in terms of preference between acts (or consequences). $A \leqslant B$ has the obvious interpretation that, if you are faced with a "choice" between two acts, the first yielding g if A obtains [71] and g' if $\sim A$ obtains, the second yielding g if B obtains and g' if $\sim B$ obtains, and you consider g at least as desirable as g' and "choose" the second act, then you regard B at least as probable as A. (This holds for all such g and g'.)

P4 asserts that $\leqslant$ as applied to events is connected:

P4   For every A, B, $A \leqslant B$ or $B \leqslant A$.

[70] On Savage's end papers this is written as $g \leqslant g'$ which we believe to be a typographical error.

[71] A obtains = some $s \in A$ obtains = A contains the true state of the world.

Together with P1, P2, P3 above and P5 below this implies, among other things, that: (1) $\leqslant$ is a weak ordering of the events; (2) $B \leqslant C$ if and only if $B \cup D \leqslant C \cup D$, provided $B \cap D = C \cap D = \emptyset$ (intersections are null);[72] and (3) $\emptyset \leqslant B$, $\emptyset \leqslant S$ for all such events B, C, D: or, in Savage's words, "$\leqslant$ as applied to events is a *qualitative probability*."

P5   There is at least one pair of consequences f, f' such that $f' < f$ ($<$ denoting strict preference).

This excludes the trivial case where all consequences are indifferent to one another.   Also derivable from the above is $B \doteq \emptyset$ if and only if B is null (in the sense of D3).   The final postulate considered here is:

P6   If $\mathbf{g} < \mathbf{h}$, then, for every consequence f, there is a partition of S (into a finite number of exclusive and exhaustive events) such that, if $\mathbf{g}$ or $\mathbf{h}$ is so modified on any one element of the partition as to take the value f at every s there, other values remaining undisturbed, then $<$ still holds between the modified $\mathbf{g}$ and $\mathbf{h}$ or between $\mathbf{g}$ and the modified $\mathbf{h}$, as the case may require.

This postulate has significance both in implying the existence of a probability measure P that strictly agrees with the qualitative probability $\leqslant$ (i.e., for every B, C, $P(B) \leqslant P(C)$ if and only if $B \leqslant C$), and in implying the existence of a utility function V, unique but for origin and scale (defined on F, the set of consquences, and on the acts, etc.), so that $V(\mathbf{f}) = \int V(f(s))\, dP(s)$.[73]

Savage also notes that P6 implies, "If $B < C$, there exists a partition of S the union of each element of which with B is less probable than C," which in turn implies, "There exist partitions of S into arbitrarily many equivalent events."   P6 also conveys the notion that no consequence is "infinitely" more desirable (or undesirable) than any other consequence. In defense of this postulate Savage (pp. 38–39) says:

Suppose, for example, that you ... consider $B < C$, that is, that you would rather stake a gain in your fortune on C rather than on B.   Consider the partition of your own world into 2^n events each of which corresponds to a particular sequence of n heads and tails, thrown by yourself, with a coin of your own choosing.   It seems to me that you could easily choose such a coin and choose n sufficiently large so that you would continue to prefer to stake your gain on C, rather than on the union of B and any particular sequence of n heads and tails.   For you to be able to do so, you need by no means consider every sequence of heads and tails equally probable.

[72] $B \cup C$ is the set of all states in either B or C and $B \cap C$ is the set of all states in both B and C. $\emptyset$ is the null set, i.e., the event consisting of no states.

[73] We are here assuming that the set of consequences, F, is finite, so that $V(\mathbf{f})$ is well defined according to the limiting process that serves to define it.

A Standard Lottery

Schlaifer (1959), in his simplified scheme for measuring probabilities, does not bother with qualitative probability or comparative relations but goes straight to numerical probabilities.[74] His scheme[75] for measuring subjective probabilities numerically is decision-oriented and deals with two hypothetical worlds: (1) a completely hypothetical world called the "standard lottery," used for comparison with (2) a pseudo-hypothetical world where the states are the actual states of the real world and the consequences are hypothetical. We are concerned with determining $P(B)$, where B is an event of the real world, either a single state or a subset of states of S. To do this, first consider a hypothetical act, say h_2, in world 2, which assigns a consequence h to all $s \in B$ and a consequence h' to all $s \in {\sim}B$. Whatever h and h' may be, $h > h'$ (i.e., h is preferred to or more valuable than h'). Next we consider a hypothetical act, say h_1, in world 1, the standard lottery. We can suppose the standard lottery to consist of N identical balls in an urn, numbered 1 through N, from which one ball is drawn in a "random" fashion (e.g., by a blind-folded person wearing heavy gloves). Let C denote the event in world 1, "one of n designated balls out of the total of N will be the one selected by the draw." Then h_1 assigns the consequence h to C and h' to ${\sim}C$, where h and h' are as before ($h > h'$). The individual is now requested to state a value of n (and designate n specific balls by number) such that $h_1 \doteq h_2$. If we assume he can do this and that he considers $h_1 \doteq h_2$ for every set of n balls he could specify,[76] and that n remains invariant for every pair h, h', with $h > h'$, then $P(C) = n/N$ (i.e., he considers each ball equally likely to be the one drawn) and $P(B) = P(C)$, yielding $P(B) = n/N$.

This also, of course, involves the question of how large to make N, which Schlaifer says should be determined by the individual. Thus, to be more explicit, it is assumed that there exists an N, say N', such that the individual is able to designate $n' \leqslant N'$, rendering $h_1 \doteq h_2$, and that:

1. For each $N \neq N'$ for which there exists an $n \leqslant N$ such that

[74] Schlaifer's book was written primarily for graduate students in business with modest mathematical backgrounds. His treatment is entirely numerical and gives practically no discussion of fundamental questions raised in this book, or, for example, in Churchman (1961a). His decision criterion is the same as is used here (maximization of expected utility). As well as we can tell (since he gives no references), his treatment of utility follows Luce and Raiffa (1957) and requests the individual to state a probability p which renders $o_j \sim (o_1, p, o_r)$ for each o_j, where $o_1 \gtrsim o_j \gtrsim o_r$.

[75] This is my interpretation. See Schlaifer (pp. 11–13) for his version. Savage's notation is used here.

[76] That is, for all $\binom{N}{n}$ ways of designating n balls of the N.

$n/N = n'/N'$, if N is used in place of N', the individual will judge $\mathbf{h}_1 \doteq \mathbf{h}_2$ by designating any n of the N balls, with $n = N(n'/N')$.

2. For each $N \neq N'$ for which there exists no $n \leqslant N$ such that $n/N = n'/N'$, for any n balls out of the N that give $n/N < n'/N'$, $\mathbf{h}_1 > \mathbf{h}_2$, and for any n balls out of the N that give $n/N > n'/N'$, $\mathbf{h}_1 < \mathbf{h}_2$ (i.e., there is no n which renders $\mathbf{h}_1 \doteq \mathbf{h}_2$).

Obviously it is also necessary to have $\sum_i P(B_i) = 1$, where B_i is any partition of S, and to have $P(B) = \sum_{s \in B} P(s)$ for all B. Hence, additional restrictions on appropriate n's and N's are also required, which we shall not consider. Few persons have such sharp judgment as required here, and for this reason we will consider bounded probability measures in Section 5.9. One scheme used will be similar to Schlaifer's.

Additional Comments

In concluding this section, several additional comments are in order. First, it is noted that Bayes' rule discussed in Section 5.2 has a great deal of use in subjective views. If we begin with initial (*a priori*) subjective probabilities and new evidence about the world is obtained, the conditional (subjective) probabilities pertaining to this evidence are combined with the *a priori* probabilities to yield *a posteriori* subjective probabilities. Under purely subjective views, we could skip explicit measurement of *a priori* and conditional probabilities (for the new evidence, given a state) and deal only with the *a posteriori* probabilities after all the evidence or experience "is in." Or we could measure *a posteriori* and conditional probabilities (for the new evidence) and compute the implied *a priori* probabilities, and so forth. In this we use the formulas

$$P(E_j \mid e) \sum_{k=1}^{n} P(E_k)P(e \mid E_k) = P(E_j)P(e \mid E_j), \qquad j = 1, \ldots, n,$$

where $\{E_j\}, j = 1, \ldots, n$, is the set of states of the world, e is the "new" experience, and the $P(E_j)$, $P(e \mid E_j)$, and $P(E_j \mid e)$ denote the *a priori* probabilities, the conditional evidence probabilities, and the *a posteriori* probabilities respectively. One may view the difference between the *a priori* and *a posteriori* probabilities as caused by the accumulation of additional experience or as a learning effect reflecting additional evidence about the true nature of the world.[77]   In some views, the $P(E_j)$ are taken

[77] See Savage (pp. 46–50) for further discussion on this, which follows his discussion of conditional personal probability. He says: "... it may be observed ... that, if the *a priori probability* ... of B_i is 0, then, no matter what ... is observed, the *a posteriori probability* of B_i ... is also 0. ... if some event is regarded as virtually impossible, then no evidence whatsoever can lend it credibility. Similarly ... if an observation x is virtually impossible on the hypothesis (i.e., given) B_i, and x is observed, then B_i becomes virtually impossible *a posteriori*."

as subjective probabilities and the $P(e \mid E_j)$ as objective probabilities,[78] since under appropriate assumptions it is possible to compute the $P(e \mid E_j)$ on objectively interpreted bases.   On this basis one could call the $P(E_j \mid e)$ "subobjective" *a posteriori* probabilities.

Second, it should be noted that a subjective view of probability does not ignore evidence in the form of relative frequencies.   In some situations, as, for example, in certain experiments under closely controlled conditions, subjective probabilities might coincide with observed relative frequencies. But we should usually find that relative frequencies, when they apply, constitute only a part of the evidence or experience that influences the individual's judgment.   Some objectivists, in criticizing subjective views, maintain that all judgments in subjective probability are nothing more or less than appraisals of relative frequencies.   They may further state that, since probabilities ought to be estimated by relative frequencies, let us expose these subjective judgments for what they really are, namely, crude estimates of objective probabilities.   That judgments of probabilities may be influenced by relative frequencies is not denied by most subjectivists, but this is only part of the story.   It seems that objectivistic critics of subjective probability who raise the foregoing point about relative frequency do not understand or appreciate the vital differences between the two conceptions.

Finally, it will be noticed that in all this discussion practically nothing has been said about the $P(o_j \mid S_i)$ with respect to the basic decision model. Under the statistical model, if the problem is originally formulated in this context, $P(o_j \mid S_i)$ will either equal 0 when o_j is not a consequence that can occur with strategy S_i, or equal the sum of one or more of the $P(E_j)$. If o_{ij} is the consequence in the ith row (S_i) and jth column (E_j) of the statistical consequence matrix and o_{ij} equals no other consequence in this row, then $P(o_{ij} \mid S_i) = P(E_j)$.

In situations where our original formulation is in the terms of the basic decision model, there may be very good reasons for not attempting to put the situation in the form of the statistical model.   For example, if Model I is used with t strategies and r consequences, then we will have rt (or fewer) probabilities to consider.   Then, following the little advertising example in Section 3.6, we could put this in the form of the statistical model, at least in some instances, by defining the jth state of the world in the form $E_j = (o_{j1}$ if S_1, o_{j2} if $S_2, \ldots, o_{jt}$ if $S_t)$, where $o_{ji} \in \mathbf{Q}$ for each S_i. In such a situation there would be r^t (or fewer) states and, thus, perhaps as many as r^t probabilities for states.[79]   But in this case we would not be

---

[78] With a frequency interpretation.

[79] In the advertising illustration of Section 3.6, $r = 2$ and $t = 2$ giving $rt = 4$, $r^t = 4$.   For $r = 10$, $t = 10$, $rt = 100$ but $r^t = 10,000,000,000$.

interested in measuring the probabilities of the states, but in measuring the probabilities of the rt (or fewer) subsets of states (i.e., events) that correspond to the $P(o_j \mid S_i)$.[80] Hence it would not serve any useful purpose (that we can see) to go to the statistical model in the case under discussion.

There may be other cases where a reformulation of the problem in basic form into the statistical form is advantageous, but whether or not this is so will depend upon the nature of the particular problem under study. In any event, if Model I or Model I ($S = A$) or Model II is employed, we shall be concerned with t probability distributions, one corresponding to each admissible strategy. For Model I there will be r arguments for each probability function where, for P_i, the ith probability function, the arguments will be the r propositions (o_j will result if strategy S_i is adopted, $j = 1, \ldots, r$). For Model I ($S = A$) or for Model II, P_i will have as its arguments the n propositions (O_j will result if strategy S_i is adopted, $j = 1, \ldots, n$).

5.7 PROBABILITY IN PRESCRIPTIVE DECISION THEORIES

As far as the general thesis of this book is concerned, the past four sections have been a means of placing us in a better position to understand and appreciate the use of probability in decision theory. To a large extent this has been accomplished in the previous section.

Personalistic, Expected-Value Theory

It should be clear from past developments that, in the type of decision situation under consideration in this book, we subscribe to probability with a subjective interpretation, along the lines of the decision-oriented subjective views. Most of our reasons can be drawn from the past discussions. They are influenced very strongly by Savage (1954).

Under a logical conception as presented in Section 5.5, it seems a hopeless task, even in the simplest decision situation, to state a clear, unambiguous evidence sentence or proposition that should be used along with hypothesis sentences such as, "S_i, if adopted, will yield o_j," or "E_j is the true state of the world." Even if we could agree upon (and here judgment enters) the correct evidence proposition to use in a given situation, the logical view is quite unable to provide us with the means for computing quantitative probabilities, except when the principle of indifference applies (which again requires a judgment).

We cannot help but agree with Savage's conjecture that the possibility

---

[80] Our intention in this is that $P(o_{j1}$ if S_1, o_{j2} if $S_2, \ldots, o_{jt}$ if $S_t) = P(o_{j1} \mid S_1)$ $P(o_{j2} \mid S_2) \ldots P(o_{jt} \mid S_t)$. $P(\cdot \mid \cdot)$ is a marginal distribution of $P(\cdot, \cdot, \ldots, \cdot)$.

of constructing an adequate logical view (leaving no room for individual judgment) is not real. If such a system of inductive logic were developed, it must be realized that judgment would be involved in selecting the very rules that are supposed to allow no judgment to enter the process of evaluation. Apparently the idea of making judgment one step removed from the evaluator does not trouble the logical positivist. In a subjective view there is, of course, not only this behind-the-scenes judgment (resulting in the axioms) but also the ever-present judgment of the individual evaluator. In spite of the differences, Savage feels it is at least imaginable that additional criteria of consistency might be added to his postulates so as to bring them closer and closer to a strict logical view, leaving little or no room for an individual's judgment. To quote Savage (p. 67):

> Neither the necessary nor the objectivistic outlook leaves any room for personal differences; both, therefore, look on any personalistic view of probability as, at best, an attempt to predict some of the behavior of abnormal, or at any rate unscientific, people.
> I would reply that the personalistic view incorporates all the universally acceptable criteria of reasonableness in judgment known to me and that, when any criteria that may have been overlooked are brought forward, they will be welcomed into the personalistic view.

Our feelings about inadequacy of a frequency conception of probability in decision theory follow from observations made in Section 5.4. To summarize, in Savage's words (p. 4):

> The difficulty in the objectivistic position is this. In any objectivist view, probabilities can apply fruitfully only to repetitive events, that is, to certain processes; and . . . it is either meaningless to talk about the probability that a given proposition is true, or this probability can be only 1 or 0, according as the proposition is in fact true or false. Under neither interpretation can probability serve as a measure of the trust to be put in the proposition. . . . if one must choose among several courses of action in the light of experimental evidence, it is not meaningful, in terms of objective probability, to compute which of these actions is most promising, that is, which has the highest expected income.[81] Holders of objectivistic views have, therefore, no recourse but to argue that it is not reasonable to assign probabilities to the truth of propositions or to calculate which of several actions is the most promising, and that the need expressed by the attempt to set up such concepts must be met in other ways, if at all.

Objectivistic Criteria

As noted in Section 3.8, the objectivist has, in some instances, tried to meet this need by proposing (what we have called) secondary criteria, primarily in the context of the statistical model. If such a criterion is thought satisfactory by a decision maker, then it seems that he is expressing

---

[81] *Author's note:* Or utility or relative value.

faith in a certain disposition about the world. In some cases this disposition or attitude may be interpreted in terms of subjective probability, whereas in other cases it cannot. For example, the Laplace criterion may be interpreted by stating that the individual considers every state of the world equally probable. If so, then for this special case, the Laplace criterion coincides with the primary criterion (maximization of expected relative value). On the other hand, the maximin utility criterion cannot be directly interpreted in terms of subjective probability, since different strategies focus on different states, the disposition being a hedge against the worst that can happen. However, after maximin has singled out a particular strategy that yields $\max_i \min_j \{V_{ij}\}$, it is theoretically possible to compute the set of all probability distributions over the states that also prescribe this same strategy under the primary criterion (assuming the relative values of the consequences have been measured on an interval scale, which will seldom be the case). The same thing may be done for any secondary criterion. In fact, if utilities are known precisely, then it is possible, although it may be extremely messy mathematically, to partition the necessarily nondenumerable set of all possible probability distributions over the states [i.e., all probability measures P that satisfy $P(E_j) \geq 0$, $\sum_{j=1}^{n} P(E_j) = 1$] in such a manner that each element of the partition prescribes one and only one strategy under the primary criterion.[82] (If this were done, one might wish to confront the decision maker with such partitions and have him decide which he feels to contain the "true" distribution.) With the addition of the complexity of a probability distribution for each of the strategies in the Model I or II formulation, similar ideas apply. The true objectivist will, of course, consider all this so much nonsense.

Even when experimental evidence, say e, of the type typically generated by statisticians is added to the picture, and the conditional probabilities $P(e \mid E_j)$ are computed (with a frequency interpretation), some particular disposition about the world may still be required if a unique strategy is to be prescribed. The typical formulation that applies here is statistical decision theory as presented by Wald (1950), who was primarily an objectivist and popularized the minimax rule.[83] Some persons who interpret the

---

[82] Probability distributions which render several strategies equal to the maximum expected relative value may be arbitrarily assigned to any one of these strategies.

[83] Although Wald's minimax rule applies to negative income (or negative utility or negative relative value), or correspondingly to the maximin of income (or utility), Savage (Chapter 9) has pointed out that in the form which Wald considered negative income, his minimax criterion is equivalent to the criterion of minimizing maximum loss, where, for a pure strategy S_i, the loss due to adopting S_i when E_j obtains is defined by $L_{ij} = \max_k V_{kj} - V_{ij}$. The typical objectivist formulation is not restricted

$P(e \mid E_j)$ under a frequency view, use instead of the minimax loss or other principle, subjective probability as it applies to *a priori* probabilities, say the $P(E_j)$. Others, who regard subjective probability like the plague and do not feel particularly inclined to commit themselves to a minimax or similar disposition, maintain that it is the statistician's job only to identify the set of what they call "admissible decision rules"[84] and not to identify one particular decision rule as the "best." With respect to individual decisions, Savage is "wholly" subjective, but he does consider an interesting application of minimax (loss) in group decision situations. For further rather cogent comments along these lines, including some notes on game theory, consult Savage (1954, particularly Chapters 6 through 11 and Chapter 13).

Traditional Decision Theory

The use of probability in what we have called traditional decision theory (after Churchman) seems mostly to center around a frequency interpretation. For example, it is clear that the typical methods and applications in operations research have been heavily influenced by the objectivistic (frequency) views of what Savage calls the British-American School of statisticians. The effect of this is readily apparent in the literature of operations research, particularly in discussions of applications of operations-research-type methods in relation to the operations-research-type models of inventory and production processes, replacement processes, service systems, etc. The popular subjects of queuing theory, Markov processes, and stochastic processes in general are, of course, probability theory and may be interpreted either from an objectivistic

---

to just pure strategies but generally considers mixed strategies of the form $(C_1 S_1, C_2 S_2, \ldots, C_t S_t)$, where $C_i \geqslant 0$ and $\sum C_i = 1$. If the "best" admissible strategy by the *minimax loss criterion* is a mixed strategy, then a pure strategy is chosen from this by using a random device which allots probabilities to the pure strategies in the "best" admissible strategy according to the C_i in this "best" strategy. In this form an *admissible strategy* is one which is not strictly dominated by any other strategy (mixed or pure) under the hypothesis of complete ignorance of the $P(E_j)$. These ideas form what Savage calls the *minimax theory* (p. 165). (We agree with him that, under an objectivistic view of probability, this is a more reasonable way of prescribing a strategy than by using the ultrapessimistic minimax negative utility criterion when used other than in the way in which Wald intended it to be used). Further sophistication is obtained when observational evidence has been accumulated and entered into the formulation.

[84] In the sense used here, a decision rule prescribes a terminal act to each possible result of experimentation, or else an objectively interpreted probability distribution over the set of terminal acts to each possible result of experimentation.

or subjectivistic position. But as applied in the processes just noted, the interpretation is usually objectivistic.

It might be recalled that any objectivistic criterion, such as maximization of expected profit, minimization of expected loss, or maximization of expected utility (with a frequency interpretation of probability), is meaningless if applied to a single decision. Nevertheless such criteria are applied to single decisions with the "justification" given that this will yield the best long-run results when applied over and over again to decisions of a repetitive nature. Sometimes it appears that this "justification" is based upon the weak law (and/or strong law) of large numbers. But for repetitive processes, the subjectivist has as much right as the objectivist to hide behind the skirts of these laws of large numbers, for they are, in fact, mathematical results arising in the deductive logic of probability theory, the same probability theory subscribed to by subjectivists as well as objectivists. Actually, as pointed out in Section 5.4, for neither viewpoint does the use of these "laws" (i.e., theorems) constitute valid justification. This sometimes drives the objectivist to justify on the basic of experience ("it works"), but if one takes Hume seriously, these arguments lead up a blind alley.[85]

We feel that this "restriction" to frequency views on the part of many operations researchers, management scientists, and similar types has impeded the progress of the development of these subjects in handling other than deterministic (nonprobabilistic) and repetitive-type probabilistic decision processes. It would, of course, be unfair not to mention that subjective probability has been used in these areas, and that there seems to be a growing awareness that this, along with the notion of utility or relative value, has great potential in dealing with problems that elude the traditional theory. For example, an intuitive conception of subjective probability has received notable attention in connection with certain scheduling procedures, such as PERT and critical path. It appears that some persons regard the use of subjective probability in these procedures as an unfortunate substitute for "objective" probability, but this misses the point. For in most applications to which PERT and critical-path techniques have been applied, there is no relevant objectivistic interpretation of probability. We also hold the opinion that some operations-research and management-science practitioners who deal with probabilistic formulations and give these (perhaps implicitly) a frequency interpretation sometimes do this in contexts where such an interpretation is entirely inapplicable.

---

[85] For additional questions raised in connection with "what is best in the long run," see Churchman (1961*a*, Chapter 5).

5.8 COMPARATIVE MEASURES OF SUBJECTIVE PROBABILITY

The Statistical Model

For simplicity, we begin with the statistical formulation with the world partitioned into states E_j, $j = 1, \ldots, n$. Our concern is with a binary relation $\geqslant$ (read "is not less probable than") applied to states or subsets of states. The following axiom "generates" a simple ranking of the $P(E_j)$:

Ordering Axiom $\geqslant$ is a weak ordering of the states.

The resulting ordering of the E_j will be denoted, by subscript convention, as

$$E_1 \geqslant E_2 \geqslant E_3 \geqslant \ldots \geqslant E_n \geqslant \emptyset,^{86} \qquad (5.11)$$

with the corresponding simple ordering of probabilities of states,

$$P(E_1) \geqslant P(E_2) \geqslant \ldots \geqslant P(E_n) \geqslant 0, \qquad \sum_{j=1}^{n} P(E_j) = 1. \qquad (5.12a)$$

If (5.11) is generated by an intuitive method, methods similar to those in Section 4.2 for obtaining an ordinal ranking of relative values may be used. In the decision-oriented approach, we use hypothetical acts, say $\mathbf{h}_1$ and $\mathbf{h}_2$, to obtain pairwise comparisons. For comparing E_j and E_k, let $h_1(E_j) = g$, $h_1(E_i) = g'$, for $i \neq j$, and $h_2(E_k) = g$, $h_2(E_i) = g'$, for $i \neq k$, where g and g' are two hypothetical consequences for which $g > g'$ (strict preference).[87] Here we assume that for all pairs g, g' with $g > g'$, either $\mathbf{h}_1 \geqslant \mathbf{h}_2$ or $\mathbf{h}_2 \geqslant \mathbf{h}_1$, and define $E_j \geqslant E_k$ if and only if $\mathbf{h}_1 \geqslant \mathbf{h}_2$ and $E_k \geqslant E_j$ if and only if $\mathbf{h}_2 \geqslant \mathbf{h}_1$. The reader may readily rewrite Savage's first four postulates to apply to this case (considering only states). For practical use, this may be shortened by supposing, e.g., that g and g' are two monetary prizes, say \$10,000 and \$1.

Although we shall not consider partial orderings of the $P(E_j)$, the discussion presented in Section 6.3 should enable the reader to formulate an analysis for dominance with such an ordering. The two extremes of a partial ordering of the $P(E_j)$ will, of course, be the null ordering with no comparisons between the $P(E_j)$ and the simple ordering (or connected partial ordering) given by (5.12a).

Other comparisons among the E_j may be obtained by considering

---

[86] $\emptyset$ is the null event whose occurrence is logically impossible. The obvious assumption applies.

[87] Note that it may be considered preferable to use $h_1(E_j) = g$, $h_1(E_k) = g'$, $h_1(E_i) = g''$ for $i \neq j, k$, and $h_2(E_j) = g'$, $h_2(E_k) = g$, $h_2(E_i) = g''$ for $i \neq j, k$, where $g > g'$ and g'' is any other consequence. This is more in line with Savage's "sure-thing principle."

sets of states or events.   With n states there are 2^n events (including the null event and set of all n states), so if n is large, it is doubtful that one would attempt a weak ordering of all events.   If, however, n were, say, equal to 3, then the eight events

$$B_1 = \emptyset, \qquad B_5 = \{E_1, E_2\},^{[88]}$$
$$B_2 = \{E_1\}, \qquad B_6 = \{E_1, E_3\},$$
$$B_3 = \{E_2\}, \qquad B_7 = \{E_2, E_3\},$$
$$B_4 = \{E_3\}, \qquad B_8 = \{E_1, E_2, E_3\},$$

might be weakly ordered.   By using pairwise comparisons, suppose it were found that $B_3 \geqslant B_4$ and $B_2 \geqslant B_7$.   We then get

$$B_8 \geqslant B_5 \geqslant B_6 \geqslant B_2 \geqslant B_7 \geqslant B_3 \geqslant B_4 \geqslant B_1$$

or

$$1 \geqslant P_1 + P_2 \geqslant P_1 + P_3 \geqslant P_1 \geqslant P_2 + P_3 \geqslant P_2 \geqslant P_3 \geqslant 0,$$

which is completely summarized by $P_2 \geqslant P_3$ and $P_1 \geqslant P_2 + P_3$, and $P_j \geqslant 0$, $\sum P_j = 1$.

When a complete ordering of events is not obtained, but only a partial ordering, the resulting comparisons may still be very useful.   Suppose, for example, that the ordinal ranking of states

$$P_1 \geqslant P_2 \geqslant \ldots \geqslant P_n \geqslant 0, \qquad \sum P_j = 1 \qquad (5.12b)$$

has been obtained.   To obtain sharper inequalities on the state probabilities, we may compare $\{E_1\}$ with $\{E_2, E_3\}$, $\{E_2, E_3, E_4\}$, ..., until we find a j such that

$$\{E_2, E_3, \ldots, E_j, E_{j+1}\} \geqslant \{E_1\} \geqslant \{E_2, E_3, \ldots, E_j\}$$

or until we find

$$\{E_1\} \geqslant \{E_2, E_3, \ldots, E_n\}.$$

An identical procedure would then be used for comparing $\{E_2\}$ against $\{E_3, E_4\}$, $\{E_3, E_4, E_5\}$, ..., then comparing $\{E_3\}$ against $\{E_4, E_5\}$, $\{E_4, E_5, E_6\}$, ..., and so forth.   The result, for $n = 6$, might be

$$\{E_2, E_3\} \geqslant \{E_1\} \geqslant \{E_2\},$$
$$\{E_2\} \geqslant \{E_3, E_4, E_5, E_6\},$$
$$\{E_4, E_5, E_6\} \geqslant \{E_3\} \geqslant \{E_4, E_5\},$$
$$\{E_4\} \geqslant \{E_5, E_6\},$$
$$\{E_5\} \geqslant \{E_6\},$$
$$\{E_6\} \geqslant \emptyset,$$

[88] B_5 is the event consisting of the states E_1 and E_2. $P(B_5)$ is the probability that either E_1 or E_2 will obtain, i.e., $P(B_5) = P(E_1 \cup E_2) = P(E_1) + P(E_2)$ since the states are mutually exclusive.

which yields the *set of inequalities* for the state probabilities

$$P_2 + P_3 \geqslant P_1 \geqslant P_2,$$
$$P_2 \geqslant P_3 + P_4 + P_5 + P_6,$$
$$P_4 + P_5 + P_6 \geqslant P_3 \geqslant P_4 + P_5 \qquad (5.13)$$
$$P_4 \geqslant P_5 + P_6,$$
$$P_5 \geqslant P_6,$$
$$P_6 \geqslant 0.$$

Later, in Sections 10.11 and 11.8, we shall consider similar sets of inequalities on relative values, but this can be done only under the assumption of additivity or valuewise independence among variables, to be explicated in Chapter 9. The idea for something similar to (5.13) stems from Churchman and Ackoff (1954), where they employed this notion in connection with relative values under additivity. Sets of inequalities like (5.13) will be analyzed in Section 6.6 in the context of the decision model. Exercise 7 at the end of this chapter presents a method for obtaining point estimates of the P_j from a set of inequalities like (5.13).

One thing to note about (5.13) is that, by the manner in which it was derived, if all greater-than-or-equal-to signs are replaced by strict inequality ($>$), it is impossible for (5.13) to be self-contradictory. That is, (5.13) is "strictly" consistent, for if $\geqslant$ is replaced by $>$, it is impossible to demonstrate that $P_j > P_j$ for any j from 1 to n.

Naturally, one may obtain sets of inequalities in slightly different fashion from the way (5.13) was obtained. If we hold to the principle of comparing $\{E_j\}$ with events containing states E_k, with $k > j$, other procedures may give weaker or stronger sets of inequalities. Weaker inequalities, such as $P_2 + P_3 + P_4 \geqslant P_1 \geqslant P_2$, would result when the decision maker does not feel sure enough of his judgments to say either $\{E_2, E_3\} \geqslant \{E_1\}$ or $\{E_1\} \geqslant \{E_2, E_3\}$. Stronger inequalities can result if the decision maker feels willing and able to render finer judgments than those required for (5.13). Given $\{E_2, E_3\} \geqslant \{E_1\} \geqslant \{E_2\}$, since we know that $\{E_2, E_3\} \geqslant \{E_2, E_4\} \geqslant \{E_2\}$, compare $\{E_1\}$ with $\{E_2, E_4\}$. Suppose $\{E_1\} \geqslant \{E_2, E_4\}$. Then compare $\{E_1\}$ with $\{E_2, E_4, E_5\}$. Suppose $\{E_2, E_4, E_5\} \geqslant \{E_1\}$. Then compare $\{E_2, E_4, E_5\}$ with $\{E_2, E_3\}$, and suppose that $\{E_2, E_3\} \geqslant \{E_2, E_4, E_5\}$. At this point we have that $\{E_2, E_4, E_5\} \geqslant \{E_1\} \geqslant \{E_2, E_4\}$. One may continue in this fashion, not only for $\{E_1\}$ versus other events but also for $\{E_2\}$ versus events containing states E_k, with $k > 2$, and so forth.

In any event it should be noted that, with our measurements of probabilities and values carried to a certain point, it may be possible to conclude that one strategy dominates all others. If so, there is no reason to carry the program of measurement any further.

Models I and II

Consider now the formulation for Model I or Model II. For generality, let e_{ij} denote the applicable one of the following three events or propositions

1. If S_i is adopted, o_j will result (Model I);
2. If A_i is adopted, O_j will result (Model I, $\mathbf{S} = \mathbf{A}$);
3. If S_i is adopted, O_j will result (Model II).

Without attempting to do this complete justice, it may be understood that each e_{ij} is an event if viewed from the statistical model to which the model form under consideration may be transformed. Furthermore, each set $\{e_{ij}\}$ for fixed i and $j = 1, \ldots, r$ is a partition of the states of a corresponding (but perhaps not completely explicit) world. Whether we view the e_{ij} in this way or as in Section 3.1,

$$\sum_{j=1}^{r} P(e_{ij}) = 1, \qquad i = 1, \ldots, t. \tag{5.14}$$

Obviously (5.14) is the same as (5.2) under Model I. In general, we shall abbreviate further:

$$P_{ij} = P(e_{ij}), \qquad i = 1, \ldots, t; j = 1, \ldots, r.$$

For Model I, r is the number of consequences, and for Model I ($\mathbf{S} = \mathbf{A}$) or Model II, r is the number of outcomes. For the three models, P_{ij} may also be written $P(o_j \mid S_i)$, $P(O_j \mid A_i)$, and $P(O_j \mid S_i)$ respectively.

For fixed i, we may attempt to generate a weak ordering of events e_{ij} of the form

$$e_{ij_1} \geqslant e_{ij_2} \geqslant \ldots \geqslant e_{ij_r} \geqslant \emptyset, \tag{5.15}$$

where $j_1, j_2, \ldots, j_r$ is a permutation of the integers $1, 2, \ldots, r$. This gives

$$P_{ij_1} \geqslant P_{ij_2} \geqslant \ldots \geqslant P_{ij_r} \geqslant 0, \qquad \sum_{k=1}^{r} P_{ij_k} = 1. \tag{5.16}$$

The rankings (5.16) for $i = 1, \ldots, t$ separate or together give, when viewed from the statistical framework, a partial ordering of events. If desirable, it is, of course, possible to attempt to generate sets of inequalities on the P_{ij} for fixed i in the fashion of (5.13).

We may also, beginning perhaps with (5.16) for several i, attempt to merge or interweave these ordinal rankings. We shall call such a ranking a mixed ordinal ranking or an interrow, intercolumn ordinal ranking. When viewed from the statistical framework, this is a partial ordering of events. For example, suppose we consider the e_{ij} for $i = 1, 2$ and obtain, say,

$$e_{i_1 j_1} \geqslant e_{i_2 j_2} \geqslant \ldots \geqslant e_{i_{2r} j_{2r}} \geqslant \emptyset,$$

or

$$P_{i_1 j_1} \geqslant P_{i_2 j_2} \geqslant \ldots \geqslant P_{i_{2r} j_{2r}} \geqslant 0, \qquad \sum_{k=1}^{2r} P_{i_k j_k} = 2, \qquad (5.17)$$

where $i_1 j_1, i_2 j_2, \ldots, i_{2r} j_{2r}$ is a permutation of $11, 12, \ldots, 1r, 21, 22, \ldots, 2r$. A caution is in order here. If $\geqslant$ in (5.17) is replaced by $>$, (5.17) may contain a contradiction. If so, this "implies" that several P_{ij} for $i = 1, 2$ are equal, and it seems advisable to check whether this is actually the case. To illustrate for $r = 3$, suppose

$$P_{11} \geqslant P_{12} \geqslant P_{23} \geqslant P_{22} \geqslant P_{13} \geqslant P_{21} \geqslant 0,$$

$$\sum_{j=1}^{3} P_{1j} = \sum_{j=1}^{3} P_{2j} = 1.$$

Noting that this says $P_{11} \geqslant P_{23}$, $P_{12} \geqslant P_{22}$, $P_{13} \geqslant P_{21}$, etc., the only way to have $\sum P_{1j} = \sum P_{2j}$ is to have $P_{11} = P_{12} = P_{23} = P_{22}$ and $P_{13} = P_{21}$.

Beginning with a "mixed" ranking such as (5.17), it is possible to attempt to generate finer inequalities on the P_{ij} involved.

Instead of starting with intrarow rankings of the form (5.15) for the event or proposition matrix

(Consequences or Outcomes)

	o_1	o_2	$\ldots$	o_r
S_1	e_{11}	e_{12}	$\ldots$	e_{1r}
S_2	e_{21}	e_{22}	$\ldots$	e_{2r}
$\vdots$	$\vdots$	$\vdots$		$\vdots$
S_t	e_{t1}	e_{t2}	$\ldots$	e_{tr}

one might wish to start with intracolumn rankings of the form

$$e_{i_1 j} \geqslant e_{i_2 j} \geqslant e_{i_3 j} \geqslant \ldots \geqslant e_{i_t j} \geqslant \emptyset, \qquad j = 1, \ldots, r, \qquad (5.18)$$

where $i_1, i_2, \ldots, i_t$ is a permutation of $1, 2, \ldots, t$. For (5.18) the sum $\sum_i P_{ij}$ will probably not equal 1.

The simplest intrarow ranking to be considered (in Section 6.5) uses just two S_i, say S_1 and S_2, and for each j specifies whether $e_{1j} \geqslant e_{2j}$ or $e_{2j} \geqslant e_{1j}$.

We will reserve critical comments on the judgments required to generate comparative measures of probability until the final section of this chapter.

5.9 INTERVAL MEASURES OF SUBJECTIVE PROBABILITY

By an interval measure in general we mean a measure which bounds each P_j (for the statistical model) or P_{ij} (in the other models) in an interval contained in $[0, 1]$. In the following discussion let B_j, $j = 1, \ldots, r$, denote a partition of the states of the world with the interpretation that (1) in the statistical model the B_j may quite likely correspond one-to-one with the $\{E_j\}$ and (2) in Model I or Model II the B_j correspond one-to-one with the e_{ij} for a fixed i.

Letting

$$P_j = P(B_j),$$

with

$$\sum_{j=1}^{r} P_j = 1, \tag{5.19}$$

a bounded interval measure of the P_j will, in general, take the form

$$\alpha_j \leqslant P_j \leqslant \beta_j, \qquad j = 1, \ldots, r, \tag{5.20}$$

with $[\alpha_j, \beta_j] \subset [0, 1]$, i.e., $0 \leqslant \alpha_j \leqslant \beta_j \leqslant 1$, and

$$\sum_{j=1}^{r} \alpha_j \leqslant 1 \leqslant \sum_{j=1}^{r} \beta_j. \tag{5.21}$$

The restriction imposed by (5.21) follows directly from (5.19) and (5.20). If $\alpha_j = \beta_j$, then we have an exact value for P_j. Another way of writing (5.20) is

$$\alpha_j \leqslant P_j \leqslant \alpha_j + \epsilon_j,$$

where $\epsilon_j = \beta_j - \alpha_j$ and represents some form of "measure of uncertainty" on the individual's part in trying to pin down P_j. In later work in connection with Model I or Model II, we shall also write

$$\alpha_{ij} \leqslant P_{ij} \leqslant \alpha_{ij} + \epsilon_{ij}, \qquad j = 1, \ldots, r,$$

$$\sum_{j=1}^{r} \alpha_{ij} \leqslant 1 \leqslant \sum_{j=1}^{r} \alpha_{ij} + \sum_{j=1}^{r} \epsilon_{ij},$$

where $P_{ij} = P(e_{ij})$, as in the previous section.

An obvious method for getting bounds on P_j is simply to ask the individual to state bounds that apply, i.e., to quote numbers α_j and β_j which to him will surely bound P_j. If he is at a total loss, $\alpha_j = 0$, $\beta_j = 1$ will always do, but will not serve to yield new information. This method of attack has the familiar ring of the intuitive approach.

We personally prefer (for reasons to be clarified in the next section) a decision-oriented approach following the line of Schlaifer's (1959) method discussed toward the end of Section 5.6. We shall let the standard lottery consist of 100 possibilities each considered (we hope) equally probable by the individual. The basic "act" in the lottery may consist of drawing one ball out of an urn of well-mixed balls numbered 1 to 100; or of rolling two ten-sided dice each with sides marked 0 to 9, the red die yielding the first digit of a two-digit number from 00 to 99, and the white die yielding the second digit;[89] and so forth. (If 1,000 possibilities are used in the lottery, add a blue die.) In the standard lottery we imagine an event $C_n = $ "one of $n \leqslant 100$ specified balls is drawn," or $C_n = $ "one of n specified numbers between 00 and 99 is rolled by the dice."[90]. To add flavor to this second way of viewing the lottery (i.e., with dice), suppose that the n numbers between 00 and 99 (if $n < 100$) are established (after n has been specified by the individual) by rolling a second pair of dice until they have given n distinct numbers. In other words, to insure more fully a notion of equally possible alternatives, the lottery is carried through in two stages: Suppose $n = 12$; then roll one pair of dice (12 or more times) until 12 distinct numbers from 00 to 99 have been generated; then roll a second pair of dice once. If the result of this last roll yields one of the 12 numbers generated by the first stage, the event C_{12} occurs. If not, then $\sim C_{12}$ occurs.

Since we are interested in B_j, we imagine the other situation to be characterized by the occurrence of either B_j or $\sim B_j$, and associate a hypothetical consequence h_1 to B_j and h_2 to $\sim B_j$, with $h_1 > h_2$. Similarly, associate h_1 with C_n and h_2 and $\sim C_n$.

Now for the standard lottery we are not going to request a value of n that makes the individual indifferent to choosing between the standard lottery and the B_j situation, but rather attempt to find two values of n, say n_1 and n_2, $n_1 \leqslant n_2$, so that:

1. For all $n \leqslant n_1$, the individual prefers the B_j situation over the standard lottery with C_n;

2. For all $n \geqslant n_2$, the individual prefers the standard lottery over the B_j situation.

In other words, for $n \leqslant n_1$, the person would rather take his chances on getting the more preferred consequence by "playing the B_j situation" than by "playing the standard lottery," the reverse being true for $n \geqslant n_2$. The bounds on $P(B_j)$ are then taken as

$$\frac{n_1}{100} \leqslant P(B_j) \leqslant \frac{n_2}{100}.$$

[89] Some readers will be aware that well-machined dice of this nature are available. They are sometimes used to generate random numbers in pencil-and-paper Monte Carlo simulation runs.

[90] C_n as used here should not be confused with C_t as used in Chapter 3.

It is, of course, desired that n_1 and n_2 be as close together as the individual can make them, but he should be allowed complete freedom in setting these bounds.

Having obtained the bounds on the P_j as given in (5.20), assuming that (5.21) is satisfied, it may be possible to refine these slightly as follows. Let $c = 1 - \sum \alpha_j \geq 0$. Then if $\epsilon_j = \beta_j - \alpha_j > c$ for any j from 1 to r, replace β_j by $\beta_j' = \alpha_j + c$. In other words, if $\sum_{j \neq k} \alpha_j + \beta_k > 1$, replace β_k with $\beta_k' = 1 - \sum_{j \neq k} \alpha_j$. Similarly, if $\alpha_k + \sum_{j \neq k} \beta_j < 1$, replace α_k with $\alpha_k' = 1 - \sum_{j \neq k} \beta_j$. The justification of these procedures follows from the fact that $\sum P_j = 1$. To illustrate, suppose for $r = 4$, initial bounds are given by

$$.06 \leq P_1 \leq .20, \quad .16 \leq P_2 \leq .27, \quad .25 \leq P_3 \leq .40, \quad .05 \leq P_4 \leq .25.$$

Since $\beta_1 + \beta_2 + \beta_3 + \alpha_4 = .92$, we may increase α_4 from .05 to .13. Similarly, since $\alpha_1 + \beta_2 + \beta_3 + \beta_4 = .98$, we may increase α_1 from .06 to .08. Point estimates of the P_j may, of course, be obtained from the bounded interval measure.[91]

5.10 COMMENTS ON MEASUREMENT OF SUBJECTIVE PROBABILITY

To conclude this chapter, we offer some further notes on the measurement of subjective probability. Since many criticisms that could be leveled at our measurement procedures are very similar to those discussed in Sections 4.3 and 4.6 in connection with measuring relative values, we shall be brief.

First, we feel that every judgment concerning probabilities (or hypothetical decision situations or relative values) is unique. If, for example, the individual provides a measure of the P_j or P_{ij} at two different times (and under different conditions) prior to implementation of a strategy, we would not be surprised to find the two incompatible. One obvious reason for this is that between the two times or intervals during which judgments are made, the individual acquires new experience (or information, data, etc.).[92] Other reasons might include: (1) The individual is lying; (2) he does not consider it worth his time to be careful in his judgments; (3) he is careful but is vague about his true preferences; (4) his value system has changed; (5) he is erratic and inconsistent, etc. As with relative values, it seems most reasonable to measure probabilities close to the time at which the decision is to be made, leaving enough time, if possible, for appropriate cogitation and reflection during the measuring process.

[91] See the exercises at the end of the chapter.

[92] The two sets of judgments may, of course, be referred to as *a priori* and *a posteriori*.

Our main reason for preferring the decision-oriented approach of measuring probabilities as opposed to the intuitive approach is that the former attempts to abstract the states or events from the real situation and make measurements of these apart from that situation so that undesirable effects that may arise from associating the events with the actual consequences might be minimized. Under an intuitive approach, where no attempt is made at this dissociation, one might expect an optimistic type to "overjudge" probabilities associated with the more desirable consequences and "underjudge" probabilities associated with less desirable consequences, and vice versa for a pessimistic type. We do not feel that, in practice, a decision-oriented method can completely do away with this association, but at least it tries. In Savage's words (p. 68):

> ...I think it clear from the formal definition of qualitative probability that the particular personalistic view sponsored here does not leave room for optimism and pessimism, however these traits be interpreted, to play any role in the person's judgment of probabilities.

For situations that are "naturals" for the statistical formulation (which is what Savage considers for the most part), it is easier to accomplish this dissociation than in the situations better suited for the basic decision model. For example, in the egg case of Section 3.6, we could add a whole string of additional acts whose consequences for the states "good" and "bad" were, say, monetary prizes, and in measuring the probabilities of the states, we could use these additional acts along with the three given. The idea of "put your money where your mouth is" seems harder to accomplish in the basic model. If it seems ridiculous to pose completely hypothetical consequences for the events "o_j if S_i," then it may be possible to use the actual consequences in **Q**, modified in an appropriate fashion. For example, the actual $o_j \in \mathbf{Q}$ could be modified by augmenting them with imaginary prizes, such as amounts of money (positive or negative), to yield such pseudohypothetical consequences as "o_j and \$100,000 in addition," "o_j and a \$5,000 penalty," "o_j and the original Mona Lisa," "o_j and a two-week-all-expenses-paid vacation to the French Riviera," "o_j and three years in jail," etc. For one who holds to the intuitive thesis expressed by Koopman (1940), this may seem a bit silly.

Another difficulty in situations of larger scope is the familiar specter of having, say, several thousand or several billion probabilities to estimate, where each proposition for consideration is a vector composite of a number of subpropositions. This will often happen where the decision situation is a sequential one with a number of stages or where the number of action variables and outcome variables is large. Obviously it would be absurd to use methods discussed thus far for analyzing the decision model under such circumstances. If the decision maker can narrow things down, then one might be in good shape, but this will often lose too much of the real situation. As was mentioned before, magnitude and complexity will be considered further in the latter part of the book under the assumption of independence of variables in the relative value sense. It will be noted that, along with the simplicity obtained for measuring values, there will be a corresponding reduction in the problem of size in connection with measuring probabilities.

EXERCISES

1. Show that the relative frequency of 1's (or 0's) in the example of a divergent sequence of relative frequencies in footnote 27 in Section 5.4 (where 2^n 1's were followed by 2^{n+1} 0's, etc.) oscillates between $1/3$ and $2/3$; that is show that no point outside $[1/3, 2/3]$ is a limit point and every point contained in $[1/3, 2/3]$ is a limit point.

2. Given the following regular sequence with pattern 10110,

$$10110101101011010110 \ldots \quad (ad\ infinitum),$$

what is the probability of a 1 in this sequence according to (*a*) von Mises, (*b*) Reichenbach?

3. Interpret the statement "the probability of rolling a seven with this pair of dice is greater than the probability of rolling an eleven," and what variations of it you may wish to consider, under (*a*) a classical view, (*b*) a frequency view, (*c*) a logical view, and (*d*) a subjective view.

4. In your own words, state why the author feels the only relevant interpretation for probability is a subjectivistic conception. If you disagree with his position, state why.

5. Rewrite Savage's first four postulates, your sole purpose being to generate a weak ordering of states (not events in general) as given by (5.11).

6. If you had to make point estimates of the P_j, given only the ranking (5.12*b*), what method would you use? State, in as few words as possible, why you think this is a "reasonable" method.

7. The author suggests the following procedure for obtaining point estimates of the P_j from a ranking such as (5.13). First, for every double inequality of the form

$$P_{j+1} + P_{j+2} + \ldots + P_{j+\alpha+1} \geqslant P_j \geqslant P_{j+1} + P_{j+2} + \ldots + P_{j+\alpha},$$

set

$$P_j = P_{j+1} + P_{j+2} + \ldots + P_{j+\alpha} + \tfrac{1}{2}P_{j+\alpha+1}. \qquad (E1)$$

Then, for every single inequality of the form

$$P_k \geqslant P_{k+1} + \ldots + P_n,$$

write

$$P_k - (P_{k+1} + \ldots + P_n) = \lambda, \qquad (E2)$$

where $\lambda > 0$. Also write $P_n = \lambda$ or $P_n - 0 = \lambda$ from $P_n \geqslant 0$. If there is one or more of the P_j on the left-hand side of (E1) appearing in (E2), substitute the right-hand side of (E1) for this P_j into (E2), and do this until (E2) contains no P_j that appears on the left-hand side of (E1).

For the P_k that now appear in (E2), solve each of these in terms of λ, beginning with $P_n = \lambda$ and working back through the P_k by decreasing subscript. Then use these λ solutions and (E1) to write each P_j on the left-hand side of (E1) in terms of λ.

At this point each P_j equals a constant times λ, say $P_j = a_j\lambda$, $j = 1, \ldots, n$. To get the point estimates for the P_j, normalize these, i.e., set $P_j = a_j/\sum a_j$.

By using this method for (5.13), show that $\lambda = 4/183$ with the point estimates for the six P_j given by

$$183(P_1, P_2, \ldots, P_6) = (71, 58, 26, 16, 8, 4),$$

and note how these satisfy the inequalities of (5.13).

8. Use the method of the previous exercise to obtain point estimates of the P_j, given

$$P_2 + P_3 + P_4 \geqslant P_1 \geqslant P_2 + P_3,$$
$$P_3 + P_4 \geqslant P_2 \geqslant P_3,$$
$$P_3 \geqslant P_4 + P_5 + P_6 + P_7 + P_8,$$
$$P_4 \geqslant P_5 + P_6 + P_7 + P_8,$$
$$P_6 + P_7 + P_8 \geqslant P_5 \geqslant P_6 + P_7,$$
$$P_7 + P_8 \geqslant P_6 \geqslant P_7,$$
$$P_7 \geqslant P_8,$$
$$P_8 \geqslant 0.$$

9. Comment on the method of Exercise 7. Can you suggest another procedure for estimating the P_j in such a case? If so, what is it? Which method do you feel is "better" if you have any such feelings, and why?

10. Consider two strategies, say S_1 and S_2, under Model I, and the probabilities P_{ij}, $i = 1, 2$; $j = 1, \ldots, r$. For each of the following mixed ordinal rankings of the form of (5.17), state what must be true of the P_{ij} in order for it to be valid:

(a) $r = 3$: $P_{11} \geqslant P_{21} \geqslant P_{12} \geqslant P_{23} \geqslant P_{13} \geqslant P_{22} \geqslant 0$;

(b) $r = 4$: $P_{21} \geqslant P_{22} \geqslant P_{11} \geqslant P_{23} \geqslant P_{12} \geqslant P_{14} \geqslant P_{24} \geqslant P_{13} \geqslant 0$;

(c) $r = 5$: $P_{11} \geqslant P_{21} \geqslant P_{12} \geqslant P_{13} \geqslant P_{22} \geqslant P_{14} \geqslant P_{23} \geqslant P_{15}$
$$\geqslant P_{24} \geqslant P_{25} \geqslant 0.$$

11. For a mixed ordinal ranking such as (5.17) with two S_i, state a simple theorem giving necessary and sufficient conditions for the corresponding strict ranking (obtained by replacing $\geqslant$ with $>$) to be valid, that is, to be consistent with $\sum P_{1j} = \sum P_{2j} = 1$.

12. With the use of the method at the end of Section 5.9, refine the bounds on the following interval measures wherever possible.

(a) $.16 \leqslant P_1 \leqslant .40$, $.20 \leqslant P_2 \leqslant .35$, $.08 \leqslant P_3 \leqslant .20$, $.24 \leqslant P_4 \leqslant .42$;

(b) $.11 \leqslant P_1 \leqslant .20$, $.29 \leqslant P_2 \leqslant .50$, $.21 \leqslant P_3 \leqslant .48$, $.34 \leqslant P_4 \leqslant .64$;

(c) $.20 \leqslant P_1 \leqslant .32$, $.12 \leqslant P_2 \leqslant .16$, $.18 \leqslant P_3 \leqslant .26$, $.24 \leqslant P_4 \leqslant .34$.

13. For a bounded interval measure of probability $\alpha_j \leqslant P_j \leqslant \beta_j$, with $\sum_{j=1}^r \alpha_j \leqslant 1 \leqslant \sum_{j=1}^r \beta_j$ and $\sum P_j = 1$, prove the theorem: If for some α_k, $\alpha_k + \sum_{j \neq k} \beta_j < 1$, then there exists no $h \neq k$ such that $\beta_h + \sum_{j \neq h} \alpha_j > 1$.

14. From what you have observed in the last exercise, give an example where the initial bounds on the P_j may be sharpened by increasing one of the α's and decreasing one of the β's.

15. Given the bounded interval measure $\alpha_j \leqslant P_j \leqslant \beta_j$, $j = 1, \ldots, r$, satisfying (5.21), present a method for obtaining point estimates of the P_j from the data. Letting P_j' denote the estimate of P_j, you must ensure that $\sum_{j=1}^r P_j' = 1$ and $\alpha_j \leqslant P_j' \leqslant \beta_j$. You should be able to defend your procedure as "reasonable."

16. If your answer in the previous exercise differs from the estimate of P_j given by $\alpha_j + (1 - \sum \alpha_j)\epsilon_j / \sum \epsilon_j$, where $\epsilon_j = \beta_j - \alpha_j$, state which method you feel is more "reasonable," and try to defend your answer. Prove that these estimates satisfy (5.20).

17. By using the method of estimating the P_j given by the previous exercise, determine the point estimates of the P_j for $r = 6$, given

$$.02 \leqslant P_1 \leqslant .10, \qquad .08 \leqslant P_4 \leqslant .12,$$
$$.28 \leqslant P_2 \leqslant .35, \qquad .18 \leqslant P_5 \leqslant .26,$$
$$.11 \leqslant P_3 \leqslant .14, \qquad .20 \leqslant P_6 \leqslant .29.$$

REFERENCES

Ackoff, R. L., *The Design of Social Research*, University of Chicago Press, Chicago, 1953.

——, with J. S. Minas and S. K. Gupta, *Scientific Method: Optimizing Applied Research Decisions*, John Wiley and Sons, New York, 1962.

Ackoff, R. L., and L. Pritzker, "The Methodology of Survey Research," *International Journal of Opinion and Attitude Research*, 5, 313–334 (1951).

Anscombe, F. J., and R. J. Aumann, "A Definition of Subjective Probability," *The Annals of Mathematical Statistics*, 34, 199–205 (1963).

Bayes, T., *Facsimiles of Two Papers by Bayes* (ed. W. E. Deming), The Graduate School, The Department of Agriculture, Washington, D.C., 1940.

Broad, C. D., *The Philosophy of Francis Bacon*, Cambridge University Press, Cambridge, 1926.

Brownlee, K. A., *Statistical Theory and Methodology in Science and Engineering*, John Wiley and Sons, New York, 1960.

Carnap, R., *Logical Foundations of Probability*, University of Chicago Press, Chicago, 1950.

———, *The Continuum of Inductive Methods*, The University of Chicago Press, Chicago, 1952.

Churchman, C. W., *Theory of Experimental Inference*, Macmillan, New York, 1948.

———, *Prediction and Optimal Decision*, Prentice-Hall, Englewood Cliffs, N.J., 1961a.

———, and R. L. Ackoff, "An Approximate Measure of Value," *Journal of Operations Research*, **2**, 172–187 (1954).

———, and L. E. Arnoff, *Introduction to Operations Research*, John Wiley and Sons, New York, 1957.

Cochran, W. G., *Sampling Technics*, John Wiley and Sons, New York, 1953.

Copeland, A. H., "Postulates for the Theory of Probability," *American Journal of Mathematics*, **63**, 741–762 (1941).

Cramer, H., *Mathematical Methods of Statistics*, Princeton University Press, Princeton, N.J., 1954.

Davidson, D., P. Suppes, and S. Siegel, *Decision Making: An Experimental Approach*, Stanford University Press, Stanford, California, 1957.

de Finetti, B., "La prévision: ses lois logiques, ses sources subjectives," *Annales de l'Institut Henri Poincaré*, **7**, 1–68 (1937).

Deming, W. E., *Some Theory of Sampling*, John Wiley and Sons, New York, 1950.

———, *Sample Design in Business Research*, John Wiley and Sons, New York, 1960.

Doob, J. L., *Stochastic Processes*, John Wiley and Sons, New York, 1953.

Ellis, R. L., "On the Foundations of the Theory of Probabilities," *Trans. Cambridge Phil. Soc.*, **8**, 1–6 (1844, read in February, 1842, first appeared in 1843).

Feller, W., *An Introduction to Probability Theory and Its Applications*, 2nd edition, John Wiley and Sons, New York, 1957.

Fisher, R. A., "The Mathematical Foundations of Theoretical Statistics," *Philosophical Transactions of the Royal Society*, A, **222**, 306–368 (1922).

Galliher, H. P., "Simulation of Random Processes," in *Notes on Operations Research 1959*, The Technology Press, Massachusetts Institute of Technology, Cambridge, Massachusetts, 1959.

Good, I. J., *Probability and The Weighing of Evidence*, Charles Griffin and Company Ltd., London, 1950.

Halmos, P. R., *Measure Theory*, D. Van Nostrand Co., New York, 1950.

Hansen, M. H., W. N. Hurwitz, and W. G. Madow, *Sampling Survey Methods and Theory*, Vol. I, John Wiley and Sons, New York, 1953a.

———, *Sampling Survey Methods and Theory*, Vol. II, John Wiley and Sons, New York, 1953b.

Hume, D., *A Treatise of Human Nature*, J. M. Dent and Sons, London, 1911.

———, *An Inquiry Concerning Human Understanding*, Liberal Arts Press, New York, 1955.

Jeffreys, H., *Theory of Probability*, Clarendon Press, Oxford, 1939.

Katz, J. J., *The Problem of Induction and Its Solution*, University of Chicago Press, Chicago, 1962.

Kendall, M. G., *The Advanced Theory of Statistics*, Vol. I, Charles Griffin and Co., London, 1947.

Keynes, J. M., *A Treatise on Probability*, first edition, Macmillan and Co., New York, 1921; second edition, 1929; Torchbook Edition with Introduction by Norwood Russell Hanson, Harper and Row, New York, 1962.

Kolmogorov, A. N., *Grundbegriffe der Wahrscheinlichkeitsrechnung*, J. Springer, Berlin, 1933; *Foundations of the Theory of Probability* (translation, edited by Nathan Morrison), Chelsea, New York, 1950.

——, and S. V. Fomin, *Elements of the Theory of Functions and Functional Analysis*, *Vol. 2, Measure. The Lebesque Integral. Hilbert Space*, Graylock Press, Albany, N.Y., 1961.

Koopman, B. O., "The Axioms and Algebra of Intuitive Probability," *Annals of Mathematics*, Ser. 2, **42**, 269–292 (1940).

——, "Intuitive Probabilities and Sequences," *Annals of Mathematics*, Ser. 2, **42**, 169–187 (1941).

Laplace, P. S. de, *Essai philosophique sur les probabilités*, Paris, 1814; *A Philosophical Essay on Probabilities* (translation), Dover Publications, New York, 1951.

——, *Théorie analitique des probabilités*, Paris, 1812, and later editions; reprinted in Laplace's *Complete Works* (*Oeuvres complétes*), *Vol. VII*, Paris, 1947.

LeBlanc, H., *Statistical and Inductive Probabilities*, Prentice-Hall, Englewood Cliffs, N.J., 1962.

Lehmann, E. L., *Testing Statistical Hypotheses*, John Wiley and Sons, New York, 1959.

Loeve, M., *Probability Theory*, 2nd edition, D. Van Nostrand Co., Princeton, N.J., 1963.

Luce, R. D., and H. Raiffa, *Games and Decisions*, John Wiley and Sons, New York, 1957.

Meyer, H. A. (ed.), *Symposium on Monte Carlo Methods*, John Wiley and Sons, New York, 1954.

Morgenthaler, G. W., "The Theory and Application of Simulation in Operations Research," in *Progress in Operations Research, Vol. I*, edited by R. L. Ackoff, John Wiley and Sons, New York, 1961.

Nagel, E., "Principles of the Theory of Probability," *International Encyclopedia of Unified Science, Vol. I, No. 6*, University of Chicago Press, Chicago, 1939, 1962.

Popper, K., *Logik der Forschung*, Vienna, 1935.

Raiffa, H., and R. Schlaifer, *Applied Statistical Decision Theory*, Division of Research, Harvard Business School, Boston, 1961.

Ramsey, F. P., *The Foundations of Mathematics and Other Logical Essays*, Harcourt, Brace and Co., New York, 1931; The Humanities Press, New York, 1950.

RAND Corporation, *A Million Random Digits with 100,000 Normal Deviates*, The Free Press, Glencoe, Ill., 1955.

Reichenbach, H., *The Theory of Probability*, English translation by Ernest H. Hutton and Maria Reichenbach, 2nd edition, University of California Press, Berkeley and Los Angeles, 1949.

Rosenblatt, M., *Random Processes*, Oxford University Press, New York, 1962.

Russell, B., *The Problems of Philosophy*, Home University Library, London, 1912.

Savage, L. J., *The Foundations of Statistics*, John Wiley and Sons, New York, 1954.

Schlaifer, R., *Probability and Statistics for Business Decisions*, McGraw-Hill, New York, 1959.

Suppes, P., and M. Winet, "An Axiomatization of Utility Based on the Notion of Utility Differences," *Management Science*, **1**, 259–270 (1955).

Taylor, A. E., *Advanced Calculus*, Ginn and Company, New York, 1955.

Venn, J., *Logic of Chance*, First Edition, 1886; Fourth Edition, Chelsea, New York, 1962.

von Mises, R., *Probability, Statistics and Truth* (original German edition 1928, 2nd edition 1936), William Hodge and Co., London, 1939; 2nd revised English edition prepared by Hilda Geiringer, Macmillan, New York, 1957.

von Neumann, J., and O. Morgenstern, *Theory of Games and Economic Behavior*, second edition, Princeton University Press, Princeton, N.J., 1947.

Wadsworth, G. P., and J. G. Bryan, *Introduction to Probability and Random Variables*, McGraw-Hill, New York, 1960.

Wald, A., "Die Wiederspruchsfreiheit des Kollektivsbegriffes der Wahrscheinlichkeitsrechnung," *Ergebnisse eines mathem. Kolloquiums, No. 8.*

————, *Statistical Decision Functions*, John Wiley and Sons, New York, 1950.

Whitehead, A. N., *Science and the Modern World*, Cambridge University Press, Cambridge, 1927.

Wilks, S. S., *Mathematical Statistics*, John Wiley and Sons, New York, 1962.

Chapter 6

ANALYSIS FOR PURE DOMINANCE

With the measures of relative values and probabilities developed in the last two chapters, we now examine the conditions under which these measures will permit us to conclude that the difference of the expected relative values of two strategies is either nonpositive or nonnegative. For definiteness, let the strategies be S_1 and S_2 with expected relative values $E(S_1)$ and $E(S_2)$.

This chapter will be devoted to an examination of the sign of $E(S_1) - E(S_2)$ within the context of Models I and II and the statistical model. If it can be determined that the sign is nonnegative, then $E(S_1) \geqslant E(S_2)$, and if it can be determined that the sign is nonpositive, then $E(S_2) \geqslant E(S_1)$. The discussion is divided into two main portions, the first dealing with measures of relative value, the latter with measures of probability, although owing to the nature of the decision models, both relative values and probabilities will appear throughout.

6.1 SUMMATION BY PARTS

Before proceeding with the analysis, we shall restate Abel's summation identity [1] or the formula for summation by parts, and note a simple theorem concerning it. The elementary observations made clear by the theorem will be used repeatedly in the sequel, as will the identity.

Abel's identity is given by

$$\sum_{j=1}^{n} a_j b_j = \sum_{k=1}^{n-1} \left(\sum_{j=1}^{k} a_j \right)(b_k - b_{k+1}) + b_n \sum_{j=1}^{n} a_j, \qquad (6.1)$$

[1] See (3.6).

where $(a_1, a_2, \ldots, a_n)$ and $(b_1, b_2, \ldots, b_n)$ are two arbitrary vectors of real numbers.

Writing $\sum a_j b_j$ in the form of (6.1) yields:

Theorem 6.1 Suppose with respect to (6.1) it is known that $b_k - b_{k+1} \geq 0$ for $k = 1, 2, \ldots, n - 1$, and that $b_n \geq 0$ whenever $\sum_{j=1}^n a_j \neq 0$, but nothing is known concerning the relative magnitudes of b_n and $b_k - b_{k+1}$, $k = 1, 2, \ldots, n - 1$. If:

 (i) $\sum_{j=1}^k a_j \geq 0$ for $k = 1, 2, \ldots, n$, then $\sum_{j=1}^n a_j b_j \geq 0$;

 (ii) $\sum_{j=1}^k a_j \leq 0$ for $k = 1, 2, \ldots, n$, then $\sum_{j=1}^n a_j b_j \leq 0$;

 (iii) $\sum_{j=1}^k a_j > 0$ for one or more k and also $\sum_{j=1}^k a_j < 0$ for one or more k, $k = 1, 2, \ldots, n$, then it cannot be concluded either that $\sum_{j=1}^n a_j b_j \geq 0$ or that $\sum_{j=1}^n a_j b_j \leq 0$.

Parts (i) and (ii) are obvious with the right-hand side of (6.1) and the first hypothesis of the theorem. In addition, if nothing is known about the relative magnitudes of b_n and the $b_k - b_{k+1}$, and $\sum_{j=1}^{k_1} a_j > 0$, $\sum_{j=1}^{k_2} a_j < 0$, $k_1 \neq k_2$, then it is easy to give two sets of b_n and the $b_k - b_{k+1}$ such that with the first (e.g., $b_{k_1} - b_{k_1+1} = 1$, all other $b_k - b_{k+1}$ and $b_n = 0$), $\sum a_j b_j > 0$, and with the second (e.g., $b_{k_2} - b_{k_2+1} = 1$, all other $b_k - b_{k+1}$ and $b_n = 0$), $\sum a_j b_j < 0$.

6.2 ANALYSIS WITH ORDINAL AND METRIC VALUE RANKINGS

The basic form of $E(S_1) - E(S_2)$ used in this section is

$$E(S_1) - E(S_2) = \sum_{k=1}^r D_k V_k, \tag{6.2}$$

where $\sum_{k=1}^r D_k = 0$ with the V_k ordered as

$$V_1 \geq V_2 \geq \ldots \geq V_r. \tag{6.3}$$

The correspondence between (6.2) and the four models considered in Chapter 3 is given in Table 6.1.

The ordinal ranking (6.3) is obviously a ranking of all the relative values from the appropriate row and second column of Table 6.1.

In any of these four cases, we shall also write

$$D_k = P_{1k} - P_{2k}, \tag{6.4}$$

with P_{1k} and P_{2k} defined in the context of the table. For example, with Model I, if $V_k \equiv V(o_j)$, then $P_{1k} - P_{2k} = P(o_j \mid S_1) - P(o_j \mid S_2)$. For Model I ($S = A$), if $V_k \equiv V(A_1, O_j)$, then $P_{1k} - P_{2k} = P(O_j \mid A_1) - 0$;

TABLE 6.1

CORRESPONDENCE BETWEEN (6.2) AND THE OTHER FORMS OF THE MODELS

In $E(S_1) - E(S_2)$ as written in (6.2)

Model	$E(S_1) - E(S_2)$ equals	r equals	D_k, the coefficient of V_k, equals
I	$\sum_{j=1}^{r} [P(o_j \mid S_1) - P(o_j \mid S_2)]V(o_j)$	r	$P(o_j \mid S_1) - P(o_j \mid S_2)$ if $V_k \equiv V(o_j)$
I (S = A)	$\sum_{j=1}^{n} P(O_j \mid A_1)V(A_1, O_j) - \sum_{j=1}^{n} P(O_j \mid A_2)V(A_2, O_j)$	$2n$	$P(O_j \mid A_1)$ if $V_k \equiv V(A_1, O_j)$ $-P(O_j \mid A_2)$ if $V_k \equiv V(A_2, O_j)$
II	$\sum_{j=1}^{n} [P(O_j \mid S_1) - P(O_j \mid S_2)]V(O_j)$	n	$P(O_j \mid S_1) - P(O_j \mid S_2)$ if $V_k \equiv V(O_j)$
Stat.	$\sum_{j=1}^{n} P(E_j)[V(o_{1j}) - V(o_{2j})]$	$2n$	$P(E_j)$ if $V_k \equiv V(o_{1j})$ $-P(E_j)$ if $V_k \equiv V(o_{2j})$

if $V_k \equiv V(A_2, O_j)$, then $P_{1k} - P_{2k} = 0 - P(O_j \mid A_2)$. The P_{1k} apply to S_1 and the P_{2k} apply to S_2. Clearly, $\sum_k P_{1k} = \sum_k P_{2k} = 1$, so that $\sum_{k=1}^{r} D_k = 0$ in every case.

The Ordinal Ranking

Using (6.1) and $\sum_{k=1}^{r} D_k = 0$, (6.2) becomes

$$E(S_1) - E(S_2) = \sum_{k=1}^{r-1} \left(\sum_{j=1}^{k} D_j \right)(V_k - V_{k+1}), \qquad (6.2a)$$

which, with theorem 6.1, gives us:

Theorem 6.2 Given the ordinal ranking (6.3) and no additional information concerning the relative values of the consequences (or outcomes), then $E(S_1) \geqslant E(S_2)$ if $\sum_{j=1}^{k} D_j \geqslant 0$ for $k = 1, 2, \ldots, r - 1$; $E(S_2) \geqslant E(S_1)$ if $\sum_{j=1}^{k} D_j \leqslant 0$ for $k = 1, 2, \ldots, r - 1$; otherwise, it cannot be concluded either that $E(S_1) \geqslant E(S_2)$ or that $E(S_2) \geqslant E(S_1)$.

With the general probability matrix with P_{ij} defined by (6.4)

$$
\begin{array}{c|cccc}
 & V_1 \geqslant V_2 \geqslant & \cdots & \geqslant V_r \\
\hline
S_1 & P_{11} & P_{12} & \cdots & P_{1r} \\
S_2 & P_{21} & P_{22} & \cdots & P_{2r}
\end{array}
$$

$E(S_1) \geqslant E(S_2)$ if $P_{11} \geqslant P_{21}$; $P_{11} + P_{12} \geqslant P_{21} + P_{22}$; $P_{11} + \cdots$
$$+ P_{1,r-1} \geqslant P_{21} + \cdots + P_{2,r-1}.$$

In Model I, if the strategies are simple courses of action, then the (expanded) probability matrix with three outcomes becomes, say,

	$V_1 \geqslant$	$V_2 \geqslant$	$V_3 \geqslant$	$V_4 \geqslant$	$V_5 \geqslant$	V_6	
$S_1 = A_1$	P_{12}	0	P_{11}	P_{13}	0	0	$P_{ij} = P(O_j \mid A_i)$,
$S_2 = A_2$	0	P_{21}	0	0	P_{22}	P_{23}	

with $E(S_1) \geqslant E(S_2)$ if $P_{12} \geqslant P_{21}$. This relation corresponds to $D_1 + D_2 \geqslant 0$ and, if it holds, then inspection of the matrix shows that all other successive sums of D_j will be nonnegative.

For the statistical model and three E_j, we have a matrix similar to that shown directly above, but now the P_{ij} in that matrix correspond to the $P(E_j)$, and we get, say,

	$V_1 \geqslant$	$V_2 \geqslant$	$V_3 \geqslant$	$V_4 \geqslant$	$V_5 \geqslant$	V_6
S_1	$P(E_2)$	0	$P(E_1)$	$P(E_3)$	0	0
S_2	0	$P(E_1)$	0	0	$P(E_2)$	$P(E_3)$

so that $E(S_1) \geqslant E(S_2)$ if $P(E_2) \geqslant P(E_1)$.

The Ordered Metrics

For a simple ordered metric measure of value, let the differences $(V_k - V_{k+1})$ be ordered by decreasing magnitude, and let $V_m^{(1)}$ represent the mth largest difference, $m = 1, 2, \ldots, r - 1$, giving the simple ordered metric ranking

$$V_1^{(1)} \geqslant V_2^{(1)} \geqslant \ldots \geqslant V_{r-1}^{(1)} \geqslant 0. \tag{6.5}$$

Also let $D_m^{(1)}$ be the coefficient of $V_m^{(1)}$ in (6.2a). That is, $D_1^{(1)}, D_2^{(1)}, \ldots, D_{r-1}^{(1)}$ correspond to the ordering of $D_1, D_1 + D_2, \ldots, \sum_{j=1}^{r-1} D_j$, indicated by the ranking (6.5).

Then (6.2a) is rewritten as

$$E(S_1) - E(S_2) = \sum_{k=1}^{r-1} D_k^{(1)} V_k^{(1)}$$

which, on using (6.1), becomes

$$E(S_1) - E(S_2) = \sum_{k=1}^{r-1} \left(\sum_{j=1}^{k} D_j^{(1)} \right) (V_k^{(1)} - V_{k+1}^{(1)}) \tag{6.6}$$

with $V_r^{(1)} = 0$. Hence, using theorem 6.1 and (6.6), we have:

Theorem 6.3 Given the ranking (6.5) and no additional information about the relative values of the consequences (or outcomes), then $E(S_1) \geqslant E(S_2)$ if $\sum_{j=1}^{k} D_j^{(1)} \geqslant 0$ for $k = 1, 2, \ldots, r - 1$; $E(S_2) \geqslant E(S_1)$ if $\sum_{j=1}^{k} D_j^{(1)} \leqslant 0$ for $k = 1, 2, \ldots, r - 1$; otherwise, it cannot be concluded either that $E(S_1) \geqslant E(S_2)$ or that $E(S_2) \geqslant E(S_1)$.

Obviously the information contained in (6.3) is embedded in (6.5) and, therefore, the ranking (6.5) is more likely to yield a definite conclusion concerning the sign of $E(S_1) - E(S_2)$ than is (6.3). We may say that the first ordered metric measure of value is stronger or more powerful than the ordinal measure.

Using the first ordered metric ranking (6.5), one can successively (attempt to) obtain a second ordered metric ranking, then a third ordered metric ranking, and so forth. For example, suppose (6.5) is known (letting $0 = V_r^{(1)}$). Then let the differences $(V_k^{(1)} - V_{k+1}^{(1)})$ be ordered by decreasing magnitude and let $V_m^{(2)}$ represent the mth largest difference, $m = 1, 2, \ldots, r - 1$, giving the second ordered metric ranking

$$V_1^{(2)} \geqslant V_2^{(2)} \geqslant \ldots \geqslant V_{r-1}^{(2)} \geqslant V_r^{(2)},$$

where $V_r^{(2)} = 0$. Letting $D_m^{(2)}$ be the coefficient of $V_m^{(2)}$ in (6.6),

$$E(S_1) - E(S_2) = \sum_{k=1}^{r=1} D_k^{(2)} V_k^{(2)}.$$

In general, we may proceed one step at a time. Suppose the nth ordered metric ranking

$$V_1^{(n)} \geqslant V_2^{(n)} \geqslant \ldots \geqslant V_{r-1}^{(n)} \geqslant V_r^{(n)} \tag{6.7}$$

is known, wherein $V_r^{(n)} = 0$. Let the differences $(V_k^{(n)} - V_{k+1}^{(n)})$ be ordered by decreasing magnitude and let $V_m^{(n+1)}$ represent the mth largest difference, $m = 1, 2, \ldots, r - 1$, with $V_r^{(n+1)} = 0$. Further, suppose that

$$E(S_1) - E(S_2) = \sum_{k=1}^{r-1} \left(\sum_{j=1}^{k} D_j^{(n)} \right) (V_k^{(n)} - V_{k+1}^{(n)}). \tag{6.8}$$

Letting $D_m^{(n+1)}$, $m = 1, \ldots, r - 1$, be the coefficient of $V_m^{(n+1)}$ in (6.8), we may write

$$E(S_1) - E(S_2) = \sum_{k=1}^{r-1} \left(\sum_{j=1}^{k} D_j^{(n+1)} \right) (V_k^{(n+1)} - V_{k+1}^{(n+1)}).$$

The generalized version of theorem 6.3 may then be expressed [2] as:

---

[2] This may also be thought of as a generalized version of theorem 6.2 if we let $D_k^{(0)} = D_k$ and $V_k^{(0)} = V_k$.

Theorem 6.4   Given the nth ordered metric ranking (6.7) and no additional information about the relative values of the consequences (or outcomes), then $E(S_1) \geqslant E(S_2)$ if $\sum_{j=1}^{k} D_j^{(n)} \geqslant 0$ for $k = 1, \ldots, r - 1$; $E(S_2) \geqslant E(S_1)$ if $\sum_{j=1}^{k} D_j^{(n)} \leqslant 0$ for $k = 1, \ldots, r - 1$; otherwise, it cannot be concluded either that $E(S_1) \geqslant E(S_2)$ or that $E(S_2) \geqslant E(S_1)$.

To illustrate these ideas, suppose for Model II that the probability matrix is known:

$$
\begin{array}{c|ccc}
 & V_1 \geqslant V_2 \geqslant V_3 & & \\
\hline
S_1 & .30 & .20 & .50 \quad \text{(3 outcomes)} \\
S_2 & .17 & .42 & .41 \\
\hline
D_j & .13 & -.22 & .09
\end{array}
$$

For the indicated ordinal ranking $D_1 = .13$, $D_1 + D_2 = -.09$, (and $D_1 + D_2 + D_3 = 0$). Suppose then that $V_1^{(1)} = V_2 - V_3$, and $V_2^{(1)} = V_1 - V_2$, with $V_1^{(1)} \geqslant V_2^{(1)} \geqslant 0$. Then $D_1^{(1)} = -.09$, $D_1^{(1)} + D_2^{(1)} = .04$. Finally suppose $V_1^{(2)} = V_1^{(1)} - V_2^{(1)}$, and $V_2^{(2)} = V_2^{(1)} - 0$, with $V_1^{(2)} \geqslant V_2^{(2)} \geqslant 0$. Then $D_1^{(2)} = -.09$, $D_1^{(2)} + D_2^{(2)} = -.05$, yielding the conclusion that $E(S_2) \geqslant E(S_1)$.

It should be apparent that the nth ordered metric measure of value is more powerful than the $(n - 1)$st ordered metric measure, since $\sum_{j=1}^{k} D_j^{(n-1)} \geqslant 0$ for $k = 1, 2, \ldots, r - 1$ implies that $\sum_{j=1}^{k} D_j^{(n)} \geqslant 0$ for $k = 1, 2, \ldots, r - 1$, whereas if $\sum_{j=1}^{k} D_j^{(n)} \geqslant 0$ for the relevant values of k, it does not necessarily follow that $\sum_{j=1}^{k} D_j^{(n-1)} \geqslant 0$. The same comments apply if $\leqslant$ replaces $\geqslant$.

The Higher Ordered Metric Ranking and The Method of Equating Coefficients

For analyzing a higher ordered metric ranking, we shall use a rather general method, called the *method of equating coefficients*. Its generality will be demonstrated in the following and in a good bit of later work. For the higher ordered metric ranking, the method of equating coefficients is described in the following four steps:

1. For the h.o.m. ranking, let the $R = r(r - 1)/2$ differences $V_j - V_k$ with $j < k$ from the ordinal ranking (6.3) be ranked by decreasing magnitude and let V_m' be the mth largest difference, giving

$$V_1' \geqslant V_2' \geqslant \ldots \geqslant V_R' \geqslant 0. \tag{6.9}$$

Write out all successive differences $V_m' - V_{m+1}'$, $m = 1, 2, \ldots, R$, from the ranking (6.9), with $V_{R+1}' = 0$. Note that each of these is nonnegative by virtue of (6.9). Some of these differences may be identical. Let T be the number of different $V_m' - V_{m+1}'$ [written in terms of the original V_j from the ordinal ranking (6.3)]. Obviously $T \leqslant R$. Let V_1'', V_2'', ..., V_T'' denote these T distinct differences. (Each $V_m' - V_{m+1}'$ is identical to one of the V_i''.)

2. Write $E(S_1) - E(S_2)$ in the form

$$E(S_1) - E(S_2) = \sum_{i=1}^{T} b_i V_i'', \qquad (6.10)$$

and also in the original form of (6.2),

$$E(S_1) - E(S_2) = \sum_{k=1}^{r} D_k V_k.$$

3. In (6.10) determine the coefficient of V_k as a linear sum of the b_i and set this coefficient equal to D_k in (6.2). (Thus, this procedure uses the method of equating coefficients of the V_k in $\sum b_i V_i'' = \sum D_k V_k$.) This will give r equations relating the b_i, $i = 1, \ldots, T$, to the D_k, $k = 1, \ldots, r$. Any one of these r equations will be linearly dependent upon the other $r - 1$ because $\sum_{k=1}^{r} D_k = 0$. Therefore we can discard one of the equations and end up with (no more than) $r - 1$ independent equations in T unknowns $(b_1, \ldots, b_T)$, with $T \geqslant r - 1$.

4. The objective at this point is to attempt to determine a $\mathbf{b} = (b_1, \ldots, b_T)$ that satisfies the $r - 1$ equations derived in step 3 such that all components of $\mathbf{b}$ are nonnegative [implying that $E(S_1) \geqslant E(S_2)$ by virtue of (6.10) and the fact that $V_i'' \geqslant 0$ for $i = 1, 2, \ldots, T$] or such that all components of $\mathbf{b}$ are nonpositive [implying that $E(S_2) \geqslant E(S_1)$].

This may be stated formally as:

Theorem 6.5 Given the system of independent linear equations of step 3 relating the b_i to the D_k; if this system has a nonnegative $\mathbf{b}$ solution $(b_i \geqslant 0$ for all i), then $E(S_1) \geqslant E(S_2)$; if it has a nonpositive $\mathbf{b}$ solution $(b_i \leqslant 0$ for all i), then $E(S_2) \geqslant E(S_1)$.

In this theorem only sufficient conditions for determining the sign of $E(S_1) - E(S_2)$ with a h.o.m. ranking are given. Can we also add, "Otherwise the sign of $E(S_1) - E(S_2)$ is indeterminate given only the h.o.m. ranking of relative values," to what has been stated in theorem 6.5? Although we suspect the answer to this question is "yes," provided the h.o.m. ranking is constructed as in Section 4.11, we are not prepared to offer a proof of this suspicion (or a counterexample to disprove it). The reader is invited to try his hand in the matter.

To look for a $\mathbf{b} \geqslant 0$ or a $\mathbf{b} \leqslant 0$, solve the $r - 1$ equations for $r - 1$ of the b_i in terms of the other $T - (r - 1)$ b_i and the D_k. This will give, for example,

$$b_1 = f_1(b_r, \ldots, b_T; D_1, \ldots, D_r),$$

$$b_2 = f_2(b_r, \ldots, b_T; D_1, \ldots, D_r), \qquad (6.11)$$

$$\vdots$$

$$b_{r-1} = f_{r-1}(b_r, \ldots, b_T; D_1, \ldots, D_r),$$

where each f_j is a linear function in the stated variables.

If we are looking for a $\mathbf{b} \geqslant 0$, then the problem has been reduced to finding values of the b_i that appear on the right-hand side of (6.11) which are nonnegative and in addition yield $f_j(\ldots) \geqslant 0$ for the $r - 1$ f_j. If we are looking for a $\mathbf{b} \leqslant 0$, we seek nonpositive b_i that appear on the right-hand side of (6.11) which yield $f_j(\ldots) \leqslant 0$ for the $r - 1$ f_j. After writing (6.11) we may also be able to conclude that a $\mathbf{b}$ solution to the $r - 1$ equalities with $\mathbf{b} \geqslant 0$ or with $\mathbf{b} \leqslant 0$ does not exist.

To illustrate this method, suppose we have obtained the h.o.m. ranking,

$$(V_1 - V_6) \geqslant (V_1 - V_5) \geqslant (V_2 - V_6) \geqslant (V_2 - V_5) \geqslant (V_3 - V_6)$$

$$\geqslant (V_4 - V_6) \geqslant (V_1 - V_4) \geqslant (V_1 - V_3) \geqslant (V_3 - V_5)$$

$$\geqslant (V_4 - V_5) \geqslant (V_1 - V_2) \geqslant (V_2 - V_4) \geqslant (V_2 - V_3)$$

$$\geqslant (V_5 - V_6) \geqslant (V_3 - V_4) \geqslant 0.$$

With steps 1 and 2, obtain

$$
\begin{aligned}
E(S_1) - E(S_2) = {} & b_1(V_5 - V_6) + b_2(V_1 - V_2 - V_5 + V_6) \\
& + b_3(V_2 - V_3 - V_5 + V_6) + b_4(V_3 - V_4) \\
& + b_5(-V_1 + 2V_4 - V_6) \\
& + b_6(V_1 - 2V_3 + V_5) \qquad (6.12) \\
& + b_7(-V_1 + V_2 + V_4 - V_5) \\
& + b_8(V_1 - 2V_2 + V_4) \\
& + b_9(-V_3 + V_4 + V_5 - V_6)
\end{aligned}
$$

wherein all value terms ( ) are nonnegative and $T = 9$. In addition, suppose that

$$E(S_1) - E(S_2) = 12V_1 - .08V_2 - .10V_3 + .09V_5 - .03V_6, \quad (6.13)$$

with the $\mathbf{P}$ matrix (corresponding to Model I) given by

	o_1	o_2	o_3	o_4	o_5	o_6
S_1	.36	.04	.06	.15	.22	.17
S_2	.24	.12	.16	.15	.13	.20
D_k	.12	−.08	−.10	0	.09	−.03

Following step 3, the coefficients of the V_k in (6.12) and (6.13) are set equal. Each is multiplied by 100 to get rid of the decimal point with the b_i written below being 100 times the b_i in (6.12). Our $r = 6$ equations are:

$$
\begin{aligned}
b_2 && -b_5 + b_6 - b_7 + b_8 && = 12, \\
-b_2 + b_3 && +b_7 - 2b_8 && = -8, \\
-b_3 + b_4 && -2b_6 && -b_9 = -10, \\
-b_4 + 2b_5 && +b_7 + b_8 + b_9 = 0, \\
b_1 - b_2 - b_3 && +b_6 - b_7 && +b_9 = 9, \\
-b_1 + b_2 + b_3 && -b_5 && -b_9 = -3.
\end{aligned}
$$

Adding the left-hand sides and right-hand sides gives $0 = 0$ so that any equation is dependent on the other five. Working with any $r - 1 = 5$ equations, and solving these for b_1, b_2, b_3, b_4, and b_6 in terms of b_5, b_7, b_8, and b_9, we get

$$
\begin{aligned}
b_1 &= 7 - b_5 - b_7 - b_9, \\
b_2 &= 6 - b_8, \\
b_3 &= -2 - b_7 + b_8, \\
b_4 &= 2b_5 + b_7 + b_8 + b_9, \\
b_6 &= 6 + b_5 + b_7.
\end{aligned}
$$

In looking for a $\mathbf{b} \geqslant 0$, we wish to find nonnegative values of b_5, b_7, b_8, and b_9 such that:

(i) $7 - b_5 - b_7 \qquad -b_9 \geqslant 0,$ i.e., $b_1 \geqslant 0,$

(ii) $6 \qquad\qquad -b_8 \qquad \geqslant 0, \qquad b_2 \geqslant 0,$

(iii) $-2 \qquad -b_7 + b_8 \qquad \geqslant 0, \qquad b_3 \geqslant 0,$

(iv) $2b_5 + b_7 + b_8 + b_9 \geqslant 0, \qquad b_4 \geqslant 0,$

(v) $6 + b_5 + b_7 \qquad\qquad \geqslant 0, \qquad b_6 \geqslant 0.$

Since b_8 has a positive coefficient in (iii) and (iv) but is restricted by (ii), make $b_8 = 6$. This gives

(i') $7 - b_5 - b_7 - b_9 \geqslant 0,$

(iii') $4 \qquad -b_7 \qquad \geqslant 0,$

(iv') $6 + 2b_5 + b_7 + b_9 \geqslant 0,$

(v') $6 + b_5 + b_7 \qquad \geqslant 0.$

In this, an obvious solution is $b_5 = b_7 = b_9 = 0$. Thus we have a $\mathbf{b} \geqslant 0$ which satisfies the original equalities: $\mathbf{b} = (7, 0, 4, 6, 0, 6, 0, 6, 0)$.

Many other $\mathbf{b} \geqslant 0$ also exist, but there is no need to go any further since we have shown that $E(S_1) \geqslant E(S_2)$.

If the method of equating coefficients is applied to an ordinal or ordered metric measure of values, the conclusions derived coincide with the results stated in theorems 6.2, 6.3, and 6.4. For example, starting with the ordinal ranking (6.3), write

$$E(S_1) - E(S_2) = b_1(V_1 - V_2) + b_2(V_2 - V_3) + \dots$$
$$+ b_{r-1}(V_{r-1} - V_r).$$

Comparing this with (6.2) and equating coefficients of the V_k gives the expected result: $b_1 = D_1$, $b_2 = D_1 + D_2$, $b_3 = D_1 + D_2 + D_3, \dots,$ $b_{r-1} = D_1 + D_2 + \dots + D_{r-1}$.

The method of equating coefficients can be applied to any set of inequalities on the V_j, $j = 1, \dots, r$, provided that the inequalities are "sufficiently rich" to yield at least one $\mathbf{b}$ solution to the set of $r - 1$ equations relating the b_i to the D_k. For example, if $D_k \neq 0$ for fixed k, then V_k must appear in at least one of the inequalities. As argued above, at least one $\mathbf{b}$ solution exists for the ordinal, ordered metrics, and higher ordered metric rankings of relative values. A $\mathbf{b}$ solution also exists for the sum ordered metric of Section 4.11. In the next section we shall specify the conditions necessary and sufficient for a $\mathbf{b}$ solution to exist in the method of equating coefficients, given a partial ordering of the V_j. As noted in Chapter 4, a partial ordering of the V_j is the "most basic" measure of the V_j that will be considered herein, and, as we shall see, unless the probability matrix associated with such an ordering has certain properties, it will be impossible to conclude that $E(S_1) \geqslant E(S_2)$ or that $E(S_2) \geqslant E(S_1)$, given only the partial ordering. It will, of course, be recalled that the ordinal ranking $V_1 \geqslant V_2 \geqslant \dots \geqslant V_r$ is a special case of a partial ordering, namely, a partial ordering where all "partialness" has been removed, or a partial ordering which is connected.

6.3 ANALYSIS WITH PARTIAL ORDERINGS OF RELATIVE VALUES

In this section it is not assumed that $V_1 \geqslant V_2 \geqslant \dots \geqslant V_r$, since we are here concerned with measures of relative value which are not as powerful as the ordinal ranking. Because of the nature of partial orderings, they are not as simple to analyze as, for example, the nicely structured ordinal and ordered metric rankings. However, with the illustrative help of *value graphs*, a relatively uncomplicated theorem will be presented which says just about all there is to say about using a partial ordering of the V_j to analyze $E(S_1) - E(S_2)$ for sign. It is not assumed that the reader is already familiar with the theory of graphs, and we will therefore make this section self-contained.

Partial Orderings and Value Graphs

To prefix the formal structure of the analysis, two examples are presented. First, suppose with $r = 5$, we have been able to determine the partial ordering $V_1 \geqslant V_2 \geqslant V_3, V_4 \geqslant V_5$ (with no comparison between V_1 and $V_4, \ldots, V_3$ and V_5). Using the method of equating coefficients, write:

$$E(S_1) - E(S_2) = b_1(V_1 - V_2) + b_2(V_2 - V_3) + b_3(V_4 - V_5),$$

in which each value difference is nonnegative. Letting D_j be the coefficient of V_j in $E(S_1) - E(S_2)$ or in (6.2), we get

$$b_1 = D_1,$$
$$b_2 - b_1 = D_2,$$
$$-b_2 = D_3,$$
$$b_3 = D_4,$$
$$b_3 = -D_5.$$

It can be readily verified that a **b** solution to this linear system exists if and only if $D_4 + D_5 = 0$. If $D_4 + D_5 \neq 0$, then $E(S_1) - E(S_2)$ as written above is not valid for any (b_1, b_2, b_3).

On the other hand, suppose we obtain the partial ranking $V_1 \geqslant V_2 \geqslant V_3$, $V_1 \geqslant V_4$, $V_2 \geqslant V_5$, which may be pictured in graph form as shown in Figure 6.1.

There the node numbered j represents V_j and a directed arc or link ($\rightarrowtail$) means $\geqslant$. The partial ranking and Figure 6.1 are equivalent, since they are simply different ways of communicating or expressing the same data. Writing

$$E(S_1) - E(S_2) = b_1(V_1 - V_2) + b_2(V_2 - V_3)$$
$$+ b_3(V_1 - V_4) + b_4(V_2 - V_5)$$

and equating coefficients,

$$b_1 + b_3 = D_1,$$
$$-b_1 + b_2 + b_4 = D_2,$$
$$-b_2 = D_3,$$
$$-b_3 = D_4,$$

gives the (unique) **b** solution

$$(b_1, b_2, b_3, b_4) = (D_1 + D_4, -D_3, -D_4, -D_5).$$

Figure 6.1   **Figure 6.2**

If (with Model I) the probability matrix is

	o_1	o_2	o_3	o_4	o_5
S_1	.3	.4	.2	0	.1
S_2	.1	.2	.4	.1	.2
D_j	.2	.2	$-.2$	$-.1$	$-.1$

(V_j is the relative value of o_j)

then $(b_1, b_2, b_3, b_4) = (.1, .2, .1, .1)$, yielding the conclusion $E(S_1) \geqslant E(S_2)$.

Now the value graph for the first example with the partial ordering $V_1 \geqslant V_2 \geqslant V_3$, $V_4 \geqslant V_5$ may be written as shown in Figure 6.2.

The difference between Figures 6.1 and 6.2 is that Figure 6.1 is connected whereas Figure 6.2 is not, where a graph is *connected* if and only if every node can be reached from every other node by traveling along the arcs in either direction.

Another example of a value graph which is not connected is shown in Figure 6.3. In this figure V_9 is isolated. For $r = 9$, this graph corresponds to the partial ordering $V_1 \geqslant V_4 \geqslant V_5 \geqslant V_6 \geqslant V_7$, $V_5 \geqslant V_8$, $V_1 \geqslant V_3 \geqslant V_6$, and $V_2 \geqslant V_3$. In Figure 6.3, additional arcs could be drawn (in particular, from V_1 to V_5 and V_8 and V_6 and V_7, from V_4 to V_8 and V_6 and V_7, from V_5 to V_7, from V_2 to V_6 and V_7, and from V_3 to

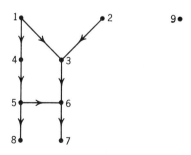

Figure 6.3

V_7), but these would serve only to clutter up the graph and would provide no additional information about the relative magnitudes of the V_j. Such arcs will be called *superfluous arcs*.

The Basic Theorem

As far as partial orderings of the V_j are concerned, it will always be possible to obtain at least one **b** solution in the method of equating coefficients if the value graph of the partial ordering is connected, it being understood that in trying to apply the method we attempt to write $E(S_1) - E(S_2)$ in the form

$$E(S_1) - E(S_2) = \sum_{i=1}^{T} b_i V'_i$$

where each V'_i is a nonnegative value difference of the form $V_j - V_k$, V_j and V_k being adjacent nodes on the value graph (connected by a directed arc), and T is the number of directed arcs in the graph containing no superfluous arcs. [An arc from V_1 to V_3 in Figure 6.1 would be superfluous as would any of the aforementioned arcs omitted from Figure 6.3.]

On the other hand, if the value graph is not connected, it will be possible to use the method of equating coefficients if and only if the sum of the D_j for each separate portion of the graph equals zero. For example, suppose for $r = 16$, one obtains the value graph shown in Figure 6.4.

This graph has four separate parts, each part being connected within itself. Then the method of equating coefficients can be used if and only if

$$\sum_{j=1}^{8} D_j = 0; \quad \sum_{j=9}^{13} D_j = 0; \quad D_{14} + D_{15} = 0; \quad D_{16} = 0.$$

These assertions will be put in the theorem to follow. Before writing the theorem, some additional notation is introduced. First, suppose the value graph of the partial ordering has K separate parts, where K equals

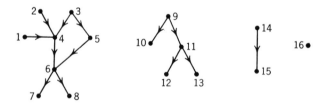

Figure 6.4

one of the integers $1, 2, \ldots, r$. Each separate part of the graph is connected within itself. Next, write $E(S_1) - E(S_2)$ according to the parts of the graph:

$$E(S_1) - E(S_2) = \sum_1 D_j V_j + \sum_2 D_j V_j + \ldots + \sum_K D_j V_j,$$

where $\sum_k D_j V_j$ refers to the kth part of the graph and $\sum_{k=1}^N (\sum_k D_j V_j) = \sum_{j=1}^r D_j V_j$. Finally, let

$$B_k = \sum_k D_j,$$

the sum of the D_j corresponding to the V_j in the kth part of the graph, with $\sum_{k=1}^K B_k = \sum_{j=1}^r D_j = 0$.

Theorem 6.6 Suppose the value graph of a partial ordering of the r V_j has K separate parts, with $\sum_k D_j V_j$ the portion of $E(S_1) - E(S_2)$ for the kth part and $B_k = \sum_k D_j$. Given only the partial ordering and no additional information about the relative magnitudes of the V_j:

(a) If $B_k = 0$ for $k = 1, 2, \ldots, K$, then it can be concluded that $E(S_1) \geqslant E(S_2)$ if and only if it can be shown that $\sum_k D_j V_j \geqslant 0$ for $k = 1, \ldots, K$. Similarly, in order to conclude that $E(S_2) \geqslant E(S_1)$, we must first be able to conclude that $\sum_k D_j V_j \leqslant 0$ for $k = 1, \ldots, K$.

For the kth part of the graph (with $B_k = 0$), let V_i', $i = 1, \ldots, T_k$, denote the nonnègative value differences for pairs of V_j connected by directed arcs and let r_k be the number of nodes (or V_j), $\sum_{k=1}^K r_k = r$. Then

$$\sum_k D_j V_j = \sum_{i=1}^{T_k} b_i V_i' \qquad (6.14)$$

will yield a set of r_k equations in T_k unknowns ($b_1, \ldots, b_{T_k}$), relating the b_i to the D_j. There exists at least one **b** solution to this set of r_k equations. Moreover, it can be concluded that $\sum_k D_j V_j \geqslant 0$ if and only if there exists a nonnegative solution (**b** $\geqslant 0$) to the equations, and it can be concluded that $\sum_k D_j V_j \leqslant 0$ if and only if there exists a nonpositive solution (**b** $\leqslant 0$).

(b) If $B_k \neq 0$ for one or more k, $k = 1, 2, \ldots, K$, then it is impossible to conclude that $E(S_1) \geqslant E(S_2)$ or that $E(S_2) \geqslant E(S_1)$.

It may be interesting to note that, as far as various rankings are concerned, this theorem specifies the absolute minimum results of measurement that one must have in order that there be an *a priori* probability greater than zero of being able to conclude either $E(S_1) \geqslant E(S_2)$ or $E(S_2) \geqslant E(S_1)$. For example, the minimum basic condition necessary (but obviously not necessarily sufficient) to determine either $E(S_1) \geqslant E(S_2)$ or $E(S_2) \geqslant E(S_1)$ if the D_j are not explicitly considered is that the V_j be measured on a partial ordinal scale such that the value graph corresponding to the partial ordering so obtained is connected. (This corresponds to $K = 1$ in the above theorem.) As noted in the theorem, however, if the D_j can be partitioned into $K > 1$ exclusive and exhaustive sets such that the sum of the D_j in each set equals zero, then it may be possible to conclude either $E(S_1) \geqslant E(S_2)$ or $E(S_2) \geqslant E(S_1)$ with a partial ordering whose value graph is not connected, but which is piecewise connected in correspondence to the partitioning of the D_j.

Outline of Proof

The proof of theorem 6.6, although involving no unusual complexities, is rather long. For this reason we shall only outline the proof, leaving justification of certain details as an exercise.[3] This outline is presented in the following four steps:

1. Since there are no inequalities between V_j in different parts of the graph (owing to the fact that the K parts are separated from one another), the sign of $E(S_1) - E(S_2)$ can be determined if and only if the $\sum_k D_j V_j$ are all either nonnegative or nonpositive. Note that, given only the partial ordering, we have no comparison between the relative magnitudes of the $\sum_k D_j V_j$, $k = 1, \ldots, K$, except when all D_j in the kth part equal zero, giving $\sum_k D_j V_j = 0$. Hereafter we will concentrate on the kth part of the graph, which will be called the kth *subgraph*.

2. For the kth subgraph, write (6.14). The resulting r_k equations relating the b_i to the D_k will be of the form

$$a_{11}b_1 + a_{12}b_2 + \ldots + a_{1T_k}b_{T_k} = D_1,$$

$$a_{21}b_1 + a_{22}b_2 + \ldots + a_{2T_k}b_{T_k} = D_2, \qquad (6.15)$$

$$\vdots$$

$$a_{r_k1}b_1 + a_{r_k2}b_2 + \ldots + a_{r_kT_k}b_{T_k} = D_{r_k},$$

where each a_{ji} is either $-1, 0$, or $+1$. For fixed i, b_i appears in one term on the right-hand side of (6.14) of the form $b_i(V_j - V_k)$. In this notation, $a_{ji} = +1$, $a_{ki} = -1$, and all other $a_{xi} = 0$ in the ith column of (6.15). Therefore, by adding the left-hand sides of (6.15), we get $\sum_{i=1}^{T_k} \sum_{j=1}^{r_k} a_{ji}b_i = 0$. Hence, a necessary condition for the existence of a solution to (6.15) is $B_k = \sum_{j=1}^{r_k} D_j = 0$.

3. $B_k = 0$ is also a sufficient condition for a solution to (6.15). To show this, begin with the kth subgraph (with no superfluous arcs). This subgraph will contain one or more *cycles* if, starting at some node, it is possible to traverse a series of arcs (ignoring the arrows) and arrive back at the starting node without passing over any arc more than once. The graph or subgraph shown in Figure 6.5 contains three cycles (1, 2, 3, 5, 1),

---

[3] See Exercise 10.

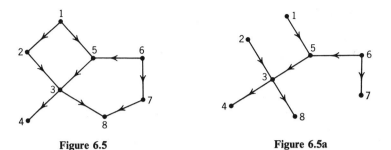

Figure 6.5   Figure 6.5a

(3, 5, 6, 7, 8, 3), and (1, 2, 3, 8, 7, 6, 5, 1), but has no superfluous arcs. In any given cycle, any one arc may be deleted without destroying the connectedness of the subgraph.   By deleting one arc at a time, reduce the subgraph to one that is still connected but contains no cycles.   For example, in Figure 6.5, if we choose to delete arcs (1, 2) and (7, 8) we get Figure 6.5a.

Deleting an arc from a subgraph with cycles is equivalent to setting one b_i in (6.14) or (6.15) equal to zero, namely, the b_i that is the coefficient of the value difference corresponding to the directed arc that is deleted.

It remains to show that for a connected subgraph with no cycles there exists a **b** solution that satisfies (6.15), having already (perhaps) set some of the $b_i = 0$ corresponding to the arcs deleted to rid the subgraph of cycles. If such a subgraph has r_k nodes, there are exactly $r_k - 1$ directed arcs (proof by induction on r_k), and hence $r_k - 1$ b_i associated with the (reduced) subgraph. If $B_k = 0$, a unique solution is obtained for these remaining b_i.   To demonstrate this solution, first label each arc with a b_i. For Figure 6.5a, this is shown in Figure 6.6.

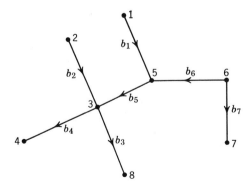

Figure 6.6

Now define:

(i) *ancestor* of b_i = part of the subgraph that the directed arc labeled b_i leads away from

(ii) *descendent* of b_i = part of the subgraph that the directed arc labeled b_i leads toward.

In Figure 6.6 the ancestor of b_6 is the part of the subgraph to the right of b_6 and the descendent of b_6 is the part of the subgraph to the left of b_6. The ancestor of b_1 is node 1 and the descendent of b_1 is the rest of the subgraph. It is not difficult to prove that:

$$b_i = +(\text{sum of the } D_j \text{ in the ancestor of } b_i), \qquad (6.16)$$

$$b_i = -(\text{sum of the } D_j \text{ in the descendent of } b_i).$$

Since $B_k = 0$, the $+$ and $-$ sums in (6.16) are indeed equal. For Figure 6.6,

$$b_1 = D_1 = -(D_2 + D_3 + \ldots + D_8),$$

$$b_2 = D_2 = -(D_1 + D_3 + D_4 + \ldots + D_8),$$

$$\vdots$$

$$b_5 = D_1 + D_5 + D_6 + D_7 = -(D_2 + D_3 + D_4 + D_8),$$

$$\vdots$$

$$b_7 = -D_7 = D_1 + \ldots + D_6 + D_8.$$

It is of course assumed that for Figure 6.5a or Figure 6.6 we are writing

$$\sum_{j=1}^{8} D_j V_j = b_1(V_1 - V_5) + b_2(V_2 - V_3) + \ldots + b_7(V_6 - V_7)$$
$$+ [0(V_1 - V_2) + 0(V_7 - V_8)].$$

Thus (6.15) has at least one solution (and many solutions if the kth part of the graph contains cycles) if and only if $B_k = 0$. From essentially the same arguments used with theorem 6.1, it follows that one can conclude $\sum_k D_j V_j \geqslant 0$ [$\sum_k D_j V_j \leqslant 0$] if and only if there is a **b** solution to (6.15) which is nonnegative [nonpositive], given only the partial ordering of the V_j.

4. If $B_k \neq 0$, then $\sum_k D_j V_j$ cannot be written in the form of (6.14). In this case, with only the partial ordering of the V_j, it is not possible to conclude either $\sum_k D_j V_j \geqslant 0$ or $\sum_k D_j V_j \leqslant 0$. For example, for the kth subgraph with cycles deleted, we may write

$$\sum_k D_j V_j = \sum_i b_i V_i' + B_k V_h \qquad (B_k \neq 0), \qquad (6.17)$$

where V_h is one of the V_j, and b_i is determined from the part of (6.16) which does not contain D_h. Even if $\mathbf{b} \geqslant 0$ in (6.17), it is not possible to conclude that $\sum_k D_j V_j \geqslant 0$, since the V_j are relative values and we can assign to V_h any positive or negative number we please in establishing an origin on the relative value scale.

In general, for the kth subgraph (which may contain cycles), we will, at best, be able to write

$$\sum_k D_j V_j = \sum_{i=1}^{T_k} b_i V_i' + B_k \left(\sum_k c_j V_j \right) \quad (B_k \neq 0),$$

where at least one $c_j \neq 0$ and it is impossible that $c_j = a(D_j/B_k)$ for some $a \neq 0$ and all j. Here again it is not possible to conclude either $\sum_k D_j V_j \geqslant 0$ or $\sum_k D_j V_j \leqslant 0$.

EXAMPLE 1. We conclude this section with an example of a partial ordering with a connected value graph which contains cycles. Suppose $r = 7$, $(D_1, D_2, \ldots, D_7) = (.02, .05, -.13, -.01, .06, -.03, .04)$, with the value graph shown in Figure 6.7.

By using $100 \sum_{j=1}^{7} D_j V_j = \sum_{i=1}^{8} b_i V_i'$ and equating coefficients, we get six independent linear equations in eight unknowns:

$$
\begin{aligned}
b_1 + b_2 \qquad\qquad\qquad\qquad &= 2, \\
-b_2 \qquad\quad +b_5 \qquad\qquad\quad &= 5, \\
b_3 + b_4 \qquad\qquad\quad &= -1, \\
-b_4 - b_5 + b_6 \qquad\quad &= 6, \\
-b_6 \qquad -b_8 &= -3, \\
b_7 \qquad &= 4.
\end{aligned}
$$

Solve the first five equations for b_1, b_2, b_3, b_4, and b_6 in terms of b_5 and b_8:

$$
\begin{aligned}
b_1 &= 7 - b_5, \\
b_2 &= -5 + b_5, \\
b_3 &= 2 + b_5 + b_8, \\
b_4 &= -3 - b_5 - b_8, \\
b_6 &= 3 - b_8.
\end{aligned}
$$

Since $b_7 > 0$, we look for a $\mathbf{b} \geqslant 0$. But by virtue of $b_4 = -3 - b_5 - b_8$, such a $\mathbf{b}$ solution does not exist. Hence the sign of $\sum_{j=1}^{7} D_j V_j$ is indeterminant with only the partial ranking

$$V_1 \geqslant V_2 \geqslant V_5 \geqslant V_6 \geqslant V_7, \qquad V_1 \geqslant V_3 \geqslant V_6, \qquad V_4 \geqslant V_3, \qquad V_4 \geqslant V_5.$$

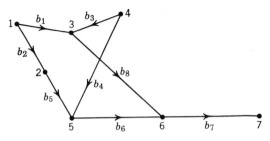

Figure 6.7

6.4 BOUNDED INTERVAL AND INTERVAL VALUE ANALYSIS

In this section we shall consider the three bounded interval measures of relative value discussed in Chapter 4 and then look at the interval measure *per se.*

First Bounded Interval Measure

The first bounded interval measure is specified as follows:

Let V_1 and V_r denote the relative values of the most desirable and least desirable consequence (or outcome) respectively, and assume that $V_1 > V_r$.

Let

$$I_j = \frac{V_j - V_r}{V_1 - V_r}, \qquad j = 1, \ldots, r,$$

be the indicated interval ratios. The first bounded interval measure is given by the inequalities

$$\alpha_j \leqslant I_j \leqslant \beta_j, \qquad j = 2, \ldots, r - 1, \tag{6.18}$$

where $1 \geqslant \beta_j \geqslant \alpha_j \geqslant 0$, $j = 2, \ldots, r - 1$, and $I_1 = 1$, $I_r = 0$. The α_j and β_j are assumed to be known. So that (6.18) may hold for $j = 1$ and $j = r$, define $\alpha_1 = \beta_1 = 1$, $\alpha_r = \beta_r = 0$.

With $E(S_1) - E(S_2) = \sum_{j=1}^{r} D_j V_j$ and $\sum_{j=1}^{r} D_j = 0$ we may write

$$\frac{E(S_1) - E(S_2)}{V_1 - V_r} = \sum_{j=1}^{r-1} D_j I_j, \tag{6.19}$$

where $E(S_1) - E(S_2)$ has the same sign as $\sum D_j I_j$, since $V_1 - V_r > 0$. Now let

$$M(S_1, S_2) = \max_{\{I_j\}} \sum_{j=1}^{r-1} D_j I_j,$$

$$m(S_1, S_2) = \min_{\{I_j\}} \sum_{j=1}^{r-1} D_j I_j.$$

Clearly,

$$M(S_1, S_2) = \sum_{j=1}^{r-1} D_j \gamma_j, \quad \gamma_j = \begin{cases} \beta_j & \text{if } D_j \geqslant 0, \\ \alpha_j & \text{if } D_j < 0, \end{cases} \quad j = 1, \ldots, r-1,$$

(6.20a)

$$m(S_1, S_2) = \sum_{j=1}^{r-1} D_j \delta_j, \quad \delta_j = \begin{cases} \beta_j & \text{if } D_j \leqslant 0, \\ \alpha_j & \text{if } D_j > 0, \end{cases} \quad j = 1, \ldots, r-1.$$

(6.20b)

This gives:

Theorem 6.7 Given the bounded interval measure (6.18) and no additional information on the relative magnitudes of the V_j, if $m(S_1, S_2) \geqslant 0$, then $E(S_1) \geqslant E(S_2)$; if $M(S_1, S_2) \leqslant 0$, then $E(S_2) \geqslant E(S_1)$; otherwise [i.e., $m(S_1, S_2) < 0 < M(S_1, S_2)$], the sign of $E(S_1) - E(S_2)$ is indeterminate.

Second Bounded Interval Measure

The second bounded interval measure, unlike the first, assumes that an ordinal ranking of the V_j has been obtained. We may denote this by $V_1 \geqslant V_2 \geqslant \ldots \geqslant V_r$. Assuming $V_1 > V_r$, let

$$L_j = \frac{V_j - V_{j+1}}{V_1 - V_r}, \quad j = 1, 2, \ldots, r-1,$$

where $L_j \geqslant 0$ by virtue of the ordinal ranking and $\sum_{j=1}^{r-1} L_j = 1$. The second bounded interval measure is given by the inequalities

$$\alpha_j \leqslant L_j \leqslant \alpha_j + \epsilon_j, \quad j = 1, \ldots, r-1,$$

(6.21)

where $1 \geqslant \alpha_j + \epsilon_j \geqslant \alpha_j \geqslant 0$, $j = 1, \ldots, r-1$, and, in addition, $\sum_{j=1}^{r-1} \alpha_j \leqslant 1 \leqslant \sum_{j=1}^{r-1} (\alpha_j + \epsilon_j)$. Using (6.2a) and letting

$$G_j = \sum_{k=1}^{j} D_k,$$

we have

$$\frac{E(S_1) - E(S_2)}{V_1 - V_r} = \sum_{j=1}^{r-1} G_j L_j, \quad \sum_{j=1}^{r-1} L_j = 1.$$

(6.22)

Let

$$M'(S_1, S_2) = \max_{\{L_j\}} \sum_{j=1}^{r-1} G_j L_j,$$

$$m'(S_1, S_2) = \min_{\{L_j\}} \sum_{j=1}^{r-1} G_j L_j.$$

Given the bounded interval measure (6.21) and no additional information on the relative magnitudes of the V_j, if $m'(S_1, S_2) \geq 0$, then $E(S_1) \geq E(S_2)$; if $M'(S_1, S_2) \leq 0$, then $E(S_2) \geq E(S_1)$; otherwise, we can conclude neither $E(S_1) \geq E(S_2)$ nor $E(S_2) \geq E(S_1)$.

To find $M'(S_1, S_2)$, first write

$$\sum_{j=1}^{r-1} G_j L_j = G_1(\alpha_1 + \delta_1) + G_2(\alpha_2 + \delta_2) + \ldots + G_{r-1}(\alpha_{r-1} + \delta_{r-1}),$$

or

$$\sum_{j=1}^{r-1} G_j L_j = \sum_{j=1}^{r-1} G_j \alpha_j + \sum_{j=1}^{r-1} G_j \delta_j,$$

in which, owing to the stated restrictions, $\sum_{j=1}^{r-1} \delta_j = 1 - \sum_{j=1}^{r-1} \alpha_j$, and $0 \leq \delta_j \leq \epsilon_j$, $j = 1, \ldots, r-1$. Since the α_j are specified, maximizing $\sum G_j L_j$ is equivalent to maximizing

$$\sum_{j=1}^{r-1} G_j \delta_j$$

subject to

$$\sum_{j=1}^{r-1} \delta_j = c \quad \text{and} \quad 0 \leq \delta_j \leq \epsilon_j, \quad j = 1, \ldots, r-1,$$

where

$$c = 1 - \sum_{j=1}^{r-1} \alpha_j.$$

To maximize $\sum G_j \delta_j$ subject to these restrictions, first order the $r-1$ G_j as $G_{j_1} \geq G_{j_2} \geq \ldots \geq G_{j_{r-1}}$, where $j_1, j_2, \ldots, j_{r-1}$ is a permutation of the integers $1, 2, \ldots, r-1$. Then, $\sum G_j \delta_j$ is clearly maximized by making δ_{j_1} as large as possible, then making δ_{j_2} as large as possible, and so forth.

Let

$$\delta_{j_1}^* = \min \{c; \epsilon_{j_1}\},$$

$$\delta_{j_2}^* = \min \{c - \delta_{j_1}^*; \epsilon_{j_2}\},$$

$$\vdots$$

$$\delta_{j_k}^* = \min \left\{c - \sum_{n=1}^{k-1} \delta_{j_n}^*; \epsilon_{j_k}\right\},$$

$$\vdots$$

$$\delta_{j_{r-1}}^* = \min \left\{c - \sum_{n=1}^{r-2} \delta_{j_n}^*; \epsilon_{j_{r-1}}\right\}.$$

For example, if $c = .5$, $\epsilon_{j_1} = .2$, $\epsilon_{j_2} = .15$, $\epsilon_{j_3} = .3$, etc., then $\delta_{j_1}^* = .2$, $\delta_{j_2}^* = .15$, $\delta_{j_3}^* = .15$, $\delta_{j_4}^* = \delta_{j_5}^* = \ldots = 0$. Obviously $\sum_{k=1}^{r-1} \delta_{j_k}^* = c$ and, by construction, the $\delta_{j_k}^*$ are successively the largest values of the δ_{j_k} that may be obtained in view of the stated restrictions. Hence,

$$M'(S_1, S_2) = \sum_{j=1}^{r-1} G_j \alpha_j + \sum_{k=1}^{r-1} G_{j_k} \delta_{j_k}^*.$$

In the same manner, with $G_{j_1} \geqslant G_{j_2} \geqslant \ldots \geqslant G_{j_{r-1}}$,

$$m'(S_1, S_2) = \sum_{j=1}^{r-1} G_j \alpha_j + \sum_{k=1}^{r-1} G_{j_k} \delta_{j_k}^0$$

where

$$\delta_{j_{r-1}}^0 = \min \{c; \epsilon_{j_{r-1}}\},$$

$$\delta_{j_{r-2}}^0 = \min \{c - \delta_{j_{r-1}}^0; \epsilon_{j_{r-2}}\},$$

$$\vdots$$

$$\delta_{j_k}^0 = \min \left\{ c - \sum_{n=k+1}^{r-1} \delta_{j_n}^0; \epsilon_{j_k} \right\},$$

$$\vdots$$

$$\delta_{j_1}^0 = \min \left\{ c - \sum_{n=2}^{r-1} \delta_{j_n}^0; \epsilon_{j_1} \right\}.$$

Third Bounded Interval Measure

For the third bounded interval measure it will be recalled from Section 4.9 that the r o_j (or O_j if Model II applies) were partitioned into $r' \leqslant r$ equivalence classes $e_1, e_2, \ldots, e_{r'}$, with $V(o_j) = V(o_k)$ if o_j and o_k were in the same equivalence class and $V(o_j) > V(o_k)$ if $o_j \in e_j$, $o_k \in e_k$, and $j < k$. Moreover, it was assumed that $r' \geqslant 3$. Letting V_j denote the relative value of any $o_k \in e_j$, we have

$$V_1 > V_2 > \ldots > V_{r'}.$$

To write $E(S_1) - E(S_2)$ in the form of (6.2) use

$$E(S_1) - E(S_2) = \sum_{j=1}^{r'} D_j' V_j, \tag{6.23}$$

where D_j' in (6.23) equals the *sum* of the D_k's in (6.2) that are the coefficients of the V_k's in (6.2) that equal V_j in (6.23). In other words the coefficient of V_j in (6.23) equals the sum of the coefficients in (6.2) on all V_k in (6.2) which have $o_k \in e_j$ (or $O_k \in e_j$). With $V_j = V(o_k \in e_j)$, the third bounded interval measure is given by

$$c_j \leqslant K_j \leqslant d_j, \qquad 0 \leqslant c_j \leqslant d_j < \infty \tag{6.24}$$

where

$$K_j = \frac{V_j - V_{j+1}}{V_{j+1} - V_{j+2}}, \qquad j = 1, \ldots, r' - 2.$$

Writing (6.23) first as

$$E(S_1) - E(S_2) = \sum_{j=1}^{r'-1} G'_j(V_j - V_{j+1}),$$

with

$$G'_j = \sum_{k=1}^{j} D'_k,$$

we get, on dividing by $V_{r'-1} - V_{r'}$,[4]

$$\frac{E(S_1) - E(S_2)}{V_{r'-1} - V_{r'}} = \sum_{j=1}^{r'-2} G'_j K_j K_{j+1} \ldots K_{r'-2} + G'_{r'-1}$$

$$= \sum_{v=1}^{r'-2} G'_v \prod_{j=v}^{r'-2} K_j + G'_{r'-1}.$$

Letting

$$M''(S_1, S_2) = \max_{\{K_j\}} \sum_{v=1}^{r'-2} G'_v \prod_{j=v}^{r'-2} K_j + G'_{r'-1},$$

$$m''(S_1, S_2) = \min_{\{K_j\}} \sum_{v=1}^{r'-2} G'_v \prod_{j=v}^{r'-2} K_j + G'_{r'-1},$$

we know that $E(S_1) \geqslant E(S_2)$ if $m''(S_1, S_2) \geqslant 0$, and $E(S_2) \geqslant E(S_1)$ if $M''(S_1, S_2) \leqslant 0$.

To find $M''(S_1, S_2)$ and $m''(S_1, S_2)$, given (6.24), we first simplify slightly by letting $r' - 2 = w$. Then

$$\sum_{v=1}^{w} G'_v \prod_{j=v}^{w} K_j = K_w G'_w + K_w K_{w-1} G'_{w-1} + \ldots + K_w K_{w-1} \ldots K_2 K_1 G'_1$$

$$= K_w[G'_w + K_{w-1}(\ldots + K_3(G'_3 + K_2(G'_2 + K_1 G'_1))\ldots)].$$

Next define $f_1, f_2, \ldots, f_w$ recursively by

$$f_1 = \max_{c_1 \leq K_1 \leq d_1} K_1 G'_1,$$

$$f_j = \max_{c_j \leq K_j \leq d_j} K_j(G'_j + f_{j-1}), \qquad j = 2, \ldots, w.$$

Since $c_j \geqslant 0$ for every j, it should be clear that

$$M''(S_1, S_2) = f_w + G'_{r'-1}.$$

---

[4] See Exercise 7 in Chapter 4.

Letting K_j^* denote the value of K_j that yields f_w,

$$K_1^* = \begin{cases} c_1 & \text{if } G_1' \leq 0, \\ d_1 & \text{if } G_1' \geq 0, \end{cases}$$

$$K_j^* = \begin{cases} c_j & \text{if } G_j' + f_{j-1} \leq 0, \\ d_j & \text{if } G_j' + f_{j-1} \geq 0, \end{cases} \qquad j = 2, \ldots, r' - 2(= w).$$

In a similar fashion if we let

$$g_1 = \min_{c_1 \leq K_1 \leq d_1} K_1 G_1',$$

$$g_j = \min_{c_j \leq K_j \leq d_j} K_j(G_j' + g_{j-1}), \qquad j = 2, \ldots, w,$$

then

$$m''(S_1, S_2) = g_w + G_{r'-1}'.$$

With K_j^0 denoting the value of K_j that yields g_w,

$$K_1^0 = \begin{cases} d_1 & \text{if } G_1' \leq 0, \\ c_1 & \text{if } G_1' > 0, \end{cases}$$

$$K_j^0 = \begin{cases} d_j & \text{if } G_j' + g_{j-1} \leq 0, \\ c_j & \text{if } G_j' + g_{j-1} > 0, \end{cases} \qquad j = 2, \ldots, r' - 2 \, (= w).$$

The reader may note that the procedure used here is an application of dynamic programming with linear functions.

Many types of bounded interval measures besides the ILK measures can, of course, be constructed and analyzed. We leave these to the reader's imagination and the exercises.[5]

Interval Measure

For an interval measure of relative values, we have:

Theorem 6.8 Given the probability matrix, measurement of the V_j on an interval scale is sufficient to establish the sign of $E(S_1) - E(S_2)$.

With the ordering $V_1 \geq V_2 \geq \ldots \geq V_r$, if $V_1 = V_r$, then $E(S_1) = E(S_2)$. If $V_1 > V_r$, then

$$\frac{E(S_1) - E(S_2)}{V_1 - V_r} = \sum_{j=1}^{r-1} D_j \frac{V_j - V_r}{V_1 - V_r}, \qquad (6.25)$$

where the right-hand side is a known, invariant real number with the hypotheses of the theorem. Since $V_1 - V_r > 0$, $E(S_1) - E(S_2)$ has the same sign as the right-hand side of (6.25).

[5] See Exercise 16.

6.5 ANALYSIS WITH INTRACOLUMN ORDERINGS OF PROBABILITIES

Thus far in this chapter we have been primarily concerned with measures of relative values of consequences or outcomes, and in most cases we have (theorem 6.2 through 6.7) specified conditions on the probabilities that must hold in connection with the various value measures in order to be able to distinguish the sign of $E(S_1) - E(S_2)$. Although some of the examples presented assumed that the probability matrix was known, it should be apparent that the sign of $E(S_1) - E(S_2)$ may be determined with less-than-perfect knowledge of the probabilities. This comment applies not only to the ordinal and metric measures of value but also is relevant in connection with the bounded interval measures. Consider, for example, equation (6.20a) or (6.20b) in connection with the first bounded interval measure. If the sign of D_j is known, then γ_j or δ_j is specified from the bounded interval measure. Then the problem of determining the sign of $M(S_1, S_2)$ or $m(S_1, S_2)$ is the same as determining the sign of a linear combination of the P_{ij}, and it may be possible to do this without knowing the P_{ij} exactly.

There does not seem to be any special reason why probabilities should be easier to measure than relative values. In different contexts or decision situations, one set of quantities may be "easier" to measure or estimate than the other set, but, in general, there are difficulties in measuring both the probabilities and relative values. In this section and the remaining sections of this chapter, we shall therefore consider several measures of probabilities discussed in Chapter 5, and for these specify conditions on the relative values that are sufficient in order to be able to reach a definite conclusion about the sign of $E(S_1) - E(S_2)$.

The first probability measure considered explicitly will be the columnar ranking of the P_{ij} in the matrix:

$$
\begin{array}{c|cccc}
 & o_1 & o_2 & \cdots & o_r \\
\hline
S_1 & P_{11} & P_{12} & \cdots & P_{1r} \\
S_2 & P_{21} & P_{22} & \cdots & P_{2r}
\end{array}
$$

This measure yields the sign of each intracolumn difference $P_{1j} - P_{2j}$ for $j = 1, \ldots, r$ but does not attempt intercolumn comparisons of the P_{ij}.

Using the form of (6.2) with $D_j = P_{1j} - P_{2j}$,

$$E(S_1) - E(S_2) = \sum_{j=1}^{r} (P_{1j} - P_{2j})V_j,$$

where V_j is the relative value of o_j. Since $\sum_j (P_{1j} - P_{2j}) = 0$, we may write

$$E(S_1) - E(S_2) = \sum_{j=1}^{r} (P_{1j} - P_{2j})(V_j - U), \qquad (6.26)$$

where U is an arbitrary constant.

The effect of varying U is to shift the origin of the value scale, and since the V_j are relative values, U may be set equal to anything we please. In particular, U may be set equal to any one of the V_j. For example, if we set $U = V_k$, then (6.26) becomes

$$E(S_1) - E(S_2) = \sum_{j \neq k} (P_{1j} - P_{2j})(V_j - V_k). \qquad (6.27)$$

Since the sign of each $P_{1j} - P_{2j}$ in (6.26) has been determined by the intracolumn rankings of the P_{ij}, we are interested in seeing if there is a U which makes each $V_j - U$ have the same sign as $P_{1j} - P_{2j}$, or which makes each $V_j - U$ have the opposite sign from that of $P_{1j} - P_{2j}$, $j = 1, \ldots, r$. If any such U exists, then it follows that one of the V_k will also have the same property in connection with (6.27). These results are summarized as:

Theorem 6.9 Given the sign of $P_{1j} - P_{2j}$ (either $\geqslant 0$ or $\leqslant 0$) for $j = 1, 2, \ldots, r$, it can be concluded that $E(S_1) \geqslant E(S_2)$ if there exists a k, $k = 1, 2, \ldots, r$, such that $V_j - V_k$ has the same sign as $P_{1j} - P_{2j}$ for all $j \neq k$. Similarly, it can be concluded that $E(S_2) \geqslant E(S_1)$ if there exists a k such that $V_j - V_k$ and $P_{1j} - P_{2j}$ have opposite signs for all $j \neq k$.

The condition on the existence of k and the signs of $V_j - V_k$ in the theorem is a sufficient condition for determining the sign of $E(S_1) - E(S_2)$. It may be asked whether, given only the intracolumn orderings of the P_{1j} and no additional information on the probabilities, this is also a necessary condition. Although we have not been able to find a counterexample to disprove the claim of necessity, we have also been unable to prove it, and we invite the reader to try his hand with the matter. It is interesting to note that, if the condition is necessary as well as sufficient, then given only the intracolumn rankings of the P_{ij}, the ordinal measure of value gives just as much information as the interval measure of value towards determining the sign of $E(S_1) - E(S_2)$, except for the possibility of equality between some of the V_j which the ordinal measure may fail to distinguish.

6.6 RANKINGS OF PROBABILITIES AND SETS OF INEQUALITIES IN THE STATISTICAL MODEL

Since rankings of probabilities in the statistical model are a bit easier to analyze than their counterparts in Models I and II (apart from the intracolumn rankings), we shall consider them first.

Ordinal Probability Ranking

We begin with the ordinal ranking

$$P(E_1) \geqslant P(E_2) \geqslant \ldots \geqslant P(E_n) \geqslant 0,$$

which will be written as

$$P_1 \geqslant P_2 \geqslant \ldots \geqslant P_n \geqslant 0, \qquad \sum_{j=1}^{n} P_j = 1. \tag{6.28}$$

For this model

$$E(S_1) - E(S_2) = \sum_{j=1}^{n} P_j V_{1j} - \sum_{j=1}^{n} P_j V_{2j},$$

$$= \sum_{j=1}^{n} P_j (V_{1j} - V_{2j}),$$

where $V_{ij} = V(o_{ij})$, the relative value of the consequence associated with strategy S_i and state E_j. For notational simplicity, let

$$W_j = V_{1j} - V_{2j}, \tag{6.29}$$

giving

$$E(S_1) - E(S_2) = \sum_{j=1}^{n} P_j W_j, \tag{6.30}$$

which, using (6.1) becomes

$$E(S_1) - E(S_2) = \sum_{j=1}^{n} \left(\sum_{k=1}^{j} W_k \right)(P_j - P_{j+1}), \qquad P_{n+1} = 0. \tag{6.31}$$

For this case, a shift in the origin of the value scale does not affect W_k by reason of (6.29). The P_j sum to 1, but if each P_j is multiplied by $a > 0$, this will not have any effect on the sign of (6.30). Hence, in connection with only the ranking (6.28), the fact that $\sum_j P_j = 1$ has nothing to do with determining the sign of $E(S_1) - E(S_2)$. Thus, using (6.31), we get:

Theorem 6.10 Given (6.28) and no additional information on the $P_j = P(E_j)$, if $\sum_{k=1}^{j} W_k \geqslant 0$ for $j = 1, \ldots, n$, then $E(S_1) \geqslant E(S_2)$; if $\sum_{k=1}^{j} W_k \leqslant 0$ for $j = 1, \ldots, n$, then $E(S_2) \geqslant E(S_1)$; otherwise the sign of $E(S_1) - E(S_2)$ is indeterminate.

For the matrix of relative values:

	$P_1 \geqslant$	$P_2 \geqslant$	$P_3 \geqslant$	$P_4 \geqslant$	$P_5 \geqslant$	P_6
S_1	6	0	17	7	80	32
S_2	4	1	13	9	83	31
W_j	2	−1	4	−2	−3	1

the partial sums of the W_j are 2, 1, 5, 3, 0, 1, so that $E(S_1) \geqslant E(S_2)$.

Sets of Inequalities

For sets of inequalities on the $P(E_j)$ or P_j as discussed in Section 5.8, we use the method of equating coefficients. This can best be illustrated by an example. Suppose, for $n = 6$,

$$P_2 + P_3 + P_4 \geqslant P_1 \geqslant P_2 + P_3,$$
$$P_3 + P_4 \geqslant P_2 \geqslant P_3,$$
$$P_4 + P_5 + P_6 \geqslant P_3 \geqslant P_4 + P_5, \qquad (6.32)$$
$$P_4 \geqslant P_5 + P_6,$$
$$P_5 \geqslant P_6,$$
$$P_6 \geqslant 0.$$

From (6.32) and (6.30), write

$$
\begin{aligned}
E(S_1) - E(S_2) &= P_1 W_1 + P_2 W_2 + P_3 W_3 + P_4 W_4 + P_5 W_5 + P_6 W_6, \\
&= a_1(P_1 - P_2 - P_3) + a_2(P_2 - P_3) + a_3(P_3 - P_4 - P_5) \\
&\quad + a_4(P_4 - P_5 - P_6) + a_5(P_5 - P_6) + a_6(P_6) \qquad (6.33) \\
&\quad + b_1(P_2 + P_3 + P_4 - P_1) + b_2(P_3 + P_4 - P_2) \\
&\quad + b_3(P_4 + P_5 + P_6 - P_3),
\end{aligned}
$$

where $a_1, \ldots, a_6$, and b_1, b_2, b_3 are yet to be determined. The last part of (6.33) has been formed from the nine inequalities in (6.32), and each P term in parenthesis is $\geqslant 0$ by virtue of (6.32). Hence, if there exists a nonnegative $\mathbf{a}, \mathbf{b}$ solution to (6.33), then $E(S_1) \geqslant E(S_2)$, and if there exists a nonpositive $\mathbf{a}, \mathbf{b}$ solution (in which every a_i and b_i is $\leqslant 0$) to (6.33), then $E(S_2) \geqslant E(S_1)$. Otherwise the sign of $E(S_1) - E(S_2)$ is indeterminate given only (6.32).

Equating the coefficients of each P_j in (6.33) gives

$$a_1 - b_1 = W_1,$$
$$-a_1 + a_2 + b_1 - b_2 = W_2,$$
$$-a_1 - a_2 + a_3 + b_1 + b_2 - b_3 = W_3,$$
$$-a_3 + a_4 + b_1 + b_2 + b_3 = W_4,$$
$$-a_3 - a_4 + a_5 + b_3 = W_5,$$
$$-a_4 - a_5 + a_6 + b_3 = W_6.$$

Suppose, for the sake of illustration, that

$$(W_1, \ldots, W_6) = (-2, 5, -2, 4, 2, -1).$$

Then, solving for a_1 through a_6 in terms of the W's and b's,

$$a_1 = b_1 - 2,$$
$$a_2 = b_2 + 3,$$
$$a_3 = b_3 - 1,$$
$$a_4 = -b_1 - b_2 + 3,$$
$$a_5 = -b_1 - b_2 + 4,$$
$$a_6 = -2b_1 - 2b_2 - b_3 + 6.$$

In trying to find a nonnegative **a**, **b** solution, we look for **b** $\geqslant 0$ that makes the right-hand sides of these six equations $\geqslant 0$, so that all the a's will be $\geqslant 0$. Trying $(b_1, b_2, b_3) = (2, 0, 1)$, we get $(a_1, \ldots, a_6) = (0, 3, 0, 1, 2, 1)$, and, therefore, conclude that $E(S_1) \geqslant E(S_2)$.

This same method may be used for more general inequality sets than (6.32). For example, it could be used in connection with

$$P_2 + P_4 + P_6 \geqslant P_1 \geqslant P_2 + P_5 + P_6,$$
$$P_3 + P_4 \geqslant P_2 \geqslant P_3 + P_5,$$
$$P_4 + P_6 \geqslant P_3 \geqslant P_5 + P_6,$$
$$P_5 + P_6 \geqslant P_4 \geqslant P_5,$$
$$P_5 \geqslant P_6,$$
$$P_6 \geqslant 0.$$

6.7 INTRAROW RANKINGS OF PROBABILITIES, MODELS I AND II

In this section we consider first the case where the P_{ij} have been ranked from largest to smallest for each row of the r-column probability matrix. The basic form for $E(S_1) - E(S_2)$ is given by (6.2), with $P_{ij} = P(o_j \mid S_i)$, $V_j = V(o_j)$, for Model I, and $P_{ij} = P(O_j \mid S_i)$, $V_j = V(O_j)$, for Model II:

$$E(S_1) - E(S_2) = \sum_{j=1}^{r} P_{1j}V_j - \sum_{j=1}^{r} P_{2j}V_j. \tag{6.34}$$

For the two strategies, S_1 and S_2, denote the two ordinal rankings for the two rows of the **P** matrix corresponding to S_1 and S_2 as

$$P_{1j_1} \geqslant P_{1j_2} \geqslant \ldots \geqslant P_{1j_r} \geqslant 0,$$
$$P_{2k_1} \geqslant P_{2k_2} \geqslant \ldots \geqslant P_{2k_r} \geqslant 0, \tag{6.35}$$

where $j_1, j_2, \ldots, j_r$ and $k_1, k_2, \ldots, k_r$ are two permutations of the integers $1, 2, \ldots, r$. Using these, (6.34) is written as

$$E(S_1) - E(S_2) = \sum_{i=1}^{r} P_{1j_i} V_{j_i} - \sum_{i=1}^{r} P_{2k_i} V_{k_i},$$

$$= \sum_{i=1}^{r} P_{1j_i}(V_{j_i} - U) - \sum_{i=1}^{r} P_{2k_i}(V_{k_i} - U).$$

Using (6.1) and taking $P_{1j_{r+1}} = P_{2k_{r+1}} = 0$,

$$E(S_1) - E(S_2) = \sum_{i=1}^{r} \left[\sum_{v=1}^{i} (V_{j_v} - U) \right] (P_{1j_i} - P_{1j_{i+1}}) \qquad (6.36)$$

$$- \sum_{i=1}^{r} \left[\sum_{v=1}^{i} (V_{k_v} - U) \right] (P_{2k_i} - P_{2k_{i+1}}).$$

From (6.35) and (6.36) it is obvious that $E(S_1) \geqslant E(S_2)$ if there exists a U such that

$$\sum_{v=1}^{i} (V_{j_v} - U) \geqslant 0 \qquad \text{for} \qquad i = 1, \ldots, r,$$

and $\qquad\qquad\qquad\qquad\qquad\qquad\qquad\qquad\qquad\qquad\qquad$ (6.37a)

$$\sum_{v=1}^{i} (V_{k_v} - U) \leqslant 0 \qquad \text{for} \qquad i = 1, \ldots, r.$$

Conditions (6.37a) can be combined as

$$\frac{1}{i} \sum_{v=1}^{i} V_{k_v} \leqslant U \leqslant \frac{1}{i} \sum_{v=1}^{i} V_{j_v}, \qquad i = 1, \ldots, r. \qquad (6.37b)$$

Setting $i = r$ in (6.37b) gives

$$\frac{1}{r} \sum_{v=1}^{r} V_{k_v} \leqslant U \leqslant \frac{1}{r} \sum_{v=1}^{r} V_{j_v},$$

and, since $\sum_{v=1}^{r} V_{k_v} = \sum_{v=1}^{r} V_{j_v} = \sum_{j=1}^{r} V_j$, if a U exists which satisfies (6.37a), this U must necessarily equal $1/r \sum_{j=1}^{r} V_j$. This result and (6.37b) yield:

Theorem 6.11 Given the rankings (6.35), it can be concluded that $E(S_1) \geqslant E(S_2)$ if

$$r \sum_{v=1}^{i} V_{k_v} \leqslant i \sum_{j=1}^{r} V_j \leqslant r \sum_{v=1}^{i} V_{j_v}, \qquad i = 1, \ldots, r - 1,$$

and it can be concluded that $E(S_2) \geqslant E(S_1)$ if

$$r \sum_{v=1}^{i} V_{j_v} \leqslant i \sum_{j=1}^{r} V_j \leqslant r \sum_{v=1}^{i} V_{k_v}, \qquad i = 1, \ldots, r - 1.$$

To illustrate, suppose $n = 4$, an interval measure of the V_j has been obtained with $(V_1, V_2, V_3, V_4) = (8, 10, 3, 1)$, and $(j_1, j_2, j_3, j_4) = (1, 2, 3, 4)$, $(k_1, k_2, k_3, k_4) = (4, 3, 2, 1)$. Corresponding to the first set of inequalities in the theorem, we get

$$i = 1: \quad 4 \leqslant 22 \leqslant 32,$$
$$i = 2: \quad 16 \leqslant 44 \leqslant 72,$$
$$i = 3: \quad 56 \leqslant 66 \leqslant 84,$$

so that $E(S_1) \geqslant E(S_2)$.

Now consider the case where, starting with the two ordinal rankings (6.35), we get inequality sets for the P_{1j} and P_{2j} similar to (6.32) with no inequalities interconnecting the P_{1j} with the P_{2j}. With the use of these two sets of inequalities and

$$E(S_1) - E(S_2) = \sum_{j=1}^{r} P_{1j}(V_j - U) - \sum_{j=1}^{r} P_{2j}(V_j - U), \qquad (6.38)$$

the method of equating coefficients of the P_{ij} is applied to determine if there exists a U for which the two sets of **a**, **b** corresponding to the two sets of inequalities (on the P_{1j} and P_{2j}) are all nonnegative or all nonpositive.

6.8 INTERROW, INTERCOLUMN PROBABILITY RANKINGS, MODELS I AND II

An ordinal ranking of the probabilities P_{1j} and P_{2j}, $j = 1, \ldots, r$, takes the form

$$P_{i_1 j_1} \geqslant P_{i_2 j_2} \geqslant \cdots \geqslant P_{i_u j_u} \geqslant 0, \qquad (6.39a)$$

where $u = 2r$ and $i_1 j_1, i_2 j_2, \ldots, i_u j_u$ is a permutation of $11, 12, \ldots, 1r, 21, 22, \ldots, 2r$. This ranking has embedded within it both the intracolumn rankings and the intrarow rankings discussed in Sections 6.5 and 6.7 and hence is more powerful than either of these. In the context of two strategies, S_1 and S_2, (6.39a) is a complete simple ordering, while the intracolumn and intrarow rankings are partial orderings of the probabilities.

For simplicity in notation, define

$$P_k = P_{i_k j_k}, \qquad (6.40)$$

so that (6.39a) may be written

$$P_1 \geqslant P_2 \geqslant \cdots \geqslant P_u \geqslant 0, \qquad (6.39b)$$

where $\sum_{k=1}^{u} P_k = 2$. Using (6.38) as the basic expression for $E(S_1) - E(S_2)$,

$$E(S_1) - E(S_2) = \sum_{k=1}^{u} P_k W_k. \qquad (6.41)$$

If $P_k = P_{1j}$ according to (6.40), then via (6.38), $W_k = V_j - U$, and if $P_k = P_{2j}$ according to (6.40), then by (6.38), $W_k = U - V_j$. The form of (6.41) is similar to (6.30), which is not entirely accidental. The reader is advised to note the differences between the two.

Applying (6.1) to (6.41) and letting $P_{u+1} = 0$,

$$E(S_1) - E(S_2) = \sum_{k=1}^{u} \left(\sum_{j=1}^{k} W_j \right)(P_k - P_{k+1}).$$

Theorem 6.12 Given (6.39a) or (6.39b), if there exists a U such that $\sum_{j=1}^{k} W_j \geq 0$ for $k = 1, \ldots, u$, then $E(S_1) \geq E(S_2)$, or if there exists a U such that $\sum_{j=1}^{k} W_j \leq 0$ for $k = 1, \ldots, u$, then $E(S_2) \geq E(S_1)$.

Starting with (6.39b) [or (6.28) in the context of the statistical model], rankings of adjacent probability differences $(P_k - P_{k+1})$ may be analyzed by a method analogous to the analysis with ordered metric value rankings discussed in Section 6.2.

In addition, standard application of the method of equating coefficients may be used in connection with any set of inequalities among the P_{1j} and P_{2j} in trying to determine the sign of $E(S_1) - E(S_2)$.

6.9 ANALYSIS WITH A BOUNDED INTERVAL MEASURE OF THE P_{ij}, MODELS I AND II

Model I $(S = A)$

A bounded interval measure of the P_{ij} for Model I when the strategies are simple courses of action and $P_{ij} = P(O_j \mid A_i)$ may be described by

$$\begin{aligned} \alpha_{1j} &\leq P_{1j} \leq \alpha_{1j} + \epsilon_{1j}, \quad j = 1, 2, \ldots, n, \\ \alpha_{2j} &\leq P_{2j} \leq \alpha_{2j} + \epsilon_{2j}, \quad j = 1, 2, \ldots, n, \end{aligned} \tag{6.42}$$

where $0 \leq \alpha_{ij} \leq \alpha_{ij} + \epsilon_{ij} \leq 1$ for $i = 1, 2; j = 1, \ldots, n$, and

$$\sum_{j=1}^{n} \alpha_{ij} \leq 1 \leq \sum_{j=1}^{n} (\alpha_{ij} + \epsilon_{ij}) \quad i = 1, 2.$$

Letting

$$P_{ij} = \alpha_{ij} + \delta_{ij},$$

with

$$0 \leq \delta_{ij} \leq \epsilon_{ij} \quad \text{and} \quad \sum_{j=1}^{n} \delta_{ij} = 1 - \sum_{j=1}^{n} \alpha_{ij}, \quad i = 1, 2,$$

we may write for Model I, when strategies are prescriptive courses of action,

$$E(A_1) - E(A_2) = \sum_{j=1}^{n} \alpha_{1j} V_{1j} - \sum_{j=1}^{n} \alpha_{2j} V_{2j} + \sum_{j=1}^{n} \delta_{1j} V_{1j} - \sum_{j=1}^{n} \delta_{2j} V_{2j}, \tag{6.43}$$

where $V_{ij} = V(A_i, O_j)$. Let the maximum and minimum values of the right-hand side of (6.43) be denoted by $M(A_1, A_2)$ and $m(A_1, A_2)$ respectively. The extremization is with respect to the δ_{ij}, subject to the stated restrictions.

To determine the values of the δ_{1j} and the δ_{2j}, $j = 1, \ldots, n$, that yield $M(A_1, A_2)$, it is sufficient to have an ordinal ranking of the V_{1j} and the V_{2j} respectively. In finding the δ_{1j} for $M(A_1, A_2)$, first assign the greatest possible weight to the δ_{1j} which is the coefficient of the largest V_{1j}, then assign the greatest possible weight to the δ_{1j} which is the coefficient of the second largest V_{1j}, and so forth, until the total allocatable weight, $1 - \sum_j \alpha_{1j}$, has been used up. In finding the δ_{2j} for $M(A_1, A_2)$, first assign the greatest possible weight to the δ_{2j} which is the coefficient of the smallest V_{2j}, etc., until $1 - \sum_j \alpha_{2j}$ has been consumed. The procedure for determining the δ_{1j} and δ_{2j} for $m(A_1, A_2)$ is just the reverse of this.

In the above notation for Model I ($S = A$), we have:

Theorem 6.13 Given the interval probability measure (6.42) and no additional information on the P_{ij}, if $m(A_1, A_2) \geq 0$, then $E(A_1) \geq E(A_2)$; if $M(A_1, A_2) \leq 0$, then $E(A_2) \geq E(A_1)$; otherwise the sign of $E(A_1) - E(A_2)$ is indeterminate.

Models I and II

For Model I in the usual form $[P_{ij} = P(o_j \mid S_i), V_j = V(o_j)]$ or for Model II $[P_{ij} = P(O_j \mid S_i), V_j = V(O_j)]$, with the measure (6.42) as it applies for either case,[6]

$$E(S_1) - E(S_2) = \sum_{j=1}^{r} (\alpha_{1j} - \alpha_{2j})V_j + \sum_{j=1}^{r} (\delta_{1j} - \delta_{2j})V_j. \qquad (6.44)$$

Theorem 6.13 applies if we replace $M(A_1, A_2)$ and $m(A_1, A_2)$ by $M(S_1, S_2)$ and $m(S_1, S_2)$ respectively, where $M(S_1, S_2)$ and $m(S_1, S_2)$ are the maximum and minimum values of the right-hand side of (6.44) with respect to the δ_{ij}.

Whereas with at least an ordinal ranking of the V_{ij} or V_j, there is no problem in assigning values of δ_{1j} and δ_{2j} to perform the extremization of (6.43) or (6.44) to give the forms for $M(A_1, A_2)$ and $m(A_1, A_2)$ or $M(S_1, S_2)$ and $m(S_1, S_2)$, troubles may arise when one is working with a measure of value which does not yield an ordinal ranking. In particular, since the first bounded interval measure of value may not yield an ordinal ranking of the V_{ij} or V_j, special problems may arise when a bounded probability measure and bounded interval value measure are used together.

---

[6] Replace n by r in (6.42) through (6.43).

With a First Bounded Interval Measure of Relative Value

For the first bounded interval measure in Model I with strategies equaling courses of actions, let $I_{ij} = (V_{ij} - V_r)/(V_1 - V_r)$, where, say, $0 \leqslant \beta_{ij} \leqslant I_{ij} \leqslant \mu_{ij} \leqslant 1$, $i = 1, 2$; $j = 1, \ldots, n$. Here V_1 and V_r are the relative values of the most desirable and least desirable consequences in the set $\{(A_i, O_j)\}$, $i = 1, 2$; $j = 1, \ldots, n$.

For this case

$$\frac{E(A_1) - E(A_2)}{V_1 - V_r} = \sum_{j=1}^{n} P_{1j}I_{1j} - \sum_{j=1}^{n} P_{2j}I_{2j}. \tag{6.45}$$

No special problems arise in analyzing for dominance, since each sum on the right-hand side of (6.45) may be dealt with separately. Given the bounded probability measure and first bounded interval measure of relative values, the maximum value or the minimum value of the right-hand side of (6.45) can be readily obtained.[7] However, when strategies are not simple courses of action for Model I or when Model II applies, the situation is drastically changed.

In this latter case

$$\frac{E(S_1) - E(S_2)}{V_1 - V_r} = \sum_{j=1}^{r-1} (P_{1j} - P_{2j})I_j, \tag{6.46}$$

with $I_j = (V_j - V_r)/(V_1 - V_r)$, $0 \leqslant \beta_j \leqslant I_j \leqslant \mu_j \leqslant 1$ for $j = 2, \ldots, r - 1$. Equation (6.46) is identical to (6.19). For definiteness, suppose we attempt to find the minimum value of the right-hand side of (6.46), subject to the restrictions on the P_{ij} and I_j imposed by the bounded probability measure (6.42)—with n replaced by r—and the first bounded interval measure of relative value, respectively. If the resultant minimum is nonnegative, we may conclude that $E(S_1) \geqslant E(S_2)$. Specifically, our problem is to minimize

$$(P_{11} - P_{21}) + (P_{12} - P_{22})I_2 + \ldots + (P_{1,r-1} - P_{2,r-1})I_{r-1}$$

with respect to the P_{ij} and I_j, subject to

$$0 \leqslant \alpha_{ij} \leqslant P_{ij} \leqslant \alpha_{ij} + \epsilon_{ij} \leqslant 1, \qquad i = 1, 2; \ j = 1, \ldots, r,$$

$$\sum_{j=1}^{r} P_{ij} = 1, \qquad i = 1, 2,$$

$$0 \leqslant \beta_j \leqslant I_j \leqslant \mu_j \leqslant 1, \qquad j = 2, \ldots, r - 1.$$

Since there is no simple algorithm for solving this problem, we shall not discuss it further.

---

[7] See Exercise 28.

Exercises 28 through 33 in the following are concerned with various other combinations of value measures and probability measures.

EXERCISES

Note: Exercises 1, 2, and 3 pertain to the case where strategies are simple courses of action.

1. Given the probability matrix

	O_1	O_2	O_3	O_4	O_5	O_6
$S_1 = A_1$	.18	.21	.06	.17	.27	.11
$S_2 = A_2$	.13	.24	.11	.08	.30	.14

what can you conclude about the sign of $E(A_1) - E(A_2)$ when:

(a) Model II applies and $V_1 \geq V_2 \geq V_3 \geq V_4 \geq V_5 \geq V_6$, where $V_j = V(O_j)$?

(b) Model I applies and $V_{11} \geq V_{21} \geq V_{12} \geq V_{22} \geq V_{13} \geq V_{14} \geq V_{23} \geq V_{24} \geq V_{15} \geq V_{25} \geq V_{16} \geq V_{26}$, where $V_{ij} = V(A_i, O_j)$?

2. Suppose with $m = 2$, $n = 8$, an ordinal ranking of the V_{ij}, $i = 1, 2$; $j = 1, \ldots, 8$, is obtained as $V_{21} \geq V_{22} \geq V_{11} \geq V_{14} \geq V_{16} \geq V_{23} \geq V_{12} \geq V_{24} \geq V_{18} \geq V_{17} \geq V_{13} \geq V_{25} \geq V_{26} \geq V_{27} \geq V_{28} \geq V_{15}$. What must be true of the P_{ij} in order to be able to conclude that $E(A_2) \geq E(A_1)$, given only the ordinal ranking of the V_{ij}?

3. Given the probability matrix

	O_1	O_2	O_3
A_1	.4	.2	.4
A_2	.3	.4	.3

what can you conclude about the sign of $E(A_1) - E(A_2)$ when:

(a) Model II applies and $V_2 - V_3 \geq V_1 - V_2 \geq 0$?

(b) Model II applies and $V_1 - V_2 \geq V_2 - V_3 \geq 0$?

(c) Model I applies and $V_{21} - V_{22} \geq V_{22} - V_{13} \geq V_{11} - V_{12} \geq V_{12} - V_{21} \geq V_{13} - V_{23} \geq 0$?

(d) Model I applies and $V_{22} - V_{13} \geq V_{11} - V_{12} \geq V_{12} - V_{21} \geq V_{21} - V_{22} \geq V_{13} - V_{23} \geq 0$?

4. Suppose $r = 8$ and one obtains the second ordered metric ranking

$(V_5 + V_7 - V_4 - V_8) \geq (V_3 + V_7 - V_4 - V_6) \geq (V_2 + V_4 - 2V_3) \geq (V_2 + V_5 - V_1 - V_6) \geq (V_3 + V_4 - V_2 - V_5) \geq (V_6 - V_7) \geq (V_1 + V_8 - V_2 - V_7) \geq 0$.

Determine the simple ordered metric ranking and ordinal ranking embedded in this second ordered metric ranking, and write a 2-by-8 probability matrix (Model I or II) which yields no conclusion about the sign of $E(S_1) - E(S_2)$, given only the ordinal or simple ordered metric ranking, but does yield the conclusion $E(S_1) \geq E(S_2)$ with the second ordered metric ranking.

5. In the statistical model with $n = 6$, $r = 12$, suppose that $(P(E_1), P(E_2), \ldots, P(E_6)) = (.21, .06, .20, .32, .12, .09)$. For two rows of the consequence matrix corresponding to S_1 and S_2,

	E_1	E_2	E_3	E_4	E_5	E_6
S_1	o_{11}	o_{12}	o_{13}	o_{14}	o_{15}	o_{16}
S_2	o_{21}	o_{22}	o_{23}	o_{24}	o_{25}	o_{26}

suppose that $V(o_{14}) \geq V(o_{23}) \geq V(o_{26}) \geq V(o_{11}) \geq V(o_{13}) \geq V(o_{24}) \geq V(o_{15}) \geq V(o_{21}) \geq V(o_{12}) \geq V(o_{22}) \geq V(o_{16}) \geq V(o_{25})$. Show that $E(S_1) \geq E(S_2)$.

6. In the statistical model with $n = 3$, suppose one obtains the simple ordered metric value ranking

$$V(o_{11}) - V(o_{23}) \geq V(o_{12}) - V(o_{13}) \geq V(o_{23}) - V(o_{22})$$
$$\geq V(o_{22}) - V(o_{12}) \geq V(o_{13}) - V(o_{21}) \geq 0.$$

Prove that $E(S_1) \geq E(S_2)$ if $P(E_1) \geq {}^1/_5 + {}^2/_5 P(E_3)$.

7. Given the probability matrix

	o_1	o_2	o_3	o_4
S_1	.20	.20	.25	.35
S_2	.10	.35	.30	.25

suppose that $V_1 \geq V_2 \geq V_3 \geq V_4$. With each of the following two higher ordered metric rankings, state what you can about the sign of $E(S_1) - E(S_2)$:

(a) $V_1 - V_4 \geq V_1 - V_3 \geq V_1 - V_2 \geq V_2 - V_4 \geq V_2 - V_3 \geq V_3 - V_4 \geq 0$.

(b) $V_1 - V_4 \geq V_1 - V_3 \geq V_2 - V_4 \geq V_1 - V_2 \geq V_2 - V_3 \geq V_3 - V_4 \geq 0$.

8. Show that, if the method of equating coefficients is applied to a simple ordered metric ranking of the V_j, $j = 1, 2, \ldots, r$, theorem 6.3 results.

9. For each of the following partial orderings of the V_j: (1) Draw the value graph of the partial ordering; (2) state whether it is connected; (3) and if any connected (sub)graph with no superfluous arcs contains cycles, identify the cycles.

(a) $V_1 \geq V_2 \geq V_3$; $V_5 \geq V_6 \geq V_7$; $V_1 \geq V_5$; $V_2 \geq V_4$ ($r = 7$).

(b) $V_1 \geq V_3 \geq V_4 \geq V_6$; $V_2 \geq V_3 \geq V_5 \geq V_6$; $V_7 \geq V_9$; $V_8 \geq V_9$
($r = 10$).

(c) $V_1 \geq V_2 \geq V_3 \geq V_4 \geq V_5 \geq V_6 \geq V_7 \geq V_8$; $V_3 \geq V_9 \geq V_6$; $V_9 \geq V_{13} \geq V_{14}$; $V_{10} \geq V_{13}$; $V_{11} \geq V_{13}$; $V_{12} \geq V_{13}$; $V_{15} \geq V_{17} \geq V_{19} \geq V_{13}$; $V_{16} \geq V_{17} \geq V_{18}$; $V_{19} \geq V_{20} \geq V_{21} \geq V_{24}$; $V_{20} \geq V_{22} \geq V_{24}$; $V_{20} \geq V_{23} \geq V_{24}$; $V_{23} \geq V_{25}$ ($r = 25$).

10. In connection with the outline of the proof of theorem 6.6, prove:

(a) If a connected graph (or subgraph) has a cycle and any one arc of the cycle is deleted, then the graph (or subgraph) will still be connected.

(*b*) A connected graph with r nodes and no cycles has exactly $r - 1$ arcs.
(*c*) (6.16).
(*d*) (6.17).

11. Given the probability matrix

	O_1	O_2	O_3	O_4
A_1	.15	.29	.25	.31
A_2	.11	.28	.28	.33

let $V_1 = V(A_1, O_1)$, $V_2 = V(A_2, O_1)$, $V_3 = V(A_1, O_2)$, $V_4 = V(A_2, O_2)$, $V_5 = V(A_1, O_3)$, $V_6 = V(A_2, O_3)$, $V_7 = V(A_1, O_4)$, $V_8 = V(A_2, O_4)$ in connection with Model I ($S = A$).

What can you conclude about the sign of $E(A_1) - E(A_2)$ with each of the following partial orderings of the V_j?

(*a*) $V_1 \geqslant V_2 \geqslant V_3 \geqslant V_4 \geqslant V_5 \geqslant V_6$; $V_1 \geqslant V_8 \geqslant V_3$; $V_7 \geqslant V_8$.
(*b*) $V_2 \geqslant V_5 \geqslant V_7 \geqslant V_8$; $V_3 \geqslant V_4 \geqslant V_1 \geqslant V_6 \geqslant V_8$.

12. Verify (6.19) and (6.22).

13. Given the probability matrix

	V_1	V_2	V_3	V_4	V_5	V_6
S_1	.22	.26	.12	.14	.10	.16
S_2	.16	.20	.21	.16	.08	.19
S_3	.24	.28	.09	.12	.06	.21
S_4	.18	.15	.28	.20	.04	.15
S_5	.05	.36	.12	.11	.15	.21
S_6	.17	.18	.20	.11	.20	.14

suppose the first bounded interval measure of relative values, $I_1 = 1$, $I_6 = 0$, and

$$.6 \leqslant I_2 \leqslant .8, \qquad .1 \leqslant I_3 \leqslant .2, \qquad .2 \leqslant I_4 \leqslant .4, \qquad .4 \leqslant I_5 \leqslant .7$$

is obtained. With this information, what strategies may be eliminated from further consideration?

14. Given the probability matrix

	O_1	O_2	O_3	O_4	O_5	O_6	O_7	O_8
S_1	.08	.16	.23	.02	.07	.19	.14	.11
S_2	.12	.17	.06	.04	.14	.09	.16	.22

suppose, under Model II, we obtain the ordinal ranking $V_1 \geqslant V_2 \geqslant V_3 \geqslant V_4 \geqslant V_5 \geqslant V_6 \geqslant V_7 \geqslant V_8$, and then get the second bounded interval measure:

$$.06 \leqslant L_1 \leqslant .13,$$
$$.12 \leqslant L_2 \leqslant .24,$$
$$.08 \leqslant L_3 \leqslant .12,$$
$$.02 \leqslant L_4 \leqslant .10,$$
$$.13 \leqslant L_5 \leqslant .31,$$
$$.10 \leqslant L_6 \leqslant .25,$$
$$.14 \leqslant L_7 \leqslant .20.$$

Compute $M'(S_1, S_2)$ and $m'(S_1, S_2)$ defined after (6.22), and state what you can conclude concerning the sign of $E(S_1) - E(S_2)$. Show that the definite conclusion arrived at with the bounded interval measure cannot be established by means of the ordinal ranking only.

15. In the third bounded interval measure of relative value, suppose $r' = 8$, $V_1 > V_2 > \ldots > V_8$, and

$$.1 \leqslant K_1 \leqslant 2, \qquad .3 \leqslant K_2 \leqslant .5, \qquad 6 \leqslant K_3 \leqslant 10,$$
$$.1 \leqslant K_4 \leqslant .4, \qquad 4 \leqslant K_5 \leqslant 5, \qquad 1 \leqslant K_6 \leqslant 2.$$

In addition, suppose the D_k' corresponding to the V_j [see (6.23)] are given as $(D_1', \ldots, D_8') = (.02, -.04, .03, -.01, -.06, -.03, .06, .03)$. Show that $E(S_1) \leqslant E(S_2)$ by determining $M''(S_1, S_2)$. Also find $m''(S_1, S_2)$.

16. In a problem with r V_j, suppose that one determines that $V_1 > V_2$, and also knows that $V_2 \geqslant V_j$ for all $j > 2$. Define a bounded interval measure on this basis along the lines of the first bounded interval measure presented in the chapter, and give a theorem which states the conditions that must apply in order to be able to conclude that $E(S_1) \geqslant E(S_2)$ or that $E(S_2) \geqslant E(S_1)$ with this bounded interval measure.

17. In connection with theorem 6.9, suppose $V_1 \geqslant V_2 \geqslant \ldots \geqslant V_n$. Then using the language and notation of theorem 6.9, prove the corollary: If there exists a k such that $V_j - V_k$ has the same sign as $P_{1j} - P_{2j}$ for all $j \neq k$, then the first condition of theorem 6.2 ($\sum_{j=1}^{k} D_j \geqslant 0$ for $k = 1, 2, \ldots, r - 1$) is satisfied.

18. Suppose that along with the intracolumn probability ranking discussed in Section 6.5, an intercolumn ranking of the absolute difference $|P_{1j} - P_{2j}|$, such as $|P_{1j_1} - P_{2j_1}| \geqslant |P_{1j_2} - P_{2j_2}| \geqslant \ldots \geqslant |P_{1j_n} - P_{2j_n}| \geqslant 0$, is obtained. Beginning with (6.26), derive a theorem which states conditions sufficient to establish the sign of $E(S_1) - E(S_2)$ given the intracolumn ranking and the intercolumn absolute difference ranking.

19. For Model II with $n = 6$ and $V_1 \geqslant V_2 \geqslant V_3 \geqslant V_4 \geqslant V_5 \geqslant V_6$, what can be concluded about the sign of $E(S_1) - E(S_2)$ if $P_{21} \geqslant P_{11}$; $P_{12} \geqslant P_{22}$; $P_{13} \geqslant P_{23}$; $P_{14} \geqslant P_{24}$; $P_{15} \geqslant P_{25}$; $P_{16} \geqslant P_{26}$?

20. For the statistical model with $n = 6$ and $P_1 \geqslant P_2 \geqslant P_3 \geqslant P_4 \geqslant P_5 \geqslant P_6 \geqslant 0$, $P_j = P(E_j)$, what can you conclude about the sign of $E(S_1) - E(S_2)$ for each of the following matrices of relative values?

		E_1	E_2	E_3	E_4	E_5	E_6
(a)	S_1	6	34	-12	8	2	1
	S_2	8	33	-5	0	2	4

		E_1	E_2	E_3	E_4	E_5	E_6
(b)	S_1	2	3	6	7	10	11
	S_2	1	4	5	8	9	12

		E_1	E_2	E_3	E_4	E_5	E_6
(c)	S_1	10	14	8	7	31	16
	S_2	4	24	13	0	20	9

21. (*Continuation.*) In connection with (*c*) above, what can you conclude about the sign of $E(S_1) - E(S_2)$, given the following set of inequalities?

$$P_2 + P_3 + P_4 + P_5 \geqslant P_1 \geqslant P_2 + P_3 + P_4,$$
$$P_3 + P_4 \geqslant P_2 \geqslant P_3,$$
$$P_4 + P_5 \geqslant P_3 \geqslant P_4,$$
$$P_4 \geqslant P_5 + P_6,$$
$$P_5 \geqslant P_6,$$
$$P_6 \geqslant 0.$$

22. For the probability matrix

	O_1	O_2	O_3	O_4
$S_1 = A_1$	P_{11}	P_{12}	P_{13}	P_{14}
$S_2 = A_2$	P_{21}	P_{22}	P_{23}	P_{24}

suppose the intrarow rankings

$$P_{11} \geqslant P_{12} \geqslant P_{13} \geqslant P_{14} \geqslant 0,$$
$$P_{23} \geqslant P_{22} \geqslant P_{21} \geqslant P_{24} \geqslant 0,$$

have been obtained, and suppose in addition that, with Model I and $V_{ij} = V(A_i, O_j)$,

$$(V_{11}, V_{12}, V_{13}, V_{14}) = (9, 7, 8, 6),$$
$$(V_{21}, V_{22}, V_{23}, V_{24}) = (12, 6, 4, 7),$$

up to an increasing linear transformation. Show that $E(S_1) \geqslant E(S_2)$.
    With the same intrarow probability rankings, suppose that

$$(V_{11}, V_{12}, V_{13}, V_{14}) = (9, 3, 14, 10),$$
$$(V_{21}, V_{22}, V_{23}, V_{24}) = (12, 4, 8, 4).$$

In this case what can be concluded about the sign of $E(S_1) - E(S_2)$?

23. Given the matrix of relative values for Model I

	O_1	O_2	O_3	O_4
$S_1 = A_1$	4	7	5	9
$S_2 = A_2$	6	8	3	8

and the ordinal ranking of the P_{ij}, $P_{21} \geqslant P_{11} \geqslant P_{12} \geqslant P_{22} \geqslant P_{23} \geqslant P_{13} \geqslant P_{24} \geqslant P_{14} \geqslant 0$, show that $E(A_2) \geqslant E(A_1)$.

24. With $n = 4$ and Model II, suppose that one obtains the ordinal ranking of the P_{ij}, $i = 1, 2; j = 1, \ldots, 4$, shown in the previous exercise. In addition, suppose the ordinal value ranking $V_2 \geqslant V_1 \geqslant V_3 \geqslant V_4$ is obtained, where $V_j = V(O_j)$. With this information, show that $E(A_1) \geqslant E(A_2)$.

25. In this chapter (6.30) and (6.41) have similar forms, but arise in different contexts. Discuss the basic differences between these two equations.

26. Given the matrix of relative values

	O_1	O_2	O_3	
$S_1 = A_1$	3	6	10	$V_{ij} = V(A_i, O_j)$
$S_2 = A_2$	5	5	8	

and the bounded probability measure

$$.2 \leqslant P_{11} \leqslant .4, \qquad .4 \leqslant P_{12} \leqslant .6, \qquad .1 \leqslant P_{13} \leqslant .3,$$
$$.1 \leqslant P_{21} \leqslant .4, \qquad .2 \leqslant P_{22} \leqslant .3, \qquad .6 \leqslant P_{23} \leqslant .8,$$

show that $E(A_2) \geqslant E(A_1)$.

27. Given the bounded probability measure of Exercise 26, suppose Model II applies, and the ordinal value ranking $V_1 \geqslant V_2 \geqslant V_3$ has been obtained, where $V_j = V(O_j)$. Show that $E(A_1) \geqslant E(A_2)$, using theorem 6.2.

28. Describe a procedure for determining when it can be concluded that either $E(A_1) \geqslant E(A_2)$ or $E(A_2) \geqslant E(A_1)$, after one has obtained a first bounded interval measure of the V_{ij} and a bounded interval measure of the P_{ij} when Model I applies with strategies equaling courses of action.

29. For the statistical model, discuss methods for analyzing $E(S_1) - E(S_2)$ for sign, given a bounded interval measure of the $P_j = P(E_j)$ of the form

$$0 \leqslant \alpha_j \leqslant P_j \leqslant \alpha_j + \epsilon_j \leqslant 1, \qquad j = 1, \ldots, n,$$

$$\sum_{j=1}^{n} \alpha_j \leqslant 1 \leqslant \sum_{j=1}^{n} (\alpha_j + \epsilon_j),$$

in conjunction with:
(a) An interval measure of the $V_{ij} = V(o_{ij})$, $i = 1, 2; j = 1, \ldots, n$.
(b) An ordinal ranking of the V_{ij}.
(c) The second bounded interval measure of the V_{ij}.

30. Given an ordinal ranking of relative values $V_1 \geqslant V_2 \geqslant \ldots \geqslant V_r$ and an ordinal ranking of the P_{ij}, $i = 1, 2; j = 1, \ldots, r$, explain a procedure for analyzing $E(S_1) - E(S_2)$ for sign. Use theorem 6.2 as a starting point.

31. Given an ordered metric ranking of relative values and an ordinal probability ranking, explain a procedure for analyzing $E(S_1) - E(S_2)$ for sign, beginning with theorem 6.3.

32. Given an ordinal ranking of relative values and a bounded probability measure for Model I or II, state conditions necessary and sufficient to determine the sign of $E(S_1) - E(S_2)$, given only the stated measures.

33. Given an ordered metric ranking of relative values and a bounded probability measure for Model I or II, state conditions necessary and sufficient to determine the sign of $E(S_1) - E(S_2)$, given no additional information on the V_j (or V_{ij}) and the P_{ij}.

Chapter 7

GENERAL ANALYSIS FOR DOMINANCE

7.1 INTRODUCTION

This chapter generalizes some of the results of the previous chapter to the situation of mixed dominance. We recall the definition from Chapter 3: Strategy S_s is dominated if there exists a vector $\mathbf{a} = (a_1, a_2, \ldots, a_t)$ with $a_i \geqslant 0$, $i = 1, \ldots, t$, $a_s = 0$, and $\sum_{i=1}^{t} a_i = 1$ such that $\sum_{i=1}^{t} a_i E(S_i) \geqslant E(S_s)$, or such that

$$\mathbf{a} \cdot \mathbf{E(S)} - E(S_s) \geqslant 0,$$

where $\mathbf{a} \cdot \mathbf{E(S)}$ indicates scalar multiplication of $(a_1, \ldots, a_t)$ and $(E(S_1), \ldots, E(S_t))$. We recall in addition that if S_s is dominated, then there exists a vector $\mathbf{C} = (C_1, \ldots, C_t)$[1] that maximizes the decision maker's total expected relative value, $C_1 E(S_1) + \ldots + C_t E(S_t)$, such that in $\mathbf{C}$, $C_s = 0$. Unless otherwise specified, $\mathbf{a}$ will always denote a t-dimensional vector whose components are nonnegative real numbers summing to one, with the sth component equal to zero.

Following the notation at the beginning of Section 6.2,

$$\mathbf{a} \cdot \mathbf{E(S)} - E(S_s) = \sum_{j=1}^{r} \left(\sum_{i=1}^{t} a_i P_{ij} - P_{sj} \right) V_j, \qquad (7.1)$$

where in:

Model I: $V_j = V(o_j)$, $P_{ij} = P(o_j \mid S_i)$, $i = 1, \ldots, t; j = 1, \ldots, r$.

Model II: $V_j = V(O_j)$, $P_{ij} = P(O_j \mid S_i)$, $i = 1, \ldots, t; j = 1, \ldots, r = n$.

Statistical Model: $V_j, j = 1, \ldots, r$ with $r = tn$ are the relative values of the tn consequences in the statistical consequence matrix. If $V_j = V(o_{i'k})$, the relative value of the consequence derived from strategy $S_{i'}$,

[1] Each C_i is nonnegative and the t C_i sum to one.

and state E_k, then $P_{i'j} = P(E_k)$, and for fixed j all other P_{ij} with $i \neq i'$ are set equal to zero.

Further elaboration on the statistical model may be helpful. In the basic formulation of the statistical model given in Section 3.6,

$$E(S_i) = \sum_{k=1}^{n} P(E_k) V(o_{ik}), \qquad i = 1, \ldots, t,$$

so that

$$
\begin{aligned}
\mathbf{a} \cdot \mathbf{E(S)} - E(S_s) &= \sum_{i=1}^{t} a_i \sum_{k=1}^{n} P(E_k) V(o_{ik}) - \sum_{k=1}^{n} P(E_k) V(o_{sk}) \\
&= \sum_{k=1}^{n} \left[\sum_{i=1}^{t} a_i V(o_{ik}) - V(o_{sk}) \right] P(E_k),
\end{aligned}
\tag{7.2}
$$

which is a turnabout of the right-hand side of (7.1), as one would expect from the formulation of the several models. If for fixed j, V_j in the notation of (7.1) is the same as $V(o_{ik})$ in the notation of (7.2), then

$$
\begin{aligned}
\left(\sum_{i=1}^{t} a_i P_{ij} - P_{sj} \right) V_j &= \left(\sum_{i=1}^{t} a_i P_{ij} - P_{sj} \right) V(o_{ik}), \\
&= \begin{cases} a_i P(E_k) V(o_{ik}) & \text{if } i \neq s, \\ -P(E_k) V(o_{ik}) & \text{if } i = s. \end{cases}
\end{aligned}
\tag{7.3}
$$

If on the right-hand side of (7.1), $\sum_{j=1}^{r}$ is split into the double sum $\sum_{j=1}^{r} = \sum_{k=1}^{n} \sum_{i=1}^{t}$, then by using (7.3) in (7.1) we may write

$$
\begin{aligned}
\mathbf{a} \cdot \mathbf{E(S)} - E(S_i) &= \sum_{k=1}^{n} \sum_{i \neq s} a_i P(E_k) V(o_{ik}) - \sum_{k=1}^{n} P(E_k) V(o_{sk}), \\
&= \sum_{k=1}^{n} \left[\sum_{i=1}^{t} a_i V(o_{ik}) - V(o_{sk}) \right] P(E_k),
\end{aligned}
$$

which is identical to (7.2).

With $\mathbf{a} \cdot \mathbf{E(S)} - E(S_s)$ written as in (7.1), we shall contract the notation one step further by defining

$$P_j(\mathbf{a}; s) = \sum_{i=1}^{t} a_i P_{ij} - P_{sj}, \qquad j = 1, \ldots, r, \tag{7.4}$$

so that (7.1) may be written as

$$\mathbf{a} \cdot \mathbf{E(S)} - E(S_s) = \sum_{j=1}^{r} P_j(\mathbf{a}; s) V_j. \tag{7.5}$$

The form thus arrived at, namely (7.5), will be used in the next section for an analysis of mixed dominance with various rankings of the V_j. In later sections, different forms, mostly dictated by convenience, will be used for $\mathbf{a} \cdot E(S) - E(S_s)$.

The reader should note that

$$\sum_{j=1}^{r} P_j(\mathbf{a}; s) = 0$$

in (7.5) for each model.

7.2 ORDINAL AND ORDERED METRIC VALUE ANALYSIS

Since the theorems that follow are straightforward generalizations of theorems in the previous chapter, proofs will be omitted.

First, suppose that the V_j in (7.5) have been ranked by decreasing magnitude on an ordinal scale giving (by subscript convention) $V_1 \geqslant V_2 \geqslant \ldots \geqslant V_r$. Then, with the use of (6.1), (7.5) may be written as

$$\mathbf{a} \cdot E(S) - E(S_s) = \sum_{k=1}^{r-1} \left[\sum_{j=1}^{k} P_j(\mathbf{a}; s) \right] (V_k - V_{k+1}), \qquad (7.6)$$

which yields:

Theorem 7.1 Given the ordinal ranking $V_1 \geqslant V_2 \geqslant \ldots \geqslant V_r$ and no additional information concerning the relative magnitudes of the V_j, it can be concluded that S_s is dominated if and only if there exists an $\mathbf{a}$ such that

$$\sum_{j=1}^{k} P_j(\mathbf{a}; s) \geqslant 0 \qquad \text{for} \qquad k = 1, 2, \ldots, r - 1.$$

Proceeding from the stated ordinal ranking, suppose the differences $(V_k - V_{k+1})$ have been ranked by decreasing magnitude on a simple ordered metric scale. Let $V_m^{(1)}$ denote the mth largest difference with $V_r^{(1)} = 0$, giving $V_1^{(1)} \geqslant V_2^{(1)} \geqslant \ldots \geqslant V_{r-1}^{(1)} \geqslant V_r^{(1)}$. Letting $P_m^{(1)}(\mathbf{a}; s)$ be the coefficient of $V_m^{(1)}$ in (7.6), we get

$$\mathbf{a} \cdot E(S) - E(S_s) = \sum_{j=1}^{r-1} P_j^{(1)}(\mathbf{a}; s) V_j^{(1)}$$

$$= \sum_{k=1}^{r-1} \left[\sum_{j=1}^{k} P_j^{(1)}(\mathbf{a}; s) \right] (V_k^{(1)} - V_{k+1}^{(1)}),$$

and hence:

Theorem 7.2 Given the ordered metric ranking $V_1^{(1)} \geqslant V_2^{(1)} \geqslant \ldots \geqslant V_{r-1}^{(1)} \geqslant 0$ and no additional information concerning the relative magnitudes of the V_j, it can be concluded that S_s is dominated if and only if there exists an **a** such that

$$\sum_{j=1}^{k} P_j^{(1)}(\mathbf{a}; s) \geqslant 0 \qquad \text{for} \qquad k = 1, 2, \ldots, r - 1.$$

Theorems 7.1 and 7.2 correspond, respectively, to theorems 6.2 and 6.3. In a manner quite analogous to the development following theorem 6.3 and leading to theorem 6.4, we could deal with the nth ordered metric ranking $(n = 2, 3, \ldots)$ in the present context. We leave this as an exercise for the reader.

For a higher ordered metric ranking, order the $R = r(r - 1)/2$ nonnegative value differences $(V_j - V_k)$ by decreasing magnitude. Let V_m' be the mth largest difference, giving the h.o.m. ranking $V_1' \geqslant V_2' \geqslant \ldots \geqslant V_R' \geqslant 0$. Consider the nonnegative adjacent differences $(V_m' - V_{m+1}')$ obtained from the h.o.m. ranking. Let T denote the number of distinct differences $(V_m' - V_{m+1}')$ and let $V_1'', V_2'', \ldots, V_T''$ denote these T distinct differences. Writing

$$\mathbf{a} \cdot \mathbf{E(S)} - E(S_s) = \sum_{j=1}^{r} P_j(\mathbf{a}; s)V_j = \sum_{v=1}^{T} b_v V_v'', \qquad (7.7)$$

and equating coefficients of the V_j we get r linear equations in the $T + t - 1$ unknowns $(b_1, b_2, \ldots, b_T; a_1, \ldots, a_{s-1}, a_{s+1}, \ldots, a_t) = (\mathbf{b}; \mathbf{a})$. One of these equations will be linearly dependent on the other $r - 1$, so we will work with only $r - 1$ of them. Our objective is to determine whether there exists a solution $(\mathbf{b}; \mathbf{a})$ to these equations such that, in the solution, $\mathbf{b} \geqslant 0$, $\mathbf{a} \geqslant 0$, and $\sum a_i = 1$. If such a solution can be found, then we can conclude that S_s is dominated. The following example illustrates the theory developed to this point.

EXAMPLE. With $t = 3$, $n = 2$, suppose Model I $(\mathbf{S} = \mathbf{A})$ is to be used with the probability matrix

	O_1	O_2	Row Sums
$S_1 = A_1$	15	85	100
$S_2 = A_2$	54	46	100
$S_3 = A_3$	90	10	100

where all P_{ij} have been multiplied by 100 to dispense with the decimal point. Suppose an ordinal ranking of the six V_j has been obtained of the form $V_1 \geqslant V_2 \geqslant \ldots \geqslant V_6$, where $V_1 = V(A_1, O_1)$, $V_2 = V(A_2, O_2)$, $V_3 = V(A_3, O_1)$, $V_4 = V(A_1, O_2)$, $V_5 = V(A_3, O_2)$, $V_6 = V(A_2, O_1)$.

Writing the matrix of probabilities of strategies for consequences, we get

	$V_1 \geqslant$	$V_2 \geqslant$	$V_3 \geqslant$	$V_4 \geqslant$	$V_5 \geqslant$	V_6
$S_1 = A_1$	15	0	0	85	0	0
$S_2 = A_2$	0	46	0	0	0	54
$S_3 = A_3$	0	0	90	0	10	0

Suppose, in addition, that the following higher ordered metric ranking has been derived:

$$(V_1 - V_6) \geqslant (V_1 - V_5) \geqslant (V_1 - V_4) \geqslant (V_1 - V_3) \geqslant (V_1 - V_2)$$
$$\geqslant (V_2 - V_6) \geqslant (V_2 - V_5) \geqslant (V_2 - V_4) \geqslant (V_2 - V_3) \quad (7.8)$$
$$\geqslant (V_3 - V_6) \geqslant (V_3 - V_5) \geqslant (V_3 - V_4) \geqslant (V_4 - V_6)$$
$$\geqslant (V_4 - V_5) \geqslant (V_5 - V_6) \geqslant 0.$$

We shall show that S_3 is dominated. First, however, it will be demonstrated that S_3 cannot be shown to be dominated with either the ordinal ranking or the ordered metric ranking embedded in (7.8), the ordered metric ranking being

$$(V_1 - V_2) \geqslant (V_2 - V_3) \geqslant (V_3 - V_4) \geqslant (V_4 - V_5) \geqslant (V_5 - V_6) \geqslant 0.$$
$$(7.9)$$

In this context, $S_s = S_3$ and $\mathbf{a} = (\alpha, 1 - \alpha, 0)$, where $0 \leqslant \alpha \leqslant 1$. We wish to analyze

$$\alpha E(S_1) + (1 - \alpha)E(S_2) - E(S_3)$$

for sign.

The following table shows $P_j(\mathbf{a}; 3)$, as defined in (7.4), $\sum_{j=1}^{k} P_j(\mathbf{a}; 3)$ as used in theorem 7.1 (ordinal analysis), and $\sum_{j=1}^{k} P_j^{(1)}(\mathbf{a}; 3)$ as used in theorem 7.2 (ordered metric analysis):

j or k	$P_j(\mathbf{a}; 3)$	$\sum_{j=1}^{k} P_j(\mathbf{a}; 3)$	$P_j^{(1)}(\mathbf{a}; 3)^2$	$\sum_{j=1}^{k} P_j^{(1)}(\mathbf{a}; 3)$
1	15α	15α	15α	15α
2	$46(1 - \alpha)$	$46 - 31\alpha$	$46 - 31\alpha$	$46 - 16\alpha$
3	-90	$-44 - 31\alpha$	$-44 - 31\alpha$	$2 - 47\alpha$
4	85α	$-44 + 54\alpha$	$-44 + 54\alpha$	$-42 + 7\alpha$
5	-10	$-54 + 54\alpha$	$-54 + 54\alpha$	$-96 + 61\alpha$
6	$54(1 - \alpha)$			

[2] The reason this column is the same as the third column is that (7.9) requires no rearrangement of the $\sum_{j=1}^{k} P_j(\mathbf{a}; 3)$ to yield the $P_j^{(1)}(\mathbf{a}; 3)$. If (7.9) had began with $(V_2 - V_3) \geqslant (V_1 - V_2)$ instead of $(V_1 - V_2) \geqslant (V_2 - V_3)$, then 15α and $46 - 31\alpha$ would exchange places in column 4.

Clearly, no α exists with $0 \leqslant \alpha \leqslant 1$ such that all entries in either column 3 or column 5 are nonnegative. Hence, the ordinal and ordered metric rankings given above are not powerful enough to show that S_3 is dominated.

By considering differences of adjacent value differences in (7.8), we get an equation in the form of (7.7):

$$15\alpha V_1 + 46(1 - \alpha)V_2 - 90V_3 + 85\alpha V_4 - 10V_5 + 54(1 - \alpha)V_6$$
$$= b_1(V_5 - V_6) + b_2(V_4 - V_5) + b_3(V_3 - V_4) + b_4(V_2 - V_3)$$
$$+ b_5(V_1 + V_6 - 2V_2) + b_6(V_2 + V_6 - 2V_3)$$
$$+ b_7(V_3 + V_6 - 2V_4) + b_8(V_4 + V_6 - 2V_5).$$

Equating coefficients of the V_j:

$$
\begin{aligned}
b_5 &= 15\alpha, \\
b_4 - 2b_5 + b_6 &= 46(1 - \alpha), \\
b_3 - b_4 \qquad - 2b_6 + b_7 &= -90, \qquad (7.10a) \\
b_2 - b_3 \qquad\qquad - 2b_7 + b_8 &= 85\alpha, \\
b_1 - b_2 \qquad\qquad\qquad - 2b_8 &= -10,
\end{aligned}
$$

where the sixth equation, for the coefficients of V_6, has been omitted, since one equation is linearly dependent on the other five. We now try to determine a nonnegative solution to (7.10a). Solving (7.10a) for b_1 through b_5 in terms of b_6, b_7, b_8, and α gives

$$
\begin{aligned}
b_5 &= 15\alpha, \\
b_4 &= 46 - 16\alpha - b_6, \\
b_3 &= -44 - 16\alpha + b_6 - b_7, \qquad (7.10b) \\
b_2 &= -44 + 69\alpha + b_6 + b_7 - b_8, \\
b_1 &= -54 + 69\alpha + b_6 + b_7 + b_8.
\end{aligned}
$$

We now try to determine $b_6 \geqslant 0$, $b_7 \geqslant 0$, $b_8 \geqslant 0$, and $0 \leqslant \alpha \leqslant 1$ so that the right-hand sides of (7.10b) are all nonnegative. Setting $b_4 = 0$ gives $b_6 = 46 - 16\alpha$, and this is inserted into the right-hand sides of b_1, b_2, and b_3, giving

$$
\begin{aligned}
b_3 &= 2 - 32\alpha - b_7, \\
b_2 &= 2 + 53\alpha + b_7 - b_8, \\
b_1 &= -8 + 53\alpha + b_7 + b_8.
\end{aligned}
$$

Setting $b_3 = 0$ gives $b_7 = 2 - 32\alpha$, whence $\alpha \leqslant 1/16$. This gives

$$
\begin{aligned}
b_2 &= 4 + 21\alpha - b_8, \\
b_1 &= -6 + 21\alpha + b_8.
\end{aligned}
$$

Setting $b_2 = 0$ gives $b_8 = 4 + 21\alpha$ and leaves

$$b_1 = -2 + 42\alpha,$$

which requires $\alpha \geqslant {}^1/_{21}$ in order for b_1 to be nonnegative. Therefore, any α in the range ${}^1/_{21} \leqslant \alpha \leqslant {}^1/_{16}$ will give a nonnegative **b** solution

$$(b_1, b_2, \ldots, b_8) = (-2 + 42\alpha, 0, 0, 0, 15\alpha, 46 - 16\alpha, 2 - 32\alpha, 4 + 21\alpha),$$

and we conclude that S_3 is dominated.

In connection with the general analysis of dominance in a problem with a large number of courses of action or strategies, there arises the problem of how to search efficiently through the S_i in trying to detect dominance. Because of the algebraic complexities that one must deal with in mixed dominance, it is most efficient to eliminate first all strategies that can be eliminated on analyzing for pure dominance. If t is large, this will quite likely cause a sizable reduction in the set of strategies that need to be analyzed further. By means of the following example, we will illustrate what seems to be an efficient procedure in connection with Model I or Model II.

Example of Analysis

Consider the probability matrix in Table 7.1 (made up from a table of random numbers for the purposes of this example). Suppose that Model I applies, and we first obtain the ordinal ranking $V_1 \geqslant V_2 \geqslant V_3 \geqslant V_4 \geqslant V_5 \geqslant V_6$, where V_j is the relative value of o_j. In analyzing this measure go through the following steps:

1. Form Table 7.2, where the entries in the jth column of Table 7.2 are $\sum_{k=1}^{j} P_{ik}$, $i = 1, 2, \ldots, 18$.

2. From theorem 6.2, S_i is dominated if there is another row in Table 7.2 whose entries are columnwise respectively greater than or equal to the entries in the row of S_i. First circle the largest element(s) in each column. If any column has a unique largest entry, then the S_i for the row of this entry cannot be shown to be dominated under the ordinal ranking $V_1 \geqslant \ldots \geqslant V_6$. In case several S_i share the largest entry in a column, look for dominance among these S_i. If there is none (with the ordinal measure), all such S_i must be kept intact; that is, no one of them can be eliminated at this stage. At this point S_3 dominates S_{11}; and S_{12} dominates S_1. Hence S_{11} and S_1 may be eliminated.

3. Next, use the rows that remain and contain circled elements to eliminate other S_i under pure dominance. For Table 7.2, S_3 dominates $S_5, S_7, S_{13}, S_{14}, S_{16}$, and S_{17}, and these latter six S_i are eliminated. Then S_{12} dominates S_9 and S_{10}; S_2 dominates no remaining S_i; and S_{15} dominates no remaining S_i. This leaves us with the following rows that have no circled elements: S_4, S_6, S_8,

and S_{18}. Looking for pure dominance among these we find that S_8 dominates S_6 and S_{18}. Thus, as far as the ordinal measure is concerned, we are left with only two S_i (S_4 and S_8) that might still be shown to be dominated under mixed dominance.

4. Try to eliminate the rows that remain and have no circled elements (S_4 and S_8) by analyzing for mixed dominance. The S_i remaining at this point are S_2, S_3, S_4, S_8, S_{12}, and S_{15}. We find that S_4 is dominated by $\frac{1}{3}S_3 + \frac{2}{3}S_8$. However, S_8 cannot be shown to

TABLE 7.1

PROBABILITY MATRIX OF STRATEGIES FOR CONSEQUENCES*

	o_1	o_2	o_3	o_4	o_5	o_6
S_1	6	17	32	3	19	23
S_2	6	24	23	27	5	15
S_3	28	15	10	26	5	16
S_4	23	9	7	32	17	12
S_5	6	9	24	36	6	19
S_6	16	11	22	18	21	12
S_7	9	29	1	21	18	22
S_8	25	4	22	23	16	10
S_9	7	17	18	15	29	14
S_{10}	8	13	21	22	21	15
S_{11}	28	8	2	29	16	17
S_{12}	16	21	18	10	21	14
S_{13}	19	4	23	26	10	18
S_{14}	20	2	5	25	18	30
S_{15}	7	24	21	25	14	9
S_{16}	13	12	20	19	12	24
S_{17}	0	17	4	9	37	33
S_{18}	12	11	0	22	43	12

* Probabilities have been multiplied by 100 (therefore, each row sums to 100 rather than 1). This table was formed from a table of random numbers.

TABLE 7.2

MATRIX FOR ANALYZING FOR DOMINANCE WITH AN ORDINAL MEASURE
OF THE V_j*

	1	2	3	4	5
S_1	6	23	⑤⑤	58	77
S_2	6	30	53	⑧⓪	85
S_3	㉘	㊸	53	79	84
S_4	23	32	39	71	88
S_5	6	15	39	75	81
S_6	16	27	49	67	88
S_7	9	38	39	60	78
S_8	25	29	51	74	90
S_9	7	24	42	57	86
S_{10}	8	21	42	64	85
S_{11}	㉘	36	38	67	83
S_{12}	16	37	⑤⑤	65	86
S_{13}	19	23	46	72	82
S_{14}	20	22	27	52	70
S_{15}	7	31	52	77	⑨①
S_{16}	13	25	45	64	76
S_{17}	0	17	21	30	67
S_{18}	12	23	23	45	88

* Greatest elements in columns are circled. This matrix was formed from Table 7.1 (see text).

be dominated by the remaining rows and is therefore retained. This exhausts the information concerning dominance provided by the ordinal ranking. We are left with S_2, S_3, S_8, S_{12}, and S_{15}.

If at this point it is judged desirable to continue with the program of value measurement, suppose the ordered metric measure $V_3 - V_4 \geqslant V_2 - V_3 \geqslant V_4 - V_5 \geqslant V_1 - V_2 \geqslant V_5 - V_6 \geqslant 0$ is obtained. Then,

TABLE 7.3

MATRIX FOR ANALYZING FOR DOMINANCE WITH THE ORDERED METRIC
MEASURE OF THE V_j: $V_3 - V_4 \geqslant V_2 - V_3 \geqslant V_4 - V_5 \geqslant V_1 - V_2 \geqslant V_5 - V_6$*

	1	2	3	4	5
S_2	53	83	163	169	254
S_3	53	⑨⑥ (96)	(175)	(203)	(287)
S_8	51	80	154	179	269
S_{12}	(55)	92	157	173	259
S_{15}	52	83	160	⁁167	258

* Greatest elements in columns are circled.   Either S_3 or S_{12} has maximum expected value.   This matrix was formed from Table 7.2 (see text).

with the S_i not eliminated from Table 7.2, Table 7.3 is formed, where the five columns are:

Column 1:   column 3 from Table 7.2;

Column 2:   columns 3 + 2 from Table 7.2;

Column 3:   columns 3 + 2 + 4 from Table 7.2;

Column 4:   columns 3 + 2 + 4 + 1 from Table 7.2;

Column 5:   columns 3 + 2 + 4 + 1 + 5 from Table 7.2.

Note that the first subscript in each successive value difference from the ordered metric ranking indicates how the new table is to be formed. Then, by using a procedure with Table 7.3 entirely similar to the procedure used for Table 7.2, we find that S_3 dominates S_2, S_8, and S_{15}. Thus, we are left with the two strategies S_3 and S_{12}, one of which has an expected value greater than or equal to the expected value of every other strategy.

From inspection of rows S_3 and S_{12} in Table 7.3, it would seem (*a priori*) that $E(S_3) \geqslant E(S_{12})$. However, such a conclusion is not justified with only the ordered metric measure. If it is considered desirable and feasible to obtain a more powerful measure of relative values, this may yield a definite conclusion concerning the sign of $E(S_3) - E(S_{12})$. In looking back through the above example, it will be noted that $E(S_3)$ is greater than or equal to $E(S_i)$ for all i, except perhaps for $i = 12$, but we cannot conclude that $E(S_{12})$ is greater than or equal to $E(S_i)$ for all $i \neq 3$, since from

Table 7.3, for example, S_{12} dominates none of the other four S_i with the ordered metric measure.

Additional Comments on Analysis: Systems of Linear Inequalities

Connected with the problem of searching through the S_i to try to weed out the strategies which can be eliminated with one or more measures of relative value is the problem of developing efficient techniques for establishing whether an $\mathbf{a} = (a_1, \ldots, a_t)$ exists that satisfies the dominance condition of, for example, theorem 7.1 or theorem 7.2. Suppose, for definiteness, we use $S_1, S_2, \ldots, S_h$ to try to dominate S_{h+1} in connection with theorem 7.1 or 7.2. With an ordinal value ranking, the problem is to determine whether an $\mathbf{a}$ exists that satisfies the system of inequalities

$$\sum_{j=1}^{k} P_j(\mathbf{a}; h + 1) \geqslant 0, \qquad k = 1, \ldots, r - 1.$$

With a first ordered metric value ranking, the problem is to determine whether an $\mathbf{a}$ exists that satisfies the system

$$\sum_{j=1}^{k} P_j^{(1)}(\mathbf{a}; h + 1) \geqslant 0, \qquad k = 1, \ldots, r - 1.$$

Either of these cases takes the following form:

Determine if there exists an $\mathbf{a} = (a_1, a_2, \ldots, a_h)$ with $a_j \geqslant 0$, $j = 1, \ldots, h$ and

$$\sum_{j=1}^{h} a_j = 1,$$

such that

$$
\begin{aligned}
c_{11}a_1 &+ c_{12}a_2 &+ \ldots + c_{1h}a_h &\geqslant b_1, \\
c_{21}a_1 &+ c_{22}a_2 &+ \ldots + c_{2h}a_h &\geqslant b_2, \\
&\vdots \\
c_{r-1,1}a_1 &+ c_{r-1,2}a_2 &+ \ldots + c_{r-1,h}a_h &\geqslant b_{r-1},
\end{aligned}
$$

where all c_{ij} and b_i are nonnegative. (The b_i are sums of the $P_{h+1,\nu}$ and the c_{ij} are sums of the $P_{j\nu}$.)

Preliminary to using, say, a linear programming approach to solve this problem, several rather simple steps can be performed which may give a definite solution or, short of this, reduce the size of the problem.

Let us first suppose that pure dominance cannot be discerned between any pair $S_j, S_k, j, k = 1, \ldots, h + 1$. Then:

1. If $\max_j c_{ij} < b_i$ for one or more i, no admissible $\mathbf{a}$ satisfies the inequalities. If $\sum_{j=1}^{h} c_{ij} \geqslant hb_i$ for all i, $\mathbf{a} = (1/h, 1/h, \ldots, 1/h)$ satisfies the inequalities.

Suppose step 1 does not do the trick, and one does not see any simple way to perturb $\mathbf{a} = (1/h, \ldots, 1/h)$ to satisfy the inequalities. Then:

2. If $\min_{j} c_{ij} \geqslant b_i$, delete the ith inequality since it holds with any admissible $\mathbf{a}$. If $\min_{j} c_{ij} < b_i$, retain the ith inequality. If one or more inequalities has been scratched, compare columns of c_{ij} in the remaining inequalities: if $c_{ij} \geqslant c_{ik}$ ($j \neq k$) for all remaining i, set $a_k = 0$ and cross off column k. If one or more columns are thus deleted, check each remaining row again to see if $\min_{j} c_{ij}$ (for remaining columns) $\geqslant b_i$. If so, delete this inequality. Then go back and compare column coefficients, etc., until no more rows or columns may be deleted. At this point check again to see if the equal-a_j solution for those a_j not set equal to zero satisfies the remaining inequalities.

If at this point a definite conclusion about the existence of $\mathbf{a}$ has not been reached, one can try a variety of things. Let us suppose we are left with m inequalities ($m \leqslant r - 1$) and n nonzero a_k ($n \leqslant h$), renumbered if necessary as $a_1, a_2, \ldots, a_n$. Dividing each remaining inequality through by its $b(> 0)$ term, our set of inequalities becomes

$$d_{11}a_1 + d_{12}a_2 + \ldots + d_{1n}a_n \geqslant 1,$$
$$d_{21}a_1 + d_{22}a_2 + \ldots + d_{2n}a_n \geqslant 1,$$
$$\vdots$$
$$d_{m1}a_1 + d_{m2}a_2 + \ldots + d_{mn}a_n \geqslant 1.$$

(Here, if $d_{ij} \geqslant d_{kj}$ for $j = 1, \ldots, n$, then the ith inequality may be scratched.) To put this in linear programming language, subtract the nonnegative slack variable a_{n+i} from the left-hand side of the ith inequality, write it as an equality, and add the restriction

$$\sum_{j=1}^{n} a_j = 1$$

to the system to give

$$d_{11}a_1 + d_{12}a_2 + \ldots + d_{1n}a_n - a_{n+1} = 1,$$
$$d_{21}a_1 + d_{22}a_2 + \ldots + d_{2n}a_n - a_{n+2} = 1,$$
$$\vdots$$
$$d_{m1}a_1 + d_{m2}a_2 + \ldots + d_{mn}a_n - a_{n+m} = 1,$$
$$a_1 + a_2 + \ldots + a_n = 1.$$

Next subtract each of the first m equations from the last one, then add the artificial variable a_{n+m+1} to the last equality to give (with $e_{ij} = 1 - d_{ij}$)

$$e_{11}a_1 + e_{12}a_2 + \ldots + e_{1n}a_n + a_{n+1} \qquad\qquad\quad = 0,$$
$$e_{21}a_1 + e_{22}a_2 + \ldots + e_{2n}a_n \qquad\quad + a_{n+2} \qquad\quad = 0,$$
$$\vdots \qquad\qquad\qquad\qquad\qquad \ddots$$
$$e_{m1}a_1 + e_{m2}a_2 + \ldots + e_{mn}a_n \qquad\qquad\quad + a_{n+m} \qquad = 0,$$
$$a_1 + \quad a_2 + \ldots + \quad a_n \qquad\qquad\qquad\qquad + a_{n+m+1} = 1,$$
$$a_j \geqslant 0, \quad j = 1, 2, \ldots, n + m + 1.$$

Beginning with the infeasible solution $(a_1, a_2, \ldots, a_{n+m+1}) = (0, 0, \ldots, 0, 1)$ with base $(a_{n+1}, a_{n+2}, \ldots, a_{n+m+1})$, we attempt to drive the artificial variable a_{n+m+1} out of the base (to get it equal to zero) and end up with a feasible solution. In this, one may use the objective function $Z = a_{n+m+1}$, to be minimized. If a feasible solution exists (with $Z = 0$), then an **a** exists for our original problem. If a feasible solution does not exist, then there is no **a** satisfying the original inequalities. Standard linear programming technics may be used to determine whether a feasible solution to the above problem does in fact exist.[3] (See references at the end of the chapter.)

7.3 THE FIRST BOUNDED INTERVAL MEASURE, MODEL I ($S = A$) AND THE STATISTICAL MODEL

Quite different things occur in the general analysis for dominance with the first bounded interval measure of value under (1) Model I with strategies equal to courses of action or the statistical model and (2) Model I ($S_i \neq A_i$) or Model II. This section deals with case 1, the next section with case 2.

For Model I ($\mathbf{S} = \mathbf{A}$), let $V_{ij} = V(A_i, O_j)$, and for the statistical model let $V_{ij} = V(o_{ij})$, the relative value of the consequence associated with S_i and E_j. In either case, $i = 1, \ldots, t; j = 1, \ldots, n$. With V_1 and V_r the relative values of the most desirable and least desirable consequences, respectively, assume $V_1 > V_r$. Letting

$$I_{ij} = \frac{V_{ij} - V_r}{V_1 - V_r},$$

the first bounded interval measure is given by

$$\alpha_{ij} \leqslant I_{ij} \leqslant \beta_{ij}, \qquad i = 1, \ldots, t; \quad j = 1, \ldots, n, \qquad (7.11)$$
$$0 \leqslant \alpha_{ij} \leqslant \beta_{ij} \leqslant 1,$$

where the V_{ij} which is V_r will have $I_{ij} = 0$ and the V_{ij} which is V_1 will have $I_{ij} = 1$.

---

[3] The author is grateful to Charles Cook for pointing out this method of dealing with the existence of **a**.

For Model I ($S = A$) with $P_{ij} = P(O_j \mid A_i)$,

$$\frac{\mathbf{a} \cdot E(S) - E(S_s)}{V_1 - V_r} = \sum_{i=1}^{t} a_i \sum_{j=1}^{n} P_{ij} I_{ij} - \sum_{j=1}^{n} P_{sj} I_{sj}, \qquad (7.12)$$

and for the statistical model with $P_j = P(E_j)$,

$$\frac{\mathbf{a} \cdot E(S) - E(S_s)}{V_1 - V_r} = \sum_{i=1}^{t} a_i \sum_{j=1}^{n} P_j I_{ij} - \sum_{j=1}^{n} P_j I_{sj}. \qquad (7.13)$$

In trying to show that the right-hand side of (7.12) or (7.13) is non-negative (if, in fact, it is), we must consider the "worst" possible situation for the I_{ij} as restricted by (7.11). This occurs when we set $I_{ij} = \alpha_{ij}$ for $i \neq s$, and set $I_{sj} = \beta_{sj}, j = 1, \ldots, n$. The right-hand sides of (7.12) and (7.13) thus minimized with respect to $\{I_{ij}\}$, subject to (7.11), are respectively

$$\sum_{i=1}^{t} a_i \sum_{j=1}^{n} \alpha_{ij} P_{ij} - \sum_{j=1}^{n} \beta_{sj} P_{sj}, \qquad (7.14)$$

$$\sum_{j=1}^{n} \left(\sum_{i=1}^{t} a_i \alpha_{ij} - \beta_{sj} \right) P_j. \qquad (7.15)$$

By manipulating the components of $\mathbf{a}$, if we can find an $\mathbf{a}$ that makes (7.14) or (7.15), as the case may be, nonnegative, then S_s is dominated. In other words, if

$$\max_{\mathbf{a}} \left(\sum_{i=1}^{t} a_i \sum_{j=1}^{n} \alpha_{ij} P_{ij} - \sum_{j=1}^{n} \beta_{sj} P_{sj} \right) \geqslant 0, \qquad (7.16)$$

or

$$\max_{\mathbf{a}} \sum_{j=1}^{n} \left(\sum_{i=1}^{t} a_i \alpha_{ij} - \beta_{sj} \right) P_j \geqslant 0, \qquad (7.17)$$

as the case may be (Model I or the statistical model), then S_s is dominated. Any admissible $\mathbf{a}$ that makes (7.14) or (7.15) $\geqslant 0$ will show that S_s is dominated. If (7.16) or (7.17) is valid under "perfect" measurement of the P_{ij} or P_j, then the more exact our actual measurements of the probabilities get, the more likely we are to uncover an $\mathbf{a}$ that permits the conclusion that S_s is dominated.

Measures of Probabilities, Model I ($S = A$)

In the remainder of this section, we shall look at several measures of the P_{ij} for Model I ($S = A$) in connection with the first bounded interval measure of value. Our point of departure will be (7.14). The same thing may, of course, be done for the statistical model.

Suppose, first, that an ordinal ranking of the P_{ij} has been obtained. Let this be of the form

$$P_1 \geqslant P_2 \geqslant \ldots \geqslant P_r \geqslant P_{r+1}, \qquad P_{r+1} = 0, \qquad (7.18)$$

where each P_k for $k \le r$ is identically one of the P_{ij}. Then write

$$\sum_{i=1}^{t} a_i \sum_{j=1}^{n} \alpha_{ij} P_{ij} - \sum_{j=1}^{n} \beta_{sj} P_{sj} = \sum_{k=1}^{r} c_k P_k, \qquad (7.19)$$

where c_k is the coefficient of the P_{ij} being denoted as P_k on the left-hand side of (7.19):

$$c_k = \begin{cases} a_i \alpha_{ij}, & \text{if } P_k = P_{ij}, \quad i \ne s, \\ -\beta_{sj}, & \text{if } P_k = P_{sj}. \end{cases}$$

From (6.1) and (7.19),

$$\sum_{k=1}^{r} c_k P_k = \sum_{j=1}^{r} \left(\sum_{k=1}^{j} c_k \right) (P_j - P_{j+1}) \qquad (7.20)$$

and this, along with (7.18) gives us:

Theorem 7.3 Given (1) the first bounded interval measure of relative value (7.11), and (2) the ordinal probability ranking (7.18), it can be concluded that S_s is dominated if there exists an **a** such that

$$\sum_{k=1}^{j} c_k \ge 0 \qquad \text{for} \qquad j = 1, 2, \ldots, r.$$

To go one step further, suppose the $P_j - P_{j+1}$ in (7.20) are ranked from greatest to least. Letting $P_k^{(1)}$ denote the kth ranked probability difference, this ranking may be rendered as

$$P_1^{(1)} \ge P_2^{(1)} \ge \ldots \ge P_k^{(1)} \ge \ldots \ge P_r^{(1)} \ge 0. \qquad (7.21)$$

Let $c_k^{(1)}$ denote the coefficient of $P_k^{(1)}$ on the right-hand side of (7.20), giving

$$\sum_{j=1}^{r} \left(\sum_{k=1}^{j} c_k \right) (P_j - P_{j+1}) = \sum_{k=1}^{r} c_k^{(1)} P_k^{(1)} = \sum_{j=1}^{r} \left(\sum_{k=1}^{j} c_k^{(1)} \right) (P_j^{(1)} - P_{j+1}^{(1)}),$$

wherein $P_{r+1}^{(1)} = 0$. This yields:

Theorem 7.4 Given (1) the first bounded interval measure of relative value (7.11), and (2) the ranking of adjacent probability differences (7.21), it can be concluded that S_s is dominated if there exists an **a** such that

$$\sum_{k=1}^{j} c_k^{(1)} \ge 0 \qquad \text{for} \qquad j = 1, 2, \ldots, r.$$

Next, suppose that a bounded probability measure of the P_{ij} has been obtained and is given by

$$\gamma_{ij} \leqslant P_{ij} \leqslant \delta_{ij}, \qquad i = 1, \ldots, t; \quad j = 1, \ldots, n,$$
$$0 \leqslant \gamma_{ij} \leqslant \delta_{ij} \leqslant 1,$$
$$\sum_{j=1}^{n} \gamma_{ij} \leqslant \sum_{j=1}^{n} P_{ij} = 1 \leqslant \sum_{j=1}^{n} \delta_{ij}, \qquad i = 1, \ldots, t.$$

(7.22)

Having already taken the "worst case" in (7.14) for the bounded interval measure of value (7.9), we now take the "worst case" of the right-hand side of (7.14) for the bounded probability measure. That is, for each $i \neq s$, determine the values of the P_{ij} as restricted by (7.22) that minimize $\sum_{j=1}^{n} \alpha_{ij} P_{ij}$, and determine the values of the P_{sj} that maximize $\sum_{j=1}^{n} \beta_{sj} P_{sj}$. Let the P_{ij} that result from this procedure be denoted as $Q_{ij}, i = 1, \ldots, t;$ $j = 1, \ldots, n.$ Then

$$\min_{\{P_{ij}\}} \min_{\{I_{ij}\}} \left(\sum_i a_i \sum_j P_{ij} I_{ij} - \sum_j P_{sj} I_{sj} \right) = \sum_{i=1}^{t} a_i \sum_{j=1}^{n} \alpha_{ij} Q_{ij} - \sum_{j=1}^{n} \beta_{sj} Q_{sj}.$$

The right-hand side of this equation is maximized with respect to $\mathbf{a}$ if the a_i with the largest coefficient ($\sum_j \alpha_{ij} Q_{ij}$) is set equal to 1 and all other a_i are set equal to zero. Specifically, we get:

Theorem 7.5   Given (1) the first bounded interval measure of relative value (7.11) and no additional information on the V_{ij}, and (2) the bounded probability measure of the P_{ij} (7.22) and no additional information on the P_{ij}, it can be concluded that S_s is dominated if and only if

$$\max_{\mathbf{a}} \min_{\{P_{ij}\}} \min_{\{I_{ij}\}} \left(\sum_i a_i \sum_j P_{ij} I_{ij} - \sum_j P_{sj} I_{sj} \right) \geqslant 0,$$

that is, if and only if

$$\max_{i \neq s} \sum_{j=1}^{n} \alpha_{ij} Q_{ij} \geqslant \sum_{j=1}^{n} \beta_{sj} Q_{sj}.$$

Finally, if the P_{ij} are known exactly, then we can conclude, given only the first bounded interval measure of relative values, that S_s is dominated if and only if there is an $i \neq s$ such that

$$\sum_j \alpha_{ij} P_{ij} \geqslant \sum_j \beta_{sj} P_{sj}.$$

It should be kept in mind that the results in this section apply only to the model forms dealt with explicitly, and not with the general Model I or Model II. The reason for this will be examined in the next section.

7.4 THE FIRST BOUNDED INTERVAL MEASURE OF RELATIVE VALUES, MODELS I AND II

For the general case of Model I or for Model II, let the first bounded interval measure be given by

$$0 \leqslant \alpha_j \leqslant I_j \leqslant \alpha_j + \epsilon_j \leqslant 1, \qquad j = 2, \ldots, r - 1, \qquad (7.23)$$
$$I_1 = 1, \qquad I_r = 0,$$

where $I_j = (V_j - V_r)/(V_1 - V_r)$, with V_1 and V_r the relative values of the most desirable and least desirable consequence (or outcome as the case may be) respectively.

Similar to (7.12), we have, with $P_{ij} = P(o_j \mid S_i)$ or $P_{ij} = P(O_j \mid S_i)$,

$$\frac{\mathbf{a} \cdot \mathbf{E(S)} - E(S_s)}{V_1 - V_r} = \sum_{i=1}^{t} a_i \sum_{j=1}^{r} P_{ij} I_j - \sum_{j=1}^{r} P_{sj} I_j, \qquad (7.24a)$$

but, unlike (7.12), the various sums of PI products are now interrelated by the common $(I_1, I_2, \ldots, I_r)$. For this reason the analysis of the first bounded interval measure for the general Model I or for Model II is more difficult than for Model I ($S = A$) or for the statistical model. Since $\sum a_i = 1$, (7.24a) can be written as

$$\frac{\mathbf{a} \cdot \mathbf{E(S)} - E(S_s)}{V_1 - V_r} = \sum_{j=1}^{r} \left\{ \sum_{i=1}^{t} a_i (P_{ij} - P_{sj}) \right\} I_j. \qquad (7.24b)$$

Since the sign of the coefficient of I_j [i.e., the sign of $\sum_i a_i (P_{ij} - P_{sj})$] can take on both positive and negative values according to different assignments of the a_i when at least one P_{ij} is greater than P_{sj} and at least one P_{ij} is less than P_{sj}, it will not be possible in many instances initially to assign I_j either the value α_j or $\alpha_j + \epsilon_j$ in minimizing the right-hand side of (7.24b) with respect to the I_j.

General Theory

If the P_{ij} are specified, then

$$\sum_{j=1}^{r-1} (P_{ij} - P_{sj}) I_j = \frac{E(S_i) - E(S_s)}{V_1 - V_r}$$

will be a function of $I_2, I_3, \ldots, I_{r-1}$, which, owing to the nature of the bounded interval measure (7.23), are presently interpreted as independent variables restricted as in (7.23). In functional notation, let

$$F_i(I_2, \ldots, I_{r-1}) = \sum_{j=1}^{r-1} (P_{ij} - P_{sj}) I_j, \qquad i \neq s,$$

or, since $I_1 = 1$,

$$F_i(I_2, \ldots, I_{r-1}) = (P_{i1} - P_{s1}) + \sum_{j=2}^{r-1} (P_{ij} - P_{sj})I_j,$$

$$i = 1, 2, \ldots, t; \quad i \neq s. \quad (7.25)$$

Putting (7.25) into (7.24) we obtain (with $a_s = 0$),

$$\frac{\mathbf{a} \cdot E(S) - E(S_s)}{V_1 - V_r} = \sum_{i=1}^{t} a_i F_i(I_2, \ldots, I_{r-1}). \quad (7.26)$$

For any given set of values for $I_2, \ldots, I_{r-1}$ which satisfy (7.23), it is clear that the right-hand side of (7.26) is maximized when the particular a_i corresponding to the largest F_i is set equal to 1 and all other $a_i = 0$. That is,

$$\max_{\mathbf{a}} \sum_{i=1}^{t} a_i F_i(I_2, \ldots, I_{r-1}) = \max_{F_i} \{F_1(I_2, \ldots, I_{r-1}); \ldots; F_t(I_2, \ldots, I_{r-1})\}.$$

Now among all admissible sets of I_j, $j = 2, \ldots, r - 1$, find a set which minimizes the right-hand side of this equation. Suppose $(I_2^0, \ldots, I_{r-1}^0)$ is such a set. Then $\max_{F_i} \{F_1(I_2, \ldots, I_{r-1}); \ldots; F_t(I_2, \ldots, I_{r-1})\}$ will be as small as possible when $(I_2, \ldots, I_{r-1}) = (I_2^0, \ldots, I_{r-1}^0)$. That is,

$$\min_{\{I_j\}} \max_{F_i} \{F_1(I_2, \ldots, I_{r-1}); \ldots; F_t(I_2, \ldots, I_{r-1})\}$$
$$= \max_{F_i} \{F_1(I_2^0, \ldots, I_{r-1}^0); \ldots; F_t(I_2^0, \ldots, I_{r-1}^0)\}. \quad (7.27)$$

Since $V_1 - V_r > 0$, $\mathbf{a} \cdot E(S) - E(S_s)$ can be made nonnegative for any given set $(I_2, \ldots, I_{r-1})$ so long as we can find an $\mathbf{a}$ that makes the right-hand side of (7.26) nonnegative. If, for some admissible set $(I_2, \ldots, I_{r-1})$ such an $\mathbf{a}$ does not exist, then, given only (7.23), it is not possible to conclude that S_s is dominated. Put in the alternate language, these observations become:

Theorem 7.6 Given the bounded interval measure (7.23) and no additional information about the relative magnitudes of the V_j, we can conclude that S_s is dominated if and only if

$$\min_{\{I_j\}} \max_{F_i} \{F_1(I_2, \ldots, I_{r-1}); \ldots; F_t(I_2, \ldots, I_{r-1})\} \geq 0.$$

This theorem applies to any measure of the P_{ij} if it is modified to read: Given the bounded interval measure (7.23) and no additional information about the relative magnitudes of the V_j, we can conclude that S_s is dominated if and only if we can conclude, with whatever measure of the P_{ij} we have at our disposal, that

$$\min_{\{I_j\}} \max_{F_i} \{F_1(I_2, \ldots, I_{r-1}); \ldots; F_t(I_2, \ldots, I_{r-1})\} \geq 0.$$

Before trying to show that S_s is dominated by a mixture of two or more other S_i, it will be most efficient to apply first theorem 6.7 and eliminate all strategies that are dominated by some other strategy. Then we can look for mixed dominance among those S_i that remain, provided, of course, that there are at least three such strategies in the reduced set. Any subset of three or more S_i in the reduced set can be used in trying to discern mixed dominance. A rule of thumb for choosing such a subset (say, of three S_i) may be helpful, such as: compute $\min_{\{I_j\}} \sum_j P_{ij} I_j = \sum_j P_{ij} \alpha_j$, pick the two S_i with the largest $\sum_j P_{ij} \alpha_j$, and try to show that a mixture of these two dominates the S_i with the smallest $\sum_j P_{ij} \alpha_j$.

A Useful Theorem

In connection with theorem 7.6, our primary interest lies in determining the sign of minimax $\{F_i\}$. In the most general situation this may require determination of the exact value of minimax $\{F_i\}$, a task which may be huge if t is large. However, in particular instances, it may be possible to find the sign of (7.27) with very little labor. For example, with F_i defined by (7.25), and I_j restricted as in (7.23), we have:

Theorem 7.7 If $\min_{\{I_j\}} \left[\sum_{i \neq s} F_i(I_2, \ldots, I_{r-1}) \right] \geq 0$, then S_s is dominated.

That is, if $\sum_{i \neq s} (P_{i1} - P_{s1}) + \sum_{j=2}^{r-1} [\sum_{i \neq s} (P_{ij} - P_{sj})] I_j$ has a minimum with respect to $(I_2, \ldots, I_{r-1})$ which is nonnegative, then minimax $\{F_i\} \geq 0$. The proof of this assertion is quite simple, consisting only of the observation that if $\min_{\{I_j\}} \sum_{i \neq s} F_i \geq 0$, then there exists no admissible $(I_2, \ldots, I_{r-1})$ that simultaneously makes all $F_i(I_2, \ldots, I_{r-1}) < 0$, in which case it cannot be true that minimax $\{F_i\} < 0$.

On the other hand, suppose that

$$\min_{\{I_j\}} \left[\sum_{i \neq s} F_i(I_2, \ldots, I_{r-1}) \right] < 0.$$

Then, if for any $\{I_j\}$ which minimizes[4] the sum of the F_i, it is true that each individual F_i is negative, it follows that minimax $\{F_i\} < 0$. However, if one or more F_i are negative and one or more positive when $\min \sum F_i < 0$, it is necessary to go further in our search for the sign of minimax $\{F_i\}$.

To illustrate theorem 7.7, suppose the following probability matrix has been estimated:

---

[4] The minimizing $\{I_j\}$ will be unique if the coefficient of each I_j in the sum is nonzero.

	o_1	o_2	o_3	o_4
S_1	.298	.163	.196	.343
S_2	.276	.303	.076	.345
S_3	.262	.223	.156	.359

with $I_1 = 1$, $.4 \leqslant I_2 \leqslant .8$, $.2 \leqslant I_3 \leqslant .7$. With the use of theorem 6.7, pure dominance cannot be established with these measures. However, using theorem 7.7, letting $i = 1, 2$; $s = 3$, we get

$$F_1 + F_2 = \sum_{i=1}^{2} (P_{i1} - P_{31}) + \sum_{j=2}^{3} \left[\sum_{i=1}^{2} (P_{ij} - P_{3j}) \right] I_j$$

$$= .05 + .02I_2 - .04I_3,$$

which is minimized when $I_2 = .4$, $I_3 = .7$. The minimum value of $F_1 + F_2$ is .03 and, by theorem 7.7, we conclude that S_3 is dominated with the above probability matrix and bounded interval measure of relative values.

Solution of Minimax $\{F_i\}$[5]

As a first step in solving for minimax $\{F_i\}$, it will be convenient to set

$$I_j = \begin{cases} \alpha_j & \text{if } P_{ij} - P_{sj} \geqslant 0 \quad \text{for every } i, \\ \alpha_j + \epsilon_j & \text{if } P_{ij} - P_{sj} \leqslant 0 \quad \text{for every } i, \\ \alpha_j + x_j & \text{otherwise,} \end{cases} \qquad (7.28)$$

and to renumber the $K \leqslant r - 2$ x_j as $x_1, x_2, \ldots, x_K$ so that, when (7.28) is put into (7.25), we get, say,

$$F_i(\mathbf{x}) = a_{i0} + a_{i1}x_1 + a_{i2}x_2 + \ldots + a_{iK}x_K \quad \text{for each } i, \qquad (7.29)$$
$$0 \leqslant x_j \leqslant \epsilon_j, \qquad j = 1, \ldots, K.$$

In this form our problem is to determine the sign of $\min_{\mathbf{x}} \max_{F_i} \{F_i(\mathbf{x})\}$ or, in the tightest case, to find $\min_{\mathbf{x}} \max_{F_i} \{F_i(\mathbf{x})\}$.

The problem of determining minimax $\{F_i\}$ is equivalent to the problem: Minimize u subject to:

$$a_{i0} + \sum_{j=1}^{K} a_{ij}x_j \leqslant u \qquad \text{for all } i \, (\neq s), \qquad (7.30)$$

$$0 \leqslant x_j \leqslant \epsilon_j, \qquad\qquad \text{for all } i \, (\neq s),$$

[5] The author is indebted to Gad Nathan for the formulation of (7.30) and (7.31) in this section.

where minimum $u = $ minimax $\{F_i\}$. To put this into a more workable linear programming form, let $u = x_{K+1} - x_{K+2} + c$, where

$$c = \max_i a_{i0},$$

and let

$$b_i = c - a_{i0} \quad \text{for each } i \ (\neq s).$$

Problem (7.30) is then equivalent to:

Maximize $x_{K+2} - x_{K+1}$ (or minimize $x_{K+1} - x_{K+2}$),

subject to: (7.31)

$$\sum_{j=1}^{K} a_{ij}x_j - x_{K+1} + x_{K+2} + x_{K+2+i} = b_i, \quad i = 1, \ldots, t \ (\neq s),$$

$$x_j \leqslant \epsilon_j, \quad j = 1, \ldots, K,$$

$$x_j \geqslant 0, \quad \text{for all } x_j,$$

where the x_{K+2+i} are slack variables (each b_i being nonnegative). (7.31) is in a standard form of an upper-bound linear programming problem and may be solved by using techniques presented by Garvin (1960, Chapter 11) or Charnes and Cooper (1961, pp. 561–562).

Suppose one is working with only three S_i and trying to show that $S_s = S_3$ dominated by a mixture of S_1 and S_2, given no pure dominance. As in (7.29) we have, say,

$$F_1(\mathbf{x}) = a_0 + a_1 x_1 + a_2 x_2 + \ldots + a_K x_K, \quad (7.32)$$

$$F_2(\mathbf{x}) = b_0 + b_1 x_1 + b_2 x_2 + \ldots + b_K x_K,$$

$$0 \leqslant x_j \leqslant \epsilon_j, \quad j = 1, \ldots, K,$$

where $a_j b_j < 0$ for $j = 1, \ldots, K$. In this case, the following theorem may be useful.

Theorem 7.8 Given that pure dominance cannot be found among S_1, S_2, and S_3, then with $S_s = S_3$:

(a) If $\max_{\mathbf{x}} F_1(\mathbf{x}) < 0$ or $\max_{\mathbf{x}} F_2(\mathbf{x}) < 0$, then minimax $\{F_1, F_2\} < 0$.

(b) If $\max_{\mathbf{x}} F_1(\mathbf{x}) \geqslant 0$ and $\max_{\mathbf{x}} F_2(\mathbf{x}) \geqslant 0$, and $\mathbf{x}^0$ is an $\mathbf{x}$ which yields minimax $\{F_1(\mathbf{x}), F_2(\mathbf{x})\}$, then

$$F_1(\mathbf{x}^0) = F_2(\mathbf{x}^0).$$

For proof of (a), suppose $\max_{\mathbf{x}} F_1(\mathbf{x}) = F_1(\mathbf{x}^*) < 0$. Then, since $a_j b_j < 0$ in (7.32), $\min_{\mathbf{x}} F_2(\mathbf{x}) = F_2(\mathbf{x}^*)$. Now $\min_{\mathbf{x}} F_2(\mathbf{x}) < 0$ since pure dominance cannot be found. Hence $\mathbf{x}^*$ makes both F_1 and F_2 negative, implying that minimax $\{F_1, F_2\}$ is negative. Similar comments apply if $\max_{\mathbf{x}} F_2(\mathbf{x}) < 0$.

Part (b) of the theorem is easily proved by contradiction, after establishing that there is at least one $\mathbf{x}$ giving $F_1(\mathbf{x}) = F_2(\mathbf{x})$. We leave this as an exercise for the reader. It can also be shown that, if the hypotheses of part (b) hold, implying $F_1(\mathbf{x}^0) = F_2(\mathbf{x}^0)$, then there is at least one minimaxing $\mathbf{x}^0 = (x_1^0, x_2^0, \ldots, x_K^0)$ in which x_j^0 equals either 0 or ϵ_j for all j from 1 to K, except perhaps for one x_j^0 which lies strictly between 0 and ϵ_j. For example, suppose

$$F_1(\mathbf{x}) = -.044 + .05x_1 - .07x_2 - .02x_3 - .01x_4,$$
$$F_2(\mathbf{x}) = -.006 - .03x_1 + .09x_2 + .04x_3 + .02x_4,$$

with $0 \leqslant x_1 \leqslant .4$, $0 \leqslant x_2 \leqslant .4$, $0 \leqslant x_3 \leqslant .1$, $0 \leqslant x_4 \leqslant .1$. Here it can be shown that $\mathbf{x}^0 = (0, {}^1/_{80}, 0, 0)$, where x_2^0 is the one x_j^0 that does not lie at either boundary.

7.5 THE SECOND BOUNDED INTERVAL MEASURE OF RELATIVE VALUES[6]

The second bounded interval measure is given by

$$\alpha_j \leqslant L_j \leqslant \alpha_j + \epsilon_j, \qquad j = 1, \ldots, r - 1, \tag{7.33}$$

$$\sum_{j=1}^{r-1} \alpha_j \leqslant \sum_{j=1}^{r-1} L_j = 1 \leqslant \sum_{j=1}^{r-1} (\alpha_j + \epsilon_j), \qquad 0 \leqslant \alpha_j \leqslant \alpha_j + \epsilon_j \leqslant 1,$$

where $L_j = (V_j - V_{j+1})/(V_1 - V_r)$. Similar to (7.26),

$$\frac{\mathbf{a} \cdot \mathbf{E}(S) - E(S_s)}{V_1 - V_r} = \sum_{\substack{i=1 \\ (i \neq s)}}^{t} a_i H_i(L_1, L_2, \ldots, L_{r-1}),$$

with

$$H_i(L_1, L_2, \ldots, L_{r-1}) = \sum_{j=1}^{r-1} \left[\sum_{k=1}^{j} (P_{ik} - P_{sk}) \right] L_j \qquad (i \neq s).$$

An argument like that leading to theorem 7.6 gives:

Theorem 7.9 Given the bounded interval measure (7.33) and no additional information about the relative magnitudes of the V_j, we can conclude that S_s is dominated if and only if

$$\min_{\{L_j\}} \max_{H_i} [H_1(L_1, \ldots, L_{r-1}); \ldots; H_t(L_1, \ldots, L_{r-1})] \geqslant 0.$$

[6] The discussion in this section applies for any model thus far considered with the appropriate interpretation of the P_{ij}. The basic form of $\mathbf{a} \cdot \mathbf{E}(S) - E(S_s)$ is given by (7.1). In all cases $V_1 \geqslant V_2 \geqslant \ldots \geqslant V_r$.

Similar to theorem 7.8, we also have: If $\min\limits_{\{L_j\}} \sum\limits_{i \neq s} H_i(L_1, \ldots, L_{r-1}) \geqslant 0$, then S_s is dominated. In addition, if $\min\limits_{\{L_j\}} \sum\limits_{i \neq s} H_i < 0$ and all H_i are negative with an L that minimizes $\sum H_i$, then minimax $\{H_i\} < 0$.

Because of the restriction $\sum L_j = 1$, it is computationally more difficult to solve for minimax $\{H_i\}$ than to solve for minimax $\{F_i\}$ from the previous section. In the present case, our problem may be stated:

Minimize u subject to:

$$H_i(L_1, \ldots, L_{r-1}) \leqslant u \qquad \text{for all } i \, (\neq s), \tag{7.34}$$

$$\alpha_j \leqslant L_j \leqslant \alpha_j + \epsilon_j, \qquad j = 1, \ldots, r - 1,$$

$$\sum_{j=1}^{r-1} L_j = 1.$$

Letting

$$L_j = \alpha_j + x_j, \qquad j = 1, \ldots, r - 1,$$

$$1 - \sum_{j=1}^{r-1} \alpha_j = c \quad (\geqslant 0),$$

H_i may be written as

$$H_i(\mathbf{x}) = a_{i0} + a_{i1}x_1 + a_{i2}x_2 + \ldots + a_{i,r-1}x_{r-1} \quad (i \neq s). \tag{7.35}$$

Then a formulation equivalent to (7.34) is given by:

Minimize u subject to:

$$a_{i0} + \sum_{j=1}^{r-1} a_{ij}x_j \leqslant u \qquad \text{for all } i \, (\neq s),$$

$$0 \leqslant x_j \leqslant \epsilon_j, \qquad j = 1, \ldots, r - 1,$$

$$\sum_{j=1}^{r-1} x_j = c.$$

This formulation is similar to (7.30) with the addition of the equality constraint $\sum x_j = c$.

To illustrate the effect of the equality constraint, suppose we are trying to show $S_s = S_3$ dominated by a mixture of S_1 and S_2, with $r = 4$. In the form of (7.35) we get

$$H_1(\mathbf{x}) = .02x_1 - .02x_2 + .3x_3,$$

$$H_2(\mathbf{x}) = .02x_1 + .3x_2 - .02x_3,$$

$$0 \leqslant x_1 \leqslant .2, \qquad 0 \leqslant x_2 \leqslant .2, \qquad 0 \leqslant x_3 \leqslant .2, \qquad x_1 + x_2 + x_3 = .2.$$

It is easily verified that minimax $\{H_1, H_2\} = .004$ with $\mathbf{x}^0 = (.2, 0, 0)$. In the previous section we would have set $x_1 = 0$ immediately (if H_1 and H_2 were replaced by F_1 and F_2), since this would simultaneously reduce F_1 and F_2, but under the constraint $\sum x_j = .2$ this cannot be done in the present case. If $H_1(\mathbf{x})$ and $H_2(\mathbf{x})$ were replaced by $F_1(\mathbf{x})$ and $F_2(\mathbf{x})$ respectively, and the equality constraint removed, we would set $x_1 = 0$, and obtain, with the use of theorem 7.8*b*,

$$-.02x_2 + .3x_3 = .3x_2 - .02x_3,$$

or

$$x_2 = x_3.$$

Putting this in $F_1(\mathbf{x})$ and $F_2(\mathbf{x})$ gives $F_1(\mathbf{x}) = F_2(\mathbf{x}) = .28x_2$. Then we set $x_2 = 0$ giving minimax $\{F_1, F_2\} = 0$.

In looking for minimax $\{H_1, H_2\}$ when three strategies are involved with $S_s = S_3$, use may be made of:

Theorem 7.10   Suppose $\min\limits_{\mathbf{x}} H_1(\mathbf{x}) < 0$; $\min\limits_{\mathbf{x}} H_2(\mathbf{x}) < 0$; for every $\mathbf{x}$ that minimizes H_1, $H_2(\mathbf{x}) > 0$; and for every $\mathbf{x}$ that minimizes H_2, $H_1(\mathbf{x}) > 0$. If $\mathbf{x}^0$ is an $\mathbf{x}$ which minimaxes $\{H_1, H_2\}$, i.e., if

$$\min_{\mathbf{x}} \max_{H_i} \{H_1(\mathbf{x}); H_2(\mathbf{x})\} = \max_{H_i} \{H_1(\mathbf{x}^0); H_2(\mathbf{x}^0)\},$$

then $H_1(\mathbf{x}^0) = H_2(\mathbf{x}^0)$.

For proof by contradiction, suppose $H_1(\mathbf{x}^0) > H_2(\mathbf{x}^0)$. If so, then $H_1(\mathbf{x}^0) = \min\limits_{\mathbf{x}} H_1(\mathbf{x})$, for otherwise we could perturb $\mathbf{x}^0$ by a small amount and reduce H_1 from $H_1(\mathbf{x}^0)$ while keeping the change in H_2 less than $H_1(\mathbf{x}^0) - H_2(\mathbf{x}^0)$. But $H_1(\mathbf{x}^0) = \min\limits_{\mathbf{x}} H_1(\mathbf{x})$ and $H_1(\mathbf{x}^0) > H_2(\mathbf{x}^0)$ together contradict the hypotheses of the theorem [they imply $0 > H_1(\mathbf{x}^0) > H_2(\mathbf{x}^0) > 0$ or $0 > 0$]. By similar reasoning, we cannot have $H_2(\mathbf{x}^0) > H_1(\mathbf{x}^0)$ under the hypotheses of the theorem. Therefore, $H_1(\mathbf{x}^0) = H_2(\mathbf{x}^0)$.

7.6   ANALYSIS WITH AN ORDINAL PROBABILITY RANKING

In this section we consider a ranking of probabilities

$$P_1 \geqslant P_2 \geqslant \ldots \geqslant P_u \geqslant 0, \tag{7.36}$$

and use the model form

$$\mathbf{a} \cdot \mathbf{E}(S) - E(S_s) = \sum_{k=1}^{u} P_k W_k. \tag{7.37}$$

Interpretation of (7.37) for the various models follows.

Statistical Model: $P_k = P(E_k)$, $W_k = \sum_{i=1}^{t} a_i V(o_{ik}) - V(o_{sk})$, $u = n$, so that (7.37) is identical to (7.2).

Model I ($S = A$): Each P_k is one of the $P(O_j \mid A_i)$, $i = 1, \ldots, m$, $j = 1, \ldots, n$, so that $u \leqslant mn$ and $\sum_k P_k = m$. If $P_k = P(O_j \mid A_i)$, then $W_k = a_i[V(A_i, O_j) - U]$ if $i \neq s$ or $W_k = -[V(A_s, O_j) - U]$ if $i = s$.

Model I (General): Each P_k is one of the $P(o_j \mid S_i)$, $j = 1, \ldots, r$, $i = 1, \ldots, t$, so that $u \leqslant rt$ and $\sum_k P_k = t$. If $P_k = P(o_j \mid S_i)$, then $W_k = a_i[V(o_j) - U]$ if $i \neq s$ or $W_k = -[V(o_j) - U]$ if $i = s$.

Model II: Each P_k is one of the $P(O_j \mid S_i)$, $j = 1, \ldots, n$, $i = 1, \ldots, t$, giving $u \leqslant nt$, $\sum_k P_k = t$. If $P_k = P(O_j \mid S_i)$, then $W_k = a_i[V(O_j) - U]$ if $i \neq s$, or $W_k = -[V(O_j) - U]$ if $i = s$.

Applying (6.1) to (7.37) gives

$$\mathbf{a} \cdot \mathbf{E}(S) - E(S_s) = \sum_{k=1}^{u-1} \left(\sum_{j=1}^{k} W_j \right)(P_k - P_{k+1}) + P_u \sum_{j=1}^{u} W_j,$$

and hence:

Theorem 7.11 Given the ranking (7.36) if there exists a U (if applicable) and $\mathbf{a}$ such that $\sum_{j=1}^{k} W_j \geqslant 0$ for $k = 1, \ldots, u$, then S_s is dominated.

For an example, suppose with Model I ($S = A$) the following matrix of relative values is obtained

	O_1	O_2	O_3
A_1	7	1	16
A_2	9	4	5
A_3	8	3	9

$m = 3, n = 3, u = 9$,

along with the probability ranking

$$P_{11} \geqslant P_{21} \geqslant P_{31} \geqslant P_{22} \geqslant P_{32} \geqslant P_{13} \geqslant P_{33} \geqslant P_{23} \geqslant P_{12} \geqslant 0.$$

We leave it to the reader to verify that pure dominance cannot be discerned with the given information. However, A_3 is dominated. In accordance with the above interpretation with $s = 3$,

$$W_1 = a_1(7 - U), \qquad W_4 = a_2(4 - U), \qquad W_7 = -9 + U,$$
$$W_2 = a_2(9 - U), \qquad W_5 = -3 + U, \qquad W_8 = a_2(5 - U),$$
$$W_3 = -8 + U, \qquad W_6 = a_1(16 - U), \qquad W_9 = a_1(1 - U).$$

After some simplification (let $a_2 = 1 - a_1$), the $\sum_{j=1}^{k} W_j \geqslant 0$ for k from 1 to 9 may be written as follows:

k	$\sum_{j=1}^{k} W_j \geqslant 0$
1	$7a_1 \geqslant Ua_1$
2	$9 \geqslant 2a_1 + U$
3	$1 \geqslant 2a_1$
4	$5 + Ua_1 \geqslant 6a_1 + U$
5	$2 + Ua_1 \geqslant 6a_1$
6	$10a_1 + 2 \geqslant 0$
7	$10a_1 + U \geqslant 7$
8	$5a_1 + Ua_1 \geqslant 2$
9	$3a_1 \geqslant 1$

We are interested in determining if there exists any pair (a_1, U) with $0 \leqslant a_1 \leqslant 1$, which simultaneously satisfies these nine inequalities. The sixth inequality may be scratched; the third and ninth require $\frac{1}{3} \leqslant a_1 \leqslant \frac{1}{2}$; and in view of this, the first requires $U \leqslant 7$. Now with $\frac{1}{3} \leqslant a_1 \leqslant \frac{1}{2}$ and $U \leqslant 7$, the second inequality is satisfied. At this point we are left with 4, 5, 7, and 8. Writing these with U on one side,

$$4: \quad U \leqslant \frac{5 - 6a_1}{1 - a_1},$$

$$5: \quad U \geqslant \frac{6a_1 - 2}{a_1},$$

$$7: \quad U \geqslant 7 - 10a_1,$$

$$8: \quad U \geqslant \frac{2 - 5a_1}{a_1}.$$

In view of 5, 7, and 8, we may try to make U as large as possible in 4. With $a_1 = \frac{1}{3}$, we get $U \leqslant \frac{9}{2}$ from 4, and observe that $(a_1, U) = (\frac{1}{3}, \frac{9}{2})$ satisfies 5, 7, and 8 as well. Hence with $(a_1, U) = (\frac{1}{3}, \frac{9}{2})$, all nine inequalities are satisfied and we conclude that A_3 is dominated.

7.7 GENERAL ANALYSIS WITH A BOUNDED PROBABILITY MEASURE

Consider first the statistical model. The bounded probability measure is

$$\alpha_k \leqslant P_k \leqslant \alpha_k + \epsilon_k, \quad k = 1, \dots, n, \quad (7.38)$$

with $0 \leqslant \alpha_k \leqslant \alpha_k + \epsilon_k \leqslant 1$ and $\sum \alpha_k \leqslant \sum P_k = 1 \leqslant \sum (\alpha_k + \epsilon_k)$, where $P_k = P(E_k)$. For the form of $\mathbf{a} \cdot \mathbf{E(S)} - E(S_s)$ use (7.2),

$$\mathbf{a} \cdot \mathbf{E(S)} - E(S_s) = \sum_{k=1}^{n} \left[\sum_{i=1}^{t} a_i V(o_{ik}) - V(o_{sk}) \right] P_k. \quad (7.2)$$

Unlike the situation for Models I and II as discussed in Section 6.9 (or that to be discussed), ordinal rankings of the $V(o_{ik})$ will not, in general, permit us to set the P_k in (7.2) initially in minimizing (7.2) subject to (7.38) and $\sum P_k = 1$, because of the leverage of the a_i. It should be clear from previous discussion that, given only the measure (7.38) and no additional information on the P_k, we can conclude that S_s is dominated if and only if

$$\max_{\mathbf{a}} \min_{\{P_k\}} \sum_{k=1}^{n} \left[\sum_{i=1}^{t} a_i V(o_{ik}) - V(o_{sk}) \right] P_k \geq 0.$$

The analysis in this case bears a striking resemblance to the analysis of the second bounded interval measure of relative values in Section 7.5. To illustrate this, first rewrite (7.2) as

$$\mathbf{a} \cdot E(S) - E(S_s) = \sum_{k=1}^{n} \sum_{i=1}^{t} a_i [V(o_{ik}) - V(o_{sk})] P_k$$

$$= \sum_{i=1}^{t} a_i \left\{ \sum_{k=1}^{n} [V(o_{ik}) - V(o_{sk})] P_k \right\}.$$

In this formulation our problem is to determine whether

$$\min_{\{P_k\}} \max_{i \neq s} \sum_{k=1}^{n} [V(o_{ik}) - V(o_{sk})] P_k \geq 0,$$

subject to

$$\sum_{k=1}^{n} P_k = 1, \qquad \alpha_k \leq P_k \leq \alpha_k + \epsilon_k, \qquad k = 1, \ldots, n.$$

In Section 7.5 our problem was to determine whether

$$\min_{\{L_k\}} \max_{i \neq s} \sum_{k=1}^{r-1} \left[\sum_{j=1}^{k} (P_{ij} - P_{sj}) \right] L_k \geq 0,$$

subject to

$$\sum_{k=1}^{r-1} L_k = 1, \qquad \alpha_k \leq L_k \leq \alpha_k + \epsilon_k, \qquad k = 1, \ldots, r-1.$$

Except for the notation, these two problems are identical, both taking the general form:
Determine whether

$$\min_{\{b_k\}} \max_{i \neq s} \sum_{k=1}^{K} c_{ik} b_k \geq 0,$$

subject to

$$\sum_{k=1}^{K} b_k = 1, \qquad \alpha_k \leq b_k \leq \alpha_k + \epsilon_k, \qquad k = 1, \ldots, K.$$

If the c_{ik} are not known precisely, additional problems arise which we shall not discuss here.

Model I or Model II

For Model I in its general form or for Model II, suppose we have obtained the bounded probability measure

$$\alpha_{ij} \leqslant P_{ij} \leqslant \alpha_{ij} + \epsilon_{ij}, \qquad i = 1, \ldots, t; \quad j = 1, \ldots, r, \qquad (7.39)$$
$$0 \leqslant \alpha_{ij} \leqslant \alpha_{ij} + \epsilon_{ij} \leqslant 1, \qquad \text{for all } i, j,$$
$$\sum_{j=1}^{r} \alpha_{ij} \leqslant \sum_{j=1}^{r} P_{ij} = 1 \leqslant \sum_{j=1}^{r} (\alpha_{ij} + \epsilon_{ij}), \qquad i = 1, \ldots, t.$$

For these cases

$$\mathbf{a} \cdot E(S) - E(S_s) = \sum_{i=1}^{t} a_i \sum_{j=1}^{r} P_{ij} V_j - \sum_{j=1}^{r} P_{sj} V_j, \qquad (7.40)$$

where, in Model I, $P_{ij} = P(o_j \mid S_i)$, $V_j = V(o_j)$, and in Model II, $P_{ij} = P(O_j \mid S_i)$, $V_j = V(O_j)$.

If an ordinal ranking of the V_j has been obtained, then we can immediately determine the values of the P_{ij} and P_{sj} that minimize the right-hand side of (7.40) with respect to $\{P_{ij}\}$ subject to (7.39) and $\sum_{j=1}^{r} P_{ij} = 1$ for $i = 1, \ldots, t$. Let the resulting value of P_{ij} thus assigned be Q_{ij}. Clearly then, we can conclude that S_s is dominated, given only the bounded probability measure and at least an ordinal measure of relative values, if and only if there exists an $\mathbf{a}$ such that we are able to show that

$$\sum_{i=1}^{t} a_i \sum_{j=1}^{r} Q_{ij} V_j - \sum_{j=1}^{r} Q_{sj} V_j \geqslant 0. \qquad (7.41)$$

Letting

$$Q_j(\mathbf{a}; s) = \sum_{i=1}^{t} a_i Q_{ij} - Q_{sj},$$

the left-hand side of (7.41) may be written as

$$\sum_{j=1}^{r} Q_j(\mathbf{a}; s) V_j, \qquad (7.42)$$

which in form is identical to

$$\sum_{j=1}^{r} P_j(\mathbf{a}; s) V_j \qquad (7.43)$$

on the right-hand side of (7.5). In (7.42) the values of the Q_{ij} have been determined, whereas in (7.43) this might not be the case. [Note that (7.42) is derived from (7.43).]

It should hardly need mentioning at this point that such measures of the V_j as the ordinal ranking, ordered metric rankings, and the second bounded interval measure may be applied to (7.42) in trying to determine whether (7.41) holds, and hence, whether S_s is dominated.

EXERCISES

1. Given the probability matrix

	O_1	O_2	O_3	O_4	O_5
S_1	.24	.18	.18	.27	.13
S_2	.20	.24	.18	.18	.20
S_3	.22	.32	.04	.16	.26
S_4	.16	.24	.40	.04	.16

show that S_2 is dominated when Model I applies and $V_1 \geqslant V_2 \geqslant V_3 \geqslant V_4 \geqslant V_5$. Can you conclude that any other S_i is dominated, given only the ordinal value ranking and the above probability matrix?

2. (*Continuation.*) If in addition to the ordinal ranking $V_1 \geqslant V_2 \geqslant V_3 \geqslant V_4 \geqslant V_5$ one obtains the information that $V_3 - V_4$ is the largest adjacent value difference [i.e., $V_3 - V_4 \geqslant \max_{j \neq 3} (V_j - V_{j+1})$], show that $\mathbf{C} = (0, 0, 0, 1)$ maximizes the total expected relative value [i.e., S_4 in the best strategy under the criterion of maximization of expected value, or $\max_i E(S_i) = E(S_4)$].

3. Consider a decision situation which involves just two outcomes, O_1 (win) and O_2 (lose). These could correspond to winning or losing a military battle, card game, golf match, etc. Suppose that a number of strategies $S_1, S_2, \ldots, S_t$ could be adopted, and that a general principle holds to the effect that (roughly) the greater the probability of winning, the greater the cost of doing so. To state this formally, let the S_i be subscripted so that

$$P(O_1 \mid S_1) < P(O_1 \mid S_2) < \ldots < P(O_1 \mid S_t).$$

Then, let us assume that it has been found that

$$\overline{V}(S_1, O_1) \geqslant \overline{V}(S_2, O_1) \geqslant \ldots \geqslant \overline{V}(S_t, O_1)$$
$$\geqslant \overline{V}(S_1, O_2) \geqslant \overline{V}(S_2, O_2) \geqslant \ldots \geqslant \overline{V}(S_t, O_2),$$

where $\overline{V}(S_i, O_j)$ represents an expected value for O_j along with one or another of the many courses of action that might result if S_i is adopted. Given only the above ranking of probabilities and the ordinal average value ranking, show that it is not possible to conclude that any S_i is dominated.

4. (*Continuation.*) Suppose that for $t = 7$ the probabilities have been estimated as follows:

	O_1 (win)	O_2 (lose)
S_1	.40	.60
S_2	.42	.58
S_3	.50	.50
S_4	.55	.45
S_5	.63	.37
S_6	.71	.29
S_7	.73	.27

and that, as above, $\overline{V}_{11} \geqslant \overline{V}_{21} \geqslant \ldots \geqslant \overline{V}_{71} \geqslant \overline{V}_{12} \geqslant \overline{V}_{22} \geqslant \ldots \geqslant \overline{V}_{72}$.

Suppose that the ordered metric ranking

$$(\overline{V}_{62} - \overline{V}_{72}) \geqslant (\overline{V}_{52} - \overline{V}_{62}) \geqslant (V_{42} - \overline{V}_{52}) \geqslant \ldots \geqslant (\overline{V}_{12} - \overline{V}_{22})$$

$$\geqslant (\overline{V}_{71} - \overline{V}_{12}) \geqslant (\overline{V}_{61} - \overline{V}_{71}) \geqslant (\overline{V}_{51} - \overline{V}_{61}) \geqslant \ldots \geqslant (\overline{V}_{11} - \overline{V}_{21}) \geqslant 0$$

is obtained. With this and the given matrix of probabilities, show that $\max_t E(S_i) = S_1$.

5. (*Continuation.*) Given the rankings of Exercise 3 (i.e., $P_{11} < P_{21} < \ldots < P_{t1}$ and $\overline{V}_{11} \geqslant \overline{V}_{21} \geqslant \ldots \geqslant \overline{V}_{t1} \geqslant \overline{V}_{12} \geqslant \ldots \geqslant \overline{V}_{t2}$) and, in addition, the ordered metric ranking of Exercise 4 (i.e., $\overline{V}_{t-1,2} - \overline{V}_{t,2} \geqslant \overline{V}_{t-2,2} - \overline{V}_{t-1,2} \geqslant \ldots \geqslant \overline{V}_{12} - \overline{V}_{22} \geqslant \overline{V}_{t1} - \overline{V}_{12} \geqslant \overline{V}_{t-1,1} - \overline{V}_{t,1} \geqslant \overline{V}_{t-2,1} - \overline{V}_{t-1,1} \geqslant \ldots \geqslant \overline{V}_{11} - \overline{V}_{21}$), $E(S_1) \geqslant E(S_2) \geqslant E(S_3) \geqslant \ldots \geqslant E(S_t)$ if $P_{t1} + t(P_{i+1,1} - P_{t1}) \leqslant 1$ for $i = 1, 2, \ldots, t - 1$. Also, $E(S_1) = \max_t E(S_i)$ if $t(P_{t1} - P_{11}) \leqslant (i - 1)(1 - P_{11})$ for $i = 2, \ldots, t$.

6. Show that the following set of inequalities has an **a** solution with $a_j \geqslant 0$, $j = 1, \ldots, 6$ and $\sum_{j=1}^{6} a_j = 1$:

$$20a_1 + 14a_2 + 10a_3 + 8a_4 + 10a_5 + 15a_6 \geqslant 12,$$
$$28a_1 + 24a_2 + 16a_3 + 24a_4 + 16a_5 + 25a_6 \geqslant 20,$$
$$34a_1 + 28a_2 + 37a_3 + 45a_4 + 30a_5 + 40a_6 \geqslant 27,$$
$$40a_1 + 44a_2 + 54a_3 + 60a_4 + 48a_5 + 44a_6 \geqslant 42,$$
$$54a_1 + 50a_2 + 60a_3 + 70a_4 + 68a_5 + 52a_6 \geqslant 58,$$
$$70a_1 + 63a_2 + 68a_3 + 80a_4 + 78a_5 + 64a_6 \geqslant 70,$$
$$81a_1 + 78a_2 + 84a_3 + 82a_4 + 90a_5 + 80a_6 \geqslant 78,$$
$$84a_1 + 83a_2 + 90a_3 + 84a_4 + 94a_5 + 84a_6 \geqslant 85.$$

7. Show that the following system of inequalities has an **a** solution with $a_j \geqslant 0$, $j = 1, \ldots, 5$ and $\sum_{j=1}^{5} a_j = 1$:

$$1.07a_1 + 1.01a_2 + .92a_3 + .82a_4 + 1.15a_5 \geqslant 1,$$
$$1.14a_1 + .98a_2 + 1.08a_3 + .91a_4 + 1.31a_5 \geqslant 1,$$
$$1.40a_1 + 1.05a_2 + .98a_3 + .90a_4 + .84a_5 \geqslant 1,$$
$$.86a_1 + .88a_2 + 1.12a_3 + 1.08a_4 + 1.06a_5 \geqslant 1,$$
$$.99a_1 + 1.10a_2 + 1.09a_3 + .98a_4 + .88a_5 \geqslant 1,$$
$$.94a_1 + .88a_2 + .96a_3 + .90a_4 + 1.20a_5 \geqslant 1,$$
$$.85a_1 + .80a_2 + 1.16a_3 + 1.05a_4 + .96a_5 \geqslant 1,$$
$$.98a_1 + .95a_2 + .90a_3 + 1.30a_4 + 1.00a_5 \geqslant 1,$$
$$.86a_1 + 1.24a_2 + 1.18a_3 + 1.02a_4 + .92a_5 \geqslant 1.$$

8. Suppose a first bounded interval value measure and a bounded probability measure are obtained for the I_{ij} and P_{ij} in connection with Model I ($S = A$) when $m = 4$, $n = 3$. The intervals for I_{ij} and P_{ij} are given in the following arrays:

	O_1	O_2	O_3
A_1	[.80, .92]	[.43, .55]	[.16, .24]
A_2	[.20, .40]	[1.00, 1.00]	[.30, .40]
A_3	[0, 0]	[.35, .45]	[.64, .70]
A_4	[.31, .40]	[.90, .98]	[.60, .72]

Bounds on
I_{ij}

	O_1	O_2	O_3
A_1	[.32, .44]	[.42, .54]	[.14, .26]
A_2	[.28, .40]	[.24, .36]	[.36, .45]
A_3	[.20, .38]	[.54, .66]	[.04, .12]
A_4	[.08, .14]	[.24, .30]	[.62, .68]

Bounds on
P_{ij}

What inequality relationships among the $E(A_i)$, $i = 1, 2, 3, 4$, do these measures yield? If it is not possible to conclude that one $E(A_i)$ is larger than all other $E(A_i)$ and there is insufficient time for further measurement before the decision (selection of one of the A_i) must be made, what do you recommend and why?

9. Along with the bounded interval value measure of Exercise 8, suppose the probability ranking $P_{42} \geqslant P_{33} \geqslant P_{23} \geqslant P_{13} \geqslant P_{12} \geqslant P_{43} \geqslant P_{32} \geqslant P_{21} \geqslant P_{22} \geqslant P_{31} \geqslant P_{11} \geqslant P_{41} \geqslant 0$ is obtained. With the probability ranking and the bounded value measure, show that $\max_i E(A_i) = E(A_4)$.

10. With three strategies, S_1, S_2, and S_3, and $n = 4$, suppose with Model II the first bounded interval measure of value

$$I_1 = 1, \qquad .7 \leqslant I_2 \leqslant .9, \qquad .1 \leqslant I_3 \leqslant .3, \qquad I_4 = 0$$

is obtained, along with the probability ranking

$$P_{22} \geqslant P_{33} \geqslant P_{11} \geqslant P_{12} \geqslant P_{24} \geqslant P_{32} \geqslant P_{34}$$
$$\geqslant P_{21} \geqslant P_{14} \geqslant P_{23} \geqslant P_{13} \geqslant P_{31} \geqslant 0.$$

What inequality relationships among $E(S_1)$, $E(S_2)$, and $E(S_3)$ do these measures yield?

11. Verify in the example illustrating theorem 7.8 that pure dominance cannot be established with the probabilities and the bounded value measure as given.

12. Given the probability matrix

	o_1	o_2	o_3	o_4	o_5
S_1	.14	.26	.34	.16	.10
S_2	.30	.18	.12	.20	.20
S_3	.20	.30	.15	.21	.14

and the first bounded interval measure under Model I,

$$I_1 = 1, \qquad .6 \leqslant I_2 \leqslant .8, \qquad .4 \leqslant I_3 \leqslant .7, \qquad .2 \leqslant I_4 \leqslant .4, \qquad I_5 = 0,$$

show that it is not possible to conclude that any S_i is dominated. (*Hint:* Make use of the observations in the paragraph following the proof of theorem 7.8).

13. Given the probability matrix

	o_1	o_2	o_3	o_4	o_5	o_6
S_1	.15	.08	.21	.23	.07	.26
S_2	.13	.22	.04	.22	.18	.21
S_3	.10	.16	.16	.26	.12	.20

and the first bounded interval measure under Model II

$$I_1 = 1, \qquad .3 \leqslant I_2 \leqslant .5, \qquad .5 \leqslant I_3 \leqslant .8,$$
$$.2 \leqslant I_4 \leqslant .4, \qquad .4 \leqslant I_5 \leqslant .5, \qquad I_6 = 0,$$

prove that S_3 is dominated.

14. Using (7.15) as a point of departure, discuss the analysis of the first bounded interval measure of relative value for the statistical model along with:

(a) An ordinal ranking of the P_j;
(b) a bounded interval measure of the P_j;
(c) sets of inequalities on the P_j.

15. With Model I, given the probability matrix

	o_1	o_2	o_3	o_4	o_5
S_1	.22	.15	.16	.29	.18
S_2	.14	.38	.15	.07	.26
S_3	.20	.20	.10	.40	.10

and the second bounded interval measure of value (with $V_1 \geqslant V_2 \geqslant V_3 \geqslant V_4 \geqslant V_5$),

$$.30 \leqslant L_1 \leqslant .35, \qquad .15 \leqslant L_2 \leqslant .25,$$
$$.15 \leqslant L_3 \leqslant .25, \qquad .20 \leqslant L_4 \leqslant .30,$$

where

$$L_j = \frac{V_j - V_{j+1}}{V_1 - V_5}, \qquad j = 1, \ldots, 4,$$

show that max $\{E(S_i)\} = E(S_3)$, i.e., that $C = (0, 0, 1)$ maximizes $C_1 E(S_1) + C_2 E(S_2) + C_3 E(S_3)$, subject to $C_i \geqslant 0$, $C_1 + C_2 + C_3 = 1$.

16. In the example following theorem 7.11, show that "pure dominance cannot be discerned with the given information."

17. Suppose Model II applies with $t = 3$, $n = 3$, and you obtain the ordinal value ranking $V_1 \geqslant V_2 \geqslant V_3$ along with the probability ranking

$$P_{11} \geqslant P_{22} \geqslant P_{31} \geqslant P_{32} \geqslant P_{23} \geqslant P_{12} \geqslant P_{13} \geqslant P_{21} \geqslant P_{33} \geqslant 0.$$

Given only this information, show that $E(S_1) \geqslant E(S_2)$ and $E(S_1) \geqslant E(S_3)$.

18. Given the matrix of relative values

	o_1	o_2
S_1	8	1
S_2	5	7
S_3	6	4

and the probability ranking $P_{11} \geqslant P_{21} \geqslant P_{31} \geqslant P_{32} \geqslant P_{22} \geqslant P_{12} \geqslant 0$, show that S_3 is dominated.

19. With the bounded probability measures given in the following array:

	o_1	o_2	o_3	o_4	o_5	o_6
S_1	[.13, .18]	[.21, .32]	[.08, .12]	[.18, .30]	[.14, .20]	[.10, .16]
S_2	[.06, .10]	[.12, .19]	[.30, .42]	[.16, .25]	[.20, .30]	[.02, .08]
S_3	[.21, .32]	[.18, .25]	[.13, .19]	[.17, .26]	[.07, .12]	[.11, .20]
S_4	[.15, .22]	[.15, .22]	[.11, .19]	[.11, .19]	[.13, .20]	[.18, .25]
S_5	[.12, .18]	[.19, .26]	[.22, .31]	[.07, .14]	[.17, .25]	[.09, .19]

show that:

(a) The ordinal ranking $V_1 \geqslant V_2 \geqslant V_3 \geqslant V_4 \geqslant V_5 \geqslant V_6$ is insufficient to allow one to conclude that any S_i is dominated.

(b) The second bounded interval measure [based on the ordinal ranking in (a)] given by $.30 \leqslant L_1 \leqslant .40, .28 \leqslant L_2 \leqslant .35, .18 \leqslant L_3 \leqslant .24, .10 \leqslant L_4 \leqslant .15,$ and $.04 \leqslant L_5 \leqslant .08$ permits only the conclusion that $E(S_3) \geqslant E(S_2)$.

20. Given the following bounds on the P_{ij}:

	o_1	o_2	o_3	o_4
S_1	[.45, .52]	[.28, .35]	[.16, .22]	[.04, .08]
S_2	[.22, .28]	[.40, .48]	[.08, .13]	[.20, .27]
S_3	[.10, .15]	[.26, .34]	[.36, .42]	[.16, .24]
S_4	[.18, .27]	[.08, .14]	[.09, .14]	[.56, .64]

suppose $V_1 \geqslant V_2 \geqslant V_3 \geqslant V_4$ in connection with Model I. Show that $\max_i \{E(S_i)\} = E(S_1)$.

REFERENCES

Charnes, A., and W. W. Cooper, *Management Models and Industrial Applications of Linear Programming*, Vol. II, John Wiley and Sons, New York, 1961.

Garvin, W. W., *Introduction to Linear Programming*, McGraw-Hill Book Company, New York, 1960.

Gass, S. I., *Linear Programming*, McGraw-Hill Book Company, New York, 1958.

Metzger, R. W., *Elementary Mathematical Programming*, John Wiley and Sons, New York, 1958.

Sasieni, M., A. Yaspan, and L. Friedman, *Operations Research—Methods and Problems*, John Wiley and Sons, New York, 1959.

Chapter 8

DENUMERABLE AND CONTINUOUS OUTCOME SPACES

With the results of the last two chapters at our disposal, we shall take a brief glance at the treatment of outcome variables which can take on a large finite or infinite number of values. To keep the discussion from getting too involved, we shall restrict it to the case where all strategies are prescriptive courses of action ($S = A$), with no conditional phrases.

The chapter begins with a short discussion of the definition of $E(A_i)$ when one or more outcome variables are involved. Then we consider situations involving only one denumerable or nondenumerable outcome variable in which the value function for this variable is monotonic [e.g., if $y_1 \geqslant y_2$, then $V(y_1) \geqslant V(y_2)$]. The analysis for this situation is called *monotonic analysis* in reference to the nature of the value function.

The final section deals with situations where the entire outcome space is partitioned into a comparatively small number of subspaces (of the same dimensionality as the original space) in trying to effect a simplification in the analysis. Analysis for dominance using the *method of partitions* will be shown to be similar to the finite discrete analysis of Model I ($S = A$) discussed in the last two chapters. This method is an exact method, not an approximation.

8.1 EXPECTED VALUE OF A COURSE OF ACTION

First, consider a situation which involves one outcome variable, say Y, such that for course of action A_i, Y can assume a denumerable number of values. Whatever the values are, they may be indexed by the set of positive integers $1, 2, \ldots$, where each integer corresponds to one and only one of the values that Y may take on. Let

277

V_{ij} = Relative value of the consequence composed of A_i
    and the jth indexed value of Y,

P_{ij} = Probability that the jth indexed value of Y
    will result if A_i is adopted.

The $V_{ij}, j = 1, 2, \ldots$, are unique up to an increasing linear transformation and $\sum_{j=1}^{\infty} P_{ij} = 1$. We shall consider the case where $P_{ij} > 0$ for a denumerable number of values of j, for otherwise the situation reduces to the finite discrete case. Then, if and only if the absolute sequence $\sum_{j=1}^{n} P_{ij}|V_{ij}|$, $n = 1, 2, \ldots$, has a limit, we define the expected value of A_i, $E(A_i)$, as the limit of the sequence $\sum_{j=1}^{n} P_{ij}V_{ij}$, $n = 1, 2, \ldots$:

$$E(A_i) = \lim_{n \to \infty} \sum_{j=1}^{n} P_{ij}V_{ij} = \sum_{j=1}^{\infty} P_{ij}V_{ij}.$$

If $E(A_i)$ is well defined, then any increasing linear transformation of the form

$$U_{ij} = aV_{ij} + b, \qquad a > 0,$$

for the V_{ij} will affect $E(A_i)$ in the obvious fashion:

$$\sum_{j=1}^{\infty} P_{ij}U_{ij} = a \sum_{j=1}^{\infty} P_{ij}V_{ij} + b.$$

If the limit of the sequence $\sum P_{ij}|V_{ij}|$ does not exist, $E(A_i)$ is not defined and the methods of this chapter may not be used.

Next, consider a situation again involving one outcome variable Y, where this time Y is continuous. Values of Y will be denoted by $y, y', y_1, y_2, \ldots$. We consider the case where Y is bounded between c and d ($c < d$), both finite. For this case let $F_i(y') = Pr(y \leqslant y' \mid A_i)$ with $F_i(c) = 0$, $F_i(d) = 1$, $F_i(y'') - F_i(y') \geqslant 0$ if $y'' > y'$, and $F_i(y)$ continuous on the right. Now let $[O_1, O_2, \ldots, O_n]$ denote a measurable n-part partition of the interval $[c, d]$. For example, one n-part partition may be taken as the set of intervals

$$O_1 = \left[c, c + \frac{d - c}{n}\right),$$

$$O_2 = \left[c + \frac{d - c}{n}, c + 2\frac{d - c}{n}\right),$$

$$\vdots$$

$$O_j = \left[c + (j - 1)\frac{d - c}{n}, c + j\frac{d - c}{n}\right),$$

$$\vdots$$

$$O_n = \left[c + (n - 1)\frac{d - c}{n}, d\right].$$

In connection with such a partition, let y_j be a value of Y contained in O_j, $j = 1, \ldots, n$, and let $V_i(y_j)$ denote the relative value of the consequence (A_i, y_j). In addition, let

$$P_i(O_j) = \int_{O_j} dF_i(y)$$

denote the probability that Y will take on a value in O_j, given A_i. With the above restrictions and notations, for a given set of y_j in connection with a given partition $[O_1, \ldots, O_n]$, the sum

$$\sum_{j=1}^{n} P_i(O_j) V_i(y_j) \qquad (y_j \in O_j)$$

is well defined. To complete the definition, let Δ denote the maximum length (or Lebesque measure) of the O_j, $j = 1, \ldots, n$. That is, if $L(O_j)$ is the Lebesque measure of O_j, then $\Delta = \max_{j} L(O_j)$. Then, if

$$\lim_{\substack{\Delta \to 0 \\ n \to \infty}} \sum_{j=1}^{n} P_i(O_j) V_i(y_j)$$

exists uniquely[1] (independent of the choices of partitions and y_j for the partitions), we define $E(A_i)$ to be this limit. If the limit exists, then write

$$E(A_i) = \lim_{\substack{\Delta \to 0 \\ n \to \infty}} \sum_{j=1}^{n} P_i(O_j) V_i(y_j) = \int_{c}^{d} V_i(y) \, dF_i(y). \qquad (8.1)$$

Extensions of the above ideas to a continuous outcome variable Y whose values are unbounded (e.g., d replaced by $+\infty$), and to a general situation involving finite, denumerable, and continuous outcome variables are possible, but we shall not explore such extensions here. In the remainder of this chapter it will be assumed that $E(A_i)$ is well defined according to the existence of the appropriate limits.

8.2 MONOTONIC ANALYSIS IN ONE OUTCOME VARIABLE

In this section we shall look at situations where only one outcome variable (Y) is involved. Values of Y will be denoted y, y', y_1, y_2, $\ldots$. We will consider the case where $V(y) \geq V(y')$ whenever $y > y'$, i.e., where the value function $V(y)$ is known to be nondecreasing in y. [Situations in which $V(y)$ is nonincreasing in y would be treated in a manner similar to that discussed here.] It may be noted that, in practice, many outcome variables have this value-monotonic property. For example, many

---

[1] Up to a positive linear transformation of the $V_i(y_j)$.

persons could be expected to attach relative values to amounts of money which increase with the amount of money, and many sprinters could be expected to attach relative values to the times it takes them to run the 100-yard dash such that the shorter the time the greater the value of the outcome.

One Denumerable Variable

For a discrete outcome variable which can take on a denumerable number of real values, let $y_1, y_2, \ldots$ denote these values with $y_1 < y_2 < \ldots$. First, consider two courses of action, A_1 and A_2 and suppose that $V(A_1, y_j) = V(A_2, y_j)$ for $j = 1, 2, \ldots$. Then we may write V_j for the relative value of y_j. In addition, let $P_{ij} = P(y_j \mid A_i)$. Then

$$E(A_1) - E(A_2) = \sum_{j=1}^{\infty} (P_{1j} - P_{2j})V_j.$$

Suppose now that $V_1 \leqslant V_2 \leqslant V_3 \leqslant \ldots$. Then, using the obvious extension of (6.1),

$$E(A_1) - E(A_2) = \sum_{k=1}^{\infty} \left[\sum_{j=1}^{k} (P_{1j} - P_{2j}) \right] (V_k - V_{k+1}), \qquad (8.2)$$

wherein $V_k - V_{k+1} \leqslant 0$ for all k. Hence, if $\sum_{j=1}^{k} (P_{1j} - P_{2j}) \geqslant 0$ for all k, we can conclude that $E(A_2) \geqslant E(A_1)$, and if $\sum_{j=1}^{k} (P_{1j} - P_{2j}) \leqslant 0$ for all k, we can conclude that $E(A_1) \geqslant E(A_2)$.

As an example, suppose that $\{P_{1j}\}$ is a Poisson distribution with parameter λ_1 and $\{P_{2j}\}$ is a Poisson distribution with parameter λ_2:

$$P_{1j} = e^{-\lambda_1} \frac{\lambda_1^{j-1}}{(j-1)!}, \qquad j = 1, 2, \ldots, \quad \lambda_1 > 0,$$

$$P_{2j} = e^{-\lambda_2} \frac{\lambda_2^{j-1}}{(j-1)!}, \qquad j = 1, 2, \ldots, \quad \lambda_2 > 0.$$

If $\lambda_1 > \lambda_2$, then $\sum_{j=1}^{k} (P_{1j} - P_{2j}) < 0$ for all k [and $E(A_1) \geqslant E(A_2)$], and if $\lambda_2 > \lambda_1$, then $\sum_{j=1}^{k} (P_{1j} - P_{2j}) > 0$ for all k [and $E(A_2) \geqslant E(A_1)$]. To show that $\sum_{j=1}^{k} (P_{1j} - P_{2j}) > 0$ for all k if $\lambda_2 > \lambda_1$, we use the identity

$$\sum_{j=1}^{k+1} e^{-\lambda} \frac{\lambda^{j-1}}{(j-1)!} = \frac{1}{k!} \int_{\lambda}^{\infty} e^{-x} x^k \, dx. \qquad (8.3)$$

With (8.3),

$$\sum_{j=1}^{k+1} (P_{1j} - P_{2j}) = \frac{1}{k!} \left[\int_{\lambda_1}^{\infty} e^{-x} x^k \, dx - \int_{\lambda_2}^{\infty} e^{-x} x^k \, dx \right],$$

$$k = 0, 1, 2, \ldots.$$

Then,

$$\sum_{j=1}^{k+1} (P_{1j} - P_{2j}) = \frac{1}{k!} \int_{\lambda_1}^{\lambda_2} e^{-x} x^k \, dx, \qquad k = 0, 1, \ldots \qquad (8.4)$$

If $\lambda_2 > \lambda_1$, the definite integral in (8.4) has a positive value and, thus, the right-hand side of (8.4) is positive. Since this holds for any nonnegative integer k, it follows that $\sum_{j=1}^{k} (P_{1j} - P_{2j}) > 0$ for $k = 1, 2, \ldots$
If $\lambda_1 > \lambda_2$, then

$$\sum_{j=1}^{k+1} (P_{1j} - P_{2j}) = -\frac{1}{k!} \int_{\lambda_2}^{\lambda_1} e^{-x} x^k \, dx, \qquad k = 0, 1, \ldots$$

yields the result that $\sum_{j=1}^{k} (P_{1j} - P_{2j}) < 0$ for $k = 1, 2, \ldots$
$V(A_1, y_j) = V(A_2, y_j)$ for $j = 1, 2, \ldots$ is the same actuality that led to Model II considered previously, except that here there are a denumerable infinity of y_j. Suppose, in general, that $V_{1j} \neq V_{2j}$ but it is true that $V_{1j} \geq V_{2j}$ for all j, i.e., that $V(A_1, y_j) \geq V(A_2, y_j)$ for all y_j. Combining this with the monotonicity assumption for V_{2j}, viz.,

(a) $\qquad V_{1j} \geq V_{2j} \qquad$ for $\qquad j = 1, 2, \ldots \qquad [V_{ij} = V(A_i, y_j)], \qquad$ (8.5)

(b) $\qquad\qquad\qquad V_{2j} \geq V_{2k} \qquad$ if $\qquad j \geq k,$

we note that, since

$$\sum_{j=1}^{\infty} P_{1j} V_{1j} \geq \sum_{j=1}^{\infty} P_{1j} V_{2j},$$

$$E(A_1) - E(A_2) = \sum_{j=1}^{\infty} P_{1j} V_{1j} - \sum_{j=1}^{\infty} P_{2j} V_{2j} \geq \sum_{j=1}^{\infty} (P_{1j} - P_{2j}) V_{2j},$$

and, therefore,

$$E(A_1) - E(A_2) \geq \sum_{k=1}^{\infty} \left[\sum_{j=1}^{k} (P_{1j} - P_{2j}) \right] (V_{2k} - V_{2,k+1}). \qquad (8.6)$$

Thus, given (8.5), if $\sum_{j=1}^{k} (P_{1j} - P_{2j}) \leq 0$ for all k, then $E(A_1) - E(A_2) \geq 0$ by (8.6). However, if $\sum_{j=1}^{k} (P_{1j} - P_{2j}) \geq 0$ for all k, and $\sum_{j=1}^{k} (P_{1j} - P_{2j}) > 0$ for at least one k, then, even though the right-hand side of (8.6) will be nonpositive, the sign of $E(A_1) - E(A_2)$ is indeterminate, given only (8.5).

For the first case where $V(A_1, y_j) = V(A_2, y_j)$ for all y_j, suppose in addition to $V(y_1) \leq V(y_2) \leq V(y_3) \leq \ldots$ it is known that

$$0 \leq V(y_{j+2}) - V(y_{j+1}) \leq V(y_{j+1}) - V(y_j) \qquad \text{for} \qquad j = 1, 2, \ldots,$$

i.e.,

$$V_{j+2} - 2V_{j+1} + V_j \leq 0 \qquad \text{for} \qquad j = 1, 2, \ldots. \qquad (8.7)$$

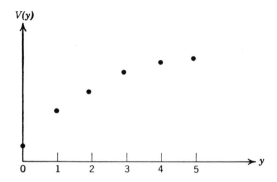

Figure 8.1

If $(y_1, y_2, y_3, \ldots) = (0, 1, 2, \ldots)$, then (8.7) is the property of downward concavity for $V(y_j)$, which may be sketched as shown in Figure 8.1. If (8.7) holds, then (8.2) may be rewritten, using (6.1), as

$$E(A_1) - E(A_2) = \sum_{k=1}^{\infty} \left[\sum_{j=1}^{k} \sum_{i=1}^{j} (P_{1i} - P_{2i}) \right] (V_{k+2} - 2V_{k+1} + V_k)$$

$$= \sum_{k=1}^{\infty} \left[\sum_{j=1}^{k} (k + 1 - j)(P_{1j} - P_{2j}) \right] (V_{k+2} - 2V_{k+1} + V_k),$$

wherein $V_{k+2} - 2V_{k+1} + V_k \leqslant 0$ for $k = 1, 2, \ldots$. Thus, if

$$\sum_{j=1}^{k} (k + 1 - j)(P_{1j} - P_{2j}) \leqslant 0 \qquad \text{for} \qquad k = 1, 2, \ldots,$$

then $E(A_1) \geqslant E(A_2)$, and if

$$\sum_{j=1}^{k} (k + 1 - j)(P_{1j} - P_{2j}) \geqslant 0 \qquad \text{for} \qquad k = 1, 2, \ldots,$$

then $E(A_2) \geqslant E(A_1)$. The above results are summarized in:

Theorem 8.1   Given a situation with one outcome variable, which can take on a denumerable number of values, $y_1, y_2, \ldots$, with $y_1 < y_2 < \ldots$:

(*a*) Suppose $V(A_1, y_j) = V(A_2, y_j)$ for $j = 1, 2, \ldots$. Then, if $V(A_1, y_1) \leqslant V(A_1, y_2) \leqslant \ldots$, $E(A_1) \geqslant E(A_2)$ if $\sum_{j=1}^{k} (P_{1j} - P_{2j}) \leqslant 0$ for $k = 1, 2, \ldots$; $E(A_2) \geqslant E(A_1)$ if $\sum_{j=1}^{k} (P_{1j} - P_{2j}) \geqslant 0$ for $k = 1, 2, \ldots$. If, in addition to $V(A_1, y_1) \leqslant V(A_1, y_2) \leqslant \ldots$, it is true that $V(A_1, y_{j+2}) - 2V(A_1, y_{j+1}) + V(A_1, y_j) \leqslant 0$, $j = 1, 2, \ldots$, then $E(A_1) \geqslant E(A_2)$ if $\sum_{j=1}^{k} (k + 1 - j)(P_{1j} - P_{2j}) \leqslant 0$ for $k = 1, 2, \ldots$; $E(A_2) \geqslant E(A_1)$ if $\sum_{j=1}^{k} (k + 1 - j)(P_{1j} - P_{2j}) \geqslant 0$ for $k = 1, 2, \ldots$.

(b) Suppose $V(A_1, y_j) \geqslant V(A_2, y_j)$ for $j = 1, 2, \ldots$, and $V(A_2, y_1) \leqslant V(A_2, y_2) \leqslant \ldots$. Then $E(A_1) \geqslant E(A_2)$ if $\sum_{j=1}^{k} (P_{1j} - P_{2j}) \leqslant 0$ for all k. Suppose further that, in connection with A_2, $V(A_2, y_{j+2}) - 2V(A_2, y_{j+1}) + V(A_2, y_j) \leqslant 0, j = 1, 2, \ldots$. Then $E(A_1) \geqslant E(A_2)$ if

$$\sum_{j=1}^{k} (k + 1 - j)(P_{1j} - P_{2j}) \leqslant 0$$

for all k.

It should be noted that theorem 8.1 applies equally well to the case where the number of values that Y can assume is finite, say n. [Replace $j = 1, 2, \ldots$ and $k = 1, 2, \ldots$ by $j = 1, 2, \ldots, n$ and $k = 1, 2, \ldots, n$.] To use the results of the theorem, it is not essential that $y_1 < y_2 < \ldots$, for, if the y_j can be ordered so that $V(A_i, y_1) \leqslant V(A_i, y_2) \leqslant \ldots$ where it is not necessarily true that $y_1 < y_2 < \ldots$, then the conclusions of the theorem still apply.

One Continuous Variable

For simplicity in examining the case where Y is a continuous outcome variable, suppose that $V(y)$ is twice differentiable with continuous derivatives, that the limits which define the following integrals exist, and that, in general, all operations that follow are theoretically legitimate. $V(y') \geqslant V(y)$ if $y' \geqslant y$ can then be expressed as $V'(y) \geqslant 0$, where $V'(y) = dV(y)/dy$. The condition of convexity[2] is $V''(y) \leqslant 0$, where $V''(y) = d^2V(y)/dy^2$.

Let $F_i(y) = P(y' \leqslant y \mid A_i)$ for $i = 1, 2$. $F_i(y)$ is the distribution function for y, given A_i. Then, when $V(A_1, y) = V(A_2, y) = V(y)$ for all y, with $F_i(c) = 0$, $F_i(d) = 1$, $c < d$, $i = 1, 2$,

$$E(A_1) - E(A_2) = \int_c^d V(y) \, dF_1(y) - \int_c^d V(y) \, dF_2(y). \tag{8.8}$$

Integrating (8.8) by parts gives

$$E(A_1) - E(A_2) = \int_c^d [-V'(y)][F_1(y) - F_2(y)] \, dy. \tag{8.9}$$

Then, if $V'(y) \geqslant 0$, (8.9) yields $E(A_1) \geqslant E(A_2)$ if $F_2(y) \geqslant F_1(y)$ for every y in $[c, d]$, and $E(A_2) \geqslant E(A_1)$ if $F_1(y) \geqslant F_2(y)$ for every y in $[c, d]$.

Integrating (8.9) by parts gives

$$E(A_1) - E(A_2) = \int_c^d V''(y) \left\{ \int_c^y [F_1(x) - F_2(x)] \, dx \right\} dy$$

$$- V'(d) \int_c^d [F_1(x) - F_2(x)] \, dx. \tag{8.10}$$

[2] To be quite proper, $V(y)$ is convex or "concave downward" if $V''(y) < 0$.

Then, if $V'(d) \geqslant 0$ and $V''(y) \leqslant 0$, (8.10) implies that $E(A_1) \geqslant E(A_2)$ if $\int_c^y F_2(x)\, dx \geqslant \int_c^y F_1(x)\, dx$ for every y in $[c, d]$, and $E(A_2) \geqslant E(A_1)$ if $\int_c^y F_1(x)\, dx \geqslant \int_c^y F_2(x)\, dx$ for every y in $[c, d]$.

If it is not generally true that $V(A_1, y) = V(A_2, y)$, but it is known that $V(A_1, y) \geqslant V(A_2, y)$ for every y in $[c, d]$, then

$$E(A_1) - E(A_2) \geqslant \int_c^d V(A_2, y)\, dF_1(y) - \int_c^d V(A_2, y)\, dF_2(y). \quad (8.11)$$

Integrating the right-hand side of (8.11) by parts gives forms identical to the right-hand sides of (8.9) and (8.10), with $V'(y)$ and $V''(y)$ being replaced by $V'(A_2, y)$ and $V''(A_2, y)$ respectively. Thus, similar to theorem 8.1 for the discrete case, we now have, when Y is a continuous variable:

Theorem 8.2 Given a situation with one continuous outcome variable Y, which can take on any value in the closed interval $c \leqslant y \leqslant d$, suppose that $V(A_2, y)$ is twice differentiable in $[c, d]$, and that the integrals in (8.8) through (8.11) are well defined, where $F_1(x) = P(y \leqslant x \mid A_1)$, $F_2(x) = P(y \leqslant x \mid A_2)$.

(a) If $V(A_1, y) = V(A_2, y)$ and $V'(A_2, y) \geqslant 0$ for all y in $[c, d]$, then $E(A_1) \geqslant E(A_2)$ if $F_2(y) \geqslant F_1(y)$ for every y in $[c, d]$, and $E(A_2) \geqslant E(A_1)$ if $F_1(y) \geqslant F_2(y)$ for every y in $[c, d]$.

In addition, if $V''(A_2, y) \leqslant 0$ for all y in $[c, d]$, then $E(A_1) \geqslant E(A_2)$ if $\int_c^y [F_2(x) - F_1(x)]\, dx \geqslant 0$ for every y in $[c, d]$, and $E(A_2) \geqslant E(A_1)$ if $\int_c^y [F_1(x) - F_2(x)]\, dx \geqslant 0$ for every y in $[c, d]$.

(b) If $V(A_1, y) \geqslant V(A_2, y)$ and $V'(A_2, y) \geqslant 0$ for all y in $[c, d]$, then $E(A_1) \geqslant E(A_2)$ if $F_2(y) \geqslant F_1(y)$ for every y in $[c, d]$.

In addition, if $V''(A_2, y) \leqslant 0$ for all y in $[c, d]$, then $E(A_1) \geqslant E(A_2)$ if $\int_c^y [F_2(x) - F_1(x)]\, dx \geqslant 0$ for every y in $[c, d]$.

To illustrate part (a) of the theorem, suppose the density functions $f_1(y) = F_1'(y)$ and $f_2(y) = F_2'(y)$ are rectangular:

$$f_1(y) = \begin{cases} 1 & \text{for } 1 \leqslant y \leqslant 2 \\ 0 & \text{otherwise,} \end{cases}$$

$$f_2(y) = \begin{cases} \frac{1}{3} & \text{for } 0 \leqslant y \leqslant 3 \\ 0 & \text{otherwise.} \end{cases}$$

Then take $c = 0$, $d = 3$. From the definitions of f_1 and f_2,

$$F_1(y) = \begin{cases} 0 & 0 \leqslant y \leqslant 1 \\ y - 1 & 1 \leqslant y \leqslant 2 \\ 1 & 2 \leqslant y \leqslant 3, \end{cases}$$

$$F_2(y) = \tfrac{1}{3} y \qquad 0 \leqslant y \leqslant 3.$$

For $0 < y < \frac{3}{2}$, $F_2(y) > F_1(y)$, and for $\frac{3}{2} < y < 3$, $F_1(y) > F_2(y)$, so that $V'(A_2, y) \geq 0$ does not, by itself, yield a definite conclusion on the sign of $E(A_1) - E(A_2)$. Next, we find that

$$\int_0^y F_1(x)\,dx = \begin{cases} 0 & 0 \leq y \leq 1 \\ (y-1)^2/2 & 1 \leq y \leq 2 \\ y - \frac{3}{2} & 2 \leq y \leq 3, \end{cases}$$

$$\int_0^y F_2(x)\,dx = y^2/6 \qquad 0 \leq y \leq 3.$$

Here it is readily seen that $\int_0^y F_2(x)\,dx > \int_0^y F_1(x)\,dx$ for $0 < y < 3$, the two being equal at $y = 0, 3$. Hence, given the conditions on $V(A_1, y)$ and $V(A_2, y)$ in part (a) of theorem 8.2, we conclude that $E(A_1) \geq E(A_2)$. The same conclusion holds if the V conditions of part (b) of the theorem apply. Figure 8.2 illustrates F_1, F_2, and $\int F_1$, $\int F_2$ for this example.

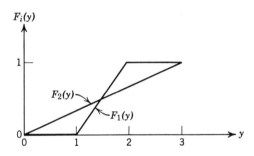

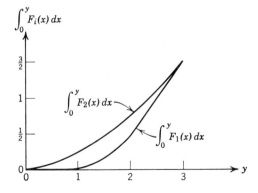

Figure 8.2

Mixed Dominance

If with m (> 2) courses of action, $A_1, A_2, \ldots, A_m$, it is true that $V(A_i, y) = V(A_j, y)$, for all (i, j) pairs over the range of y, then the analysis for mixed dominance is straightforward. For example, with Y denumerable, if $V(y_1) \leqslant V(y_2) \leqslant \ldots$, then we can conclude that A_s is dominated if there exists an **a** ($a_s = 0$, $a_i \geqslant 0$ for $i \neq s$, and $\sum a_i = 1$) such that

$$\sum_{j=1}^{k} \left(\sum_{i=1}^{m} a_i P_{ij} \right) \leqslant \sum_{j=1}^{k} P_{sj} \quad \text{for} \quad k = 1, 2, \ldots,$$

where $P_{ij} = P(y = y_j \mid A_i)$. For Y continuous and $V'(y) \geqslant 0$, we can conclude that A_s is dominated if there exists an **a** such that

$$\sum_{i=1}^{m} a_i F_i(y) \leqslant F_s(y) \quad \text{for every } y \in [c, d],$$

where $F_i(x) = P(y \leqslant x \mid A_i)$ and $F_i(c) = 0$, $F_i(d) = 1$ for $i = 1, 2, \ldots, m$.

8.3 THE METHOD OF PARTITIONS

When one is faced with outcome variables that have a very large finite or infinite number of values, it may be desirable to take the entire set of outcomes (which may be infinite) and partition this set into a manageable number of exclusive and exhaustive subsets, say, $O_1, O_2, \ldots, O_n$, and then approximate $E(A_i)$ by

$$E(A_i) \doteq \sum_{j=1}^{n} P(O_j \mid A_i) V(A_i, y_j),$$

where $y_j \in O_j, j = 1, \ldots, n$.[3] If $V(A_i, y_j)$ were constant over all $y_j \in O_j$, this equation would be exact, but we would usually expect $V(A_i, y_j)$ to vary as y_j ranges over O_j; hence the approximation. With such approximations, one could use the methods of analysis for dominance discussed in the last two chapters, but the "conclusions" reached would only be as good as the approximations and might very well reverse themselves with different partitions and different choices of points in the resulting sets of these partitions. Hence, it would be desirable to have available a method, based upon partitions of the values of outcome variables, that would allow a conclusion such as $E(A_1) \geqslant E(A_2)$ to hold with certainty. This section explores such a method.

Two Preliminary Cases

To explain the method, we shall begin with several simple cases and then present the general theory. First, suppose we are working with only

---

[3] The y_j are the original outcomes. These have been grouped into sets of original outcomes (O_j), which may also be viewed as (new) outcomes. Each original outcome y_j is a point in one and only one of the O_j.

one outcome variable (Y) which can assume a large finite or infinite number of values.[4] Partition the values of Y into n sets, say $O_1, \ldots, O_n$, such that each value of Y is contained in one and only one set. For course of action A_i and "outcome" O_j, let $P_{ij} = P(O_j \mid A_i)$ be the probability that Y will realize a value in the set O_j if A_i is adopted, where $\sum_{j=1}^{n} P_{ij} = 1$ for each A_i. Consider two courses of action, A_1 and A_2, for which $V(A_1, y) = V(A_2, y) = V(y)$ for each $y \in Y$. For a given O_j, suppose it is possible to identify a point in Y, say y_j', that is at least as preferable to the decision maker as any point in O_j; and suppose that it is possible to identify a point in Y, say y_j'', such that any point in O_j is at least as valuable to the decision maker as y_j''. Then

$$V(y_j'') \leqslant V(y) \leqslant V(y_j') \qquad \text{for all } y \in O_j.$$

If such points (y_j'', y_j') can be determined for each $O_j, j = 1, 2, \ldots, n$, then clearly[5]

$$\sum_{j=1}^{n} P_{ij} V(y_j'') \leqslant E(A_i) \leqslant \sum_{j=1}^{n} P_{ij} V(y_j'). \qquad (8.12)$$

Letting

$$E(A_i'') = \sum_{j=1}^{n} P_{ij} V(y_j''),$$

$$E(A_i') = \sum_{j=1}^{n} P_{ij} V(y_j'),$$

we may write (8.12) as $E(A_i'') \leqslant E(A_i) \leqslant E(A_i')$. Obviously,

$$E(A_1) \geqslant E(A_2) \qquad \text{if} \quad E(A_1'') \geqslant E(A_2'), \qquad (8.13)$$
$$E(A_2) \geqslant E(A_1) \qquad \text{if} \quad E(A_2'') \geqslant E(A_1').$$

If we are trying, by means of (8.13), to determine whether $E(A_1) \geqslant E(A_2)$ our interest lies in determining the sign of $E(A_1'') - E(A_2')$,

$$E(A_1'') - E(A_2') = \sum_{j=1}^{n} P_{ij} V(y_j'') - \sum_{j=1}^{n} P_{2j} V(y_j'). \qquad (8.14)$$

The right-hand side of (8.14) has a form similar to that analyzed in Chapter 6 under Model I $(\mathbf{S} = \mathbf{A})$. Indeed, if we let $V_{1j} = V(y_j'')$ and $V_{2j} = V(y_j')$, then (8.14) has the form $\sum P_{1j} V_{1j} - \sum P_{2j} V_{2j}$. Hence, with various measures of the P_{ij} and the $V(y_j')$, $V(y_j'')$, the sign of $E(A_1'') - E(A_2')$

---

[4] It is not essential that Y be defined so that it realizes numerical values. In general, Y describes an outcome space (or sample space) the points of which need not be numbers.

[5] Assuming that $E(A_i)$ is well defined.

can be analyzed by the methods of Chapter 6. In this respect it should be noted that in measuring the P_{ij} all the values that Y can assume are relevant, whereas in measuring the $V(y'_j)$ and $V(y''_j)$ only the points $y'_1, \ldots, y'_n, y''_1, \ldots, y''_n$ are used.

If it can be concluded that $E(A''_1) - E(A'_2) \geq 0$, then $E(A_1) \geq E(A_2)$, but if it is concluded that $E(A''_1) - E(A'_2) \leq 0$, then this implies neither $E(A_1) \geq E(A_2)$ nor $E(A_2) \geq E(A_1)$, so that in order to be able to conclude that $E(A_2) \geq E(A_1)$, it is generally necessary to analyze

$$E(A''_2) - E(A'_1) = \sum_{j=1}^{n} P_{2j}V(y''_j) - \sum_{j=1}^{n} P_{1j}V(y'_j) \qquad (8.15)$$

for sign. If $E(A''_2) - E(A'_1) \geq 0$, then $E(A_2) \geq E(A_1)$; otherwise we cannot reach a definite conclusion on the sign $E(A_1) - E(A_2)$ with the use of (8.15).

In the event that the signs of (8.14) and (8.15) are determined to be nonpositive, this still yields no conclusion about the sign of $E(A_1) - E(A_2)$.

For a second case, suppose that the above structure applies, except that it is not true that $V(A_1, y) = V(A_2, y)$ for all $y \in Y$. In this case, for the jth member of the partition O_j, determine (if possible) points $y'_{1j}, y''_{1j}, y'_{2j}, y''_{2j}$ in Y such that

$$V(A_1, y''_{1j}) \leq V(A_1, y) \leq V(A_1, y'_{1j}), \qquad \text{for all } y \in O_j,$$

$$V(A_2, y''_{2j}) \leq V(A_2, y) \leq V(A_2, y'_{2j}), \qquad \text{for all } y \in O_j.$$

Then

$$\sum_{j=1}^{n} P_{1j}V(A_1, y''_{1j}) \leq E(A_1) \leq \sum_{j=1}^{n} P_{1j}V(A_1, y'_{1j}),$$

$$\sum_{j=1}^{n} P_{2j}V(A_2, y''_{2j}) \leq E(A_2) \leq \sum_{j=1}^{n} P_{2j}V(A_2, y'_{2j}).$$

If we let $E(A''_i) = \sum P_{ij}V(A_i, y''_{ij})$ and $E(A'_i) = \sum P_{ij}V(A_i, y'_{ij})$, then (8.13) applies for this case. For example, if it can be concluded that $E(A''_1) \geq E(A'_2)$, then $E(A_1) \geq E(A_2)$. Writing

$$E(A''_1) - E(A'_2) = \sum_{j=1}^{n} P_{1j}V(A_1, y''_{1j}) - \sum_{j=1}^{n} P_{2j}V(A_2, y'_{2j}),$$

we note again that this takes the same form as $\sum P_{1j}V_{1j} - \sum P_{2j}V_{2j}$ and may be analyzed by the methods of Chapter 6 applicable to Model I ($S = A$).

Some Problems of Partitions

Before presenting the generalizations of this method, several comments are in order. The method is based on the supposition that, for a set of points (O_j) in outcome space, it is possible to identify, for each course of action, two points whose relative values bound the relative values of all points in O_j under the given course of action. It is not essential to the method that the two points be elements of O_j. If y'_{ij} and y''_{ij} are any two points in Y for which

$$V(A_i, y''_{ij}) \leqslant V(A_i, y) \leqslant V(A_i, y'_{ij}) \qquad \text{for all } y \in O_j,$$

then the method applies. For example, if O_j is the half-open interval $[0, 1)$, and $V(A_i, y)$ is strictly increasing on this interval, we can take $y'_{ij} = 1$, although the point $y = 1$ is not an element of O_j. Normally we would try to select y'_{ij} and y''_{ij} from O_j, since this will generally give us the greatest *a priori* chance of determining the sign of $E(A_1)$ $- E(A_2)$, using the given partition.

In this connection there may arise a natural difficulty when the range of an outcome variable is unbounded. For example, suppose Y is a continuous random variable which can take on any value $y \geqslant 0$. In any partition with a finite number of parts, there must necessarily be at least one O_j which is unbounded. If the O_j are chosen as nonoverlapping adjacent intervals, the right-most of these will be, say, $O_n = [a, \infty]$. If $V(A_i, y)$ is strictly increasing in y (but finite for any finite y), then there is no y' such that $V(A_i, y') \geqslant V(A_i, y)$ for all $y \in O_n$. The practical resolution of this difficulty is to truncate the range of Y at some finite value, say M, and consider only $y \in [0, M]$. Since for any given $\epsilon > 0$ it is possible, in theory at least, to choose an M sufficiently large so that $P(y > M \mid A_i)$ $< \epsilon$ for all A_i under consideration, the inaccuracy introduced by the truncation should not be cause for grave concern, particularly if $V''(A_i, y)$ $\leqslant 0$ [i.e., if the rate of increase in $V(A_i, y)$ decreases as y gets larger]. If outcome variables with infinite ranges are truncated to provide finite ranges, it will no longer be true that $\sum_{j=1}^{n} P_{ij} = 1$, but if the truncating values are chosen properly, $\sum_{j=1}^{n} P_{ij}$ will be so close to unity that the error introduced by assuming that $\sum_j P_{ij} = 1$ should be negligible.

How many parts a partition should have and how the various parts should be defined are matters of judgment, guided by available information concerning probabilities and relative values. If one partition does not yield a conclusion about the sign of $E(A_1) - E(A_2)$, one may wish to define another partition and see if this permits a definite conclusion. For example, we may form a new partition from the old one by partitioning each O_j in the first partition into, say, two parts, thus doubling the number of O_j. In general, the larger the number of parts in a partition, the greater the likelihood of being able to conclude either $E(A_1) \geqslant E(A_2)$ or $E(A_2) \geqslant E(A_1)$. However, increasing the number of parts will also increase the amount of effort required to analyze $E(A_1'') - E(A_2')$ or

$E(A_2'') - E(A_1')$ for sign, including the effort required to measure the relative values.

General Theory

In the general case with two courses of action, let N be the number of outcome variables, the variables being $Y_1, Y_2, \ldots, Y_N$. For those Y_j having infinite ranges, truncate these in a manner so that the error of truncation will be negligible. Let **Y** denote the resulting N-dimensional outcome space. Partition **Y** into n parts, say $O_1, O_2, \ldots, O_n$. Let $P_{ij} = P(O_j \mid A_i)$ for $j = 1, 2, \ldots, n$ be the probability function on the partition, given A_i. Now for each O_j determine (if possible) four N-dimensional points, say $\mathbf{y}_{1j}'$, $\mathbf{y}_{1j}''$, $\mathbf{y}_{2j}'$, and $\mathbf{y}_{2j}''$, each of which belongs to **Y**, such that

$$V(A_1, \mathbf{y}_{1j}'') \leqslant V(A_1, \mathbf{y}) \leqslant V(A_1, \mathbf{y}_{1j}') \qquad \text{for all } \mathbf{y} \in O_j,$$
$$V(A_2, \mathbf{y}_{2j}'') \leqslant V(A_2, \mathbf{y}) \leqslant V(A_2, \mathbf{y}_{2j}') \qquad \text{for all } \mathbf{y} \in O_j. \tag{8.16}$$

Each point **y**, $\mathbf{y}_{1j}'$, and so forth, is, of course, an N-dimensional point of the form $\mathbf{y} = (y_1, y_2, \ldots, y_N)$, where y_j is a member of the set of elements defined by $Y_j, j = 1, 2, \ldots, N$.

Then, let

$$E(A_i') = \sum_{j=1}^{n} P_{ij} V(A_i, \mathbf{y}_{ij}'), \qquad i = 1, 2,$$

$$E(A_i'') = \sum_{j=1}^{n} P_{ij} V(A_i, \mathbf{y}_{ij}''), \qquad i = 1, 2. \tag{8.17}$$

From (8.16) and (8.17),

$$E(A_1'') \leqslant E(A_1) \leqslant E(A_1'),$$
$$E(A_2'') \leqslant E(A_2) \leqslant E(A_2').$$

Then, $E(A_1) \geqslant E(A_2)$ if $E(A_1'') \geqslant E(A_2')$, or $E(A_2) \geqslant E(A_1)$ if $E(A_2'') \geqslant E(A_1')$. Analysis of $E(A_1'') - E(A_2')$ or $E(A_2'') - E(A_1')$ for sign can be conducted by the methods of Chapter 6 as applied to Model I ($\mathbf{S} = \mathbf{A}$).

In the special case where $V(A_1, \mathbf{y}) = V(A_2, \mathbf{y})$ for all $\mathbf{y} \in \mathbf{Y}$, we may take $\mathbf{y}_{2j}' = \mathbf{y}_{1j}'$ and $\mathbf{y}_{2j}'' = \mathbf{y}_{1j}''$. If possible $\mathbf{y}_{1j}'$, $\mathbf{y}_{1j}''$, $\mathbf{y}_{2j}'$, $\mathbf{y}_{2j}''$ should be determined from the elements of O_j or, if this is not possible, from elements near the "boundary" of O_j.

In extending this to the analysis of mixed dominance, let A_s be a course of action we are trying to show to be dominated by a combination of A_i, $i = 1, \ldots, m; i \neq s$. With the use of the same n-part partition as defined above, for each O_j determine (if possible) m points in **Y**, say, $\mathbf{y}_{ij}$, $i = 1, 2, \ldots, m$, such that

$$V(A_i, \mathbf{y}_{ij}) \leqslant V(A_i, \mathbf{y}), \qquad \text{for all } \mathbf{y} \in O_j \ (i \neq s),$$
$$V(A_s, \mathbf{y}_{sj}) \geqslant V(A_s, \mathbf{y}), \qquad \text{for all } \mathbf{y} \in O_j.$$

Then, let

$$E(A_i^*) = \sum_{j=1}^{n} P_{ij} V(A_i, y_{ij}), \qquad i = 1, 2, \ldots, m.$$

If it is then possible to determine an **a** ($a_s = 0$, $a_i \geqslant 0$, $\sum_{i=1}^{m} a_i = 1$) such that

$$\sum_{i \neq s} a_i E(A_i^*) \geqslant E(A_s^*),$$

we can conclude that A_s is dominated. The methods used to analyze

$$\sum_{i \neq s} a_i E(A_i^*) - E(A_s^*) = \mathbf{a} \cdot \mathbf{E(A^*)} - E(A_s^*)$$

for sign are similar to those presented in Chapter 7 under Model I ($\mathbf{S} = \mathbf{A}$).

EXERCISES

NOTE: These exercises are concerned with situations involving just one outcome variable Y, either discrete or continuous, and two courses of action, A_1 and A_2. Unless otherwise stated, assume $V(A_1, y) = V(A_2, y)$, with the common value function denoted by $V(y)$. The limits which define $E(A_1)$ and $E(A_2)$ are assumed to exist.

1. Suppose Y has a geometric distribution, given A_1 or A_2:

$$P_{1j} = p^{j-1}(1 - p), \qquad j = 1, 2, \ldots \quad (0 < p < 1),$$
$$P_{2j} = q^{j-1}(1 - q), \qquad j = 1, 2, \ldots \quad (0 < q < 1),$$

where $P_{ij} = P(y = j \mid A_i)$, $j = 1, 2, \ldots$. If $V(y)$ decreases as y increases, $y = 1, 2, \ldots$ show that $E(A_1) \geqslant E(A_2)$ if $q \geqslant p$ and $E(A_2) \geqslant E(A_1)$ if $p \geqslant q$. $[\sum_{j=1}^{k} a^{j-1} = (1 - a^k)/(1 - a)$ if $a \neq 1.]$

2. Suppose Y is continuous, and has an exponential distribution given A_i:

$$f_1(y) = \lambda_1 e^{-\lambda_1 y}, \qquad y \geqslant 0 \quad (\lambda_1 > 0),$$
$$f_2(y) = \lambda_2 e^{-\lambda_2 y}, \qquad y \geqslant 0 \quad (\lambda_2 > 0),$$

where $f_i(y) = dF_i(y)/dy$, or $F_i(y) = \int_0^y \lambda_i e^{-\lambda_i x} \, dx = P(y' \leqslant y)$. Given $V'(y) \geqslant 0$, show that $E(A_1) \geqslant E(A_2)$ if $\lambda_2 \geqslant \lambda_1$ and $E(A_2) \geqslant E(A_1)$ if $\lambda_1 \geqslant \lambda_2$.

3. With Y continuous, suppose the density function of $y \mid A_i$ is normal with mean μ_i and variance σ_i^2:

$$f_i(y) = \frac{1}{\sqrt{2\pi} \, \sigma_i} e^{-(y - \mu_i)^2 / 2\sigma_i^2} \qquad \text{for all } y \quad (\text{from } -\infty \text{ to } +\infty).$$

With $F_i(y) = \int_{-\infty}^{y} f_i(x) \, dx$, prove that:

(a) $F_1(y) \geqslant F_2(y)$ for all y if and only if $\sigma_1 = \sigma_2$, $\mu_2 \geqslant \mu_1$. {*Hint:* Use the fact that $F_i(y) = \Phi[(y - \mu_i)/\sigma_i]$, where Φ is the distribution function for a normal variate with mean 0 and variance 1, with $\Phi(a) > \Phi(b)$ if and only if $a > b$.}

(b) If $\mu_1 = \mu_2$, then $\int_{-\infty}^{y} F_1(x)\,dx \geqslant \int_{-\infty}^{y} F_2(x)\,dx$ for all y if and only if $\sigma_1 \geqslant \sigma_2$. (*Hint:* Make use of the symmetry property of the normal distribution.)

(c) Generalize part (b) to: $\int_{-\infty}^{y} F_1(x)\,dx \geqslant \int_{-\infty}^{y} F_2(x)\,dx$ for all y if and only if $\sigma_1 \geqslant \sigma_2$ and $\mu_2 \geqslant \mu_1$. Similarly, $\int_{-\infty}^{y} F_2(x)\,dx \geqslant \int_{-\infty}^{y} F_1(x)\,dx$ if and only if $\sigma_2 \geqslant \sigma_1$ and $\mu_1 \geqslant \mu_2$.

(d) If $V'(y) \geqslant 0$ and $V''(y) \leqslant 0$ for all y, what conclusions can be made concerning the sign of $E(A_1) - E(A_2)$ in each of the following cases?

(i) $(\mu_1, \sigma_1) = (4, 1)$, $(\mu_2, \sigma_2) = (6, 2)$.

(ii) $(\mu_1, \sigma_1) = (100, 10)$, $(\mu_2, \sigma_2) = (90, 20)$.

(iii) $(\mu_1, \sigma_1) = (-3, 4)$, $(\mu_2, \sigma_2) = (3, 3)$.

(iv) $(\mu_1, \sigma_1) = (100, 2)$, $(\mu_2, \sigma_2) = (-100, 1)$.

4. For Y continuous, suppose the density functions of $y \mid A_1$ and $y \mid A_2$ are respectively

$$f_1(y) = \begin{cases} 1 & 0 \leqslant y \leqslant 1 \\ 0 & \text{elsewhere} \end{cases}$$

$$f_2(y) = \begin{cases} 3y^2 & 0 \leqslant y \leqslant 1 \\ 0 & \text{elsewhere.} \end{cases}$$

Show that $E(A_1) \geqslant E(A_2)$ if $V'(y) \leqslant 0$ for $y \in [0, 1]$.

5. For Y continuous, suppose the distribution functions of $y \mid A_1$ and $y \mid A_2$ are respectively

$$F_1(y) = \begin{cases} 0 & y \leqslant 0 \\ y & 0 \leqslant y \leqslant 1 \\ 1 & y \geqslant 1 \end{cases}$$

$$F_2(y) = \begin{cases} 0 & y \leqslant 0 \\ y^3 - {}^3/_2 y^2 + {}^3/_2 y & 0 \leqslant y \leqslant 1 \\ 1 & y \geqslant 1. \end{cases}$$

Show that, given only $V'(y) \geqslant 0$ for $y \in [0, 1]$, no conclusion may be reached concerning the sign of $E(A_1) - E(A_2)$, but that with $V'(y) \geqslant 0$ and $V''(y) \leqslant 0$, we can conclude that $E(A_1) - E(A_2) \geqslant 0$.

6. Suppose Y is discrete, and the probability functions of $y \mid A_1$ and $y \mid A_2$ follow binomial distributions:

$$P_{1j} = \binom{n}{j} p^j (1 - p)^{n-j}, \qquad j = 0, 1, \ldots, n \quad (0 < p < 1),$$

$$P_{2j} = \binom{n}{j} q^j (1 - q)^{n-j}, \qquad j = 0, 1, \ldots, n \quad (0 < q < 1),$$

where $P_{ij} = P(y = j \mid A_i)$, $j = 0, 1, \ldots, n$. Show that $\sum_{j=0}^{k} (P_{1j} - P_{2j}) \geqslant 0$

if and only if $q \geqslant p$, and, similarly, that $\sum_{j=0}^{k} (P_{1j} - P_{2j}) \leqslant 0$ if and only if $p \geqslant q$. Make use of the identity, for $0 < t < 1$,

$$\sum_{j=0}^{k} \binom{n}{j} t^{j} (1-t)^{n-j} = (n-k) \binom{n}{k} \int_{0}^{1-t} x^{n-k-1} (1-x)^{k} \, dx.$$

On this basis, give the sign of $E(A_1) - E(A_2)$ for each of the following cases:

(a) $V(y)$ increases as y increases, $(p, q) = (.6, .8)$.

(b) $V(y)$ decreases as y increases, $(p, q) = (.4896, .4986)$.

(c) $V(y)$ increases as y increases, $(p, q) = (.02, .01)$.

Chapter 9

VALUEWISE INDEPENDENCE OF VARIABLES

9.1 INTRODUCTION

Our discussion of independence began in Section 1.4 where, among other things, an example was offered to illustrate the notion of independence, and analogies to independence in other contexts were drawn. The reasons for considering independence were briefly stated in Section 1.4 and discussed in more detail in Section 4.3 in connection with our consideration of measures of relative value. In many decision situations, independence will not, in fact, hold, and if independence is assumed in such cases considerable error may be introduced. This indicates the need for some caution on the part of the individual or research worker when involved in making a decision as to whether to assume independence in what degree. This is, if you please, a matter of subjective judgment in which one must try to weigh the distortion that may be caused by assuming independence (not really knowing how critical this will be) against the gains in economy of analysis that may result under independence. In Section 9.7 we shall begin to consider ways in which decision situations may be reformulated so as to make the assumption of independence (if it does come to that) more tenable and less objectionable, after considering ways of testing for independence in Section 9.6.

It will be recalled that the primary reasons for considering independence of variables in the relative value sense are purely practical in nature. Concern with independence stems from the desire to simplify. Under independence, this simplification or reduction comes about in one of two ways. First, independence may reduce the number of entities requiring value measurement. This is particularly significant if the number of elements in the product of all action and outcome variables that have positive probabilities of occurrence with one or more strategies (i.e., the total number of consequences) is close to the total number of elements in the product set. However, in some cases (e.g., in some situations under certainty to be discussed in Chapter 10), independence may actually increase the number of entities requiring value measurement. In such cases, this increase may be more than offset by the simplicity that can occur in making preference judgments. Thus, the second kind of simplification due to independence deals with an individual's ability to measure relative values. Under independence, preference judgments need only be taken over pairs (or triples, etc.) of consequences which differ with respect to the values of just a few variables, as opposed to consequences which differ with respect to the values of many variables. Very often the choice between independence or not is a choice between "divide and conquer with approximation" or "don't divide and don't conquer at all."

In discussing valuewise independence of variables, it will be shown in Section 9.4 what effect this has upon the decision model. In Section 9.5 we will discuss value measures, but leave detailed discussion of the relative values of the variable's values under independence to the remaining chapters of the book.

Before approaching the formal development in Section 9.3, let us digress for a moment to consider a partial history of independence.

9.2 HISTORICAL AND OTHER COMMENTS

The notion of independence, far from being a recent development in value or utility theory, appeared in the writings of economists more than a century ago. Although any short explanation or history of their thought cannot hope to present an accurate picture of their intentions, we shall, with apology to the economists, take a brief glance backwards.

In the language of economics, we shall consider a set of commodity bundles X, where every $x \in X$ is a vector of amounts of specific goods or services. That is, $x = (x_1, x_2, \ldots, x_n)$, where x_i denotes the amount of the ith good or commodity (be it shoes, butter, bread, olive oil, etc.) in the commodity bundle. The units of x_i are pairs, or pounds, or loaves, or gallons, etc. We might, for example, take X to be the set of all commodity bundles available to an individual consumer during the course of one year, where X is limited according to the consumer's disposable income, and the availability and prices of the various goods. During the year, the individual will acquire one and only one of the $x \in X$. It is generally assumed that the x_i are continuous variables, so that operations such as differentiation may be used. It hardly seems necessary to say that economists were and are interested in the study of consumer behavior (among other things), and have attempted to interpret and understand the devious ways of *Homo sapiens* in the market place.

With this brief introduction, let us look at a patch of history. According to Samuelson (1947):

> As early as 1854, Gossen is credited with presenting what is essentially marginal utility. He assumed this to be a decreasing linear function of the quantity of any particular good. The utility function would therefore be as follows:
>
> $$U = K + (a_1 x_1 - b_1 x_1^2) + (a_2 x_2 - b_2 x_2^2) + \ldots \qquad (1)$$
>
> Jevons, writing fifteen years later, proposed that the utility function be written as the sum of utilities pertaining to each good separately.
>
> $$U = V_1(x_1) + V_2(x_2) + \ldots + V_n(x_n), \qquad (2)$$
>
> where the functions V_i obey the law of diminishing marginal utility.* Specifically,
>
> $$V_i'(x_i) > 0, \qquad (3)$$
> $$V_i''(x_i) < 0.$$
>
> In his *Mathematical Psychics* (1881), Edgeworth, going further than Jevons, suggested that the requirement that utility be a sum of functions pertaining to each good was an unnecessary and indeed unjustifiable assumption. He proposed, therefore, that the utility function be written in the form†
>
> $$U = \phi(x_1, \ldots, x_n), \qquad (4)$$
>
> where ϕ is any joint function of the quantities of all goods, and where
>
> $$\phi_{ij} = \frac{\partial^2 \phi}{\partial x_i \, \partial x_j} \gtreqless 0. \qquad (i \neq j) \qquad (5)$$
>
> * Walras and Marshall also made the assumption that utility may be written as in (2). In the case of Marshall, . . . it is not clear whether he really intended to be taken literally when making the assumption that utilities are independent, or whether he regarded this as an approximation for small movements under certain conditions.
>
> † Professor Irving Fisher is also credited with the independent discovery of this possibility at a later date (p. 93).

From Samuelson's comments it seems clear that the notion of independence of utilities as expressed by (2) appeared prior to the idea of a joint utility function defined over commodity bundles, as expressed by (4). In this book, we have felt it quite natural to begin with a form like (4), defined over consequences, and then consider the case of independence of variables.[1] The equation which describes independence here will be of similar form to (2), e.g.,

$$V(x_1, x_2, \ldots, x_n) = V_1(x_1) + V_2(x_2) + \ldots + V_n(x_n), \qquad (9.1)$$

[1] Since the turn of the century, economists working in utility theory and interested in independence (and interdependence) have usually proceeded from the more general form of (4).

where the left-hand side of (9.1) is of the same form as the right-hand side of (4).[2]   The form (1) represents an "additional" assumption to that of (2); namely, it gives a quadratic form to the utility of the amount of each commodity.   Since the x_i are considered as continuous variables in the above excerpt, conditions (3) state that the utility of the ith good increases at a decreasing rate with the amount, similar to the conditions in the monotonicity section of the previous chapter (Section 8.2).   The purpose of (5) is to illustrate that in (4) no specific assumption is being made about independence.

Although not particularly relevant to our immediate discussion of independence, the continuation of Samuelson's remarks does have a bearing on the discussion of decisions under certainty in the next chapter:

By the end of the nineteenth century many writers, notably Pareto, had come to the realization that it was an unnecessary and unwarranted assumption that there even exist utility as a *cardinal* magnitude.   Since only more or less comparisons are needed for consumer's behaviour and not comparisons of how much more or less, it is only necessary that there exist an *ordinal* preference field.   For any two combinations of goods, respectively $(x_1^0, \ldots, x_n^0)$ and $(x_1^1, \ldots, x_n^1)$, or for brevity, (X^0) and (X^1), it is only necessary that the consumer be able to place them in one of the following mutually exclusive categories.

  a. (X^0) preferred to (X^1)

  b. (X^1) preferred to (X^0) (6)

  c. (X^0) and (X^1) equally preferred or indifferent.

For convenience, we may attach a number to each combination; this is assumed to be a continuous differentiable function.   This function (or rule of numbering) may be written

$$\phi = \phi(X) = \phi(x_1, \ldots, x_n). \qquad (7)$$

It is so constructed that the following three conditions correspond to the above three respectively:

  a′. $\phi(X^1) < \phi(X^0)$

  b′. $\phi(X^0) < \phi(X^1)$ (8)

  c′. $\phi(X^0) = \phi(X^1)$.

ϕ may be designated as a utility index.   The one parameter family of loci defined by

$$\phi(x_1, x_2, \ldots, x_n) = C,$$

where C is regarded as a parameter, are designated as indifference loci.
It is clear that any function

$$U = F(\phi), \qquad F'(\phi) > 0 \qquad (9)$$

defined by any monotonic transformation of ϕ, is also a utility index.   For

$$\phi(X^1) \gtreqless \phi(X^0) \quad \text{implies} \quad U(X^1) \gtreqless U(X^0),$$

[2] In (9.1) V_j denotes a function defined over the values of the jth good or, in the context of this monograph, the values of the jth variable.

respectively. The converse also holds. Thus, from any one utility index all others can be derived by a suitable functional transformation. To summarize, our ordinal preference field may be written

$$U = F[\phi(x_1, \ldots, x_n)], \qquad F'(\phi) > 0, \tag{10}$$

where ϕ is any one cardinal index of utility.

It is clear that the choice of any one numbering system or utility index is arbitrary. The indifference loci are left unchanged by any alteration of the tags attached to each, provided ordinal relationships are maintained. In order, therefore, to avoid the asymmetry of employing any one favored utility index, many writers (Pareto, W. E. Johnson, Hicks and Allen, *et al.*) have suggested that a notation be employed which is dependent only upon the invariant elements of the ordinal preference field, namely, the indifference loci [pp. 93–95].

The point being stressed in this excerpt is that, in discussing the utility of certain alternatives (where no probabilities are involved), it suffices to have an ordering of the alternatives as opposed, for example, to a utility function unique up to an increasing linear transformation. Conceptually, it has been helpful to characterize such an ordering with a utility index given by (7) and (8), unique only up to a monotonic increasing transformation, as noted in (9). A utility index is intended to be a faithful representation only of the preference and indifference relations between certain alternatives (or commodity bundles in the economic context), and comparisons between absolute utility differences are not considered meaningful or relevant under a utility index. In order that a utility index exist over a set X of certain alternatives, or commodity bundles, it is necessary (but not sufficient—see Exercise 12) that for any two x, x' in X, either (*a*), (*b*), or (*c*) in (6) holds and that $\gtrsim$ is transitive. These two conditions are similar to axioms 1 and 2 of the von Neumann-Morgenstern axioms in Section 1.3. (If we then go on to admit the other axioms in Section 1.3, we get a cardinal utility function, unique except for origin and scale.)

An indifference locus (otherwise known as indifference surface, trade-off surface, or equivalence class) is a set of $x \in X$, such that all x in this set are equally preferred to one another, and any x not in this set is either more preferable or less preferable than each x in the set. According to the suggestion in the last part of the above excerpt, the ordinal preference field could be characterized by a family of sets $\{X(C)\}$, where C is a continuous parameter, say, from 0 to 1 ($0 \leqslant C \leqslant 1$), and where each $X(C)$ is an indifference locus such that, if $x \in X(C_0)$ and $x' \in X(C_1)$, then $C_0 \geqslant C_1$ if and only if $x \gtrsim x'$. In this book we are not much concerned with indifference loci. However, in the context of finite sets, we used this notion (under the name of equivalence classes) in connection with the third bounded interval measure of relative value discussed in Section 4.9.

This discussion serves to illustrate that, if the set of strategies **S** in a decision situation is composed entirely of certain alternatives, then we need go no further than to identify a strategy (or alternative, or consequence) that is at least as desirable as every other $S_i \in$ **S**. However, as argued previously,[3] it may be quite difficult for an individual to determine his preference between two such alternatives, especially when each is composed of a sizable vector of values of the variables. For this reason we shall consider the problem of decision making under "certainty," using the independence assumption, in Chapter 10.

Getting back to our history of independence, again in the context of economics, as the utility function [(2) in the first excerpt from Samuelson] of Jevons[4] came to be questioned because of its independence implications, the terms *complementarity* and *competitiveness* among various goods arose in the literature; see, e.g., Auspitz and Lieben (1889). Irving Fisher, who was greatly influenced by Jevons (1871) and Auspitz and Lieben (1889), considered these aspects in his celebrated *Mathematical Investigations in the Theory of Value and Prices* (1925, first read in 1892). Part I of this two-part monograph deals with independence. Part II considers the effect that interactions among various goods have on (his kind of) utilities:

Hitherto it has been assumed that the utility of a commodity is a function of the quantity of that commodity alone. It is true that it depends upon that quantity more than any other and the analysis of Part I is a necessary first approximation. In astronomy the attraction of the sun on the earth is first studied alone to determine the earth's motion; next the moon's influence is admitted, then the occasional "perturbations" due to planets and comets. Absolute accuracy is never attained for the earth's motion is a function of the mass and position of every body in the universe.

So also the utility of the 100th lb. of butter (100 lbs. per year) depends mostly on that 100 lbs. It would not be perceptibly influenced by a change in the quantity of clothing, but it would be perceptibly reduced if the amount of *bread* consumed were reduced from 300 loaves to 200, for bread and butter go together.

It is needful here to distinguish carefully between two ways in which the quantity of one commodity can affect the utility of others. Even under the supposition of Part I, a change in the price of clothes affected a change in the individual valuation of money and so changed the quantity of bread consumed and so in turn changed the marginal utility and price of bread. But under our new supposition, a change in the price of butter directly changes the utility of the *same quantity* of bread. In the first case marginal utility of bread can change only after a change in its *quantity*. In the second the marginal utility of the *same* amount of bread changes . . ..

It will be seen that this sort of dependence of particular commodities is

---

[3] See Section 4.3.

[4] *The Theory of Political Economy*, 1871.

very common. Articles are bought with reference to each other, oil with reference to the number of lamps used, bed linen to the number of beds, bureaus to the quantity of clothes to be stored, ...

The cases above instanced are cases of "completing" articles. Under the head of "competing" articles, come mineral oil and other oils, various "qualities" of any article as meats, grades of flour, etc., while under production almost every two articles are competing.

. . . the utility of a commodity usually varies so much more under a variation in the quantity of that commodity than under variations of other commodities that the relations discussed in Part I may be regarded as good first approximations. Especially is this true if the interdependent commodities are grouped . . . so as to eliminate all the really important influences of commodities on each other [pp. 64–67].

Although no attempt will be made to define the relative value (cardinal utility) of a value of a variable (quantity of a commodity), except when independence is assumed or to formalize the notion of complementing or competing variables (commodities), we will appeal freely to the reader's intuition on matters of interactions among variables in a value sense. The foregoing quote is offered mainly to help develop a feeling for the idea of valuewise interactions (be they complementing, competing, or some other kind). In the last few lines of this quote, Fisher presents a defense for independence, following up his opening statement. Particular attention is directed to the final sentence since the grouping notion is pursued later on.

9.3 FUNCTIONAL INDEPENDENCE WITH FINITE SETS

This section formalizes the notion of independence of variables with respect to a real-valued function f. The theory developed here applies primarily to finite sets, although it can be extended quite simply to denumerable sets. In this development use is made of certain aspects of the theory of graphs. The theory in this section will be applied to valuewise independence in the next section.

The basic notions are:

1. Two finite sets, X and Y, each with at least one element. Moreover, no two elements of X are identical and no two elements of Y are identical. The element(s) of X will be denoted $x, x', \ldots$, and the element(s) of Y will be denoted $y, y', \ldots$.

2. An ordered pair (x, y) with $x \in X$, $y \in Y$. The set of all ordered pairs (x, y) is the product set $X \times Y$.

3. A nonnull subset of $X \times Y$, denoted by Z. That is, Z is a set of ordered pairs (x, y), where $(x, y) \in Z$ implies $(x, y) \in X \times Y$, but $(x, y) \in X \times Y$ does not necessarily imply that $(x, y) \in Z$ unless X and Y each have only one element or unless $Z = X \times Y$.

4. A real-valued function f defined on the elements of Z. The value that f takes on for $(x, y) \in Z$ will be denoted $f(x, y)$.

It should be noted that the elements of X and Y may be taken to be anything we please. For example, we could have $X = \{$beauty, dog, horse$\}$ and $Y = \{$apple, orange, 4, George Washington$\}$.

Using the primitives given above, let

$$X_0 = \text{set of all } x \in X \text{ that appear in the first place}$$
$$\text{of one or more } (x, y) \in Z,$$

$$Y_0 = \text{set of all } y \in Y \text{ that appear in the second place}$$
$$\text{of one or more } (x, y) \in Z.$$

By the definitions of X_0 and Y_0, $Z \subset X_0 \times Y_0$: read "Z is contained in $X_0 \times Y_0$" or "Z is a subset of $X_0 \times Y_0$."

Almost Independence

Our first important definition concerns almost independence:

Definition 9.1 X and Y are *almost independent* with respect to f if and only if there exist real-valued functions f_1 defined on X_0 and f_2 defined on Y_0 such that

$$f_1(x) + f_2(y) = f(x, y), \tag{9.2}$$

for every $(x, y) \in Z$.

If Z has only one element (x, y), i.e., $Z = \{(x, y)\}$, then X and Y are almost independent with respect to f, since in (9.2) we can assign $f_1(x)$ any value we please and then let $f_2(y) = f(x, y) - f_1(x)$. If either X_0 or Y_0 has only one element, then X and Y are almost independent with respect to f. For example, if

$$Z = \{(x_0, y_0), (x_0, y_1), (x_0, y_2), \ldots, (x_0, y_n)\},$$

let $f_1(x_0) = 0$, and define $f_2(y_j)$ by $f_2(y_j) = f(x_0, y_j)$ for $j = 0, 1, \ldots, n$; or we could let $f_2(y_0) = 0$, define $f_1(x_0)$ by $f_1(x_0) = f(x_0, y_0)$ and define $f_2(y_j)$ for $j > 0$ by $f_2(y_j) = f(x_0, y_j) - f(x_0, y_0)$.

Let us now see what conditions on f must hold in general in order for X and Y to be *almost independent* with respect to f. To do this, we shall use some graph theoretic notions. As in Section 6.3, it is not assumed the reader is necessarily familiar with graph theory, so the discussion will be self-contained.[5]

Definition 9.2 (x, y) and (x', y') are *adjacent* if and only if (x, y), $(x', y') \in Z$ and $x = x'$ or $y = y'$ (but not both).

---

[5] Another reason for doing this is that the language of the theory of graphs is not entirely standard. For a reference, see Berge (1962).

The graph of Z, denoted Γ_Z, is formed as follows:

Definition 9.3   Let the $(x, y) \in Z$ be called *nodes*.   Any two nodes of Z are connected by a *link* if and only if the nodes are adjacent (two adjacent nodes define a link).   The set of all nodes and links is Γ_Z.

If

$$Z = \{(x_1, y_1), (x_1, y_2), (x_2, y_1), (x_2, y_2),$$
$$(x_2, y_3), (x_3, y_3), (x_4, y_4), (x_5, y_4)\},$$

Γ_Z may be portrayed as shown in (9.3) (the dots are nodes and the lines joining adjacent nodes are links, labeled as $a, b, \ldots, h$):

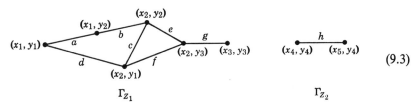

$$(9.3)$$

Definition 9.4   A *simple chain* is a sequence of links, all different, where each link is attached to the next link by one of its nodes, and to the preceding link by the other node.

In (9.3), (a, b), (a, b, c, f, e), (g, e, b, a, d, f), and (h) are among the set of all simple chains.

Definition 9.5 Γ_Z is *connected* if and only if there is a simple chain going between each distinct pair of nodes.

Obviously the graph of (9.3) is not connected since, for example, there is no simple chain between (x_3, y_3) and (x_4, y_4).   However (9.3) does have two *connected subgraphs*, $\Gamma_{Z_1} = \{(x_1, y_1), (x_1, y_2), (x_2, y_1), (x_2, y_2), (x_2, y_3),$ $(x_3, y_3), a, b, c, d, e, f, g\}$ and $\Gamma_{Z_2} = \{(x_4, y_4), (x_5, y_4), h\}$.

Definition 9.6   A *connected subgraph* of Γ_Z is a set of nodes and links between these nodes in Γ_Z, where each distinct pair of nodes in the set is joined by a simple chain.   A connected subgraph is *maximal* if there is no link joining a node of the connected subgraph to some node not in the connected subgraph.

In (9.3) there are two maximal connected subgraphs, Γ_{Z_1} and Γ_{Z_2} as defined above.   Although $\{(x_1, y_1), (x_1, y_2), (x_2, y_2), a, b\}$ in (9.3) is a connected subgraph, it is not maximal.   For any graph, the union of maximal connected subgraphs is the total graph [e.g., $\Gamma_Z = \Gamma_{Z_1} + \Gamma_{Z_2}$

in (9.3)]. Obviously a graph is connected if and only if there is a single maximal connected subgraph.

In considering the conditions on f that must hold in order to render X and Y almost independent with respect to f, it is sufficient to examine a maximal connected subgraph of Γ_Z, since no two maximal connected subgraphs have either an $x \in X_0$ or a $y \in Y_0$ in common, and thus there is no connection between them.

Lemma 9.1 X and Y are almost independent with respect to f if and only if for each maximal connected subgraph Γ_{Z_k} of Γ_Z there exist functions f_1 and f_2 such that

$$f_1(x) + f_2(y) = f(x, y)$$

for every $(x, y) \in \Gamma_{Z_k}$.

For Γ_{Z_2} in (9.3) we may take $f_1(x_4) = 0$, $f_2(y_4) = f(x_4, y_4)$, and $f_1(x_5) = f(x_5, y_4) - f(x_4, y_4)$ as a solution to the two equations

$$f_1(x_4) + f_2(y_4) = f(x_4, y_4),$$
$$f_1(x_5) + f_2(y_4) = f(x_5, y_4).$$

It should be noted that the $f(x_i, y_j)$ are given numbers, and the $f_1(x_i)$ and $f_2(y_j)$ are "unknowns" to be obtained as a solution to the set of equations

$$f_1(x_i) + f_2(y_j) = f(x_i, y_j) \tag{9.4a}$$

for all $(x_i, y_j) \in \Gamma_{Z_k}$. That is, functions f_1 and f_2 exist for Γ_{Z_k} if and only if the system (9.4a) has a solution. For notational simplicity, let

$$u_i = f_1(x_i),$$
$$v_j = f_2(y_j),$$
$$c_{ij} = f(x_i, y_j),$$

so that (9.4a) may be written as

$$u_i + v_j = c_{ij} \tag{9.4b}$$

for all $(x_i, y_j) \in \Gamma_{Z_k}$. In these terms we now state:

Lemma 9.2 If the system of equations

$$u_i + v_j = c_{ij}$$

for all (x_i, y_j) in a maximal connected subgraph Γ_{Z_k} of Γ_Z has a solution, this solution is unique up to the addition of an arbitrary constant to each u_i and the subtraction of the same constant from each v_j.

If (9.4b) has a solution, it can be obtained as follows:

1a. Pick a specific node, say $(x_{i_0}, y_{j_0}) \in \Gamma_{z_k}$ and assign u_{i_0} and v_{i_0} any two numbers that satisfy $u_{i_0} + v_{j_0} = c_{i_0 j_0}$. If Γ_{z_k} has only one node, we are finished. If not,

1b. (x_{i_0}, y_{j_0}) has at least one adjacent node, either of the form (x_{i_0}, y_{j_1}), $y_{j_1} \neq y_{j_0}$, or (x_{i_1}, y_{j_0}), $x_{i_1} \neq x_{i_0}$. For an adjacent node of the form (x_{i_0}, y_{j_1}), we get $v_{j_1} = c_{i_0 j_1} - u_{i_0}$. For an adjacent node of the form (x_{i_1}, y_{j_0}), we find $u_{i_1} = c_{i_1 j_0} - v_{j_0}$.

1c. Since every node in Γ_{z_k} can be reached by a simple chain from (x_{i_0}, y_{j_0}), continue the procedure of (1b), taking one new node at a time and solving for the unknown u_i or v_j in the $u_i + v_j = c_{ij}$ equation for that node. Thus, having specified u_{i_0} and v_{j_0}, every u_i and v_j corresponding to the x_i and y_j of Γ_{z_k} is uniquely determined.

If $\{u_i\}$ and $\{v_j\}$ is one solution to the system (9.4b), then so is $\{u_i + a\}$ and $\{v_j - a\}$, for if $u_i + v_j = c_{ij}$, then $(u_i + a) + (v_j - a) = c_{ij}$.

To see why a system such as (9.4b) may not have a solution, consider the maximal connected subgraph shown in Figure 9.1. There the number $c_{ij} = f(x_i, y_j)$ is written in place of the node (x_i, y_j). Starting with c_{11}, assign u_1 and v_1 numbers which satisfy $u_1 + v_1 = c_{11}$. Proceeding clockwise around the graph,

$$v_2 = c_{12} - u_1,$$
$$u_2 = c_{22} - v_2 = c_{22} - c_{12} + u_1,$$
$$v_1 = c_{21} - u_2 = c_{21} - c_{22} + c_{12} - u_1.$$

But we also have

$$v_1 = c_{11} - u_1.$$

Hence, a u, v solution for this 4-node subgraph exists if and only if

$$c_{21} - c_{22} + c_{12} - u_1 = c_{11} - u_1$$

or

$$c_{11} - c_{12} + c_{22} - c_{21} = 0,$$

i.e., if and only if

$$f(x_1, y_1) - f(x_1, y_2) + f(x_2, y_2) - f(x_2, y_1) = 0.$$

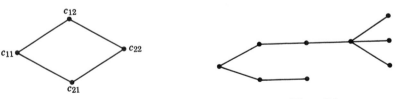

Figure 9.1   Figure 9.2

The 4-node graph (Figure 9.1) contains what is called a *cycle*.

Definition 9.7 A *cycle* (or simple cycle) is a simple chain which has the same number of nodes as links, with every node a component of exactly two links.

In (9.3), (a, b, c, d), (c, e, f), and (a, b, e, f, d) are the three cycles of Γ_{z_1}. If a maximal connected subgraph has no cycles, there is one and only one simple chain between any two nodes. For example, Figure 9.2 has no cycles and there is exactly one simple chain between any two nodes. If this is the case, then there can be no difficulty in the procedure given above for solving for the u_i and v_j. We state this as:

Lemma 9.3 The system of equations

$$u_i + v_j = c_{ij}$$

for all (x_i, y_j) in a maximal connected subgraph Γ_{z_k} has a solution if Γ_{z_k} has no cycles.

A second method [Sasieni, Yaspan, and Friedman (1959, Chapter 8)] for obtaining a u, v solution if one exists or of determining that no solution exists is to construct a matrix of the c_{ij} and perform a border evaluation of this matrix, as follows:

2a. Let Γ_{z_k} be a maximal connected subgraph with $x_1, x_2, \ldots, x_n$ and $y_1, y_2, \ldots, y_m$ the x's and y's that appear in one or more (x, y) $\in \Gamma_{z_k}$. Construct an n-by-m matrix of the c_{ij},

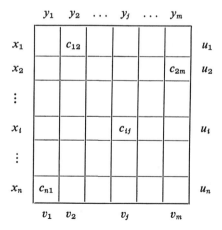

where c_{ij} is written in the cell for the ith row and jth column if $(x_i, y_j) \in \Gamma_{z_k}$. If $(x_i, y_j) \notin \Gamma_{z_k}$, then cell (i, j) is left blank. Since Γ_{z_k} is connected, each occupied cell has at least one other occupied cell in its row or column.

2b. Pick any row or column to start.   Suppose we pick the first row.   Assign to u_1 any number whatever and write this to the right of row 1.   Since we want $u_i + v_j = c_{ij}$, if c_{1j} is defined we must have $v_j = c_{1j} - u_1$.   For each occupied cell $(1, j)$ in the first row, write v_j at the bottom of the jth column, where $v_j = c_{1j} - u_1$.

2c. Pick any column for which v_j has been evaluated and calculate u_i for the rows that have an occupied cell in the jth column.   If $v_j = c_{1j} - u_1$ has been computed and c_{ij}, $i \neq 1$, appears in cell (i, j), we get $u_i = c_{ij} - v_j$.

2d. Continue this procedure, going from row to column to row, etc., until all the u_i and v_j have been evaluated and satisfy $u_i + v_j = c_{ij}$ for each $(x_i, y_j) \in \Gamma_{z_k}$, or until it is clear that it is impossible to have $u_i + v_j = c_{ij}$ for all $(x_i, y_j) \in \Gamma_{z_k}$.

To show further the correspondence between the matrix-method and graph-theoretic approach, begin by writing the c_{ij} matrix for all the $(x_i, y_j) \in Z$.   Suppose here there are n elements in X_0 and m elements in Y_0.   The c_{ij} matrix will then have the form shown above.   If the rows and column of this total matrix can be rearranged so that the matrix can be partitioned as follows

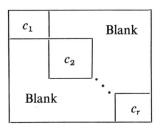

then each nonblank block corresponds to a maximal connected subgraph Γ_{z_k}.   The matrix for (9.3) is

	y_1	y_2	y_3	y_4
x_1	c_{11}	c_{12}		
x_2	c_{21}	c_{22}	c_{23}	
x_3			c_{33}	
x_4				c_{44}
x_5				c_{54}

In the first block, corresponding to Γ_{z_1}, there is one *loop*—($c_{11}, c_{12}, c_{22}, c_{21}$) —corresponding to the cycle (a, b, c, d) in (9.3).   It will be noted that a u, v solution exists for the 3-by-3 block if and only if $c_{11} - c_{12} + c_{22} - c_{21} = 0$. In formulating the basic theorem which concerns the existence of a u, v solution in a maximal connected subgraph, we shall use the partitioned matrix which corresponds to the maximal connected subgraph.

Definition 9.8 A *loop* is a cycle in which no two consecutive links have the same x_i or the same y_j in all three nodes which define the two consecutive links.

As done above, it will often be convenient to write a loop in terms of the c_{ij} associated with the successive nodes of the loop. In the 3-by-3 diagonal matrix above, the loop $(c_{11}, c_{12}, c_{22}, c_{21})$ can be pictured by first replacing the c_{ij} with dots, then tracing a path from one dot back around to itself by a succession of alternating horizontal and vertical moves, changing direction only in a cell with a dot (Figure 9.3):

Figure 9.3

In Figure 9.4, two of the four loops are sketched in:

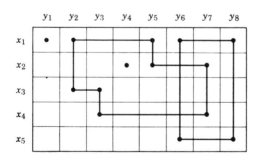

Figure 9.4

These two loops are identified as $(c_{12}, c_{15}, c_{25}, c_{27}, c_{47}, c_{43}, c_{33}, c_{32})$ and $(c_{16}, c_{18}, c_{58}, c_{56})$. The third loop is $(c_{12}, c_{18}, c_{58}, c_{56}, c_{16}, c_{15}, c_{25}, c_{27}, c_{47}, c_{43}, c_{33}, c_{32})$, and the fourth loop is $(c_{12}, c_{16}, c_{56}, c_{58}, c_{18}, c_{15}, c_{25}, c_{27}, c_{47}, c_{43}, c_{33}, c_{32})$. Another example is given by Figure 9.5, where the loop is $(c_{12}, c_{13}, c_{23}, c_{21}, c_{31}, c_{32})$.

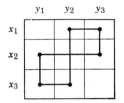

Figure 9.5

From definition 9.8, it is not hard to show that any loop contains an even number of nodes, at least four in number. Also note that every loop is a cycle (by definition) but not every cycle is a loop. Our next definition concerns loop numbers.

Definition 9.9 Given a loop $(c_{i_1 j_1}, c_{i_1 j_2}, c_{i_2 j_2}, c_{i_2 j_3}, \ldots, c_{i_n j_1})$, the *loop number*, denoted as $\psi(c_{i_1 j_1}, \ldots, c_{i_n j_1})$, is defined by

$$\psi = |c_{i_1 j_1} - c_{i_1 j_2} + c_{i_2 j_2} - c_{i_2 j_3} + \ldots - c_{i_n j_1}|.$$

That is, the loop number is the absolute value of the alternating-sign sum of the c_{ij} in the loop.

For the examples given above,

$$\psi(c_{11}, c_{12}, c_{22}, c_{21}) = |c_{11} - c_{12} + c_{22} - c_{21}|$$

$$\psi(c_{12}, c_{15}, c_{25}, c_{27}, c_{47}, c_{43}, c_{33}, c_{32})$$
$$= |c_{12} - c_{15} + c_{25} - c_{27} + c_{47} - c_{43} + c_{33} - c_{32}|.$$

These developments bring us to a statement which is stronger than lemma 9.3:

Lemma 9.4 The system of equations

$$u_i + v_j = c_{ij}$$

for all $(x_i, y_i) \in \Gamma_{z_k}$, where Γ_{z_k} is a maximal connected subgraph, has a solution if Γ_{z_k} has no loops.

Finally, this leads to the basic theorem:

Theorem 9.1 In a maximal connected subgraph Γ_{z_k}, there exists a solution to the system of equations

$$u_i + v_j = c_{ij},$$

i.e.,

$$f_1(x_i) + f_2(y_j) = f(x_i, y_j)$$

for all $(x_i, y_j) \in \Gamma_{z_k}$ if and only if the loop number of each loop in Γ_{z_k} equals zero.

To see why ψ must equal zero for any loop in order that a solution exist, suppose that a solution does exist. If this is so, then $c_{ij} = u_i + v_j$. Now replace c_{ij} by $u_i + v_j$ in the definition of ψ:

$$\psi(c_{i_1 j_1}, c_{i_1 j_2}, c_{i_2 j_2}, c_{i_2 j_3}, \ldots, c_{i_n j_1})$$

$$= |(u_{i_1} + v_{j_1}) - (u_{i_1} + v_{j_2}) + (u_{i_2} + v_{j_2}) - (u_{i_2} + v_{j_3}) + \ldots - (u_{i_n} + v_{j_1})|$$

$$= |(u_{i_1} - u_{i_1}) + (v_{j_1} - v_{j_1}) + (u_{i_2} - u_{i_2}) + (v_{j_2} - v_{j_2}) + \ldots + (u_{i_n} - u_{i_n})|$$

$$= 0.$$

If $\psi \neq 0$ for some loop, it is clearly impossible to have $c_{ij} = u_i + v_j$ for all c_{ij} in the loop.

Suppose that $\psi = 0$ for every loop. Then, for any given loop, we can delete any one of the $u_i + v_j = c_{ij}$ equations, since it is linearly dependent on the other $u_i + v_j = c_{ij}$ equations in the loop. (This is the same thing as making a blank cell out of one of the cells in the c_{ij} matrix which is in the loop.) In this way we can "break up" all the loops and end up with a reduced system of equations $u_i + v_j = c_{ij}$ in which all the equations are linearly independent. This, of course, is the situation in lemma 9.4. If the c_{ij} matrix for Γ_{z_k} is an n-by-m matrix, then there are $n + m - 1$ unknowns (instead of $n + m$, since one of the $n + m$ u_i and v_j can be arbitrarily set to begin with) in the system of linearly independent equations. Hence, the number of equations that remain in the reduced set is no greater than $n + m - 1$, and by virtue of being linearly independent, there is at least one solution to the system (having first set $u_1 = \alpha$, say).[6] But by lemma 9.2 the solution is unique (except for changes in α), and hence there must be exactly $n + m - 1$ equations. This says that if the c_{ij} matrix associated with a maximal connected subgraph Γ_{z_k} is an n-by-m matrix, and if Γ_{z_k} has no loops, then there are $n + m - 1$ nonempty cells in the matrix, or $n + m - 1$ nodes in Γ_{z_k}.

Independence

These developments finally bring us to the definition of independence.

Definition 9.10 X and Y are *independent* with respect to f if and only if there exist real-valued functions f_1 defined on X_0 and f_2 defined on Y_0, both unique except for origin, such that

$$f_1(x) + f_2(y) = f(x, y) \tag{9.5}$$

for every $(x, y) \in Z$.

---

[6] If Γ_{z_k} has no loops, then in the c_{ij} matrix, starting at a given occupied cell, there is one and only one "path" of alternate horizontal-vertical moves changing direction in occupied cells leading to any other occupied cell. Since this is so, there can be no conflict in making a border evaluation of a c_{ij} matrix with no loops.

From the preceding definitions and lemma 9.2, we get:

Theorem 9.2a X and Y are independent with respect to f if and only if (1) X and Y are almost independent with respect to f; (2) Γ_Z is connected.

From theorem 9.1 we get:

Theorem 9.2b X and Y are independent with respect to f if and only if (1) Γ_Z is connected; (2) the loop number of each loop in Γ_Z equals zero.

The reader will note that almost independence is a necessary but not sufficient condition for independence. We also require that Γ_Z be connected so that f_1 and f_2 are unique up to the transformations $f_1(x) + a$, $f_2(y) - a$. If Γ_Z is not connected and X and Y are almost independent, then f_1 and f_2 are unique up to $f_1(x) + a$, $f_2(y) - a$ (lemma 9.2) on any given maximal connected subgraph of Γ_Z, but over-all uniqueness does not hold. For example, if $\Gamma_{Z_1} + \Gamma_{Z_2} = \Gamma_Z$, then f_1 and f_2 may be changed to $f_1(x) + a$, $f_2(y) - a$ on Γ_{Z_1} without a corresponding change on Γ_{Z_2}. Consider this further with respect to (9.3). Let:

$$X_0 = \{x_1, x_2, x_3, x_4, x_5\} = \{\text{red, orange, yellow, green, blue}\},$$
$$Y_0 = \{y_1, y_2, y_3, y_4\} = \{\text{cat, pig, dog, horse}\},$$

$$
\begin{aligned}
c_{11} &= f(x_1, y_1) = f(\text{red, cat}) &&= 8, \\
c_{12} &= f(x_1, y_2) = f(\text{red, pig}) &&= 5, \\
c_{21} &= f(x_2, y_1) = f(\text{orange, cat}) &&= 16, \\
c_{22} &= f(x_2, y_2) = f(\text{orange, pig}) &&= 13, \\
c_{23} &= f(x_2, y_3) = f(\text{orange, dog}) &&= 34, \\
c_{33} &= f(x_3, y_3) = f(\text{yellow, dog}) &&= -15, \\
c_{44} &= f(x_4, y_4) = f(\text{green, horse}) &&= 9, \\
c_{54} &= f(x_5, y_4) = f(\text{blue, horse}) &&= 19.
\end{aligned}
$$

Since $\psi(c_{11}, c_{12}, c_{22}, c_{21}) = |8 - 5 + 13 - 16| = 0$, X and Y are almost independent (but not independent). If we let $f_1(\text{red}) = \alpha$, $f_1(\text{green}) = \beta$, then the f_1, f_2 solution can be written as

$$
\begin{aligned}
f_1(\text{red}) &= \alpha, & f_2(\text{cat}) &= 8 - \alpha, \\
f_1(\text{orange}) &= 8 + \alpha, & f_2(\text{pig}) &= 5 - \alpha, \\
f_1(\text{yellow}) &= -41 + \alpha, & f_2(\text{dog}) &= 26 - \alpha, \\
f_1(\text{green}) &= \beta, & f_2(\text{horse}) &= 9 - \beta, \\
f_1(\text{blue}) &= 10 + \beta,
\end{aligned}
$$

where α and β are (arbitrary) parameters that may be assigned any numerical values we please.

For later usage we will require:

Theorem 9.3 If X and Y are independent with respect to f for one particular set of values $f(x, y)$, $(x, y) \in Z$, when f is unique only up to an increasing linear transformation, then the functions f_1 and f_2 will in general be unique up to increasing linear transformations with arbitrary origins and a common unit measurement.

If f_1 and f_2 satisfy definition 9.10 for a particular set of values $f(x, y)$ for all $(x, y) \in Z$, and we then make the transformation $af + b$, $a > 0$, (9.5) becomes

$$af(x, y) + b = af_1(x) + b_1 + af_2(y) + b_2.$$

Thus, if X and Y are independent with respect to f, and f is unique only up to an increasing linear transformation, then f_1 and f_2 have a common unit measurement, i.e., if f_1 undergoes the transformation

$$af_1(x) + b \qquad (a > 0),$$

then f_2 must correspondingly be transformed according to

$$af_2(y) + c,$$

where b and c are arbitrary constants.

To conclude this section, we shall consider the special but important case of $Z = X_0 \times Y_0$, where every ordered pair (x, y) with $x \in X_0$ and $y \in Y_0$ is an element of Z. For this case we have:

Theorem 9.4 If $Z = X_0 \times Y_0$, then X and Y are independent with respect to f if and only if

$$f(x, y) - f(x', y) = f(x, y') - f(x', y') \qquad (9.6)$$

for every $x, x' \in X_0, y, y' \in Y_0$.

For $Z = X_0 \times Y_0$, (9.6) is obviously a necessary condition for independence, since it simply says that each 4-node loop has a loop number equal to zero. In view of theorem 9.2b, theorem 9.4 implies that, if (9.6) holds, then every loop in Γ_Z has loop number zero. To show the sufficiency of (9.6), instead of showing that it implies that every loop has a loop number equal to zero, perform the following border evaluation of the n-by-m c_{ij} matrix:

First, take $u_1 = 0$. This gives $v_j = c_{1j}$ for $j = 1, \ldots, m$. Then, consider each column in succession and write out the u_i solution for each row past the first, $i = 2, \ldots, n$. This is illustrated as follows:

$$\begin{array}{ccccc}
 & y_1 & y_2 & y_3 & \cdots & y_m
\end{array}$$

	y_1	y_2	y_3	$\cdots$	y_m
x_1	c_{11}	c_{12}	c_{13}		c_{1m}
x_2	c_{21}	c_{22}	c_{23}		c_{2m}
x_3	c_{31}	c_{32}	c_{33}		c_{3m}
$\vdots$					
x_n	c_{n1}	c_{n2}	c_{n3}		c_{nm}

$$\begin{array}{ccccc}
c_{11} & c_{12} & c_{13} & \cdots & c_{1m}
\end{array}$$

$$v_j \text{ (from } u_1 = 0\text{)}.$$

The u_i solution for $i = 2, \ldots, n$ is as obtained from:

Col. 1	Col. 2	$\ldots$	Col. m
$c_{21} - c_{11}$	$c_{22} - c_{12}$		$c_{2m} - c_{1m}$
$c_{31} - c_{11}$	$c_{32} - c_{12}$		$c_{3m} - c_{1m}$
$c_{n1} - c_{11}$	$c_{n2} - c_{12}$		$c_{nm} - c_{1m}$

It is apparent from this that there is independence if (and only if)

$$c_{i1} - c_{11} = c_{i2} - c_{12} = c_{i3} - c_{13} = \ldots = c_{im} - c_{1m}$$

for $i = 2, \ldots, n$, which amounts to the same thing as (9.6).

The Value Function

In the next section we shall use the notion of independence with respect to the value function V, but we will not pursue the idea of almost independence. The main reason for introducing almost independence in the present context is to demonstrate more clearly what is meant by independence *per se* and to show precisely what is involved in this latter notion.

The fact that we do not deal with almost independence in the sequel does not imply that we consider it of little use in value theory. It does mean, however, that we consider independence a more useful notion than almost independence. Although almost independence is not considered further, the interested reader is encouraged to explore the concept in connection with the decision model, particularly when almost independence holds but independence does not.

9.4 VALUEWISE INDEPENDENCE

With the results of the previous section at hand, we are in a fairly good position to consider independence of variables with respect to the value function V. We begin with the following preliminaries:

1. $X_j, j = 1, \ldots, n$, represents the set of all variables (action variables and/or outcome variables and/or mixed variables[7]) under explicit consideration in the decision situation. Each variable X_j is a finite set and we write $x_j \in X_j, x'_j \in X_j, \ldots$ to note that $x_j, x'_j, \ldots$ are elements of X_j. The values of any one variable are mutually exclusive.

2. $X = X_1 \times X_2 \times \ldots \times X_n$, is the product set of the X_j. Each $x \in X$ is a vector of the form $x = (x_1, x_2, \ldots, x_n), x_j \in X_j, j = 1, 2, \ldots, n$.

3. $S = \{S_i\}, i = 1, \ldots, t$, is the set of t admissible *strategies* under explicit consideration in the decision situation, where

$$\sum_{x \in X} P(x \mid S_i) = 1, \qquad i = 1, \ldots, t,$$

$P(x \mid S_i)$ being the probability that $x \in X$ will occur, given S_i, with $\sum_{x \in X}$ denoting summation over all $x \in X$.

4. X_0 is the set of all $x \in X$ for which $\sum_{i=1}^t P(x \mid S_i) > 0$. That is, $x \in X_0$ if and only if $P(x \mid S_i) > 0$ for at least one $S_i \in S$. X_0 is the set of *consequences* and X is the set of *pseudoconsequences*. Obviously, $X_0 \subset X$.

Next, partition the n variables $X_1, X_2, \ldots, X_n$ into two nonnull subsets, such that each X_j appears in one and only one subset. This partition may be structured in any manner we please. Let $\{X_1, \ldots, X_k\}$ be the first member of the partition and $\{X_{k+1}, \ldots, X_n\}$ be the second member,[8] with $1 \leqslant k < n$, and let

$$\begin{aligned} Y_1 &= X_1 \times X_2 \times \ldots \times X_k, \\ Y_2 &= X_{k+1} \times X_{k+2} \times \ldots \times X_n. \end{aligned} \qquad (9.7)$$

Then $Y_1 \times Y_2 = X$. With $y_1 \in Y_1$ and $y_2 \in Y_2$, $x = (y_1, y_2)$, $y_1 = (x_1, x_2, \ldots, x_k)$, and $y_2 = (x_{k+1}, \ldots, x_n)$.

Now let the value function V be defined on a subset Z of the set of pseudoconsequences X, where every consequence in X_0 is an element of Z (i.e., $X_0 \subset Z \subset X$), such that Γ_Z is connected when Z is viewed as being a set of ordered pairs $(y_1, y_2), y_1 \in Y_1, y_2 \in Y_2$.[9]

---

[7] See Section 2.4.

[8] This may require a relabeling of the variables.

[9] If Γ_{X_0} is connected then we may take $Z = X_0$. However, when Γ_{X_0} is not connected, we include in Z some pseudoconsequences which are not actual consequences in order to have Γ_Z connected so that the definition of independence can be used. In this connection, also note the last few paragraphs of Section 9.5.

Then, according to theorem 9.2b, Y_1 and Y_2 are independent with respect to V if and only if the loop number of each loop in Γ_Z equals zero. For example, if the 4-node loop $[(y_{11}, y_{21}), (y_{11}, y_{22}), (y_{12}, y_{22}), (y_{12}, y_{21})]$, with $y_{jk} \in Y_j$, appears in Γ_Z, then we would require

$$\psi = |V(y_{11}, y_{21}) - V(y_{11}, y_{22}) + V(y_{12}, y_{22}) - V(y_{12}, y_{21})| = 0.$$

If $Y_1 \text{ I } Y_2$ (short for " Y_1 and Y_2 are independent with respect to V defined on Z"), then we can write

$$V(y_1, y_2) = V_1(y_1) + V_2(y_2) \tag{9.8}$$

for all $(y_1, y_2) \in Z$, where V_1 and V_2 are value functions defined over Y_{10} and Y_{20} respectively, having arbitrary origins and a common unit measurement (see theorem 9.3). In this,

$Y_{j0} = $ set of all $y_j \in Y_j$ that appear in one or more $x \in Z, j = 1, 2.$

Suppose $Y_1 \text{ I } Y_2$ and $k \geqslant 2$ in (9.7). Partition the k variables in the definition of Y_1 into two sets, say $\{X_1, \ldots, X_s\}$ and $\{X_{s+1}, \ldots, X_k\}$ with $1 \leqslant s < k$, and let

$$Y_{11} = X_1 \times \ldots \times X_s,$$
$$Y_{12} = X_{s+1} \times \ldots \times X_k,$$

so that $Y_{11} \times Y_{12} = Y_1$. Consider the graph of the ordered pairs $(y_{11}, y_{12}) \in Y_{10}$, with $y_{11} \in Y_{11}$, $y_{12} \in Y_{12}$. The function of concern, defined over the $(y_{11}, y_{12}) \in Y_{10}$ is V_1, as given in (9.8). If the graph of the ordered pairs $(y_{11}, y_{12}) \in Y_{10}$ is connected and if the loop number of every loop in this graph equals zero (where ψ is defined with respect to V_1) then we may write

$$V_1(y_{11}, y_{12}) = V_{11}(y_{11}) + V_{12}(y_{12}) \tag{9.9}$$

for all $(y_{11}, y_{12}) \in Y_{10}$. Putting (9.9) back into (9.8) gives

$$V(y_1, y_2) = V(y_{11}, y_{12}, y_2) = V_{11}(y_{11}) + V_{12}(y_{12}) + V_2(y_2) \tag{9.10}$$

for all $(y_{11}, y_{12}, y_2) \in Z$. In (9.10) the three value functions V_{11}, V_{12}, and V_2 are unique up to positive linear transformations with a common unit measurement (or a common scale multiplier), for

$$aV(y_1, y_2) + b = aV_{11}(y_{11}) + aV_{12}(y_{12}) + aV_2(y_2) + b.$$

In the above, with

$$Y_1 \times Y_2 = X,$$
$$Y_{11} \times Y_{12} = Y_1,$$

independence of Y_{11} and Y_{12} was defined only if $Y_1 \text{ I } Y_2$. If $Y_{11} \text{ I } Y_{12}$ (i.e., Y_{11} and Y_{12} are independent with respect to V_1), then we could further partition any one of the sets $\{X_1, \ldots, X_s\}$, $\{X_{s+1}, \ldots, X_k\}$, or $\{X_{k+1}, \ldots, X_n\}$ that has two or more variables and consider independence over the two product sets of the two-part partition.

Continuing in this fashion, one can obtain, say, an m-part partition of the n variables $\{X_j\}$, $j = 1, \ldots, n$, with $m \leqslant n$, where the parts of the partition are

$$\{X_1, \ldots, X_{k_1}\}, \{X_{k_1+1}, \ldots, X_{k_2}\}, \ldots, \{X_{k_{m-1}+1}, \ldots, X_n\},$$

$$1 \leqslant k_1 < k_2 < \ldots < k_{m-1} < n,$$

such that, letting

$$Y_1 = X_1 \times \ldots \times X_{k_1},$$
$$Y_2 = X_{k_1+1} \times \ldots \times X_{k_2},$$
$$\vdots$$
$$Y_m = X_{k_{m-1}+1} \times \ldots \times X_n,$$

one has

$$V(y_1, y_2, \ldots, y_m) = V_1(y_1) + V_2(y_2) + \ldots + V_m(y_m), \quad (9.11)$$

with $y_j \in Y_j$, $j = 1, \ldots, m$, for all $(y_1, y_2, \ldots, y_m) \in Z$. If (9.11) holds and $V_1, V_2, \ldots, V_m$ are unique up to positive linear transformations with a common unit measurement, then we may say that $Y_1, Y_2, \ldots, Y_m$ are mutually valuewise independent variables, written as

$$Y_1 \, I \, Y_2 \, I \, \ldots \, I \, Y_m.$$

Although some of the Y_j may be products of two or more of the original variables X_j, there should be no confusion if we also refer to the Y_j as variables.

If $m = 3$ and $Y_1 \, I \, Y_2 \, I \, Y_3$, we could arrive at this conclusion either by showing that $Y_1 \times Y_2 \, I \, Y_3$ and then that $Y_1 \, I \, Y_2$, or by showing that $Y_1 \times Y_3 \, I \, Y_2$ and then that $Y_1 \, I \, Y_3$, or by showing that $Y_2 \times Y_3 \, I \, Y_1$ and then that $Y_2 \, I \, Y_3$.

Expected Relative Value of S_i

Given

$$Y_1 \times Y_2 \times \ldots \times Y_m = X_1 \times X_2 \times X_3 \times \ldots \times X_n = X \quad (m \leqslant n),$$
$$(9.12)$$

$$Y_1 \, I \, Y_2 \, I \, \ldots \, I \, Y_m, \quad (9.13)$$

with

$$V(x) = V(y_1, y_2, \ldots, y_m) = V_1(y_1) + V_2(y_2) + \ldots + V_m(y_m)$$
$$(9.14)$$

by virtue of our definition of (9.13), $E(S_i)$, the expected relative value of strategy S_i, may be reduced as follows:

$$E(S_i) = \sum_{x \in X_0} P(x \mid S_i)V(x)$$

$$= \sum_{(y_1,\ldots,y_m) \in X_0} P(y_1,\ldots,y_m \mid S_i)[V_1(y_1) + \ldots + V_m(y_m)]$$

$$= \sum_{y_1 \in Y_{10}} P(y_1 \mid S_i)V_1(y_1) + \ldots + \sum_{y_m \in Y_{m0}} P(y_m \mid S_i)V_m(y_m), \quad (9.15)$$

where Y_{j0} is the set of all $y_j \in Y_j$ that appear in one or more $x \in X_0$, and

$$P(y_j \mid S_i) = \sum_{y_1} \ldots \sum_{y_{j-1}} \sum_{y_{j+1}} \ldots$$

$$\sum_{y_m} P(y_1,\ldots,y_{j-1},y_j,y_{j+1},\ldots,y_m \mid S_i).$$

In (9.15),

$$\sum_{y_j \in Y_{j0}} P(y_j \mid S_i) = 1, \quad j = 1,\ldots,m; \quad i = 1,\ldots,t,$$

$$\sum_{i=1}^{t} P(y_j \mid S_i) > 0 \quad \text{for every } y_j \in Y_{j0}, \quad j = 1,\ldots,m,$$

where, as defined above, $P(y_j \mid S_i)$ is the marginal probability of the occurrence of $y_j \in Y_{j0}$, given S_i. In the extreme case where all the original variables are mutually valuewise independent, (9.15) may be written as

$$E(S_i) = \sum_{x_1} P(x_1 \mid S_i)V_1(x_1) + \ldots + \sum_{x_n} P(x_n \mid S_i)V_n(x_n) \quad i = 1,\ldots,t.$$

If, in considering the *difference* of the expected values of two strategies, say $E(S_i) - E(S_k)$, the two terms from (9.15)

$$\sum_{y_j} P(y_j \mid S_i)V_j(y_j), \quad \sum_{y_j} P(y_j \mid S_k)V_j(y_j)$$

cancel one another out for all $S_i, S_k \in \mathbf{S}$, we might say that Y_j is irrelevant for value measurement purposes. We note that, sufficient for

$$\sum_{y_j} P(y_j \mid S_i)V_j(y_j) - \sum_{y_j} P(y_j \mid S_k)V_j(y_j) = 0$$

for all $S_i, S_k \in \mathbf{S}$, is

(1) $V_j(y_j) = c \quad$ for all $y_j \in Y_{j0}$,

as is

(2) $P(y_j \mid S_i) = P(y_j \mid S_k) \quad$ for all $y_j \in Y_{j0}; \quad S_i, S_k \in \mathbf{S}$.

Condition (1), if valid, says that the decision maker is indifferent as to what value $y_j \in Y_{j0}$ occurs, and condition (2) asserts that the probability of the occurrence of any $y_j \in Y_{j0}$ is the same regardless of the strategy adopted.

9.5 INDEPENDENCE AND VALUE MEASURES

Let us return to the independence equation

$$V(y_1, y_2, \ldots, y_m) = V_1(y_1) + V_2(y_2) + \ldots + V_m(y_m),$$

and look briefly at value measures for the $V_j(y_j)$—which will be considered in much greater detail in the next several chapters.

One measure that suggests itself immediately is an ordinal ranking of the relative values of the values of a given Y_j. Let

$$\{y_{j1}, y_{j2}, \ldots, y_{jn_j}, y_{j0}\} = Y_{j0},$$

and let the ordinal ranking over Y_{j0} be written as

$$V_j(y_{j1}) \geqslant V_j(y_{j2}) \geqslant \ldots \geqslant V_j(y_{jn_j}) \geqslant V_j(y_{j0}).$$

If this can be done for each valuewise independent variable, there will be n ordinal rankings, one for each variable. Very often such a ranking will "suggest itself" quite naturally, particularly when the values $y_{jk} \in Y_{j0}$ are quantitative and V_j is monotonic increasing or decreasing in the values of Y_{j0}. It might then be possible, for each Y_j, to obtain an ordered metric ranking or a bounded interval measure over the $V_j(y_{jk})$, $k = 0, 1, \ldots, n_j$, and to apply these to the m separate parts of the difference

$$E(S_1) - E(S_2) = \sum_{k=0}^{n_1} [P(y_{1k} \mid S_1) - P(y_{1k} \mid S_2)]V_1(y_{1k})$$

$$+ \sum_{k=0}^{n_2} [P(y_{2k} \mid S_1) - P(y_{2k} \mid S_2)]V_2(y_{2k}) \qquad (9.16)$$

$$\vdots$$

$$+ \sum_{k=0}^{n_m} [P(y_{mk} \mid S_1) - P(y_{mk} \mid S_2)]V_m(y_{mk})$$

in analyzing $E(S_1) - E(S_2)$ for sign. With separate measures of the $V_j(y_{jk})$, $k = 0, 1, \ldots, n_j$, for each j, it is not unlikely that one will find different signs for the various parts of the right-hand side of (9.16); for example,

$$\sum_{k=0}^{n_1} [P(y_{1k} \mid S_1) - P(y_{1k} \mid S_2)]V_1(y_{1k}) \geqslant 0 \qquad (9.17a)$$

and

$$\sum_{k=0}^{n_2} [P(y_{2k} \mid S_1) - P(y_{2k} \mid S_2)]V_2(y_{2k}) \leqslant 0. \qquad (9.17b)$$

In such a case, it might be said that, according to (9.17a), S_1 is more effective than S_2 for Y_1; and, according to (9.17b), that S_2 is more effective than S_1 for Y_2.

Method 1 for Inter-V_j Comparisons

It should be obvious then that comparisons are required in many cases between the $V_j(y_{jk})$ for different j. There are several ways in which this may be done. One method considers comparisons of metric differences of the form $V_j(y_{jk_1}) - V_j(y_{jk_2})$ for different j. We shall illustrate this approach by using (9.16). First, let

$$p_{jk}^i = P(y_{jk} \mid S_i), \qquad j = 1, \ldots, m; \quad k = 0, 1, \ldots, n_j,$$
$$v_{jk} = V_j(y_{jk}).$$

Then (9.16) may be written as

$$E(S_1) - E(S_2) = \sum_{k=0}^{n_1} (p_{1k}^1 - p_{1k}^2)v_{1k} + \sum_{k=0}^{n_2} (p_{2k}^1 - p_{2k}^2)v_{2k} + \ldots$$
$$+ \sum_{k=0}^{n_m} (p_{mk}^1 - p_{mk}^2)v_{mk}. \quad (9.18)$$

Application of Abel's identity (6.1) yields

$$E(S_1) - E(S_2) = \sum_{k=1}^{n_1} \left[\sum_{v=1}^{k} (p_{1v}^1 - p_{1v}^2) \right](v_{1k} - v_{1,k+1}) + \ldots$$
$$+ \sum_{k=1}^{n_m} \left[\sum_{v=1}^{k} (p_{mv}^1 - p_{mv}^2) \right](v_{mk} - v_{m,k+1}), \quad (9.19)$$

where $v_{j,n_j+1} = v_{j0}$, $p_{j,n_j+1}^i = p_{j0}^i$. Since

$$\sum_{k=0}^{n_j} (p_{jk}^1 - p_{jk}^2) = \sum_{k=1}^{n_j+1} (p_{jk}^1 - p_{jk}^2) = 0 \qquad \text{for each } j,$$

the jth sum on the right-hand side of (9.19) contains n_j terms instead of n_j+1 terms. Given the ordinal rankings

$$v_{j1} \geqslant v_{j2} \geqslant \ldots \geqslant v_{jn_j} \geqslant v_{j0}, \qquad j = 1, \ldots, m,$$

each difference $v_{jk} - v_{j,k+1}$ in (9.19) is nonnegative. Moreover, it is generally meaningful to compare any two such differences since the m value functions $V_1, \ldots, V_m$ have a common unit measure. For example, one might attempt to obtain a complete ordering of the $r = \sum n_j$ nonnegative differences,

$$v_{jk} - v_{j,k+1}, \qquad j = 1, \ldots, m; \quad k = 1, \ldots, n_j.$$

Let such a ranking be

$$v_1' \geqslant v_2' \geqslant \ldots \geqslant v_r' \geqslant 0, \qquad (9.20)$$

where each v_k' is one of the $v_{jk} - v_{j,k+1}$, and vice versa, and let q_k be the coefficient of v_k' in (9.19). Then (9.19) becomes

$$E(S_1) - E(S_2) = \sum_{k=1}^{r} q_k v_k'. \qquad (9.21)$$

With (9.21) we can obtain a theorem concerning what conclusions can be made on the sign of $E(S_1) - E(S_2)$, given (9.20). Or one could try to obtain tight bounds on certain ratios of value differences such as

$$w_j = \frac{v_j'}{v_{j-1}'}, \qquad j = 2, \ldots, r.$$

Letting $w_1 = 1$, (9.21) may be put in the following form:

$$\frac{E(S_1) - E(S_2)}{v_1'} = \sum_{k=1}^{r} q_k \prod_{j=1}^{k} w_j.$$

We will explore the above measures further in Section 11.5.

Method 2 for Inter-V_j Comparisons

The second method for tying together the $V_j(y_{jk})$ for various j employs the fact that the origins of the m value functions $V_j, j = 1, \ldots, m$, may be set as we please. One way of doing this is to pick one y_{jk} from each Y_{j0}, say y_{jk_j}, and set

$$V_1(y_{1k_1}) = V_2(y_{2k_2}) = \ldots = V_m(y_{mk_m}),$$

where $0 \leqslant k_j \leqslant n_j, j = 1, \ldots, m$. Different ways of picking the y_{jk_j} (one for each j) will obviously interconnect the $V_j(y_{jk})$ for the n value functions V_j in different ways. For example, it is often convenient to let $y_{jk_j} = y_{j0}$, $j = 1, \ldots, m$, given the m ordinal rankings

$$v_{j1} \geqslant v_{j2} \geqslant \ldots \geqslant v_{jn_j} \geqslant v_{j0}, \qquad j = 1, \ldots, m, \qquad (9.22)$$

$v_{jk} = V_j(y_{jk})$. In other words set [10]

$$v_{10} = v_{20} = \ldots = v_{m0} = v_{r+1}, \qquad (9.23)$$

where v_{j0} is the relative value of the *least desirable* value in Y_{j0}, according to (9.22).[11] Then, beginning with the m ordinal rankings (9.22), we may

[10] v_{r+1} is designated as the common value of the v_{j0}.

[11] In the sequel we shall use the convention established by (9.23). It should be kept in mind, however, that other ways may be used to interconnect the m value functions. If the reader finds some other way of doing this more advantageous than (9.23), he should have little trouble in carrying through an analysis with the different setting of origins after studying the next two chapters.

attempt to obtain a mixed ordinal ranking or an interconnected ordinal ranking of all the v_{jk}, $j = 1, \ldots, m$; $k = 1, \ldots, n_j$. With $r = \sum_{j=1}^{m} n_j$, there will be $r + 1$ terms in this ranking, which will be $v_{j1}, \ldots, v_{jn_j}$, $j = 1, \ldots, m$, and v_{r+1}, the common value of the v_{j0} as indicated in (9.23). Let v_α be the αth ranked v_{jk} in the mixed ordinal ranking of all the v_{jk} when (9.23) is used, and p_α be coefficient of v_α in (9.18), with

$$p_{r+1} = \sum_{j=1}^{m} (p_{j0}^1 - p_{j0}^2).$$

The mixed ordinal ranking will be

$$v_1 \geqslant v_2 \geqslant \ldots \geqslant v_r \geqslant v_{r+1}, \tag{9.24}$$

and (9.18) may be written as

$$E(S_1) - E(S_2) = \sum_{\alpha=1}^{r} p_\alpha v_\alpha + p_{r+1} v_{r+1} = \sum_{\alpha=1}^{r+1} p_\alpha v_\alpha. \tag{9.25a}$$

Since

$$\sum_{\alpha=1}^{r+1} p_\alpha = 0,$$

or

$$p_{r+1} = -\sum_{\alpha=1}^{r} p_\alpha,$$

(9.25a) may be rewritten as

$$E(S_1) - E(S_2) = \sum_{\alpha=1}^{r} p_\alpha (v_\alpha - v_{r+1}). \tag{9.25b}$$

Since the common origin, v_{r+1}, may be set equal to whatever we please there is no harm in setting $v_{r+1} = 0$ so long as we do not get tricked into believing that the zero arises from anything other than an arbitrary convention. Setting $v_{r+1} = 0$, (9.24) becomes

$$v_1 \geqslant v_2 \geqslant \ldots \geqslant v_r \geqslant 0,$$

and (9.25a) or (9.25b) becomes

$$E(S_1) - E(S_2) = \sum_{\alpha=1}^{r} p_\alpha v_\alpha.$$

From this point we may go on to try to obtain a mixed ordered metric ranking of the v_{jk}, which ranks the r value difference $(v_\alpha - v_{\alpha+1})$, $\alpha = 1, \ldots, r$, from greatest to least. Or we may attempt one or more of the other measures described in the next several chapters (see, in particular, Sections 11.2 through 11.4).

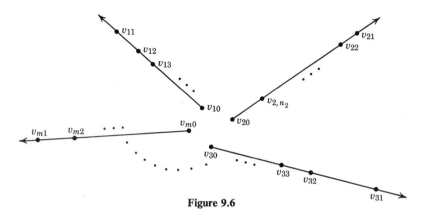

Figure 9.6

To see more clearly what happens when the v_{j0} are set equal to one another as in (9.23) and a mixed ordinal ranking results, consider the following illustration. First, visualize the relative values v_{jk} as being points on a straight line or axis. Do this for each value function V_j. Pictorially, we may illustrate the v_{jk} for each j as shown in Figure 9.6. We recall that all lines have a common unit measurement, so that if one of the m axes is uniformly compressed or stretched by a multiplier a, every other axis must be compressed or stretched accordingly. Next, in setting $v_{10} = v_{20} = \ldots = v_{m0} = v_{r+1}$, take the m axes and tie them together at the ends indicated by the v_{j0}. After some rotation of the m axes, this may be pictured as in Figure 9.7. Finally, collapse the m axes onto the v

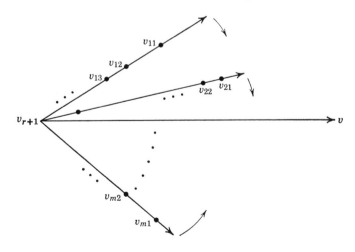

Figure 9.7

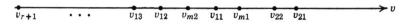

Figure 9.8

axis in Figure 9.7 by rotating them in the directions indicated by the curved arrows. This gives our mixed value axis, shown in Figure 9.8.

Preference Judgments

In procedures used to obtain preference judgments that lead to a measure of relative values of the values of a variable or variables, it seems most meaningful to consider preference judgments between (or among) consequences or pseudoconsequences in Z ($X_0 \subset Z \subset X$) of the form $x = (y_1, y_2, \ldots, y_m)$, where $y_j \in Y_j$, $j = 1, \ldots, m$, and then to use

$$V(y_1, \ldots, y_n) = V_1(y_1) + \ldots + V_m(y_m) \tag{9.26}$$

to yield statements about the $V_j(y_j)$. After looking at several illustrative examples, we shall comment briefly on some difficulties that might be encountered.

Let $\{y_{jk}\}$ be the values of Y_{j0}, where the second subscript on y does not necessarily reflect an ordinal ranking and may be different for different Y_{j0}.

EXAMPLE 1.   We wish to determine if $V_1(y_{11}) \geqslant V_1(y_{12})$ or $V_1(y_{12}) \geqslant V_1(y_{11})$. Take two consequences [12] in Z of the form

$$x = (y_{11}, y_{2k}, \ldots, y_{mk}),$$
$$x' = (y_{12}, y_{2k}, \ldots, y_{mk}).$$

If $x \gtrsim x'$, then $V(x) \geqslant V(x')$ or, using (9.26), $V_1(y_{11}) + V_2(y_{2k}) + \ldots + V_m(y_{mk}) \geqslant V_1(y_{12}) + V_2(y_{2k}) + \ldots + V_m(y_{mk})$ which reduces to $V_1(y_{11}) \geqslant V_1(y_{12})$. If $x' \gtrsim x$, then $V_1(y_{12}) \geqslant V_1(y_{11})$.

EXAMPLE 2.   Suppose $V_1(y_{11}) \geqslant V_1(y_{12})$ and $V_2(y_{23}) \geqslant V_2(y_{24})$. We wish to compare $V_1(y_{11}) - V_1(y_{12})$ and $V_2(y_{23}) - V_2(y_{24})$. Take two consequences in Z of the form

$$x = (y_{11}, y_{24}, y_{3k}, \ldots, y_{mk}),$$
$$x' = (y_{12}, y_{23}, y_{3k}, \ldots, y_{mk}).$$

If $x \gtrsim x'$, then $V(x) \geqslant V(x')$ or, using (9.26),

$$V_1(y_{11}) + V_2(y_{24}) + \sum_{j=3}^{m} V_j(y_{jk}) \geqslant V_1(y_{12}) + V_2(y_{23}) + \sum_{j=3}^{m} V_j(y_{jk}),$$

[12] And/or pseudoconsequences.

which reduces to $V_1(y_{11}) - V_1(y_{12}) \geqslant V_2(y_{23}) - V_2(y_{24})$. If $x' \gtrsim x$, then $V_2(y_{23}) - V_2(y_{24}) \geqslant V_1(y_{11}) - V_1(y_{12})$.

EXAMPLE 3. Suppose we have the m ordinal rankings

$$V_j(y_{j1}) \geqslant V_j(y_{j2}) \geqslant \ldots \geqslant V_j(y_{jn_j}) \geqslant V_j(y_{j0}), \qquad j = 1, \ldots, m$$

and set

$$V_1(y_{10}) = V_2(y_{20}) = \ldots = V_m(y_{m0}) = v_{r+1}.$$

We wish to determine whether $V_1(y_{11}) \geqslant V_2(y_{21})$ or vice versa. Take two consequences in Z of the form

$$x = (y_{11}, y_{20}, y_{3k}, \ldots, y_{mk}),$$
$$x' = (y_{10}, y_{21}, y_{3k}, \ldots, y_{mk}).$$

If $x \gtrsim x'$, then by (9.26),

$$V_1(y_{11}) + V_2(y_{20}) + \sum_{j=3}^{m} V_j(y_{jk}) \geqslant V_1(y_{10}) + V_2(y_{21}) + \sum_{j=3}^{m} V_j(y_{jk}),$$

which reduces to $V_1(y_{11}) \geqslant V_2(y_{21})$, since we have set $V_2(y_{20}) = V_1(y_{10})$. If we had not taken $V_1(y_{10}) = V_2(y_{20})$, then $x \gtrsim x'$ gives

$$V_1(y_{11}) - V_1(y_{10}) \geqslant V_2(y_{21}) - V_2(y_{20}).$$

Either way $x \gtrsim x'$ says that the difference in relative value between the most desirable and least desirable values of Y_{20} is not greater than the difference in relative value between the most desirable and least desirable values of Y_{10}.

EXAMPLE 4. Beginning as in example 3, suppose we get the mixed ordinal ranking

$$V_1(y_{11}) \geqslant V_2(y_{21}) \geqslant V_1(y_{12}) \geqslant \ldots \geqslant v_{r+1}.$$

We wish to compare $V_1(y_{11}) - V_2(y_{21})$ and $V_2(y_{21}) - V_1(y_{12})$. This cannot be done with a simple comparison as above, so consider three consequences in Z of the form

$$x = (y_{11}, y_{20}, y_{3k}, \ldots, y_{mk}),$$
$$x' = (y_{12}, y_{20}, y_{3k}, \ldots, y_{mk}),$$
$$x'' = (y_{10}, y_{21}, y_{3k}, \ldots, y_{mk}),$$

where $x \gtrsim x'' \gtrsim x'$ by the mixed ordinal ranking. Let $(x, \frac{1}{2}, x')$ be the hypothetical gamble "yielding" either x or x', each with probability $\frac{1}{2}$. If $(x, \frac{1}{2}, x') \gtrsim x''$, then

$$\frac{1}{2}V(x) + \frac{1}{2}V(x') \geqslant V(x'').$$

Multiplying through by 2 and using (9.26), we get

$$V_1(y_{11}) + V_2(y_{20}) + \sum_{j=3}^{m} V_j(y_{jk}) + V_1(y_{12}) + V_2(y_{20}) + \sum_{j=3}^{m} V_j(y_{jk})$$

$$\geqslant 2V_1(y_{10}) + 2V_2(y_{21}) + 2\sum_{j=3}^{m} V_j(y_{jk}),$$

which, since we have set $V_1(y_{10}) = V_2(y_{20})$, yields

$$V_1(y_{11}) - V_2(y_{21}) \geqslant V_2(y_{21}) - V_1(y_{12}).$$

If $x'' \gtrsim (x, \frac{1}{2}, x')$, then $V_2(y_{21}) - V_1(y_{12}) \geqslant V_1(y_{11}) - V_2(y_{21})$.

In each of these examples the consequences compared were in Z, which by definition is the set of consequences (and pseudoconsequences) which were taken as the arguments of V. The important point is that the consequences considered differed only with respect to the values of the variables we were interested in and the values of all other variables were identical in the two (or three) consequences. If independence does in fact hold, then it is immaterial what values are chosen for the variables that are not of direct interest, so long as the values chosen give elements in Z. Indeed, it may be more efficient not to specify explicit values for the variables that are not of direct interest, with the understanding that the values "chosen" for the Y_j not of direct concern are the same in each consequence at hand. If this is done, we might adopt a notation showing only the values of the variables which are different. To illustrate, for:

Example 1: Let $x = (y_{11})$, $x' = (y_{12})$ where x, $x' \in Z$, with the implication that x and x' are alike in all respects except for the value of Y_{10}.

Example 2: Let $x = (y_{11}, y_{24})$, $x' = (y_{12}, y_{23})$, where x, $x' \in Z$, with the understanding that x and x' are alike in all respects except for the values of Y_{10} and Y_{20}.

Example 3: Let $x = (y_{11}, y_{20})$, $x' = (y_{10}, y_{21})$.

Example 4: Let $x = (y_{11}, y_{20})$, $x' = (y_{12}, y_{20})$, $x'' = (y_{10}, y_{21})$.

If $X_0 = Y_{10} \times Y_{20} \times \ldots \times Y_{m0}$, or if one takes $Z = Y_{10} \times Y_{20} \times \ldots \times Y_{m0}$ and all the pseudoconsequences in Z that are not consequences (i.e., not in X_0) make sense to the individual in so far as he can render value judgments over them, then Z is sufficiently rich to yield consequences or pseudoconsequences as required for the comparisons in the examples given above. However, in many cases, restrictions of one sort or another among variables may preclude sizable portions of $Y_{10} \times Y_{20} \times \ldots \times Y_{m0}$ from appearing in Z, if for no other reason than that the pseudo-consequences in such omitted portions of $Y_{10} \times Y_{20} \times \ldots \times Y_{m0}$ may be "ridiculous" or meaningless to the individual as regards his value judgments. With Z restricted to be less than all of $Y_{10} \times Y_{20} \times \ldots$ $\times Y_{m0}$ or X, it may be impossible to find two $x \in Z$ that satisfy examples 1, 2, or 3 above.[13]   In example 1, y_{11} and y_{12} may appear in no two members of Z which are alike in all respects other than the value of Y_{10}.   For example, any $x \in Z$ that has y_{11} in it becomes, on replacing y_{11} with y_{12}, $x' \notin Z$.   In such a situation y_{11} and y_{12} cannot be directly compared and we must go through some intermediary $x \in Z$ to get a comparison between y_{11} and y_{12}.   While it is my feeling that this kind of difficulty is not too likely to occur in practice, it should be pointed out that we cannot indiscriminately compare (or pretend, in theory, to compare) any two elements of $Y_{10} \times Y_{20} \times \ldots \times Y_{m0}$ or of $X = Y_1 \times Y_2 \times \ldots \times Y_m$. Some caution should be exercised in assuring that such a comparison is meaningful to the decision maker.

As the reader may have detected by this time, the reasons for taking V to be defined over a set (Z) which includes not only the set of actual consequences (X_0) but also perhaps many pseudoconsequences $x \in X$ that are not in X_0 are (1) to have Γ_Z connected so that independence would be meaningful (it might be that Γ_{Z_0} is not connected with respect to every two-part partition of the variables) and (2) to have the basic set of arguments of V sufficiently rich enough to provide direct comparisons of the relative values of the values of the variables as in the above four examples.   The greater the number of $x \in X$ when $x \notin X_0$ that are included in Z, the greater the number of loops that will arise in the graph that deals with ordered pairs $(a, b) \in Z$, and hence there will be more work in trying to demonstrate that $A \, I \, B$ $(a \in A, b \in B, A \times B = X)$.   Since independence will usually be stated as an assumption and, except perhaps for a nominal amount of "verification," we will not attempt to prove it a valid (or nonvalid) hypothesis, a large number of loops in Γ_Z should not cause great concern.   In fact, from a practical viewpoint, if Γ_{X_0} [with respect to $(a, b) \in X_0$] is connected and has a large number of loops, that is all the more reason for considering independence.

In some cases the x's included in Z that are not in X_0 may arise from possible strategies that have been discarded as less desirable than others still under consideration (we might say that these are pseudoconsequences which were once actual consequences), and in other cases these x's may be nothing other than figments of the formulation, there being no feasible strategy known to have positive probability for them.   Particular attention will be given to this latter kind of pseudoconsequence in the next chapter.   In the next several chapters we will be quite liberal in presuming that Z contains elements sufficient to provide the several value measures to

---

[13] Γ_Z is assumed in any event to be connected whenever Z is written as a set of ordered pairs of the form $(a, b) \in Z$.

be discussed. Again, we caution that in some decision situations there may be difficulty in trying to make comparisons such as those given in the previous examples and those to be given in the sequel.

9.6 TESTING FOR INDEPENDENCE

In this section we shall discuss ways in which one may attempt to verify the valuewise independence of two variables or to demonstrate that two variables are not valuewise independent.

$$Z = X \times Y$$

Let us first consider the case where the value function V is taken to be defined over ordered pairs $(x, y) \in Z$, with $x \in X$, $y \in Y$, $X \times Y = Z$. For this situation, theorem 9.4 (with f replaced by V) specifies the conditions on V that must hold for $X \, I \, Y$. If the $V(x, y)$ for all $(x, y) \in Z$ have been measured on an interval scale, then there seems to be no particular reason to even consider independence, since we already know everything about the relative values of the consequences. The problem of interest here is not to take a set of numbers—$V(x, y)$—and plug them into the equations for the loop numbers ψ, but rather to determine if the loop numbers equal zero when the $V(x, y)$ have not been precisely determined. This may sound like a lot of double talk, so let us see what one may do.

For the case at hand, with $Z = X \times Y$, let $X = \{x_1, x_2, \ldots, x_n\}$ and $Y = \{y_1, y_2, \ldots, y_m\}$. According to theorem 9.4, $X \, I \, Y$ if and only if

$$V(x_i, y_j) - V(x_r, y_j) = V(x_i, y_k) - V(x_r, y_k) \qquad (9.27)$$

for all $x_i, x_r \in X$, $y_j, y_k \in Y$. The system of equations (9.27) can be reduced a good bit by using the obvious properties of the equality relation, to read: $X \, I \, Y$ if and only if

$$V(x_i, y_j) - V(x_n, y_j) = V(x_i, y_m) - V(x_n, y_m) \qquad (9.28a)$$

$$V(x_i, y_j) + V(x_n, y_m) = V(x_i, y_m) + V(x_n, y_j) \qquad (9.28b)$$

for all $(x_i, y_j) \in Z$. Altogether there are $(n - 1)(m - 1)$ equations like (9.28b), for $i = 1, \ldots, n - 1$, $j = 1, \ldots, m - 1$, that require verification in order that $X \, I \, Y$. If any one of these $(n - 1)(m - 1)$ equations does not in fact hold good, then X and Y are not independent with respect to V. If n and m are large, then in practice it will not be possible to test to see if all $(n - 1)(m - 1)$ equations do hold, but a random sampling of (i, j) pairs, $1 \leqslant i \leqslant n - 1$, $1 \leqslant j \leqslant m - 1$, should serve to provide evidence as to the warrantability of the assertion that $X \, I \, Y$.

In view of past discussion (particularly Chapter 4), one can test for the validity of

$$V(x_i, y_j) + V(x_n, y_m) = V(x_i, y_m) + V(x_n, y_j)$$

for a given $(x_i, y_j) \in Z$ by determining whether the individual is indifferent between the two hypothetical 50-50 gambles:

$$a = [(x_i, y_j), \tfrac{1}{2}, (x_n, y_m)], \qquad b = [(x_i, y_m), \tfrac{1}{2}, (x_n, y_j)]. \tag{9.29}$$

[Instead of using the probability $\tfrac{1}{2}$ as such, one might work with an event E^* whose subjective probability equals $\tfrac{1}{2}$.] With $[(x_i, y_j), \tfrac{1}{2}, (x_r, y_k)]$, the gamble "yielding" (x_i, y_j) with probability $\tfrac{1}{2}$ or (x_r, y_k) with probability $\tfrac{1}{2}$, if the subject is indifferent to a choice between a and b as defined in (9.29), then

$$V[(x_i, y_j), \tfrac{1}{2}, (x_r, y_k)] = \tfrac{1}{2}V(x_i, y_j) + \tfrac{1}{2}V(x_r, y_k),$$

and

$$V[a] = V[b] \qquad \text{if and only if } a \sim b,$$

yield (9.28*b*) directly.

Other evidence can also be used for testing whether $X \mathrel{I} Y$, given $X \times Y = Z$. For example, one might obtain a strict preference ordering of some of the $(x_i, y_j) \in Z$, of the form

$$V(x_{i_1}, y_{j_1}) > V(x_{i_2}, y_{j_2}) > \ldots > V(x_{i_r}, y_{j_r}), \tag{9.30}$$

then write $V(x_{i_k}, y_{j_k}) = u_{i_k} + v_{j_k}$, plug this back into (9.30), and determine whether

$$u_{i_1} + v_{j_1} > u_{i_2} + v_{j_2} > \ldots > u_{i_r} + v_{j_r} \tag{9.31}$$

is internally consistent. If (9.31) is consistent, then (9.30) supports independence (but is obviously not sufficient for $X \mathrel{I} Y$), but if (9.31) has internal contradictions of the form $u_i > u_i$ or $v_j > v_j$, then (9.30) shows that it is not true that $X \mathrel{I} Y$.

$Z \neq X \times Y$

In cases where $Z \subset X \times Y$ but $Z \neq X \times Y$, and the graph Γ_Z of the ordered pairs $(x_i, y_j) \in Z$ is connected (see Section 9.3), in order to show that $X \mathrel{I} Y$ it is necessary to show that the loop number of every loop in Γ_Z equals zero.[14] As in the case where $Z = X \times Y$, it may be sufficient

---

[14] If Γ_Z is connected but has no loops, then $X \mathrel{I} Y$. However, in such a case it is questionable whether independence is of any use.

to know whether $\psi = 0$ for some of the simpler loops, since many loops with a large number of nodes may be decomposed into several loops each with a smaller number of nodes. Any four-node loop can be treated by the method of 50-50 gambles given previously. It is more difficult to deal with 6-node, 8-node, ... loops. Consider the following 6-node loop:

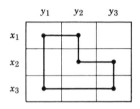

Figure 9.9

Letting $V_{ij} = V(x_i, y_j)$, the loop number is

$$\psi = |V_{11} - V_{12} + V_{22} - V_{23} + V_{33} - V_{31}|.$$

Obviously $\psi = 0$ if and only if

$$V(x_1, y_1) + V(x_2, y_2) + V(x_3, y_3) = V(x_1, y_2) + V(x_2, y_3) + V(x_3, y_1).$$

To test this, one might consider comparing the two hypothetical gambles

$$a = [(x_1, y_1), \tfrac{1}{3}, (x_2, y_2), \tfrac{1}{3}, (x_3, y_3)],$$

$$b = [(x_1, y_2), \tfrac{1}{3}, (x_2, y_3), \tfrac{1}{3}, (x_3, y_1)],$$

where $[z_1, \tfrac{1}{3}, z_2, \tfrac{1}{3}, z_3]$ is the lottery in which z_1, z_2, and $z_3 \in Z$ "occur" with equal probability. If $a \sim b$, then $\psi = 0$. With an 8-node loop we would require gambles with four $z_i \in Z$ in each gamble.

9.7 FORMULATING FOR INDEPENDENCE

In virtually all decision situations in which independence is used it must be taken as an assumption. The first reason for this is that it is simply too great a task to attempt complete verification of the independence hypothesis[15]—the effort might be better spent on other things. The second and perhaps more important reason for stating independence as an assumption is because it often yields an approximation (to a very complicated state of affairs). Although in many instances it may be a good approximation, it is nevertheless an approximation and should be recognized as such. It may also be an approximation which must be made in order to treat a problem analytically or "objectively."

[15] If it is in fact true.

Since independence is often an approximation, care should be taken in employing the assumption of independence. This most obviously concerns how the relevant variables are grouped to yield the variables which are assumed to be mutually independent. In the notation of Section 9.4, we start with the original variables

$$X_1, X_2, \ldots, X_n,$$

and end up with the set of variables assumed to be mutually independent:

$$Y_1, Y_2, \ldots, Y_m, \quad m \leqslant n,$$

where each Y_j is identically one of the X_j or the product of two or more X_j, and

$$Y_1 \times Y_2 \times \ldots \times Y_m = X_1 \times X_2 \times \ldots \times X_n = X.$$

In dividing the n X_j into m groups, it seems reasonable that one would usually be motivated by:

1. A desire to put variables which are valuewise interdependent into the same group;

2. a desire to put variables which are valuewise independent into different groups;

3. a desire to have m large, as close to n as is "reasonably possible."

In these desires, (2) and (3) are complementary to one another but (1) and (3) are clearly in conflict, a fact which has been noted previously. On the one hand, it is desirable to reduce the number of entities whose relative values need to be measured in some way or another—which may be part of the reason for desire (3)—and on the other hand, we do not want to distort the situation by too gross an approximation.

Since it may be true that all variables interact with one another in a relative value sense, the matter is not simply one of "deciding" which variables are interdependent and which are independent, but becomes a matter of "how much" interdependence. In terms of the value function V, the amount of interdependence between, say, Y_1 and Y_2 with $Y_1 \times Y_2 = X$ could be defined in several ways, but we shall not even attempt to write down one way, since it would be of very little use.[16] The decision maker, with appropriate guidance from the research worker, should be able to judge which variables interact most with one another in a relative value sense and should be able to make an intelligent grouping of the original variables into "mutually independent" sets. In doing this, one

---

[16] If enough were known about the $V(x)$ to make use of a definition of amount of interdependence it is doubtful whether one would have any need to make an assumption of independence.

should be careful not to confuse valuewise interdependent with stochastic interdependence or "causal" dependence.

In considering the decision situation with an eye toward independence, it may be possible to combine several variables into one variable, not by the product notion, but simply by some arithmetic operation. For example, if several variables are measured in the same units (e.g., dollars), they most probably will be quite interdependent in the relative value sense and some linear combination of these variables might be as appropriate to the decision maker for his purposes of making value judgments as a vector of the values of the variables. If one is using a small, finite subset of all possible values a variable can take on for value measurement purposes, such a procedure could serve to further reduce the number of entities requiring value measurement.

In the first part of the next chapter we shall explore the problems of formulating for independence in more detail. While the comments given there are primarily directed towards decision making under certainty, most of the discussion is applicable to the general case of decision making under uncertainty and will not be repeated in Chapter 11.

EXERCISES

1. Given the set of ordered pairs,

$$Z = \{(x_1, y_1), (x_1, y_2), (x_1, y_3), (x_1, y_4), (x_2, y_3), (x_2, y_4),$$

$$(x_2, y_5), (x_2, y_6), (x_3, y_5), (x_3, y_7), (x_4, y_6), (x_4, y_7)\},$$

with $x_i \neq x_j$ if $i \neq j$, and $y_i \neq y_j$ if $i \neq j$: (a) Draw the graph Γ_Z, according to the definition of Section 9.3. (b) Identify all the cycles in Γ_Z. (c) Identify all the loops in Γ_Z. (d) Is Γ_Z connected?

2. (*Continuation.*) Let f be a real-valued function defined over the $(x_i, y_j) \in Z$, with $c_{ij} = f(x_i, y_j)$. Draw the c_{ij} matrix, identify the loops in it, and state the conditions on the c_{ij} that must hold in order for X and Y to be independent with respect to f.

3. Repeat Exercises 1 and 2 after adding the node (x_4, y_1) to Z.

4. Analyze the following set of ordered pairs according to the theory of Section 9.3:

$$Z = \{(x_1, y_2), (x_1, y_4), (x_1, y_7), (x_1, y_{10}), (x_2, y_1), (x_3, y_4), (x_3, y_6), (x_3, y_9),$$

$$(x_4, y_7), (x_4, y_{11}), (x_5, y_8), (x_6, y_3), (x_7, y_1), (x_7, y_{12}), (x_8, y_2), (x_8, y_{10}),$$

$$(x_9, y_1), (x_{10}, y_1), (x_{10}, y_{12}), (x_{11}, y_4), (x_{11}, y_5), (x_{11}, y_9), (x_{12}, y_3),$$

$$(x_{12}, y_7), (x_{12}, y_{11})\}.$$

5. Is the following set of ordered pairs connected?

$$Z = \{(1, 2), (apple, pie), (apple, cider), (1, piece),$$

$$(1, jug), (Kentucky, pie), (gold, piece), (Kentucky, jug)\}.$$

6. (*Continuation.*) Suppose a real-valued function f is defined on the ordered pairs in Exercise 5, with

$$f(Z) = \{-3, 7, 0, 4, 16, 9, -14, 32\}.$$

Give functions f_1 and f_2 over X and Y that satisfy $f_1(x) + f_2(y) = f(x, y)$ for all eight $(x, y) \in Z$.

7. Show that X and Y are independent with respect to f if and only if X and Y are independent with respect to f', where

$$f'(x, y) = af(x, y) + b, \qquad a \neq 0,$$

for all $(x, y) \in Z$.

8. *Conditional independence.* In a decision situation suppose there are three variables of interest, say, X, Y, and W. Suppose further that X has n values, Y has m values, and W has 2 values:

$$X = \{x_1, x_2, \ldots, x_n\}$$
$$Y = \{y_1, y_2, \ldots, y_m\}$$
$$W = \{w_1, w_2\},$$

with $Z = X \times Y \times W$, where Z is the set of consequences. It is apparent that there is no independence among X, Y, and W. However, it is judged that for any given y_j,

(a) $$V(x_i, y_j, w_1) - V(x_i, y_m, w_1)$$

is the same for all $x_i \in X$; and for any given y_j,

(b) $$V(x_i, y_j, w_2) - V(x_i, y_m, w_2)$$

is the same for all $x_i \in X$. Argue, then, that one can write

(1) $$V(x_i, y_j, w_1) = f_1(x_i) + f_2(y_j),$$
(2) $$V(x_i, y_j, w_2) = g_1(x_i) + g_2(y_j).$$

What restrictions must the functions f_1, f_2, g_1, and g_2 obey concerning origins and unit measurements?

Rewrite $E(S_\alpha)$, the expected value of strategy S_α, using (1) and (2).

Originally, with no independence of any kind, there were $2mn$ entities requiring value measurement. How many entities require value measurement under the *conditional independence* as defined by (1) and (2)? How many entities would require value measurement if it were true that $X \mathbin{I} Y \mathbin{I} W$?

9. (*Continuation.*) Extend the theory of Exercise 8 to cover a situation where there are $p > 2$ elements in W, i.e., $W = \{w_1, w_2, \ldots, w_p\}$, and for any given y_j and w_k it is judged that

$$V(x_i, y_j, w_k) - V(x_i, y_m, w_k)$$

is the same for all $x_i \in X$.

10. Suppose in Exercises 1 and 2 that X I Y, with

$$V(x_i, y_j) = V_1(x_i) + V_2(y_j),$$

and suppose that ordinal rankings on X and Y are, respectively,

$$V_1(x_1) \geqslant V_1(x_2) \geqslant V_1(x_3) \geqslant V_1(x_4),$$
$$V_2(y_1) \geqslant V_2(y_2) \geqslant \ldots \geqslant V_2(y_7).$$

Discuss how each of these would be obtained, using only the elements of Z in Exercise 1 for simple preference comparisons.

11. (*Continuation.*)   In Exercise 10, suppose the ordinal ranking over Y remains as shown, but it is found for X that

$$V_1(x_2) \geqslant V_1(x_1),$$
$$V_1(x_2) \geqslant V_1(x_3),$$
$$V_1(x_3) \geqslant V_1(x_4).$$

(*a*) Give two 50-50 gambles that could be used to find out whether $V_1(x_1) \geqslant V_1(x_3)$ or $V_1(x_3) \geqslant V_1(x_1)$. The gambles are to be of the form $(a, {}^1/_2, b)$, where $a, b \in Z$.

(*b*) Suppose from (*a*) it is found that $V_1(x_3) \geqslant V_1(x_1)$, and you now want a comparison between $V_1(x_1)$ and $V_1(x_4)$. Give two three-consequence gambles, of the form (a, b, c), where a, b, and c occur with equal probability $(\frac{1}{3})$, that could be used to find out whether $V_1(x_1) \geqslant V_1(x_4)$ or $V_1(x_4) \geqslant V_1(x_1)$.

12. *Lexicographic ordering.* Let $X = [0, \infty)$, $Y = [0, \infty)$, $Z - X \times Y$. Given that (x, y) is preferred to (x', y') if and only if $x > x'$ or $x = x'$ and $y > y'$ and that $(x, y) \sim (x', y')$ if and only if $x = x'$ and $y = y'$ prove: there exists no real-valued function V on Z such that $V(x, y) \geq V(x', y')$ if and only if $(x, y) \simeq (x', y')$. [This leads to vector or *multidimensional utilities*, discussed in Part III of Thrall, Coombs, and Davis (1954).]

REFERENCES

Auspitz and Lieben, *Untersuchungen über die Theorie des Preises*, Duncker and Humblot, Leipzig, 1889.

Berge, C., *The Theory of Graphs and Its Applications*, translated by Alison Doig, John Wiley and Sons, New York, 1962.

Fisher, I., *Mathematical Investigations in the Theory of Value and Prices*, Yale University Press, New Haven, 1925.

Samuelson, P. A., *Foundations of Economic Analysis*, Harvard University Press, Cambridge, 1961 (copyright, 1947).

Sasieni, M., A. Yaspan, and L. Friedman, *Operations Research—Methods and Problems*, John Wiley and Sons, New York, 1959.

Thrall, R. M., C. H. Coombs, and R. L. Davis (eds). *Decision Processes*, John Wiley and Sons, New York, 1954.

Chapter 10

INDEPENDENCE AND CERTAINTY

10.1 INTRODUCTION

There are many common decision situations which may profitably be treated as decision making under certainty, although the appearance of certainty generally arises out of a simplification of a situation which involves uncertainty. That is, for practical reasons, one may often reduce a noncertain situation to a "certain" one, either by making explicit simplifying assumptions or by ignoring or not making explicit various elements which would complicate the situation and propel it from the conceptually simpler category of decision making under certainty to a category of decision making under risk or uncertainty. It may fairly be said that certainty, as used herein, is in itself inadequate to describe the content of this chapter and is somewhat of a misnomer.[1] However, we will use the term in place of a bulkier description such as "certainty by virtue of simplification."

To illustrate, suppose an individual is involved in purchasing a life insurance policy, buying a car or house, considering a number of job opportunities, or trying to decide where to spend his vacation. In everyday life and language it seems that most persons involved in making a decision of this type attempt, however crudely, to "weigh the factors" or "consider the pros and cons or advantages and disadvantages of each alternative," and in some manner come up with a satisfactory choice. In doing so, however, very often only concrete aspects are dealt with explicitly while subtler aspects of the situation are not considered directly. To each

---

[1] We might go so far as to say that there is nothing as uncertain as certainty. Our inability to predict the uncertain may necessitate setting our sights only on what is certain and can mentally be dealt with in a reasonably short period of time.

alternative (insurance policy, house, job, or what have you) there corresponds exactly one consequence which describes various characteristics of the alternative. Probable implications of the alternatives for the more distant, uncertain future are formally suppressed.

The situation considered in this chapter is, of course, a special case of the general decision situation of Chapter 2, namely, decision making under "certainty." To analyze this type of situation the assumption of independence of variables in the relative value sense is used, although this need not always be done (and may be quite unnecessary). The situation of this chapter is also a special case of the situation treated in the next chapter where uncertainty is dealt with. The final section of the present chapter will begin the transition from certainty to uncertainty by considering a special case under uncertainty which in structure is almost identical to the certainty situation.

The discussions of the next several sections, leading up to the analysis of dominance under certainty and independence, is designed to apply to formulation of the decision problem under certainty, although as noted at the end of Chapter 9, many of the remarks made in these sections will also apply to the uncertainty case of the final chapters. The methods of analysis presented in this chapter are primarily concerned with:

1. Determining when one alternative or prospect under certainty has a larger relative value than another prospect.

However, these methods can also be used for:

2. Determining when one course of action has a larger relative value than another course of action in a general decision problem, when it is assumed that the courses of action (A_i) and outcomes (O_j) are valuewise independent of one another so that

$$V(A_i, O_j) = V_1(A_i) + V_2(O_j).$$

That is, the methods used here can apply to determining when $V_1(A_i) \geqslant V_1(A_k)$, for example. They can also be used for determining whether $V_2(O_j) \geqslant V_2(O_k)$, and for:

3. Determining when one consequence has a larger relative value than another in a general decision situation, i.e., when $V(o_j) \geqslant V(o_k)$, where o_j and o_k are consequences of the form (A_i, O_j).

Application of the methods given here requires the assumption of independence among variables, as noted above. Cases (2) and (3) may be considered to be by-products of the present analysis and will not be discussed *per se* either here or in the next chapter, since our basic interest lies in determining whether one *strategy* has an expected relative value larger than the expected relative value of another *strategy*.[2]

It should be noted that the terminology used in this chapter deviates to some degree from that used previously. The main reason for this is the addition of a bit of local color. In addition, some of the new terms agree more with the more common usage in the literature. For a concise "dictionary":

Alternative or prospect—consequence

Performance variable —action variable (and, in some cases, outcome variable)

Conceptual prospect —pseudoconsequence

10.2 FORMULATION

In general, we are here concerned with the type of situation in which an individual has in mind attaining one thing from a group of similar (but by no means identical) things in order to satisfy certain of his, and perhaps other people's, needs, goals, or objectives. Within the total group of similar things from which he is planning to choose one, it may be quite possible, in fact, to choose more than one. However, for simplicity it is assumed that, after attaining one of the alternatives, he has sufficiently satisfied his needs (for the time being) so that the situation which stimulated his choice is no longer relevant to him.

Suppose an individual is buying a house (or car or insurance policy) for himself or his family. After considering a set of houses (or cars or insurance policies) and having made a purchase of one element in the set at a certain time, he will generally no longer be interested in purchasing some other element(s) in the set at that time (although within a few years he may decide to purchase another house or another car, etc., by which time the set of alternatives from which he will choose may be quite different from the previous set[3]). If the individual were considering buying, say, two cars at one time, then the basic elements of the set of alternatives could be taken to be pairs of cars rather than individual cars. In any event, it is assumed that one can formulate the set of alternatives so that exactly one will be selected by the individual.

In order not to give the impression that this chapter deals only with the

---

[2] In the present context a strategy would read "select alternative A_i."

[3] Time, of course, is only relative to the type of item under consideration. For the person who buys his lunch at some restaurant every day, there will be a daily decision on what to have for lunch. Having had one lunch on a given day, he will probably not be interested in obtaining a second lunch that same day, so we may say that his culinary and gustatory needs have been satisfied for the time being (a period of several hours, perhaps).

purchase of goods and services, we mention other situations in which the theory might be applied.   Following is a brief list:

1. An engineer, faced with the responsibility of designing a light bulb (machine tool, die, airplane wing, bridge, etc.) must make a choice among a conceptually huge number of alternative designs.

2. A scientist, wishing to conduct an experiment to test one or more hypotheses, must select an experimental design from a vast number of possible experimental designs.

3. A president of a company has just lost his executive vice president and must recommend to the board an individual he would like to have fill the vacancy.

4. A politician's campaign manager, whose candidate is about to campaign for re-election, must choose a campaign tour through his constituency.

Developing Admissible Alternatives

As noted in Chapter 2, once we have identified the type of thing which we wish to choose (car, light bulb design, campaign tour, etc.), the first task is to search out, develop, and identify a set of feasible and admissible alternatives (from the viewpoint of the decision maker) from which to choose.   For the type of situation considered in this chapter, this is often the most important phase of the research and, perhaps, the most difficult and time consuming.   Before giving examples, we shall try to outline the general nature of the task that is faced in getting a "good" list of alternatives.

Usually there is a huge number of possible alternatives or prospects that might be considered.   Very often, it will require a great deal of effort on the part of the individual or research worker to search out and discover feasible alternatives.[4]   In this process, we will seldom know whether our efforts have uncovered the "best" alternative(s).   In addition, in the search for and learning about good prospects, a law of diminishing returns will set in, however hard it is to tell just when.   The task of developing a set of alternatives may terminate when time or money has run low or when the individual decision maker feels that the set so far obtained contains at least one satisfactory prospect.   Or, on the notion of diminishing returns, the individual may, at a certain time, feel that what he can expect to gain by continuing the search for more alternatives will be more than offset by what he can expect to lose by postponing the major decision and he thus makes a selection at that time.   Many persons will find that they

---

[4] In some engineering design problems, for example, it may take months or years just to develop one feasible design, let alone a number of alternative feasible designs from which to choose.

make many decisions at points in time roughly governed by this principle.

The process of attaining a "final" list of admissible alternatives is a sequential one. As time progresses, one will develop or discover new alternatives, some of which may get added to the list for further consideration, others being discarded on the spot as less than desirable. Moreover, as additional prospects are added to the list, others already on the list may be dropped because one or more new ones are judged to be superior. At any given point in time, one will have a list of prospects (either mental or written), but at different points in time this list (or these lists) may look quite different. Thus, we actually go through a progression of lists of alternatives, adding and paring as we go along. Finally, for one or more reasons, we go no further in our quest for new alternatives and contemplate the prospects on the most recent list (i.e., the "final" list), settling down to the task of selecting one of these.

In this process the importance of identifying and making use of good sources of information should be recognized. A great deal of time and effort may be saved by first finding out what "helps" are available and then using these efficiently. Few people who go to a library in search of a specific volume will go directly to the stacks and begin scanning the titles in the hope of finding it. Instead, they will use the card catalog and indexing system to determine its stack location.

Examples

Let us now look at this process applied to two of the situations cited earlier. In buying a house in a large city, there may be thousands of houses on the market when the individual begins his search. Generally, he will constrain his quest to several specific neighborhoods and will have in mind a general type of house that he wishes to purchase. He may be wise to engage the advice of one or more real estate offices, since there he can attain a listing of available houses, locations, approximate characteristics of these houses, and approximate prices, taxes, etc. He will probably scan the classified section of one or more newspapers every day and use the information contained therein. He might consult friends who live in the neighborhood(s) he is considering and use their advice. He might wish to visit the offices of the local government to obtain information on taxes, zoning laws, improvements, and so forth. As he proceeds, he will select certain houses for further consideration and may keep a list of those in which he is interested. After visiting some of these, he may decide he is no longer interested in several, and so takes them off his list. Others may have to be deleted owing to their sale to someone else. Finally, he gets a list of a small number of feasible and apparently satisfactory prospects.

He may look further into these, noting more carefully their characteristics, bargaining with the seller over price, etc., until after due consideration of the factors important to him, he makes a choice and buys a house.

In designing an experiment, a scientist, if he is not already familiar with the literature on the design of experiments, may do well to consult colleagues who are better versed on this subject and to undertake (with advice from others perhaps) a search of relevant literature on the general subject, and in particular in areas close to that in which he is working. He will want to know how others have set up similar experiments, may consult their publications, and correspond with them to get their opinions on how he might proceed or their views on specific procedures he is considering. In designing his experiment, he will continually be making choices on how not to do or how to do such and such until he comes up with one or more designs he considers satisfactory for his purposes. He may wish to run a pilot experiment or experiments to test his design(s). In this situation a number of secondary decisions may be required in connection with various aspects of the experiment.

When one is involved in making up a list of alternatives and in so doing deletes or discards certain possibilities from further consideration, one will have in mind a number of factors or characteristics of the alternatives that are being used (either implicitly or explicitly) in making these decisions. In addition, when one gets a "final" list, these same factors (to be called performance variables) will come into play in deciding among the remaining alternatives. It may be fairly said that the reason why any given prospect on the final list appears thereon is that there is no other prospect on that list which is clearly better in the preliminary judgment of the decision maker (or the research worker). What is needed then is a more detailed analysis of these prospects, similar to that discussed in previous chapters.

What we shall do here, unlike what has been done before, is to suppress deliberately uncertainties in the situation in order to treat the problem of choice as a problem under "certainty." Although uncertainties may have an effect on the individual's value judgments, they will not be considered explicitly. The method used in analyzing this type of situation is developed below.

10.3 OUTLINE OF METHOD

The procedure employed in this approximation method has the following steps:

    1. Identify a set of performance variables[5] relevant to the alternatives and important to the decision maker.

[5] Which, in previous terms, may be viewed either as action variables or, on occasion, as outcome variables.

2. For each prospect on the list, identify one value of each performance variable which adequately describes the prospect with respect to the variable. Equate each prospect to its corresponding values of the performance variables.

3. Assume that the performance variables are valuewise independent, that is, the relative value of an alternative or prospect to the decision maker equals the sum of relative values of the values of the performance variables which identify the prospect. By methods similar to those given previously applied to conceptual (not necessarily actual) prospects, measure the relative values of the values of the performance variables on various scales.

4. Use the results of value measurements to analyze for dominance between and among alternatives.

10.4 PERFORMANCE VARIABLES AND THEIR VALUES

Perhaps the best way to indicate what we mean by performance variables is to give several examples of situations and present lists of items that might be called "performance variables" in these situations.

First, reconsider the situation where an individual is looking for a house to purchase. Among the characteristics (performance variables) of houses that he considers important may be the following:

1. Number of rooms.
2. Number of bedrooms.
3. Number of bathrooms.
4. Age of house.
5. Kind of garage.
6. Nature of basement.
7. Number of floors.
8. Outside materials.
9. Inside materials.
10. Type of heating system.
11. Size of kitchen.
12. "Permanent" appliances in kitchen.
13. Estimated cost of fixing up the property (inside and outside improvements).
14. Price being asked for property.
15. Size of lot.
16. Civic improvements to property (sewers, sidewalks, etc.).
17. Current yearly taxes.
18. Distance from closest school.
19. Amount of traffic on facing street.

Each house that he seriously considers purchasing may be described by its values of the performance variables. For example, a house which has

6 rooms, 3 bedrooms, 1 bathroom, is 10 years old, has an attached two-car garage (codified as 3), a full basement with concrete floor (codified as 4) may be described by the vector $(6, 3, 1, 10, 3, 4, \ldots)$. To be able to specify values of any performance variable for different houses, one must have an idea of what each variable means and how to make observations and measurements with respect to it. That is, an operational definition of each variable is required, although it may not be vital to have a very exacting operational definition for every variable. For example, one should have an idea of what does and does not constitute a room, so that on visiting a house one can observe its structural and other characteristics and, by means of one's idea (or definition) of "room," count the number of rooms contained therein. Ackoff (1962, Chapter 5) points out the difficulties involved in defining such a thing as "room," and demonstrates that what appears to be an easy thing to define may, in fact, be very hard (if not impossible) to define exactly. He also points out that our operational definitions should be designed to serve the purposes to which we wish to put them in a particular situation. Thus, in looking at houses for the purpose of buying one, an individual may be satisfied with a quite crude and unwritten idea of how to identify a "room" when he sees one, whereas in a detailed survey of housing in various residential districts where different persons will be interviewing households in the different districts, a more exacting written definition of "room" may be required.

For each performance variable there may be as many relevant values as there are alternatives under consideration. Letting **A** denote the set of alternatives, with members $A_1, A_2, \ldots, A_m$, the number of relevant values of each performance variable will be less than or equal to m. There will be fewer than m values for a variable when two or more prospects have the same value for that variable (e.g., many houses of interest may have three bedrooms). The number of values will, of course, be dependent upon how detailed one wishes to get in defining performance variables. Very seldom (if ever) will two things be precisely identical, but they may be treated as identical relative to the purposes of the inquiry.

In requiring one value of each variable to correspond to any given alternative, we will often be suppressing uncertainties. For example, no one knows exactly what it will cost to fix up a given house to put it into the shape desired. However, an approximate estimate of this cost may be derived, the goodness of the approximation depending in part upon how much effort one wishes to put into making the estimate. For the house searcher, a crude judgment of this cost may serve his purposes. (A company bidding on a large defense contract may spend much time and money in getting a good estimate to guide their bidding strategy.) The present method says, in effect, that we will act as if the estimate of the true value of a performance variable were, in fact, the true value. If one wishes to consider several values of a performance variable for a given alternative (with probabilities corresponding to the several values), then the present model is not applicable.[6]

As a second, somewhat different, example of a list of performance variables, consider a situation involving the design of an engine to be used in a new automobile. Suppose that the rest of the automobile has been designed and is given as fixed, placing certain restrictions on engine design. Various feasible alternative engine designs may be proposed. The performance variables considered relevant may include the following:

1. Initial tooling-up cost to produce an engine.
2. Unit cost of producing an engine (independent of tooling-up cost), including parts, materials, labor, machine running costs, and so forth.
3. Engine weight.
4. Total car weight.
5. Maximum horse power.
6. Displacement.
7. Compression ratio.
8. Starting torque.
9. Type of gasoline required for most efficient performance.
10. Average MPG gasoline consumption.
11. Miles between oil changes.
12. Engine life in miles.

Each proposed engine will be described by a value for each performance variable. Here again, in order to use the present method, one value of each variable must be identified for each alternative, ignoring obvious uncertainties. In this situation it is quite likely that more than one person will make the decision of what engine to put into mass production, in which case an extension of the present methods of value measures is required (which we shall not consider). It is also a virtual certainty that scores of secondary decisions will be made during the design phase. If, in fact, more than one feasible design does eventually come off the drawing boards, pilot models of the "best" of these may be built and tested to give better estimates of the values of certain performance variables. [Such tests will generally be made anyway, in order to iron out bugs in the design(s).]

---

[6] But the analysis of the next chapter is applicable to such a situation.

In either of the situations cited above (and in most others one could imagine), the number of potential performance variables will be quite large. If we wished to take the time, at least several hundred variables could be listed for either of these situations. There are several ways of proceeding at this stage. One is to select a subset of performance variables most important to the decision maker and work only with these, ignoring the rest. (We have already arrived at the point where every alternative in the "final" list has been judged admissible, and thus it will not be catastrophic to ignore some of the less critical variables in the program of value measurement.) The number of variables selected in relation to the total number that might be considered would usually be expected to depend upon the over-all importance of the particular decision situation to the decision maker. If the decision must be made hurriedly or is of little consequence to the individual, it might not be feasible or economical to even attempt to make out a list of performance variables. On the other hand, if the decision is quite important (e.g., concerning an important part of the nation's defense, or materially affecting the future solvency of a corporation), explicit consideration of more than, say, one hundred performance variables might be justified.

A second way of dealing with a large potential number of performance variables is first to select a small number (say 6 to 10) of the more critical of these and to analyze the alternatives with respect to this small number of variables. Then add an additional half-dozen or so variables to those previously selected for explicit consideration, analyze the alternatives with respect to the augmented set, and compare the results obtained with the results of the first analysis. If the two sets of results agree in their conclusions with respect to the alternatives, the individual may be satisfied and consider going no further. If the results of the second analysis contradict the results of the first analysis, one may wish to add another group of variables and perform a new analysis with respect to the new, larger set of factors.

A third method would be to select a specified number of variables, analyze the alternatives with respect to these, and repeat the process several times, each time selecting a new set of variables to work with. If the results remained fairly invariant with respect to the different sets of variables, one might feel justified in inferring a general preference ordering over the set of alternatives.

In the remainder of this chapter we shall deal with a specified number (n) of performance variables and proceed as if this were *the* relevant set, keeping in mind that it is really a subset of the set of all performance variables and may be subject to change if one so wishes.

10.5 PROSPECTS AND CONCEPTUAL PROSPECTS

In terms of values of performance variables, each actual prospect or alternative A_i is equated to an n-dimensional vector of values. To symbolize this, let

X_j = the jth performance variable, $j = 1, 2, \ldots, n$,

x_{ij} = the value of X_j associated with A_i, $i = 1, \ldots, m$; $j = 1, \ldots, n$.

Then

$$A_i = (x_{i1}, x_{i2}, \ldots, x_{in}), \qquad i = 1, \ldots, m.$$

The matrix of the values of the performance variables that are taken to be relevant can be arrayed as follows:

	X_1	X_2	$\ldots$	X_j	$\ldots$	X_n
A_1	x_{11}	x_{12}	$\ldots$	x_{1j}	$\ldots$	x_{1n}
A_2	x_{21}	x_{22}	$\ldots$	x_{2j}	$\ldots$	x_{2n}
$\vdots$	$\vdots$					
A_i	x_{i1}	x_{i2}	$\ldots$	x_{ij}	$\ldots$	x_{in}
$\vdots$	$\vdots$					
A_m	x_{m1}	x_{m2}	$\ldots$	x_{mj}	$\ldots$	x_{mn}

Thus, for the performance variable X_j, there will be m (or fewer) relevant values $x_{1j}, x_{2j}, \ldots, x_{mj}$. That is, we may take

$$X_j = \{x_{1j}, x_{2j}, \ldots, x_{mj}\}.^7$$

If two values of X_j are identical, this will be expressed with the usual identity sign. For example, $x_{2j} = x_{5j}$ means that x_{2j} and x_{5j} are identical.

Because of the nature of the model employed here, frequent use will be made of conceptual prospects in the programs of obtaining relative value measures. A *conceptual prospect* is any n-dimensional vector of values $(x_{i_1 1}, x_{i_2 2}, \ldots, x_{i_n n})$, where $x_{i_k k}$ is one of the relevant values of X_k. In the case where $i_1 = i_2 = \ldots = i_n$, a conceptual prospect reduces to one of the actual or available prospects.

In other words, a conceptual prospect is formed by selecting one relevant value from each performance variable. Thus, if we were dealing with two

---

[7] The reader should note that the double subscript notation here is the reverse of that in Section 9.5. There we took, in effect, $Y_j = \{y_{j1}, y_{j2}, \ldots, y_{jn_j}\}$, where in y_{jk} the *first* subscript identified the variable. In $X_j = \{x_{1j}, x_{2j}, \ldots, x_{mj}\}$ the *second* subscript identifies the parent variable. Within this chapter we will be consistent in the latter convention whenever double subscripts are used.

actual prospects $A_1 = (x_{11}, x_{12})$ and $A_2 = (x_{21}, x_{22})$, with $x_{11} \neq x_{21}$, $x_{12} \neq x_{22}$, then there would be four conceptual prospects (x_{11}, x_{12}), (x_{11}, x_{22}), (x_{21}, x_{12}), and (x_{21}, x_{22}). If the situation were an m-by-n one as illustrated in the above matrix, then there would be no more than m^n conceptual prospects.

Conceptual Prospects and Value Measurement

In measuring relative values of the x_{ij}, we will practically never use all of the conceptual prospects and, generally, will need only a fairly small subset of the total set for this purpose.

The idea of using conceptual prospects in measuring relative values may get one into troubles which can be avoided by reformulating the set of performance variables. The primary difficulty one might encounter would be due to some kind of relation between performance variables. For example, suppose that the value of X_k is uniquely determined, given the value of X_j. Then, if $x_{1j} \neq x_{2j}$ and $x_{1k} \neq x_{2k}$, the conceptual prospects $(\dots, x_{1j}, \dots, x_{2k}, \dots)$ and $(\dots, x_{2j}, \dots, x_{1k}, \dots)$ are nonsense. In such a case X_j and X_k would be reformulated as one performance variable instead of two. A more complicated situation arises if the value of X_j is functionally dependent upon the values of two or more different performance variables. If $x_j = f(x_k, \dots, x_v)$, where $x_j \in X_j$, etc., this situation may be handled by replacing X_j with $f(\dots)$.

A slightly different relational complication may arise owing to inequality restrictions. For example, if X_1 were the number of rooms in a house and X_2 the number of bedrooms, we would have $x_{i1} \geqslant x_{i2}$ for any actual prospect. It might happen that some x_{i1} is less than some x_{k2}, $i \neq k$, in which case any conceptual prospect with $x_{i1} < x_{k2}$ is nonsense. (Imagine a 3-room house with 4 bedrooms). Here again we may avoid the difficulty by putting X_1 and X_2 together into a new variable, say X_1', where each value of X_1' has two components (number of rooms, number of bedrooms). If the occurrence of conceptual prospects which violate inequality restrictions is rare, then one may wish not to combine the possible offenders into one inclusive performance variable unless and until he is forced to do so in making value measurements.

What we are suggesting here is that the performance variables be so defined as to make (almost) every conceptual prospect capable of intellectual attainment. In other words, we want these prospects to "make sense" to the individual who will have to make value judgments or preference judgments between (at least some of) them. The intention in using a conceptual prospect which is not an actual prospect is that the individual be able to conceive of such a prospect as being possible, although we may not have learned about the existence of such a prospect or do not have the knowledge or technical ability to construct it. For example, one conceptual but as yet undiscovered prospect for "house" may be a 7-room, 3-bedroom, brick, on an acre of ground with a swimming pool, etc., at a total selling price of $10,000. As a second example, one might be able to conceive of the possibility of an automobile engine weighing 50 pounds, costing $10 to produce, and being able to develop 340 horsepower, while having no real idea how to design or construct such an item. Although both of these prospects may be a bit unrealistic, many individuals would be willing to grant that "somewhere, sometime, such a prospect may be realized," i.e., that it is not impossible.

The reason for using conceptual prospects, as noted in the previous chapter, is to enable an individual to make preference judgments with a minimum of confusion and uncertainty. Frequent use will be made of pairs of conceptual prospects which differ only in the values of from one to about four performance variables. It is our contention that, as the number of performance variables which have different values for the two prospects increases, the more difficult it will be (generally speaking) for an individual to discriminate preferentially between them. This will be especially true when there are many values in the first alternative which are more desirable than their correspondents in the second alternative and, in addition, there are many values (for different performance variables) in the second alternative which are more desirable than their correspondents in the first alternative. Most of the actual prospects that require further analysis would be expected to be of this type, since the individual's preliminary judgment has failed to distinguish a clear preference between any two of them, leaving him in a state of ambiguity that we shall attempt to resolve.

10.6   MODEL III

The basic model used in this chapter is a rather simple, special case of the general decision model. Since it is assumed that each A_i has probability one for an n-dimensional vector $(x_{i1}, x_{i2}, \ldots, x_{in})$,

$$E(A_i) = V(A_i) = V(x_{i1}, x_{i2}, \ldots, x_{in}), \qquad i = 1, 2, \ldots, m,$$

where the expected relative value of alternative A_i equals the relative value of A_i.[8]   As noted in Section 9.2, to identify an alternative that maximizes the decision maker's total relative value, it is only necessary to rank the A_i or $(x_{i1}, \ldots, x_{in})$ on an ordinal preference scale and select the alternative

[8] For this model "expected relative value of A_i" and "relative value of A_i" are equivalent.

that is ranked highest in desirability.[9]   However, as indicated above and in previous chapters, the individual may be unsure concerning his preferences between and among the various prospects in **A**.   (In fact, it is assumed at the start that he is unable to distinguish clearly the more desirable member of any pair of two A_i from **A**.)

In trying to resolve this ambiguity, the assumption of independence of performance variables in the relative value sense will be used.   With this assumption

$$V(A_i) = V_1(x_{i1}) + V_2(x_{i2}) + \ldots + V_n(x_{in}),$$

where V_j is a value function defined on the relevant values of the performance variable $X_j, j = 1, 2, \ldots, n$.   Each V_j has arbitrary origin, but the n V_j have a common (though arbitrarily set) unit measurement.

The relative value of any conceptual prospect $(x_{i_1 1}, x_{i_2 2}, \ldots, x_{i_n n})$, with the assumption of independence, may be written as

$$V(x_{i_1 1}, x_{i_2 2}, \ldots, x_{i_n n}) = V_1(x_{i_1 1}) + V_2(x_{i_2 2}) + \ldots + V_n(x_{i_n n}).$$

$$(10.1)$$

It will be noted that the assumption of independence in this model will generally *increase* the number of entities requiring value measurements. If we start with m alternatives, then without the assumption there are m items to consider.   But having made the assumption, we may have as many as mn entities (values of performance variables) to deal with, although this in itself should not cause alarm, since it will enable us to deal with a problem that might otherwise be incapable of further analysis.

Before going on to analyze for dominance of alternatives, one further comment and caution seems advisable.   If one has good reason for suspecting that two (or more) performance variables should not be taken as valuewise independent (with respect to each other) they should be combined into one performance variable.[10]   If there is reason to believe that no performance variable is "approximately" valuewise independent with respect to the other $n - 1$ performance variables, then there might be no gain in assuming independence because of the distortion of the actual situation that results.

---

[9] Obviously, an ordinal preference ranking is not even required.   All that we need do is identify an A_i whose relative value is at least as great as the relative value of any other A_i.

[10] This corresponds to dividing the original variables into mutually independent groups as discussed in Chapter 9.

10.7 MIXED ORDINAL ANALYSIS WITH TWO PROSPECTS

In this section we shall analyze a mixed ordinal ranking for two prospects. For definiteness, let the two prospects be

$$A_1 = (x_{11}, x_{12}, \ldots, x_{1n}),$$
$$A_2 = (x_{21}, x_{22}, \ldots, x_{2n}),$$

with relative values

$$V(A_i) = V_1(x_{i1}) + V_2(x_{i2}) + \ldots + V_n(x_{in}), \quad i = 1, 2.$$

Without loss in generality assume that $x_{1j} \neq x_{2j}$, so that all performance variables differ in their values for the two alternatives. [If $x_{1j} = x_{2j}$, then $V_j(x_{1j})$ and $V_j(x_{2j})$ cancel out in the difference $V(A_1) - V(A_2)$.]

The Mixed Ordinal Ranking

For each j, $j = 1, \ldots, n$, identify the *less desirable value* of X_j, call it z_j, and set

$$V_1(z_1) = V_2(z_2) = \ldots = V_n(z_n) = 0. \qquad (10.2)$$

This establishes a common origin for the n value functions. There remain n relative values $V_j(x_j)$, $j = 1, \ldots, n$, where x_j is the *more desirable value* of X_j.

Letting

$(x_j) =$ conceptual prospect of the form $(z_1, \ldots, z_{j-1}, x_j, z_{j+1}, \ldots, z_n)$, obtain a weak ordering of the n (x_j). Since, with (10.1) and (10.2),

$$V((x_j)) = V_j(x_j),$$

this weak ordering, if of the form

$$(x_{j_1}) \gtrsim (x_{j_2}) \gtrsim \ldots \gtrsim (x_{j_n}),$$

yields the mixed ordinal ranking

$$V_{j_1}(x_{j_1}) \geqslant V_{j_2}(x_{j_2}) \geqslant \ldots \geqslant V_{j_n}(x_{j_n}) \geqslant 0. \qquad (10.4a)$$

Letting

$$v_k = V_{j_k}(x_{j_k}), \quad k = 1, \ldots, n, \qquad (10.3)$$

we have

$$v_1 \geqslant v_2 \geqslant \ldots \geqslant v_n \geqslant 0. \qquad (10.4b)$$

In view of (10.2),

$$V(A_1) - V(A_2) = \sum_{k=1}^{n} c_k v_k, \qquad (10.5)$$

where

$$
c_k =
\begin{cases}
+1 & \text{if } v_k \text{ is the relative value of the value of a} \\
& \text{performance variable in } A_1, \\
-1 & \text{if } v_k \text{ is the relative value of the value of a} \\
& \text{performance variable in } A_2.
\end{cases}
\tag{10.6}
$$

Since the ranking (10.4b) is basic to this section, it should be pointed out that the method presented above is not the only method for obtaining this ranking. As in Section 9.5, the individual may be asked to make pairwise comparisons between pairs of conceptual prospects such as (x_1, z_2) and (z_1, x_2), where each of these two has a similar (but unspecified) value for each of the variables $X_3, X_4, \ldots, X_n$. If $(x_1, z_2) \gtrsim (z_1, x_2)$, then $V_1(x_1) \geqslant V_2(x_2)$. In any event, the usual assumptions of connectedness and transitivity apply.

It may be noted by the reader that (10.4b) is similar to (9.20), since (10.4a) may also be viewed as a ranking of n value differences $V_j(x_j) - V_j(z_j), j = 1, \ldots, n$. Actually, we may define

$$
v_k = V_{j_k}(x_{j_k}) - V_{j_k}(z_{j_k}),
\tag{10.7}
$$

where v_k is the kth ranked relative value difference $V_j(x_j) - V_j(z_j)$. Setting $V_{j_k}(z_{j_k}) = 0$ gives (10.3). By the device of (10.2) we see that the mixed ordinal ranking (10.4b) is, in fact, a complete (simple) ranking of the n value differences $V_j(x_j) - V_j(z_j), j = 1, \ldots, n$.

If, in obtaining a mixed ordinal ranking of the $V_j(x_{ij})$, $i = 1, 2$; $j = 1, \ldots, n$, we had interconnected the n values functions $V_1, V_2, \ldots, V_n$ by arbitrarily choosing a common origin, say by taking

$$
V_1(x_{i_1 1}) = V_2(x_{i_2 2}) = \ldots = V_n(x_{i_n n}),
\tag{10.8}
$$

where each i_j equals either 1 (for A_1) or 2 (for A_2), it is clear that the mixed ordinal ranking with the other n $V_j(x_{ij})$ will give a partial ordering of the v_k as defined by (10.7). Moreover, this partial ordering will, in fact, be a complete ordering if and only if we take (1) $x_{i_j j} = z_j$ for all j in (10.8)—as was done in (10.2)—or (2) $x_{i_j j} = x_j$ for all j.

Applying (6.1) to (10.5) gives

$$
V(A_1) - V(A_2) = \sum_{j=1}^{n-1} \left(\sum_{k=1}^{j} c_k \right)(v_j - v_{j+1}) + v_n \sum_{k=1}^{n} c_k,
\tag{10.9}
$$

which along with (10.4b) yields:

Theorem 10.1 Given the ranking (10.4b) and no additional information concerning the $V_j(x_{ij})$, $i = 1, 2; j = 1, \ldots, n$,

$$V(A_1) \geqslant V(A_2) \quad \text{if } \sum_{k=1}^{j} c_k \geqslant 0 \quad \text{for} \quad j = 1, 2, \ldots, n;$$

$$V(A_2) \geqslant V(A_1) \quad \text{if } \sum_{k=1}^{j} c_k \leqslant 0 \quad \text{for} \quad j = 1, 2, \ldots, n.$$

Otherwise, the sign of $V(A_1) - V(A_2)$ is indeterminate.

The observations concerning the interconnections of the n value functions $V_1, \ldots, V_n$ in the paragraphs containing (10.7) and (10.8) are summarized in:

Theorem 10.2 If the mixed ordinal ranking (10.4b) as derived on the basis of (10.2) does not yield a definite conclusion about the sign of $V(A_1) - V(A_2)$, then no other mixed ordinal ranking, based on (10.8), will yield a definite conclusion about the sign of $V(A_1) - V(A_2)$.

EXAMPLE. To illustrate theorem 10.1, suppose $n = 5$ with the matrix of the values of the five variables as shown in Figure 10.1, where the circled element in each column of the original matrix identifies the *less desirable* (z_j) of the two values. The five conceptual prospects used in the mixed ordinal ranking are:

$$(x_1) = (x_1, z_2, z_3, z_4, z_5),$$
$$(x_2) = (z_1, x_2, z_3, z_4, z_5),$$
$$(x_3) = (z_1, z_2, x_3, z_4, z_5),$$
$$(x_4) = (z_1, z_2, z_3, x_4, z_5),$$
$$(x_5) = (z_1, z_2, z_3, z_4, x_5).$$

If $(x_1) \gtrsim (x_2) \gtrsim (x_3) \gtrsim (x_5) \gtrsim (x_4) \gtrsim (z_1, z_2, z_3, z_4, z_5)$, then the ordinal ranking is

$$V_1(x_1) \geqslant V_2(x_2) \geqslant V_3(x_3) \geqslant V_5(x_5) \geqslant V_4(x_4) \geqslant 0,$$

or

$$v_1 \geqslant v_2 \geqslant v_3 \geqslant v_4 \geqslant v_5 \geqslant 0.$$

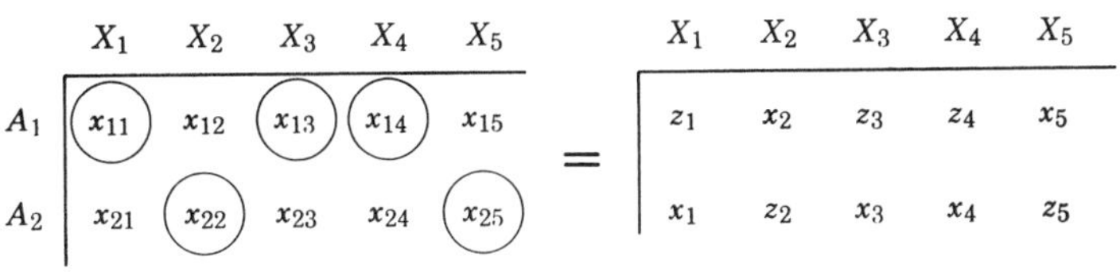

	X_1	X_2	X_3	X_4	X_5			X_1	X_2	X_3	X_4	X_5
A_1	x_{11}	x_{12}	x_{13}	x_{14}	x_{15}	=		z_1	x_2	z_3	z_4	x_5
A_2	x_{21}	x_{22}	x_{23}	x_{24}	x_{25}			x_1	z_2	x_3	x_4	z_5

Figure 10.1

Using (10.6),

$$(c_1, c_2, c_3, c_4, c_5) = (-1, 1, -1, 1, -1),$$

so that, similar to (10.5),

$$V(A_1) - V(A_2) = -v_1 + v_2 - v_3 + v_4 - v_5.$$

The partial sums of the c_k are

$$(c_1, c_1 + c_2, \ldots, c_1 + c_2 + c_3 + c_4 + c_5) = (-1, 0, -1, 0, -1),$$

so that, according to theorem 10.1, $V(A_2) \geqslant V(A_1)$.

10.8   MIXED DOMINANCE WITH A MIXED ORDINAL RANKING

In the present context the usual definition of dominance is modified slightly to read as follows:

Definition 10.1   Prospect A_s is dominated if and only if there exists a real-valued vector $\mathbf{a} = (a_1, \ldots, a_m)$ with $a_i \geqslant 0$, $i = 1, \ldots, m$, $a_s = 0$, $\sum a_i = 1$, such that

$$\sum_{i \neq s} a_i V(A_i) \geqslant V(A_s),$$

or such that

$$\sum_{j=1}^{n} \left[\sum_{i=1}^{m} a_i V_j(x_{ij}) - V_j(x_{sj}) \right] \geqslant 0. \tag{10.10}$$

In generating the mixed ordinal ranking, first identify the *least desirable* value of each X_j, say z_j, and set

$$V_1(z_1) = V_2(z_2) = \ldots = V_n(z_n) = 0. \tag{10.11}$$

Let r denote the number of distinct values of the n variables $X_1, \ldots, X_n$, which are different from the z_j.   [Assuming each X_j has at least two distinct values to begin with (including z_j), then $n \leqslant r \leqslant (m - 1)n$.]   Then obtain a mixed weak ordering of the r conceptual prospects formed by combining one of the r values of the variables different from the z_j with the z_j for the other $n - 1$ variables.   This weak ordering will then give the mixed ordinal ranking of the form

$$v_1 \geqslant v_2 \geqslant \ldots \geqslant v_r \geqslant 0, \tag{10.12}$$

where each $V_j(x_{ij})$, $x_{ij} \neq z_j$, is one of the v_k.

Finally let c_k' be the coefficient of v_k on the left-hand side of (10.10). Since (10.11) has already knocked out n terms in that expression, each c_k'

will equal either minus one [if v_k is one of the $V_j(x_{sj})$] or a linear combination of the a_i ($i \neq s$). Accordingly, we have

$$\sum_{j=1}^{n} \sum_{i=1}^{m} a_i V_j(x_{ij}) - \sum_{j=1}^{n} V_j(x_{sj}) = \sum_{k=1}^{r} c_k' v_k,$$

and

$$\sum_{k=1}^{r} c_k' v_k = \sum_{j=1}^{r-1} \left(\sum_{k=1}^{j} c_k' \right)(v_j - v_{j+1}) + v_r \sum_{k=1}^{r} c_k',$$

in which $v_j - v_{j+1} \geqslant 0$ and $v_r \geqslant 0$ according to (10.12). This gives the obvious:

Theorem 10.3 If there exists an **a** ($a_s = 0$; $a_i \geqslant 0$, $i \neq s$; $\sum a_i = 1$) that renders

$$\sum_{k=1}^{j} c_k' \geqslant 0 \qquad \text{for } j = 1, 2, \ldots, r,$$

then A_s is dominated. If such an **a** does not exist, then, given only the ranking (10.12), one cannot conclude that A_s is dominated.

10.9 A BOUNDED MEASURE WITH TWO PROSPECTS

Beginning with the ranking (10.4b) for two A_i,

$$v_1 \geqslant v_2 \geqslant \ldots \geqslant v_n \geqslant 0,$$

where each v_k is one of the $V_j(x_j) - V_j(z_j)$ and vice versa, assume that $v_{n-1} > 0$ and let

$$u_k = \frac{v_k}{v_{k-1}}, \qquad k = 2, \ldots, n. \tag{10.13}$$

Then, since

$$u_2 u_3 \ldots u_k = \frac{v_k}{v_1},$$

(10.5) may be rewritten as

$$f(A_1, A_2) = \frac{V(A_1) - V(A_2)}{v_1} = c_1 + \sum_{k=2}^{n} c_k(u_2 u_3 \ldots u_k).$$

From (10.4b) and (10.13) it is clear that $0 \leqslant u_k \leqslant 1$ for $k = 2, \ldots, n$. Suppose that one obtains bounds on the u_k given by

$$\alpha_k \leqslant u_k \leqslant \beta_k, \qquad k = 2, \ldots, n, \tag{10.14}$$

where $0 \leqslant \alpha_k \leqslant \beta_k \leqslant 1$. Letting

$$M(A_1, A_2) = \max f(A_1, A_2) \qquad \text{subject to (10.14),}$$
$$m(A_1, A_2) = \min f(A_1, A_2) \qquad \text{subject to (10.14),}$$

we have:

Theorem 10.4   If $M(A_1, A_2) \leqslant 0$, then $V(A_2) \geqslant V(A_1)$; if $m(A_1, A_2) \geqslant 0$, then $V(A_1) \geqslant V(A_2)$; if $m(A_1, A_2) < 0 < M(A_1, A_2)$ and our only information on the $V_j(x_{ij})$, $i = 1, 2; j = 1, \ldots, n$, is given by (10.4$b$) and (10.14), then the sign of $V(A_1) - V(A_2)$ is indefinite.

To illustrate how the bounds on u_k may be obtained, suppose for definiteness that

$$u_2 = \frac{v_2}{v_1} = \frac{V_1(x_{11}) - V_1(x_{21})}{V_3(x_{23}) - V_3(x_{13})}.$$

Knowing that $V_3(x_{23}) - V_3(x_{13}) \geqslant V_1(x_{11}) - V_1(x_{21})$, write

$$V_3(x_{23}) - V_3(x_{13}) = b[V_1(x_{11}) - V_1(x_{21})],$$

where $b \geqslant 1$.   Then, have the decision maker consider how many times greater his difference in preference between x_{23} and x_{13} is compared to his difference in preference between x_{11} and x_{21}, and have him specify two numbers, say b_1 and b_2 with $1 \leqslant b_1 \leqslant b_2$, such that the interval $[b_1, b_2]$ contains the "true" multiple b.   Then take

$$\alpha_2 = \frac{1}{b_2}, \qquad \beta_2 = \frac{1}{b_1}; \qquad \alpha_2 \leqslant u_2 \leqslant \beta_2.$$

Alternatively, one could proceed as follows.   Let (x_{11}, x_{13}), (x_{21}, x_{23}), and (x_{21}, x_{13}) be three conceptual prospects which contain the same values for the variables $X_2, X_4, \ldots, X_n$; and let (x, p, y) be a hypothetical gamble "yielding" x with probability p or y with probability $1 - p$.   Suppose that the individual can specify two values of p, say p_1 and p_2, with $0 \leqslant p_1 \leqslant p_2 \leqslant 1$, such that

$$(x_{11}, x_{13}) \succsim ((x_{21}, x_{23}), p, (x_{21}, x_{13})) \qquad \text{for all } p \leqslant p_1;$$
$$((x_{21}, x_{23}), p, (x_{21}, x_{13})) \succsim (x_{11}, x_{13}) \qquad \text{for all } p \geqslant p_2.$$

Then, with the usual assumptions for this sort of thing (e.g., the individual's preferences agree with the mathematical expectation interpretation of the gamble as implied by the von Neumann-Morgenstern axioms), we have

$$V_1(x_{11}) + V_3(x_{13}) \geqslant p_1[V_1(x_{21}) + V_3(x_{23})]$$
$$+ (1 - p_1)[V_1(x_{21}) + V_3(x_{13})],$$

which reduces to $u_2 \geqslant p_1$, and

$$p_2[V_1(x_{21}) + V_3(x_{23})] + (1 - p_2)[V_1(x_{21}) + V_3(x_{13})]$$
$$\geqslant V_1(x_{11}) + V_3(x_{13})$$

which reduces to $u_2 \leqslant p_2$. Thus we take $\alpha_2 = p_1$, $\beta_2 = p_2$ as the bounds on u_2.

To compute[11] $M(A_1, A_2)$ and $m(A_1, A_2)$, let

$$f_{n+1} = 0,$$
$$f_j = \max_{\alpha_j \leqslant u_j \leqslant \beta_j} u_j(c_j + f_{j+1}), \qquad j = n, n-1, \ldots, 2,$$

and

$$g_{n+1} = 0,$$
$$g_j = \min_{\alpha_j \leqslant u_j \leqslant \beta_j} u_j(c_j + g_{j+1}), \qquad j = n, n-1, \ldots, 2.$$

Then

$$M(A_1, A_2) = c_1 + f_2,$$
$$m(A_1, A_2) = c_1 + g_2.$$

10.10 ORDERED METRIC ANALYSIS WITH TWO PROSPECTS

Beginning with (10.4*b*),

$$v_1 \geqslant v_2 \geqslant \ldots \geqslant v_n \geqslant 0, \tag{10.4b}$$

this section explains how one can obtain an ordered metric ranking of the v_j, i.e., a ranking of the adjacent differences $v_j - v_{j+1}, j = 1, \ldots, n$, where $v_{n+1} = 0$ according to (10.2), and states what conclusions can be reached with this ranking.

First, suppose we have obtained an ordered metric ranking of the form

$$v_{j_1} - v_{j_1+1} \geqslant v_{j_2} - v_{j_2+1} \geqslant \ldots \geqslant v_{j_n} - v_{j_n+1} \geqslant 0, \tag{10.15}$$

rewritten as

$$w_1 \geqslant w_2 \geqslant \ldots \geqslant w_n \geqslant 0 \tag{10.16}$$

on letting

$$w_k = v_{j_k} - v_{j_k+1}.$$

Then, let s_k be the coefficient of w_k in (10.9), so that

$$s_k = \sum_{\alpha=1}^{j_k} c_\alpha.$$

---

[11] The reasoning of this approach is found in Section 6.4 under the third bounded interval measure.

Then

$$V(A_1) - V(A_2) = \sum_{k=1}^{n} s_k w_k$$

$$= \sum_{j=1}^{n-1} \left(\sum_{k=1}^{j} s_k \right)(w_j - w_{j+1}) + w_n \sum_{k=1}^{n} s_k,$$

which, along with (10.16) allows us:

Theorem 10.5 Given the ranking (10.16) and no additional information about the relative values $V_j(x_{ij})$, $i = 1, 2; j = 1, \ldots, n$,

$$V(A_1) \geqslant V(A_2) \quad \text{if } \sum_{k=1}^{j} s_k \geqslant 0 \quad \text{for } j = 1, 2, \ldots, n;$$

$$V(A_2) \geqslant V(A_1) \quad \text{if } \sum_{k=1}^{j} s_k \leqslant 0 \quad \text{for } j = 1, 2, \ldots, n.$$

Otherwise, the sign of $V(A_1) - V(A_2)$ is indefinite.

Preference Judgments

To obtain the ordered metric ranking (10.15), proceed by a sequence of paired comparisons (with the usual assumptions of connectedness and transitivity). By a given comparison we wish to determine an inequality between, say, $v_\alpha - v_{\alpha+1}$ and $v_\beta - v_{\beta+1}$. For definiteness, suppose $\beta > \alpha$. Two cases of interest present themselves:

1. $\beta > \alpha + 1$.
2. $\beta = \alpha + 1$.

Consider case 1 first. Having set $V_j(z_j) = 0$ for $j = 1, \ldots, n$, with z_j the less desirable value of X_j, let

$$x_j = \text{value of a variable whose relative value is } v_j. \tag{10.17}$$

That is, v_j is the relative value of the more desirable value (x_j) of one of the variables, $j = 1, \ldots, n$. For case 1

$$v_\alpha \geqslant v_{\alpha+1} \geqslant v_\beta \geqslant v_{\beta+1}$$

and $x_\alpha, x_{\alpha+1}, x_\beta, x_{\beta+1}$ are all different. Letting (x_h, x_i) be the conceptual prospect containing x_h and x_i $(h \neq i)$ and the $n - 2$ z_j for the $n - 2$ X_j which differ from the performance variables for x_h and x_i, if

$$(x_\alpha, x_{\beta+1}) \gtrsim (x_{\alpha+1}, x_\beta),$$

then [12]

$$v_\alpha - v_{\alpha+1} \geqslant v_\beta - v_{\beta+1};$$

---

[12] $V(x_\alpha, x_{\beta+1}) = v_\alpha + v_{\beta+1}$, etc.

if
$$(x_{\alpha+1}, x_\beta) \gtrsim (x_\alpha, x_{\beta+1}),$$
then
$$v_\beta - v_{\beta+1} \geqslant v_\alpha - v_{\alpha+1}.$$

Although it may be possible to obtain the complete ranking (10.15) from comparisons of the above type, this will generally not happen and we must consider case 2 where $x_{\alpha+1} = x_\beta$. The above simple comparisons cannot be used for this case since $(x_{\alpha+1}, x_\beta)$ is not defined (and does not make any sense) when $x_{\alpha+1} = x_\beta$. For case 2 begin with

$$v_\alpha \geqslant v_{\alpha+1} \geqslant v_{\alpha+2},$$

with $x_\alpha, x_{\alpha+1}, x_{\alpha+2}$ all different. Our interest lies in comparing $v_\alpha - v_{\alpha+1}$ and $v_{\alpha+1} - v_{\alpha+2}$. With (10.17), let (x_k) be the conceptual prospect containing x_k and the $n - 1$ z_j for the $n - 1$ X_j which differ from the performance variable for x_k.

The most direct way of attaining our end is simply to ask "Is the difference in preference between (x_α) and $(x_{\alpha+1})$ greater than or equal to or less than or equal to the difference in preference between $(x_{\alpha+1})$ and $(x_{\alpha+2})$?" If the answer is "greater than or equal to," then we take $v_\alpha - v_{\alpha+1} \geqslant v_{\alpha+1} - v_{\alpha+2}$, and if the response is "less than or equal to," we take $v_{\alpha+1} - v_{\alpha+2} \geqslant v_\alpha - v_{\alpha+1}$.

A second method for case 2 is to have the individual compare $(x_{\alpha+1})$ and the 50-50 gamble $((x_\alpha), \frac{1}{2}, (x_{\alpha+2}))$. If $(x_{\alpha+1}) \gtrsim ((x_\alpha), \frac{1}{2}, (x_{\alpha+2}))$, then $v_{\alpha+1} - v_{\alpha+2} \geqslant v_\alpha - v_{\alpha+1}$, and if $((x_\alpha), \frac{1}{2}, (x_{\alpha+2})) \gtrsim (x_{\alpha+1})$, then $v_\alpha - v_{\alpha+1} \geqslant v_{\alpha+1} - v_{\alpha+2}$.

Other Possibilities

No attempt will be made to derive an ordered metric ranking from (10.12) to be used in analyzing three or more alternatives for mixed dominance. This could be done by using gambles, for example, but in light of other methods to be presented in the next section, it would be of questionable value. Similarly, we shall not consider a higher ordered metric ranking here.

10.11 SETS OF INEQUALITIES BY SIMPLE COMPARISONS

This section explains a fairly simple but seemingly quite powerful method of analyzing $V(A_1) - V(A_2)$ for sign, using sets of inequalities among the v_j. The basic method for deriving the inequalities is due to Churchman and Ackoff (1954). We shall work with the derived inequalities as such and not attempt (in this section) to attach numerical values to the v_j as they suggested.[13]

---

[13] One method of doing this follows the presentation in Exercise 7 of Chapter 5.

Deriving Sets of Inequalities

We begin with the ordinal ranking for two prospects

$$v_1 \geqslant v_2 \geqslant \ldots \geqslant v_n \geqslant 0. \tag{10.4b}$$

As in (10.17), let x_j denote the value (of a performance variable) whose relative value is $v_j, j = 1, \ldots, n$, and let $(x_j, x_{j+1}, \ldots, x_k)$ be the conceptual prospect containing $x_j, x_{j+1}, \ldots, x_k$ $(k \geqslant j)$ and the $j - 1 + n - k$ z_j corresponding to the $j - 1 + n - k$ performance variables which differ from the performance variables for $x_j, \ldots, x_k$.

The procedure for obtaining the inequalities we shall work with is described as follows:

For each $(x_j), j = 1, \ldots, n$, compare (x_j) successively with (x_{j+1}, x_{j+2}), $(x_{j+1}, x_{j+2}, x_{j+3})$, $(x_{j+1}, x_{j+2}, x_{j+3}, x_{j+4}), \ldots$, until an n_j is determined such that

$$(x_{j+1}, \ldots, x_{n_j}) \gtrsim (x_j) \gtrsim (x_{j+1}, \ldots, x_{n_j-1}), \qquad (j + 2 \leqslant n_j \leqslant n),$$

or until

$$(x_j) \gtrsim (x_{j+1}, x_{j+2}, \ldots, x_n).$$

Setting

$$V_j(z_j) = 0 \qquad \text{for all } j,$$

$$V(x_j, x_{j+1}, \ldots, x_k) = v_j + v_{j+1} + \ldots + v_k,$$

these expressions of preference give rise to the set of inequalities

$$v_2 + v_3 + \ldots + v_{n_1} \geqslant v_1 \geqslant v_2 + v_3 + \ldots + v_{n_1-1} \quad \text{or} \quad v_1 \geqslant v_2 + \ldots + v_n,$$

$$v_3 + v_4 + \ldots + v_{n_2} \geqslant v_2 \geqslant v_3 + v_4 + \ldots + v_{n_2-1} \quad \text{or} \quad v_2 \geqslant v_3 + \ldots + v_n,$$

$$\vdots \tag{10.18}$$

$$v_{j+1} + \ldots + v_{n_j} \geqslant v_j \geqslant v_{j+1} + \ldots + v_{n_j-1} \quad \text{or} \quad v_j \geqslant v_{j+1} + \ldots + v_n,$$

$$\vdots$$

$$v_{n-1} + v_n \geqslant v_{n-2} \geqslant v_{n-1} \qquad\qquad\quad \text{or} \quad v_{n-2} \geqslant v_{n-1} + v_n,$$

$$\qquad\qquad\qquad\qquad\qquad\qquad\qquad\qquad\qquad v_{n-1} \geqslant v_n, \quad v_n \geqslant 0.$$

Method of Equating Coefficients

The treatment of (10.18) is similar to the treatment of sets of inequalities on probabilities in Section 6.6. In summary, each of the

$$K \, (n \leqslant K \leqslant 2n - 2)$$

nonnegative relative value differences from (10.18) is multiplied by an undetermined coefficient and a sum formed as in (10.20) below. This is then set equal to $\sum c_j v_j$; coefficients of each v_j are set equal to one another;

and the resulting set of equations is inspected for a nonnegative or non-positive solution to the a, b, coefficients. In the present context, this procedure is illustrated by the following example.

Suppose we have obtained the following system of inequalities for $n = 7$:

$$v_2 + v_3 + v_4 \geqslant v_1 \geqslant v_2 + v_3,$$

$$v_3 + v_4 \geqslant v_2 \geqslant v_3$$

$$v_4 + v_5 + v_6 + v_7 \geqslant v_3 \geqslant v_4 + v_5 + v_6$$

$$v_4 \geqslant v_5 + v_6 + v_7 \qquad (10.19)$$

$$v_6 + v_7 \geqslant v_5 \geqslant v_6$$

$$v_6 \geqslant v_7$$

$$v_7 \geqslant 0.$$

From these eleven inequalities, write

$$\begin{aligned}
V(A_1) - V(A_2) &= a_1(v_1 - v_2 - v_3) + a_2(v_2 - v_3) \\
&\quad + a_3(v_3 - v_4 - v_5 - v_6) \\
&\quad + a_4(v_4 - v_5 - v_6 - v_7) + a_5(v_5 - v_6) \\
&\quad + a_6(v_6 - v_7) + a_7(v_7) \qquad (10.20) \\
&\quad + b_1(v_2 + v_3 + v_4 - v_1) \\
&\quad + b_2(v_3 + v_4 - v_2) \\
&\quad + b_3(v_4 + v_5 + v_6 + v_7 - v_3) \\
&\quad + b_5(v_6 + v_7 - v_5).
\end{aligned}$$

The first seven terms with coefficients a_1 through a_7 come from the seven right-hand side inequalities, and the last four terms with coefficients b_1, b_2, b_3, and b_5 come from the four left-hand side inequalities. Equating the coefficient of each v_j in (10.20) to c_j gives the following 7 equations in 11 unknowns:

$$a_1 - b_1 = c_1,$$

$$a_2 - a_1 + b_1 - b_2 = c_2,$$

$$a_3 - a_2 - a_1 + b_1 + b_2 - b_3 = c_3,$$

$$a_4 - a_3 + b_1 + b_2 + b_3 = c_4, \qquad (10.21)$$

$$a_5 - a_4 - a_3 + b_3 - b_5 = c_5,$$

$$a_6 - a_5 - a_4 - a_3 + b_3 + b_5 = c_6,$$

$$a_7 - a_6 - a_4 + b_3 + b_5 = c_7.$$

Since all ( ) terms in (10.20) are nonnegative according to (10.19), $V(A_1) \geqslant V(A_2)$ if there exists a solution to the system (10.21) in which all

a's and b's are nonnegative. Similarly, $V(A_2) \geqslant V(A_1)$ if a solution to (10.21) can be found in which all a's and b's are nonpositive. To look for such a solution, rewrite the system (10.21) with a_1 through a_7 on the left-hand side of the equal signs and $b_1, \ldots, b_5$ on the right-hand side.

First, suppose $(c_1, \ldots, c_7) = (1, -1, -1, -1, 1, 1, -1)$. Then, after a small amount of algebraic labor, (10.21) may be rewritten as

$$a_1 = 1 + b_1,$$
$$a_2 = b_2,$$
$$a_3 = b_3,$$
$$a_4 = -1 - b_1 - b_2,$$ (10.22)
$$a_5 = -b_1 - b_2 + b_5,$$
$$a_6 = -2b_1 - 2b_2,$$
$$a_7 = -2 - 3b_1 - 3b_2 - b_3 - b_5.$$

In order to get the a's and b's all of the same sign, it is first necessary to set $a_6 = b_1 = b_2 = 0$ by virtue of the equation $a_6 = -2(b_1 + b_2)$. But $b_1 = b_2 = 0$ imply $a_1 = 1$ and $a_4 = -1$. Since it is impossible to obtain a uniform sign solution to (10.22), the system of inequalities (10.19) does not permit us to conclude either $V(A_1) \geqslant V(A_2)$ or $V(A_2) \geqslant V(A_1)$.

Next, suppose $(c_1, \ldots, c_7) = (1, -1, 1, -1, -1, -1, -1)$. Then (10.21) gives

$$a_1 = 1 + b_1,$$
$$a_2 = b_2,$$
$$a_3 = 2 + b_3,$$
$$a_4 = 1 - b_1 - b_2,$$ (10.23)
$$a_5 = 2 - b_1 - b_2 + b_5,$$
$$a_6 = 4 - 2b_1 - 2b_2,$$
$$a_7 = 4 - 3b_1 - 3b_2 - b_3 - b_5.$$

Setting all the b's equal to zero gives nonnegative a's and we conclude that $V(A_1) \geqslant V(A_2)$.

In general, if n is small (no greater than about 20), it will usually be possible to arrive at a conclusion concerning a set of equations such as (10.23) in a short time, using little more than inspection and common sense. In fact, the major part of the effort of analysis may come just in writing these equations and checking to make sure they are correct. If n is larger than about 20, the analysis of such a set of equations may take a bit more time, but we do not visualize insurmountable difficulties.[14]

[14] Readers familiar with the techniques of linear programming may note that the system (10.18) or any one similar to it may be analyzed by programming methods. However, since we do not believe that these techniques for the problem presented here are as efficient as the methods outlined above, they have been omitted.

Concluding Remarks

In concluding the discussion of independence and certainty, the question is again raised of what to do if the above analysis yields no definite conclusion concerning the sign of $V(A_1) - V(A_2)$. In our opinion, if this happens, then it is probably not worth the effort to try to obtain additional information on the v_j. This opinion is based on two other opinions or "observations." The first of these is that, in order to obtain the system (10.18), the individual is generally required to make some pretty fine discriminatory preference judgments, particularly if n is large, and although he (presumably) has been able to state his preferences in the procedure described at the beginning of this section, he may very likely entertain some doubt concerning the exactness of his preference statements. [If his doubts are strong enough, one could relax that procedure to yield such inequalities as $v_2 + v_3 + v_4 + v_5 + v_6 \geqslant v_1 \geqslant v_2 + v_3$, where the individual is quite sure of his preferences $(x_2, x_3, x_4, x_5, x_6) \gtrsim (x_1) \gtrsim (x_2, x_3)$ but is unable to get any finer bounds such as $(x_2, x_3, x_4, x_5) \gtrsim (x_1) \gtrsim (x_2, x_3, x_4)$ with any degree of certainty. If this relaxation is admitted, the above methods still apply in their entirety.]

Our second observation is that, if the analysis fails to conclude either $V(A_1) \geqslant V(A_2)$ or $V(A_2) \geqslant V(A_1)$, then, relative to other alternatives that have been eliminated by one of the methods described in this chapter, $V(A_1)$ and $V(A_2)$ will be "almost equal."

10.12 BOOLEAN VARIABLES, INDEPENDENCE, AND UNCERTAINTY

In concluding this chapter, we begin the transition from certainty to uncertainty under independence. The substance of this section is due primarily to Churchman and Ackoff (1954), and the formulation presented is, in part, the author's interpretation of their article. In appearance, their formulation and the one given below may not, at first, bear too great a resemblance, but we shall attempt to show that their theory, as it may apply to an individual, is a rather approximate special case of the general theory described in this book. It is also our opinion that, although approximate and special, the "theory" that follows may be a very powerful tool if used properly.

For the purposes of value measurement, we will be concerned with n Boolean (i.e., two-valued) variables $X_1, X_2, \ldots, X_n$. The two values of X_j are taken to be exclusive and exhaustive and will be denoted as z_j and x_j, $j = 1, \ldots, n$, with z_j the less desirable value of X_j and x_j the more desirable value of X_j. In Churchman and Ackoff's formulation, the x_j, $j = 1, 2, \ldots, n$, are called *objectives*; the z_j are not explicitly mentioned.

Letting y_j denote a value of X_j (either x_j or z_j), a consequence will have the form $(y_1, y_2, \ldots, y_n)$, and altogether there are 2^n such consequences. Assuming that the n variables are mutually valuewise independent, we have, as before,

$$V(y_1, y_2, \ldots, y_n) = V_1(y_1) + V_2(y_2) + \ldots + V_n(y_n).$$

As in (10.2), set

$$V_1(z_1) = V_2(z_2) = \ldots = V_n(z_n) = 0,$$

specifying a common origin for the n value functions $V_1, \ldots, V_n$. In the same manner as in Section 10.7 obtain a mixed ranking of the relative values of the n objectives, $x_1, \ldots, x_n$. Letting (x_j) denote the consequence $(z_1, \ldots, z_{j-1}, x_j, z_{j+1}, \ldots, z_n)$, we can, without loss in generality, suppose that

$$(x_1) \gtrsim (x_2) \gtrsim \ldots \gtrsim (x_n) \gtrsim (z_1, \ldots, z_n),$$

so that we have the ranking

$$v_1 \geqslant v_2 \geqslant \ldots \geqslant v_n \geqslant 0,$$

where

$$v_j = V_j(x_j).$$

To obtain measures of the v_j more powerful than the ordinal ranking, any of the methods and resulting measures presented previously in the chapter (when two prospects were under consideration) may be used. Churchman and Ackoff give particular attention to systems of inequalities such as (10.18) and (10.19). They go one step beyond these inequalities by assigning numerical values to the v_j, $j = 1, \ldots, n$, that are consistent with the inequalities. In doing this, the individual is first requested to give rough estimates of the v_j (say, on the basic of setting $v_1 = 1$) in accord with the ordinal ranking, which are then adjusted by using the higher powered inequalities such as (10.19).

It should be mentioned that, in terms used in this book, the n Boolean variables $X_1, \ldots, X_n$, are essentially outcome variables. That is, with a given course of action or strategy, there is generally a positive probability of occurrence for either value of X_j (which probabilities must add to one). If we consider strategies $S_1, S_2, \ldots, S_t$, and let

$$p_{ij} = P(x_j \mid S_i),$$

$$q_{ij} = P(z_j \mid S_i),$$

then

$$p_{ij} + q_{ij} = 1, \qquad i = 1, \ldots, t.$$

In this theory, the expected relative value of S_i, $E(S_i)$, is given by

$$E(S_i) = \sum_{j=1}^{n} p_{ij}v_j, \qquad i = 1, \ldots, t,$$

so that

$$E(S_1) - E(S_2) = \sum_{j=1}^{n} (p_{1j} - p_{2j})v_j,$$

similar to (10.5). If c_j in the previous sections of this chapter, excluding 10.8, is replaced by $p_{1j} - p_{2j}$, then all previous methods and results that applied to $V(A_1) - V(A_2)$ now apply to $E(S_1) - E(S_2)$. Unlike the main case examined in this chapter, the same v_j apply to *all* S_i, $i = 1, \ldots, t$, so that in analyzing for mixed dominance the number of v_j will not increase as additional strategies are brought into the picture.

Since the variables of interest for relative value measurement purposes are essentially outcome variables, action variables enter the picture only in the statements of courses of action and/or strategies and in the resultant effect on the p_{ij}. This is quite similar to Model II discussed in Sections 3.5 and 4.13 [where we had $V(A_i, O_j) = V(O_j)$] with the added feature of independence of outcome variables.

In the illustrations of their method it is clear that many of the two-valued variables X_j are not "naturally" two-valued in basic form but are made so by the formulation. For example, one objective (x_j) may be "to attain at least 6% return on investment." The corresponding z_j would be "to attain less than 6% return on investment." The two "values" x_j and z_j then *define* X_j. It is clear that (under clarification of the time during which return on investment is to be computed), one and only one of these two values will result from a given course of action or strategy. The underlying variable, "return on investment"—call it y—may be viewed as a continuous variable, and, to define x_j and z_j, we partition all the possible values of y into two sets, the one set defining x_j ($y \geqslant .06$), the other set defining z_j ($y < .06$). This amounts to the kind of partitioning of an outcome variable discussed in Section 8.3. The (implicit) assumption that goes along with this type of treatment of an outcome variable is that the value function over the domain of definition of the variable (supposing it to be continuous) is a step function. That is, $V(y)$ is assumed to have a constant magnitude on each part of the partition of y. For y equaling return or investment, $V(y)$ would look as shown in Figure 10.2. In partitioning the values of a variable into two sets such as was done for y in Figure 10.2, particular importance is attached to the point at which the two parts of the partition "meet" (e.g., $y = .06$ in Figure 10.2). The value which divides x_j and z_j is generally taken to be a value which

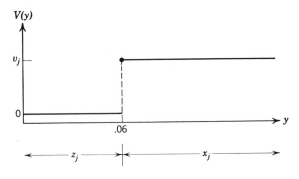

Figure 10.2

represents a "satisfactory achievement" in the eyes of the decision maker (or decision makers). For this reason, the above methods are often referred to as *satisficing* methods. Although some of the x_j may not be particularly well defined for value measurement purposes [e.g., we would expect $V(y)$ to vary over the range given by x_j], it has been found, according to Churchman and Ackoff, that many individuals are able to make value judgments over the x_j with very little difficulty.

EXERCISES[15]

1. Describe several decision situations you have been involved in over the past several years for which you could have used the methods described in this chapter. Comment on whether or not you think application of these methods would have enabled you to arrive at a more satisfactory alternative(s) than you actually selected.

2. Describe a decision situation you expect to face in the near future which may be analyzed by the methods of this chapter. Identify at least six performance variables (and, preferably, at least 20) that you think will be important, and try to give an indication of the relative significance or importance of these with respect to each other. Do you think a reformulation of the performance variables will be required before using the idea of conceptual prospects and independence in obtaining value measures? If so, be specific.

3. For the two alternatives $A_1 = (x_{11}, x_{12}, x_{13}, x_{14}, x_{15}, x_{16})$, $A_2 = (x_{21}, x_{22}, x_{23}, x_{24}, x_{25}, x_{26})$, suppose that the less desirable values of the six performance variables are $(x_{11}, x_{12}, x_{23}, x_{24}, x_{15}, x_{16})$. Let $v_{21}, v_{22}, v_{13}, v_{14}, v_{25}$, and v_{26} be the relative values of the other six values. If a simple mixed ordinal ranking of these relative values is to be obtained, what ordinal rankings (if any) will enable one to conclude that $V(A_1) \geqslant V(A_2)$? On the other hand, what must be true of an ordinal ranking in this situation so that one cannot conclude that $V(A_2) \geqslant V(A_1)$?

[15] Independence of values and the certainty hypothesis are to be assumed unless otherwise stated.

4. Prove the following theorem. Suppose there are n relevant performance variables such that two prospects, A_1 and A_2, differ with respect to each performance variable. Identify the less desirable value of each performance variable and let m be the number of "less desirable values" in A_1 with $n - m$ the number of "less desirable values" in A_2. Then, if $2m < n$, it will be impossible to conclude that $V(A_1) \geqslant V(A_2)$ with a mixed ordinal ranking of relative values.

5. With $n = 7$ and three alternatives, suppose the three values of each performance variable differ with respect to the alternatives. With $A_i = (x_{i1}, x_{i2}, \ldots, x_{i7})$ for $i = 1, 2, 3$, suppose the least desirable values of the seven X_j are $x_{21}, x_{32}, x_{23}, x_{34}, x_{35}, x_{26}$, and x_{27} respectively. [These values are $z_1, z_2, \ldots, z_7$ respectively.] With v_{ij} denoting the relative value of x_{ij}, suppose an ordinal ranking over the values yields $v_{14} \geqslant v_{22} \geqslant v_{37} \geqslant v_{24} \geqslant v_{25} \geqslant v_{31} \geqslant v_{11} \geqslant v_{12} \geqslant v_{13} \geqslant v_{15} \geqslant v_{16} \geqslant v_{33} \geqslant v_{36} \geqslant v_{17} \geqslant v_0$, where v_0 is the common relative value of the seven z_j. Show that it is not possible on the basis of this ranking to discern pure dominance, but that there exists an α with $0 \leqslant \alpha \leqslant 1$ such that one can conclude $\alpha V(A_1) + (1 - \alpha)V(A_2) \geqslant V(A_3)$, and thus that A_3 is dominated.

6. Prove the following theorem. Suppose there are three alternatives which differ with respect to each performance variable. Let n be the number of relevant performance variables. Suppose one has obtained a mixed ordinal ranking of the relative values of the values of the performance variables as described in the procedure above (10.12). If $n \leqslant 5$ and pure dominance (between any two A_i) cannot be determined from the ranking, then it will not be possible to eliminate any A_i on an analysis for mixed dominance. Furthermore, $n = 5$ is the largest value of n for which this holds true.

7. Following the development in Section 10.9, what can you conclude about $V(A_1) - V(A_2)$ for each of the following?

(a) $(c_1, \ldots, c_5) = (-1, -1, 1, 1, 1)$,

$.4 \leqslant u_2 \leqslant .7$, $.8 \leqslant u_3 \leqslant 1.0$, $.2 \leqslant u_4 \leqslant .5$, $.4 \leqslant u_5 \leqslant .6$.

(b) $(c_1, \ldots, c_8) = (1, -1, -1, -1, -1, -1, -1, -1)$,

$.2 \leqslant u_2 \leqslant .5$, $.1 \leqslant u_3 \leqslant .2$, $.5 \leqslant u_4 \leqslant .8$, $.2 \leqslant u_5 \leqslant .4$,

$.7 \leqslant u_6 \leqslant .9$, $.6 \leqslant u_7 \leqslant .8$, $.3 \leqslant u_8 \leqslant .5$.

(c) $(c_1, \ldots, c_6) = (1, 1, -1, -1, -1, -1)$,

$.8 \leqslant u_2 \leqslant .9$, $.7 \leqslant u_3 \leqslant .9$, $.9 \leqslant u_4 \leqslant 1.0$,

$.8 \leqslant u_5 \leqslant .9$, $.9 \leqslant u_6 \leqslant 1.0$.

8. For two prospects and $n = 5$, suppose one has an ordinal ranking like (10.4b) of the form $v_1 \geqslant v_2 \geqslant v_3 \geqslant v_4 \geqslant v_5 \geqslant 0$, where $v_1, \ldots, v_5$ are the relative values of the values $x_{11}, x_{22}, x_{23}, x_{24}, x_{25}$ respectively. Suppose, further, that one has obtained the ordered metric ranking $v_2 - v_3 \geqslant v_3 - v_4 \geqslant v_4 - v_5 \geqslant v_1 - v_2 \geqslant v_5 \geqslant 0$. Show then that $V(A_2) \geqslant V(A_1)$.

Note: Exercises 9 through 15 apply to Section 10.11.

9. Assuming that an individual is capable of expressing a preference between any (x_j) and $(x_r, \ldots, x_s)$ with $r, \ldots, s$ all greater than j, develop a stepwise procedure for obtaining finer bounds on the v_j than those given by the procedure that led to the system (10.18). [*Hint:* Consider (x_1). If $(x_2, x_3) \gtrsim (x_1)$, compare (x_1) with (x_2, x_4), and so forth.]

10. Analyze the following triangular sets of inequalities by the method of equating coefficients, and state your conclusion for each set [i.e., whether $V(A_1) \geqslant V(A_2)$, etc.].

(a) $(c_1, \ldots, c_7) = (-1, 1, 1, -1, -1, 1, 1)$.

$$
\begin{aligned}
v_1 - v_2 - v_3 - v_4 - v_5 \quad &\geqslant 0, \\
- v_2 + v_3 + v_4 \quad &\geqslant 0, \\
v_3 - v_4 \quad &\geqslant 0, \\
v_4 - v_5 - v_6 - v_7 &\geqslant 0, \\
v_5 - v_6 \quad &\geqslant 0, \\
v_6 - v_7 &\geqslant 0, \\
v_7 &\geqslant 0.
\end{aligned}
$$

(b) $(c_1, \ldots, c_8) = (-1, 1, 1, -1, -1, 1, -1, -1)$.

$$
\begin{aligned}
-v_1 + v_2 \quad + v_4 \quad\quad\quad + v_8 &\geqslant 0, \\
v_2 - v_3 - v_4 \quad\quad &\geqslant 0, \\
v_3 \quad - v_5 \quad - v_7 \quad &\geqslant 0, \\
- v_4 \quad + v_6 + v_7 + v_8 &\geqslant 0, \\
v_5 - v_6 \quad\quad &\geqslant 0, \\
v_6 - v_7 - v_8 &\geqslant 0, \\
v_7 - v_8 &\geqslant 0, \\
v_8 &\geqslant 0.
\end{aligned}
$$

(c) $(c_1, \ldots, c_7) = (1, -1, -1, -1, -1, -1, 1)$.

$$
\begin{aligned}
v_1 - v_2 - v_3 - v_4 - v_5 - v_6 \quad &\geqslant 0, \\
v_2 \quad &\geqslant 0, \\
v_3 \quad &\geqslant 0, \\
v_4 \quad &\geqslant 0, \\
v_5 \quad &\geqslant 0, \\
v_6 \quad &\geqslant 0, \\
v_7 &\geqslant 0.
\end{aligned}
$$

11. Develop a simple algorithm for analyzing triangular sets of inequalities like those in Exercise 10 in trying to determine the sign of $V(A_1) - V(A_2)$.

12. Prove the theorem: Given ($10.4b$), if $v_1 \geq v_2 + v_3 + \ldots + v_n$ or if $c_1 = c_2$ and $v_2 \geq v_3 + v_4 + \ldots + v_{n-1}$, then $V(A_1) \geq V(A_2)$ if $c_1 = 1$ and $V(A_2) \geq V(A_1)$ if $c_1 = -1$.

13. Analyze the following systems of inequalities to see if you can conclude either $V(A_1) \geq V(A_2)$ or $V(A_2) \geq V(A_1)$.

(a) $(c_1, \ldots, c_8) = (1, -1, 1, 1, -1, -1, -1, -1)$.

$$v_2 + v_3 \geq v_1 \geq v_2$$
$$v_3 + v_4 + v_5 + v_6 \geq v_2 \geq v_3 + v_4 + v_5$$
$$v_4 + v_5 \geq v_3 \geq v_4$$
$$v_5 + v_6 \geq v_4 \geq v_5$$
$$v_6 + v_7 + v_8 \geq v_5 \geq v_6 + v_7$$
$$v_7 + v_8 \geq v_6 \geq v_7$$
$$v_7 \geq v_8$$
$$v_8 \geq 0.$$

(b) $(c_1, c_2, \ldots, c_6) = (1, -1, -1, 1, -1, -1)$.

$$v_2 + v_3 \geq v_1 \geq v_2$$
$$v_3 + v_4 + v_5 + v_6 \geq v_2 \geq v_3 + v_4 + v_5$$
$$v_4 + v_5 + v_6 \geq v_3 \geq v_4 + v_5$$
$$v_5 + v_6 \geq v_4 \geq v_5$$
$$v_5 \geq v_6$$
$$v_6 \geq 0.$$

14. What justification does the author have for asserting, "... the system of inequalities (10.19) does not permit us to conclude either $V(A_1) \geq V(A_2)$ or $V(A_2) \geq V(A_1)$," in the paragraph above (10.23)?

15. Prove that there is no nonpositive solution to (10.23) by using only the equations given in (10.23).

16. In connection with the Boolean variable model of Section 10.12, suppose p_{1j} and p_{2j}, $j = 1, \ldots, 8$, have been estimated as follows:

		\multicolumn{8}{c}{j}
		1	2	3	4	5	6	7	8
i	1	.8	.1	.7	.6	.5	.3	1.0	.2
	2	.4	.4	.9	.5	.2	.8	.8	.1

State what you can about the sign of $E(S_1) - E(S_2)$, given the information on the v_j, $j = 1, \ldots, 8$, contained in:

(a) Exercise 7b.
(b) Exercise 10b.
(c) Exercise 13a.

REFERENCES

Ackoff, R. L., with S. K. Gupta and J. S. Minas, *Scientific Method: Optimizing Applied Research Decisions*, John Wiley and Sons, New York, 1962.

Churchman, C. W., and R. L. Ackoff, "An Approximate Measure of Value", *Operations Research*, 2, 172–187 (1954).

Chapter 11

INDEPENDENCE AND UNCERTAINTY

In this penultimate chapter, we shall consider the general decision model under independence of variables in the relative value sense, the models in the previous chapter being special cases of Model IV presented in the following. Model IV is itself a special case of Model I.

11.1 MODEL IV

The groundwork for Model IV was laid in Sections 9.4 and 9.5. For our general model under independence, there are m mutually valuewise independent variables

$$Y_1, Y_2, \ldots, Y_m,$$

where some of the Y_j may be action variables, others may be outcome variables, and still others may be mixed variables.[1] The elements of Y_j will be denoted y_j or $y_{j0}, y_{j1}, \ldots, y_{jn_j}$. That is,

$$Y_j = \{y_{j0}, y_{j1}, \ldots, y_{jn_j}\}, \qquad j = 1, \ldots, m.$$

The assumption of independence states that

$$V(y_1, y_2, \ldots, y_m) = V_1(y_1) + V_2(y_2) + \ldots + V_m(y_m),$$

where $V_1, \ldots, V_m$ are m value functions with arbitrary origins and a common metric. V_j is the value function defined on Y_j.

Subscript Conventions

Throughout this chapter the following two subscript conventions will be used:

[1] See Section 2.4 for definitions of these terms.

1. For each Y_j, the $n_j + 1$ values of Y_j will be labeled $y_{j0}, y_{j1}, \ldots, y_{jn_j}$, where

$$V_j(y_{j1}) \geqslant V_j(y_{j2}) \geqslant \ldots \geqslant V_j(y_{jn_j}) \geqslant V_j(y_{j0}).$$

2. The variables Y_j will be numbered so that

$$V_1(y_{11}) - V_1(y_{10}) \geqslant V_2(y_{21}) - V_2(y_{20})$$
$$\geqslant V_3(y_{31}) - V_3(y_{30}) \geqslant \ldots \geqslant V_m(y_{m1}) - V_m(y_{m0}) \geqslant 0. \quad (11.1)$$

According to (1), y_{j1} is the most desirable value of Y_j, and y_{j0} is the least desirable value of Y_j. According to (2), the variable Y_1 has the largest relative value difference between its most desirable and least desirable values, the variable Y_2 has the next largest relative value difference between its most and least desirable values, ..., and Y_m has the smallest relative value difference between its most desirable and least desirable values.

Letting

$$v_{jk} = V_j(y_{jk}), \qquad j = 1, \ldots, m; \quad k = 0, 1, \ldots, n_j,$$

the m ordinal rankings in (1) are

$$v_{11} \geqslant v_{12} \geqslant v_{13} \geqslant \ldots \geqslant v_{1n_1} \geqslant v_{10},$$
$$v_{21} \geqslant v_{22} \geqslant v_{23} \geqslant \ldots \geqslant v_{2n_2} \geqslant v_{20},$$
$$\vdots \qquad\qquad\qquad\qquad\qquad\qquad (11.2)$$
$$v_{m1} \geqslant v_{m2} \geqslant v_{m3} \geqslant \ldots \geqslant v_{mn_m} \geqslant v_{m0},$$

and the ranking (11.1) is

$$v_{11} - v_{10} \geqslant v_{21} - v_{20} \geqslant \ldots \geqslant v_{m1} - v_{m0} \geqslant 0. \quad (11.3)$$

In making the above subscript conventions, it is assumed that the individual is able to render the value judgments required to give (11.2) and (11.3). The types of preference statements required for these should be clear by this point. As noted in Chapter 9, the values of a variable will often exhibit a natural order similar to the preference ordering over those values. If a given variable Y_j is the product of two or more non-independent variables, the ordinal relative value ranking over the values of Y_j may be more difficult to obtain. The ranking (11.3) may be obtained either by direct reference to a comparison of the differences in preference between the most and least desirable values of the variables or by comparing consequences which differ only in two variables. For example, $v_{11} - v_{10} \geqslant v_{21} - v_{20}$ could come from $(y_{11}, y_{20}) \gtrsim (y_{10}, y_{21})$, where (y_{11}, y_{20}) and (y_{10}, y_{21}) are any two consequences which have the indicated values of Y_1 and Y_2 and agree with one another in the values of the other $m - 2$ variables.

As before, for the sake of convenience, set

$$v_{10} = v_{20} = \ldots = v_{m0} = 0 \tag{11.4}$$

to specify the interconnection of the m value functions. With (11.4), (11.3) may be rewritten as

$$v_{11} \geqslant v_{21} \geqslant \ldots \geqslant v_{m1} \geqslant 0. \tag{11.5}$$

$E(S_i)$ *for Model IV*

In the decision situation let $S_1, \ldots, S_t$ be the admissible strategies (**S**) of concern, and let $E(S_i)$ be the relative value of strategy S_i. Then

$$E(S_i) = \sum_{j=1}^{m} \sum_{k=1}^{n_j} p_{jk}^i v_{jk}$$

$$= \sum_{k=1}^{n_1} p_{1k}^i v_{1k} + \sum_{k=1}^{n_2} p_{2k}^i v_{2k} + \ldots + \sum_{k=1}^{n_m} p_{mk}^i v_{mk}, \tag{11.6}$$

where

$$p_{jk}^i = P(y_{jk} \mid S_i), \quad \text{for all } i, j, k. \tag{11.7}$$

In order that the S_i be properly defined, we require

$$\sum_{k=0}^{n_j} p_{jk}^i = 1, \quad i = 1, \ldots, t; \quad j = 1, \ldots, m.$$

Since v_{j0} has been set equal to zero and, therefore, does not appear in (11.6), p_{j0}^i does not appear in (11.6). Since

$$p_{j0}^i + \sum_{k=1}^{n_j} p_{jk}^i = 1,$$

$$\sum_{k=1}^{n_j} p_{jk}^i \leqslant 1,$$

so that the p_{jk}^i for fixed i and j that appear explicitly in (11.6) need not add to 1. In fact, it may happen that $\sum_{k=1}^{n_j} p_{jk}^i = 0$ (if $p_{j0}^i = 1$).

As has been the case throughout this book, our primary interest lies in determining an $S_i \in \mathbf{S}$ that has an expected relative value at least as great as the expected relative value of any other $S_i \in \mathbf{S}$.

Probabilities

In making the assumption of independence, if it is a reasonably good assumption, not only will less effort and expense be involved in measuring relative values but also it will probably be much easier to make or obtain estimates of the probabilities. Instead of having to work with joint probability functions (n-dimensional, where n may equal 10 to 20 in some cases), under independence (valuewise, not stochastic) we are concerned only with marginal probability functions as in (11.7). In order to estimate the p_{jk}^i, there is generally no need to go back to the basic joint function to find p_{jk}^i from a sum as in (9.15).

In much of this chapter we will act as if acceptable estimates of the p_{jk}^i have been obtained, although in Section 11.7 a bounded measure of the p_{jk}^i is considered. For some of the Y_j that are action variables (if there be any), certain of the p_{jk}^i may equal 1. For all outcome variables, most of the p_{jk}^i will be strictly between 0 and 1. It may be noted that there will generally be many more probabilities to estimate than relative values. Although the same set of relative values $\{v_{jk}\}, j = 1, \ldots, m; k = 0, 1, \ldots, n_j$, applies to every strategy, each strategy S_i has its own set of probabilities $\{p_{jk}^i\}, j = 1, \ldots, m; k = 0, 1, \ldots, n_j$.

In estimating the p_{jk}^i for a fixed i and j, it may be advantageous to use other probabilities in making these estimates. As an example, suppose Y_4 is the first variable, in terms of the passage of time, to have its value determined. Let Y_4 be an action variable whose value is uniquely specified, given strategy S_1, and suppose that $p_{43}^1 = 1$, i.e., $P(y_{43} \mid S_1) = 1$. Suppose then that Y_2 is the next variable to have its value determined on the time scale, and that Y_2 is an outcome variable with

$$p_{2k}^1 = P(y_{2k} \mid y_{43}, S_1).$$

Next, let Y_6 be an action variable whose value, given S_1, depends upon the value taken by Y_2. To keep things simple, suppose $n_2 = 2, n_6 = 1$, and that, given S_1, y_{60} is adopted if y_{20} results and y_{61} is adopted if either y_{21} or y_{22} occurs. Then

$$p_{60}^1 = p_{20}^1, \qquad p_{61}^1 = p_{21}^1 + p_{22}^1 = 1 - p_{20}^1.$$

Our next variable to have its value determined will be, say, Y_1, an outcome variable. For Y_1 it may be advantageous to consider first the conditional probability distributions

$$P(y_{1k} \mid y_{60}, S_1), \qquad k = 0, 1, \ldots, n_1,$$

and

$$P(y_{1k} \mid y_{61}, S_1), \qquad k = 0, 1, \ldots, n_1,$$

and then to use

$$p_{1k}^1 = p_{60}^1 P(y_{1k} \mid y_{60}, S_1) + p_{61}^1 P(y_{1k} \mid y_{61}, S_1)$$
$$= p_{20}^1 P(y_{1k} \mid y_{60}, S_1) + (1 - p_{20}^1) P(y_{1k} \mid y_{61}, S_1), \qquad k = 0, \ldots, n_1.$$

Many readers will realize that a decision situation of the type just described in part might be advantageously formulated and dealt with in the fashion of dynamic programming. Since such situations are quite common, most of the final chapter will be devoted to consideration of the time-sequential decision process under independence and conditional independence of relative values. If the stochastic process which describes the occurrence of events of interest over time is Markovian in nature, our task becomes quite a bit easier.

Some Special Cases of Model IV

The model given by (11.6), dubbed *Model IV*, has a number of special cases which may be of interest in their own right. For example, going back to earlier notation, suppose that each strategy is identical to a prescriptive course of action $A_i \in \mathbf{A}$. Writing the consequences as ordered pairs of descriptive courses of action and outcomes, (A_i, O_j), with $A_i \in \mathbf{A}$, $O_j \in \mathbf{O}$, consider the situation where the courses of action and outcomes are valuewise independent, say,

$$V(A_i, O_j) = W(A_i) + U(O_j), \qquad (11.8)$$

where W is a value function on $\mathbf{A}$, U is a value function on $\mathbf{O}$, and W and U have a common unit measurement. Using (11.8), the expected value of course of action A_i may be written

$$E(A_i) = W(A_i) + \sum_{O_j \in \mathbf{O}} P(O_j \mid A_i)U(O_j). \qquad (11.9)$$

Obviously $E(A_1) \geqslant E(A_2)$ if $W(A_1) \geqslant W(A_2)$ and if

$$\sum_{O_j \in \mathbf{O}} [P(O_j \mid A_1) - P(O_j \mid A_2)]U(O_j) \geqslant 0.$$

The methods of Chapters 6 and 7 as they apply to Model I may be used for comparing the $\sum P(O_j \mid A_i)U(O_j)$, since this sum is essentially the form found in Model I. If the outcome variables can be partitioned into a set of mutually valuewise independent variables, then the methods of this chapter are applicable in comparing the $\sum P(O_j \mid A_i)U(O_j)$ for the various A_i.

Comparisons of the $W(A_i)$ in (11.9) may be made directly, or, if this is too difficult and the action variables can be partitioned into a set of mutually (valuewise) independent variables, then the methods of Chapter 10 may be used to compare the $W(A_i)$.

If the strategies contain conditional phrases (and thus are more general than prescriptive courses of action) and if (11.8) holds, then in place of (11.9) we have

$$E(S_i) = \sum_{A_k \in \mathbf{A}} P(A_k \mid S_i)W(A_k) + \sum_{O_j \in \mathbf{O}} P(O_j \mid S_i)U(O_j), \qquad (11.10)$$

where

$$\sum_{A_k \in \mathbf{A}} P(A_k \mid S_i) = 1, \qquad \sum_{O_j \in \mathbf{O}} P(O_j \mid S_i) = 1$$

for each $S_i \in \mathbf{S}$. Hence, the methods of Chapters 6 and 7 as they apply to

Model I may be used in comparing the $\sum P(A_k \mid S_i)W(A_k)$ for the various S_i and in comparing the $\sum P(O_j \mid S_i)U(O_j)$ for the various strategies. If one finds it necessary to obtain a combined analysis of the two terms on the right-hand side of (11.10)—as will usually be the case—then the methods of this chapter are applicable. The models given by (11.9) and (11.10) are, of course, special cases of (11.6) since (11.9) or (11.10) can be expressed in the form

$$E(S_i) = \sum_{j=1}^{2} \sum_{k=1}^{n_j} p_{jk}^i v_{jk}.$$

Values of Variables and Partitions

In the general model under independence, it is desirable, if possible, to keep the n_j, $j = 1, \ldots, m$, fairly small for the purposes of making comparative judgments and estimating probabilities. The extreme in this sense was illustrated in Section 10.12, where for each outcome variable we took $n_j = 1$ (i.e., $n_j + 1 = 2$, giving 2 values for each outcome variable). For practical purposes, it is desirable to have n_j less than about 6 or 7. With n_j no more than about 6, it should be possible to obtain some fairly powerful measures of relative values for each variable under consideration. If separate value measures are first obtained for each independent variable, we may then "tie these together" by considering a value measure which includes values of all the different variables. One way of doing this is presented in the next two sections. Following that, measures interconnecting all the v_{ij} are considered.

In attempting to keep the n_j small, we will quite often be dealing with approximations brought on by the formulation. For example, some of the variables considered may naturally be continuous variables whose ranges are partitioned to give the y_{jk}. For practical reasons, such treatment, though approximate, may be entirely satisfactory in the decision situation under consideration. Nevertheless, in Section 11.6, analysis with partitions of the type discussed in Section 8.3 will be presented.

A Simple Case of Analysis

Before going on to other value measures, we note that it may be possible to determine the sign of, say, $E(S_1) - E(S_2)$, with only the ordinal rankings given by (11.2). From (11.6),

$$E(S_1) - E(S_2) = \sum_{j=1}^{m} \sum_{k=1}^{n_j} (p_{jk}^1 - p_{jk}^2)v_{jk}, \tag{11.11}$$

which, using Abel's summation identity, becomes

$$E(S_1) - E(S_2) = \sum_{j=1}^{m} \sum_{k=1}^{n_j} \left[\sum_{v=1}^{k} (p_{jv}^1 - p_{jv}^2) \right](v_{jk} - v_{j,k+1}) \tag{11.12}$$

on letting $v_{j,n_j+1} = v_{j0}$. Since $v_{jk} - v_{j,k+1} \geqslant 0$ for all j, k according to (11.2),

$$E(S_1) \geqslant E(S_2) \quad \text{if} \quad \sum_{v=1}^{k} (p_{jv}^1 - p_{jv}^2) \geqslant 0$$

$$\text{for } j = 1, \ldots, m, \ k = 1, \ldots, n_j;$$

$$E(S_2) \geqslant E(S_1) \quad \text{if} \quad \sum_{v=1}^{k} (p_{jv}^1 - p_{jv}^2) \leqslant 0$$

$$\text{for } j = 1, \ldots, m, \ k = 1, \ldots, n_j.$$

It is also possible to tie in the ranking (11.5) along with those in (11.2), and to make maximal use of the resulting $m + 1$ rankings in analyzing (11.11) for sign.[2]

11.2 AN ANALYSIS WITH BOUNDED INTERVAL MEASURES, I

This section discusses bounded interval measures of the type presented in Section 10.9 for each variable considered separately, and then for the most and least desirable values of all m variables to give an interconnection among the separate value functions. This is one of the easier value measures to derive and may also be one of the more powerful. The next section considers a similar approach by using a slightly different bounded interval measure, similar in form to the second bounded interval measure in Section 4.8.

Bounded Interval Measures for Each Y_j

Beginning with (11.2) and (11.4), let

$$u_{jk} = \frac{v_{jk} - v_{j0}}{v_{j,k-1} - v_{j0}} = \frac{v_{jk}}{v_{j,k-1}}, \quad j = 1, \ldots, m; \ k = 2, \ldots, n_j.$$

$$(11.13)$$

For a fixed j, the bounded interval measure for Y_j is given by

$$\alpha_{jk} \leqslant u_{jk} \leqslant \beta_{jk}, \quad k = 2, \ldots, n_j, \quad (11.14)$$

where $0 \leqslant \alpha_{jk} \leqslant \beta_{jk} \leqslant 1$. To obtain α_{jk} and β_{jk} for a given j and k, one may try several methods, similar to those in Section 10.9. First, we may have the decision maker consider how many times greater his difference in preference between $y_{j,k-1}$ and y_{j0} is compared to his difference in preference between y_{jk} and y_{j0}, and then have him specify two numbers, say b_1 and b_2 with $1 \leqslant b_1 \leqslant b_2$, that bound the "true" multiple and give

[2] See Exercise 1.

b_1 [difference in preference between y_{jk} and y_{j0}]

$\leqslant$ [difference in preference between $y_{j,k-1}$ and y_{j0}]

$\leqslant b_2$ [difference in preference between y_{jk} and y_{j0}]

or

$$b_1(v_{jk} - v_{j0}) \leqslant (v_{j,k-1} - v_{j0}) \leqslant b_2(v_{jk} - v_{j0}), \qquad (11.15)$$

or

$$\frac{1}{b_2} \leqslant u_{jk} \leqslant \frac{1}{b_1}.$$

By this method $\alpha_{jk} = 1/b_2$ and $\beta_{jk} = 1/b_1$. The individual should try to make b_1 and b_2 as close as possible while still feeling sure that (11.15) holds.

A second method for obtaining α_{jk} and β_{jk} uses the comparison of (y_{jk}) with the gamble $((y_{j,k-1}), p, (y_{j0}))$, where (y_{jk}), $(y_{j,k-1})$, and (y_{j0}) are three consequences (or pseudoconsequences) which differ only in the value of Y_j. Letting p_1 denote a value of p for which the decision maker feels certain that $(y_{jk}) \gtrsim ((y_{j,k-1}), p, (y_{j0}))$, we get

$$v_{jk} \geqslant p_1 v_{j,k-1} + (1 - p_1)v_{j0}$$

or

$$u_{jk} \geqslant p_1.$$

Similarly, letting p_2 denote a value of p for which the individual feels certain that $((y_{j,k-1}), p, (y_{j0})) \gtrsim (y_{jk})$, we get

$$p_2 v_{j,k-1} + (1 - p_2)v_{j0} \geqslant v_{jk},$$

or

$$u_{jk} \leqslant p_2.$$

In this method, $\alpha_{jk} = p_1$ and $\beta_{jk} = p_2$, assuming, of course, that $p_1 \leqslant p_2$. It is desirable to have p_1 and p_2 close together.

Initial Bounds on $E(S_1) - E(S_2)$

With $E(S_i)$ given by (11.6), consider the difference in the expected relative values of two strategies, S_1 and S_2:

$$E(S_1) - E(S_2) = \sum_{k=1}^{n_1} (p_{1k}^1 - p_{1k}^2)v_{1k} \qquad (11.11)$$

$$+ \sum_{k=1}^{n_2} (p_{2k}^1 - p_{2k}^2)v_{2k} + \ldots + \sum_{k=1}^{n_m} (p_{mk}^1 - p_{mk}^2)v_{mk}.$$

With u_{jk} given by (11.13), let $u_{j1} = 1$ for $j = 1, \ldots, m$. Then, as the reader may readily verify,

$$E(S_1) - E(S_2) = v_{11} \sum_{k=1}^{n_1} (p_{1k}^1 - p_{1k}^2) \prod_{v=1}^{k} u_{1v}$$

$$+ v_{21} \sum_{k=1}^{n_2} (p_{2k}^1 - p_{2k}^2) \prod_{v=1}^{k} u_{2v} + \ldots \qquad (11.16)$$

$$+ v_{m1} \sum_{k=1}^{n_m} (p_{mk}^1 - p_{mk}^2) \prod_{v=1}^{k} u_{mv}.$$

Now let

$$h_j = \min_{\{\alpha_{jk} \leqslant u_{jk} \leqslant \beta_{jk}\}} \sum_{k=1}^{n_j} (p_{jk}^1 - p_{jk}^2) \prod_{v=1}^{k} u_{jv}, \qquad (11.17a)$$

$$H_j = \max_{\{\alpha_{jk} \leqslant u_{jk} \leqslant \beta_{jk}\}} \sum_{k=1}^{n_j} (p_{jk}^1 - p_{jk}^2) \prod_{v=1}^{k} u_{jv}, \qquad (11.17b)$$

where h_j and H_j are computed in the same manner as in Section 10.9. Specifically, letting

$$f_{j,n_j+1} = 0,$$
$$f_{jk} = \max_{\alpha_{jk} \leqslant u_{jk} \leqslant \beta_{jk}} u_{jk}(p_{jk}^1 - p_{jk}^2 + f_{j,k+1}), \qquad k = n_j, \ldots, 2,$$

and

$$g_{j,n_j+1} = 0,$$
$$g_{jk} = \min_{\alpha_{jk} \leqslant u_{jk} \leqslant \beta_{jk}} u_{jk}(p_{jk}^1 - p_{jk}^2 + g_{j,k+1}), \qquad k = n_j, \ldots, 2,$$

we get

$$h_j = p_{j1}^1 - p_{j1}^2 + g_{j2}, \qquad j = 1, \ldots, m,$$
$$H_j = p_{j1}^1 - p_{j1}^2 + f_{j2}, \qquad j = 1, \ldots, m.$$

Then, from (11.16), (11.17a), and (11.17b),

$$\sum_{j=1}^{m} h_j v_{j1} \leqslant E(S_1) - E(S_2) \leqslant \sum_{j=1}^{m} H_j v_{j1}. \qquad (11.18)$$

A Bounded Interval Measure for the v_{j1}

We now obtain a bounded interval measure with the $v_{j1}, j = 1, \ldots, m,$ and use this to complete the analysis. Let

$$u_1 = 1,$$

$$u_j = \frac{v_{j1} - v_{j0}}{v_{j-1,1} - v_{j-1,0}} = \frac{v_{j1}}{v_{j-1,1}}, \qquad j = 2, \ldots, m, \qquad (11.19)$$

having set $v_{j0} = 0$ for all j in (11.4). By the ranking (11.3) or (11.5),

$0 \leqslant u_j \leqslant 1$ for all j. Our bounded interval measure of the u_j may be written

$$\alpha_j \leqslant u_j \leqslant \beta_j, \qquad j = 2, \ldots, m, \tag{11.20}$$

where $0 \leqslant \alpha_j \leqslant \beta_j \leqslant 1$. This measure of relative value gives the desired interconnection among the m value functions for the m variables. The bounds on the u_j are obtained either by directly comparing $(v_{j1} - v_{j0})$ and $(v_{j-1,1} - v_{j-1,0})$ or by using gambles as follows. Let $(y_{j-1,0}, y_{j1})$, $(y_{j-1,1}, y_{j0})$, and $(y_{j-1,0}, y_{j0})$ be three consequences which differ only in their values for Y_{j-1} and Y_j. Then, let α_j be a value of p for which the individual is sure that $(y_{j-1,0}, y_{j1}) \gtrsim ((y_{j-1,1}, y_{j0}), p, (y_{j-1,0}, y_{j0}))$, so that

$$v_{j-1,0} + v_{j1} \geqslant \alpha_j v_{j-1,1} + \alpha_j v_{j0} + (1 - \alpha_j)v_{j-1,0} + (1 - \alpha_j)v_{j0},$$

or

$$u_j \geqslant \alpha_j.$$

Similarly, let β_j be a value of p for which the individual is sure that $((y_{j-1,1}, y_{j0}), p, (y_{j-1,0}, y_{j0})) \gtrsim (y_{j-1,0}, y_{j1})$, giving

$$u_j \leqslant \beta_j.$$

Completing The Analysis

From the definition of u_j in (11.19),

$$\sum_{j=1}^{m} h_j v_{j1} = v_{11} \sum_{j=1}^{m} h_j \prod_{k=1}^{j} u_k,$$

$$\sum_{j=1}^{m} H_j v_{j1} = v_{11} \sum_{j=1}^{m} H_j \prod_{k=1}^{j} u_k,$$

so that, from (11.18),

$$\min_{\{\alpha_j \leqslant u_j \leqslant \beta_j\}} \sum_{j=1}^{m} h_j \prod_{k=1}^{j} u_k \leqslant \frac{E(S_1) - E(S_2)}{v_{11}} \leqslant \max_{\{\alpha_j \leqslant u_j \leqslant \beta_j\}} \sum_{j=1}^{m} H_j \prod_{k=1}^{j} u_k.$$

Let

$$m(S_1, S_2) = \min \sum_{j=1}^{m} h_j \prod_{k=1}^{j} u_k, \tag{11.21}$$

$$M(S_1, S_2) = \max \sum_{j=1}^{m} H_j \prod_{k=1}^{j} u_k. \tag{11.22}$$

Then, with

$$f_{m+1} = 0,$$

$$f_j = \max_{\alpha_j \leqslant u_j \leqslant \beta_j} u_j(H_j + f_{j+1}), \qquad j = m, m-1, \ldots, 2,$$

and
$$g_{m+1} = 0,$$
$$g_j = \min_{\alpha_j \leqslant u_j \leqslant \beta_j} u_j(h_j + g_{j+1}), \qquad j = m, m - 1, \ldots, 2,$$
$$m(S_1, S_2) = h_1 + g_2,$$
$$M(S_1, S_2) = H_1 + f_2.$$

Finally, we arrive at:

Theorem 11.1 Given the bounded interval measures (11.14) and (11.20) and no additional information on the v_{jk}, $E(S_1) \geqslant E(S_2)$ if $m(S_1, S_2) \geqslant 0$; $E(S_2) \geqslant E(S_1)$ if $M(S_1, S_2) \leqslant 0$; otherwise, if $m(S_1, S_2) < 0 < M(S_1, S_2)$, the sign of $E(S_1) - E(S_2)$ is indeterminate.

In finding the extrema $m(S_1, S_2)$ and $M(S_1, S_2)$, we have gone through a two-step process, first minimizing and maximizing with respect to the separate bounded interval measures for the m variables as in (11.17a) and (11.17b), then "minimizing with the minima" and "maximizing with the maxima" with the interconnecting bounded interval measure (11.20) as in (11.21) and (11.22). This whole process may be expressed by a single equation. According to the definitions of u_{jk} and u_j in (11.13) and (11.19), we may write, beginning with (11.16),

$$f(S_1, S_2) = \frac{E(S_1) - E(S_2)}{v_{11}} = \sum_{j=1}^{m} \left[\sum_{k=1}^{n_j} (p_{jk}^1 - p_{jk}^2) \prod_{v=1}^{k} u_{jv} \right] \prod_{\alpha=1}^{j} u_\alpha.$$
(11.23)

Then
$$m(S_1, S_2) = \min f(S_1, S_2)$$
subject to
$$u_{11} = u_{21} = \ldots = u_{m1} = u_1 = 1;$$
$$\alpha_{jk} \leqslant u_{jk} \leqslant \beta_{jk} \quad \text{for} \quad j = 1, \ldots, m; k = 2, \ldots, n_j;$$
$$\alpha_j \leqslant u_j \leqslant \beta_j \quad \text{for} \quad j = 2, \ldots, m,$$

and $M(S_1, S_2) = \max f(S_1, S_2)$, subject to the same restrictions given for $m(S_1, S_2)$.

Approximate Numerical Measure of Values

If desired, an approximate numerical measure for the v_{jk} may be obtained by assigning v_{11} any number > 0, say $v_{11} = 1$, and by estimating the u_{jk} and the u_j as $\bar{u}_{jk}$ and $\bar{u}_j$ respectively, where

$$\bar{u}_{jk} = \frac{\alpha_{jk} + \beta_{jk}}{2}, \qquad j = 1, \ldots, m; \ k = 2, \ldots, n_j, \qquad (11.24)$$

$$\bar{u}_j = \frac{\alpha_j + \beta_j}{2}, \qquad j = 2, \ldots, m. \qquad (11.25)$$

The heuristic reasoning for estimating u_{jk} or u_j as the mid-points between the bounds on these ratios of relative value differences is simply that inside the intervals $[\alpha_{jk}, \beta_{jk}]$ or $[\alpha_j, \beta_j]$ the individual is in doubt about his preferences whereas outside these intervals he is not.[3] We might have some cause to expect that, roughly at the mid-point of the interval $[\alpha_{jk}, \beta_{jk}]$, the individual will be most in doubt about which way his preference swings, and such a mid-point may therefore be viewed "like a point of indifference."

Since

$$\frac{v_{j1}}{v_{11}} = u_2 u_3 \ldots u_j, \qquad j = 2, \ldots, m,$$

$$\frac{v_{jk}}{v_{j1}} = u_{j2} u_{j3} \ldots u_{jk}, \qquad j = 1, \ldots, m; \quad k = 2, \ldots, n_j,$$

our estimates, using (11.24) and (11.25), will be

$$v_{11} = 1,$$

$$\bar{v}_{j1} = \left(\frac{\alpha_2 + \beta_2}{2}\right)\left(\frac{\alpha_3 + \beta_3}{2}\right) \ldots \left(\frac{\alpha_j + \beta_j}{2}\right), \qquad j = 2, \ldots, m,$$

$$\bar{v}_{1k} = \left(\frac{\alpha_{12} + \beta_{12}}{2}\right) \ldots \left(\frac{\alpha_{1k} + \beta_{1k}}{2}\right), \qquad k = 2, \ldots, n_1,$$

$$\bar{v}_{jk} = \left(\frac{\alpha_2 + \beta_2}{2}\right) \ldots \left(\frac{\alpha_j + \beta_j}{2}\right)\left(\frac{\alpha_{j2} + \beta_{j2}}{2}\right) \ldots \left(\frac{\alpha_{jk} + \beta_{jk}}{2}\right),$$

$$j = 2, \ldots, m; k = 2, \ldots, n_j,$$

$$v_{10} = v_{20} = \ldots = v_{m0} = 0,$$

or, for $\bar{v}_{j1}$, $\bar{v}_{1k}$, and $\bar{v}_{jk}$,

$$\bar{v}_{j1} = \frac{\displaystyle\prod_{\nu=2}^{j} (\alpha_\nu + \beta_\nu)}{2^{j-1}}, \qquad \bar{v}_{1k} = \frac{\displaystyle\prod_{\nu=2}^{k} (\alpha_{1\nu} + \beta_{1\nu})}{2^{k-1}},$$

$$\bar{v}_{jk} = \prod_{\nu=2}^{j} (\alpha_\nu + \beta_\nu) \frac{\displaystyle\prod_{\nu=2}^{k} (\alpha_{j\nu} + \beta_{j\nu})}{2^{j+k-2}}.$$

To illustrate, suppose $m = 3$, $n_1 = 2$, $n_2 = 3$, $n_3 = 4$, with

$$.6 \leqslant u_2 \leqslant .8, \qquad .7 \leqslant u_3 \leqslant .9,$$
$$.6 \leqslant u_{12} \leqslant .8,$$
$$.4 \leqslant u_{22} \leqslant .7, \qquad .8 \leqslant u_{23} \leqslant 1.0,$$
$$.5 \leqslant u_{32} \leqslant .7, \qquad .2 \leqslant u_{33} \leqslant .4, \qquad .7 \leqslant u_{34} \leqslant 1.0.$$

[3] These statements are, of course, approximate.

The approximate numerical measure of the v_{jk} will then be, rounded to two decimal places,

$$(v_{11}, \bar{v}_{12}, v_{10}) = (1.00, .70, 0)$$

$$(\bar{v}_{21}, \bar{v}_{22}, \bar{v}_{23}, v_{20}) = (.70, .39, .35, 0)$$

$$(\bar{v}_{31}, \bar{v}_{32}, \bar{v}_{33}, \bar{v}_{34}, v_{30}) = (.56, .34, .10, .09, 0).$$

One can, of course, check such a numerical assignment against other measures of the v_{jk} such as the complete mixed ordinal ranking given in (11.39).

Before attempting to compute $m(S_1, S_2)$ or $M(S_1, S_2)$ it may be to one's advantage to plug the approximate numerical values of the v_{jk} into $E(S_1) - E(S_2)$ and determine the value, call it $\bar{f}(S_1, S_2)$, of this difference with the $\bar{v}_{jk}$. Since we have set $v_{11} = 1$,

$$m(S_1, S_2) \leqslant \bar{f}(S_1, S_2) \leqslant M(S_1, S_2),$$

so that, if $\bar{f}(S_1, S_2) \geqslant 0$, we will then look at $m(S_1, S_2)$, and if $\bar{f}(S_1, S_2) \leqslant 0$, we will look at $M(S_1, S_2)$. It is also quite possible that one may not even wish to fool around with $m(S_1, S_2)$ and $M(S_1, S_2)$, and simply proceed on the sign of $\bar{f}(S_1, S_2)$ in "determining" which strategy is the more desirable.

11.3 AN ANALYSIS WITH BOUNDED INTERVAL MEASURES, II

As in the previous section, we begin with the rankings (11.2) and (11.3) and use (11.4) to specify a common origin for the m value functions $V_1, \ldots, V_m$. Defining $v_{j,n_j+1} = v_{j0} = 0$ for all j, use Abel's identity (6.1) on each term of (11.11) to yield

$$
\begin{aligned}
E(S_1) - E(S_2) = &\sum_{k=1}^{n_1} \left[\sum_{v=1}^{k} (p_{1v}^1 - p_{1v}^2) \right](v_{1k} - v_{1,k+1}) \\
&+ \sum_{k=1}^{n_2} \left[\sum_{v=1}^{k} (p_{2v}^1 - p_{2v}^2) \right](v_{2k} - v_{2,k+1}) + \ldots \quad (11.12) \\
&+ \sum_{k=1}^{n_m} \left[\sum_{v=1}^{k} (p_{mv}^1 - p_{mv}^2) \right](v_{mk} - v_{m,k+1}).
\end{aligned}
$$

Dividing and multiplying the jth term in (11.12) by v_{j1} or $v_{j1} - v_{j0}$ and letting

$$q_{jk} = \sum_{v=1}^{k} (p_{jv}^1 - p_{jv}^2),$$

$$L_{jk} = \frac{v_{jk} - v_{j,k+1}}{v_{j1} - v_{j0}} = \frac{v_{jk} - v_{j,k+1}}{v_{j1}}$$

for $j = 1, \ldots, m$; $k = 1, \ldots, n_j$, gives

$$E(S_1) - E(S_2) = v_{11} \sum_{k=1}^{n_1} q_{1k} L_{1k} + v_{21} \sum_{k=1}^{n_2} q_{2k} L_{2k} \qquad (11.26)$$

$$+ \ldots + v_{m1} \sum_{k=1}^{n_m} q_{mk} L_{mk}.$$

Bounds on L_{jk}

Noting that

$$\sum_{k=1}^{n_j} L_{jk} = \frac{v_{j1} - v_{j2}}{v_{j1} - v_{j0}} + \frac{v_{j2} - v_{j3}}{v_{j1} - v_{j0}} + \ldots + \frac{v_{jn_j} - v_{j0}}{v_{j1} - v_{j0}} = 1$$

for each j, the bounded interval measure for Y_j in this section is given by, say,

$$a_{jk} \leqslant L_{jk} \leqslant a_{jk} + b_{jk}, \qquad k = 1, \ldots, n_j, \qquad (11.27)$$

in which

$$0 \leqslant a_{jk} \leqslant a_{jk} + b_{jk} \leqslant 1,$$

$$\sum_{k=1}^{n_j} a_{jk} \leqslant 1 \leqslant \sum_{k=1}^{n_j} (a_{jk} + b_{jk}), \qquad (11.28)$$

$$\sum_{k=1}^{n_j} L_{jk} = 1.$$

The bounds on L_{jk} may be obtained either by direct judgment in comparing the difference in preference between y_{jk} and $y_{j,k+1}$ with the difference in preference between y_{j1} and y_{j0}, or by comparing the two gambles $((y_{jk}), p, (y_{j0}))$ and $((y_{j,k+1}), p, (y_{j1}))$, from which

$$L_{jk} \geqslant \frac{1-p}{p} \quad \text{if} \quad ((y_{jk}), p, (y_{j0})) \gtrsim ((y_{j,k+1}), p, (y_{j1}));$$

$$L_{jk} \leqslant \frac{1-p}{p} \quad \text{if} \quad ((y_{j,k+1}), p, (y_{j1})) \gtrsim ((y_{jk}), p, (y_{j0})).$$

Initial Bounds on $E(S_1) - E(S_2)$

Letting

$$h'_j = \min_{\{L_{jk}\}} \sum_{k=1}^{n_j} q_{jk} L_{jk},$$

$$H'_j = \max_{\{L_{jk}\}} \sum_{k=1}^{n_j} q_{jk} L_{jk},$$

subject to (11.27) and (11.28), we get from (11.26),

$$\sum_{j=1}^{m} h'_j v_{j1} \leqslant E(S_1) - E(S_2) \leqslant \sum_{j=1}^{m} H'_j v_{j1}. \qquad (11.29)$$

The minimization and maximization of each $\sum_k q_{jk}L_{jk}$ proceeds as in Section 6.4 for the second bounded interval measure. To find h'_j and H'_j, first rank the q_{jk} for the given j from largest to smallest. With $k_1, \ldots, k_{n_j}$ a permutation of $1, 2, \ldots, n_j$, this ranking of the q_{jk} will be of the form

$$q_{jk_1} \geqslant q_{jk_2} \geqslant \ldots \geqslant q_{jk_{n_j}}.$$

Then write

$$\sum_{k=1}^{n_j} q_{jk}L_{jk} = \sum_{k=1}^{n_j} q_{jk}a_{jk} + \sum_{k=1}^{n_j} q_{jk}\epsilon_{jk}$$

in which

$$0 \leqslant \epsilon_{jk} \leqslant b_{jk}, \qquad \sum_{k=1}^{n_j} \epsilon_{jk} = 1 - \sum_{k=1}^{n_j} a_{jk} = c_j.$$

We then have

$$h'_j = \sum_{k=1}^{n_j} q_{jk}a_{jk} + \sum_{k=1}^{n_j} q_{jk}\epsilon^0_{jk},$$

where

$$\epsilon^0_{jk_{n_j}} = \min\{b_{jk_{n_j}}; c_j\},$$

$$\epsilon^0_{jk_v} = \min\left\{b_{jk_v}; c_j - \sum_{\alpha=v+1}^{n_j} \epsilon^0_{jk_\alpha}\right\}, \qquad v = n_j - 1, n_j - 2, \ldots, 1,$$

and

$$H'_j = \sum_{k=1}^{n_j} q_{jk}a_{jk} + \sum_{k=1}^{n_j} q_{jk}\epsilon^*_{jk},$$

where

$$\epsilon^*_{jk_1} = \min\{b_{jk_1}; c_j\},$$

$$\epsilon^*_{jk_v} = \min\left\{b_{jk_v}; c_j - \sum_{\alpha=1}^{v-1} \epsilon^*_{jk_\alpha}\right\}, \qquad v = 2, 3, \ldots, n_j.$$

Applying Abel's identity to the bounds on $E(S_1) - E(S_2)$ in (11.29) gives

$$\sum_{j=1}^{m}\left(\sum_{k=1}^{j} h'_k\right)(v_{j1} - v_{j+1,1}) \leqslant E(S_1) - E(S_2)$$

$$\leqslant \sum_{j=1}^{m}\left(\sum_{k=1}^{j} H'_k\right)(v_{j1} - v_{j+1,1}), \quad (11.30)$$

where $v_{m+1,1} = 0$. From the ranking $v_{11} \geqslant v_{21} \geqslant \ldots \geqslant v_{m1} \geqslant 0$, each $v_{j1} - v_{j+1,1}$ is nonnegative. Let

$$L_j = \frac{(v_{j1} - v_{j0}) - (v_{j+1,1} - v_{j+1,0})}{v_{11} - v_{10}} = \frac{v_{j1} - v_{j+1,1}}{v_{11}}, \qquad j = 1, \ldots, m.^4$$

[4] Let $v_{m+1,1} = v_{m0} = 0$ giving $L_m = (v_{m1} - v_{m0})/(v_{11} - v_{10}) = v_{m1}/v_{11}$.

Then (11.30) may be rendered as

$$\sum_{j=1}^{m} g_j L_j \leqslant \frac{E(S_1) - E(S_2)}{v_{11}} \leqslant \sum_{j=1}^{m} G_j L_j, \qquad (11.31)$$

where

$$g_j = \sum_{v=1}^{j} h'_v,$$

$$G_j = \sum_{v=1}^{j} H'_v,$$

$$\sum_{j=1}^{m} L_j = 1. \qquad (11.32)$$

Bounds on L_j

Let the bounds on L_j be given by

$$a_j \leqslant L_j \leqslant a_j + b_j, \qquad j = 1, \ldots, m, \qquad (11.33)$$

where $0 \leqslant a_j \leqslant a_j + b_j \leqslant 1$, $\sum a_j \leqslant 1 \leqslant \sum(a_j + b_j)$. Since the relative values of the values of either two Y_j (for L_1 and L_m) or three Y_j (for $L_2, \ldots, L_{m-1}$) are found in L_j, it is somewhat more difficult to obtain bounds on L_j than on L_{jk} (which involves but one Y_j).

The bounds on L_1 may be obtained in a manner similar to the bounds on u_2 as defined by (11.19), since

$$L_1 = \frac{(v_{11} - v_{10}) - (v_{21} - v_{20})}{v_{11} - v_{10}} = 1 - u_2.$$

If $\alpha_2 \leqslant u_2 \leqslant \beta_2$, then $1 - \beta_2 \leqslant L_1 \leqslant 1 - \alpha_2$. The bounds on

$$L_m = \frac{v_{m1} - v_{m0}}{v_{11} - v_{10}}$$

may be obtained either by comparing $v_{m1} - v_{m0}$ with $v_{11} - v_{10}$ directly, or by comparing (y_{10}, y_{m1}) with $((y_{11}, y_{m0}), p, (y_{10}, y_{m0}))$. The bounds on L_j for $2 \leqslant j \leqslant m - 1$ may be obtained by comparing $(y_{10}, y_{j1}, y_{j+1,0})$ with $((y_{11}, y_{j0}, y_{j+1,1}), p, (y_{10}, y_{j0}, y_{j+1,1}))$. If a_j is a p for which the individual is sure that

$$(y_{10}, y_{j1}, y_{j+1,0}) \gtrsim ((y_{11}, y_{j0}, y_{j+1,1}), p, (y_{10}, y_{j0}, y_{j+1,1})),$$

then

$$v_{10} + v_{j1} + v_{j+1,0}$$
$$\geqslant a_j(v_{11} + v_{j0} + v_{j+1,1}) + (1 - a_j)(v_{10} + v_{j0} + v_{j+1,1}),$$

$$(v_{j1} - v_{j0}) - (v_{j+1,1} - v_{j+1,0}) \geqslant a_j(v_{11} - v_{10}),$$

$$L_j \geqslant a_j.$$

Similarly, if $a_j + b_j$ is a p for which the individual is sure that

$$((y_{11}, y_{j0}, y_{j+1,1}), p, (y_{10}, y_{j0}, y_{j+1,1})) \gtrsim (y_{10}, y_{j1}, y_{j+1,0}),$$

then

$$L_j \leqslant a_j + b_j.$$

Completing the Analysis

From (11.31) let

$$m'(S_1, S_2) = \min_{\{L_j\}} \sum_{j=1}^{m} g_j L_j, \tag{11.34a}$$

$$M'(S_1, S_2) = \max_{\{L_j\}} \sum_{j=1}^{m} G_j L_j, \tag{11.34b}$$

which may be written, using (11.33), as

$$m'(S_1, S_2) = \sum_{j=1}^{m} g_j a_j + \min_{\{\epsilon_j\}} \sum_{j=1}^{m} g_j \epsilon_j,$$

$$M'(S_1, S_2) = \sum_{j=1}^{m} G_j a_j + \max_{\{\epsilon_j\}} \sum_{j=1}^{m} G_j \epsilon_j,$$

subject to

$$0 \leqslant \epsilon_j \leqslant b_j, \qquad \sum_{j=1}^{m} \epsilon_j = 1 - \sum_{j=1}^{m} a_j = c.$$

Given

$$g_{j_1} \leqslant g_{j_2} \leqslant \ldots \leqslant g_{j_m},$$

$$m'(S_1, S_2) = \sum g_j a_j + \sum g_j \epsilon_j^0,$$

where

$$\epsilon_{j_1}^0 = \min\{b_{j_1}; c\},$$

$$\epsilon_{j_\nu}^0 = \min\left\{b_{j_\nu}; c - \sum_{\alpha=1}^{\nu-1} \epsilon_{j_\alpha}^0\right\}, \qquad \nu = 2, 3, \ldots, n.$$

Given

$$G_{k_1} \geqslant G_{k_2} \geqslant \ldots \geqslant G_{k_m},$$

$$M'(S_1, S_2) = \sum G_j a_j + \sum G_j \epsilon_j^*,$$

where

$$\epsilon_{k_1}^* = \min\{b_{k_1}; c\},$$

$$\epsilon_{k_\nu}^* = \min\left\{b_{k_\nu}; c - \sum_{\alpha=1}^{\nu-1} \epsilon_{k_\alpha}^*\right\}, \qquad \nu = 2, 3, \ldots, n.$$

Given only the rankings (11.27) and (11.33), the most we can say about

$$f(S_1, S_2) = \frac{E(S_1) - E(S_2)}{v_{11}}$$

is that

$$m'(S_1, S_2) \leqslant f(S_1, S_2) \leqslant M'(S_1, S_2).$$

This analysis gives:

Theorem 11.2 Given the bounded interval measures (11.27) and (11.33) and no additional information on the v_{jk}, $E(S_1) \geqslant E(S_2)$ if $m'(S_1, S_2) \geqslant 0$; $E(S_2) \geqslant E(S_1)$ if $M'(S_1, S_2) \leqslant 0$; otherwise, if $m'(S_1, S_2) < 0 < M'(S_1, S_2)$, the sign of $E(S_1) - E(S_2)$ is indeterminate.

Instead of using the bounded interval measure (11.33) to complete the analysis after obtaining (11.29), one could proceed from (11.29) by using the bounded interval measure given by (11.20) in the previous section, similar to the treatment of (11.18).

Approximate Numerical Measure of Values

In the present context, an approximate numerical measure of the v_{jk} may be obtained from estimates of the L_j and L_{jk}. Calling these estimates $\bar{L}_j$ and $\bar{L}_{jk}$, we cannot use the mid-points of the intervals $[a_j, a_j + b_j]$ and $[a_{jk}, a_{jk} + b_{jk}]$, since there is no assurance that $\sum_j (a_j + b_j/2) = 1$ or that $\sum_k (a_{jk} + b_{jk}/2) = 1$. By (11.28) and (11.32), one should make sure that

$$\sum_{j=1}^{m} \bar{L}_j = 1; \quad \sum_{k=1}^{n_j} \bar{L}_{jk} = 1, \quad j = 1, \ldots, m. \quad (11.35)$$

Letting

$$c = 1 - \sum_{j=1}^{m} a_j; \quad c_j = 1 - \sum_{k=1}^{n_j} a_{jk}, \quad j = 1, \ldots, m,$$

one could take

$$\bar{L}_j = a_j + c \frac{b_j}{\displaystyle\sum_{j=1}^{m} b_j}, \quad j = 1, \ldots, m, \quad (11.36)$$

$$\bar{L}_{jk} = a_{jk} + c_j \frac{b_{jk}}{\displaystyle\sum_{k=1}^{n_j} b_{jk}}, \quad j = 1, \ldots, m; \; k = 1, \ldots, n_j, \quad (11.37)$$

which not only insure that[5] $a_j \leqslant \bar{L}_j \leqslant a_j + b_j$ and $a_{jk} \leqslant \bar{L}_{jk} \leqslant a_{jk} + b_{jk}$ but also satisfy (11.35).

[5] $c \leqslant \sum_j b_j$ and $c_j \leqslant \sum_{jk} b_k$.

Setting
$$v_{11} = 1$$
gives
$$\bar{v}_{j1} = \sum_{v=j}^{m} \bar{L}_v, \qquad j = 2, \ldots, m, \tag{11.38a}$$

$$\bar{v}_{1k} = \sum_{v=k}^{n_1} \bar{L}_{1v}, \qquad k = 2, \ldots, n_1, \tag{11.38b}$$

$$\bar{v}_{jk} = \bar{v}_{j1} \sum_{v=k}^{n_j} \bar{L}_{jv}, \qquad j = 2, \ldots, m; \; k = 2, \ldots, n_j. \tag{11.38c}$$

Letting
$$\bar{f}'(S_1, S_2) = f(S_1, S_2)$$
with the above approximations of the v_{jk}, we have that
$$m'(S_1, S_2) \leqslant \bar{f}'(S_1, S_2) \leqslant M'(S_1, S_2).$$
$\bar{f}'(S_1, S_2)$ may be used in a manner similar to $\bar{f}(S_1, S_2)$, as discussed at the end of the previous section.

11.4 THE MIXED ORDINAL RANKING AND OTHER VALUE MEASURES

Mixed Ordinal Ranking

A mixed ordinal ranking of the v_{jk}, starting with (11.2), (11.3), and (11.4), takes the form
$$v_1 \geqslant v_2 \geqslant \ldots \geqslant v_r \geqslant 0, \tag{11.39}$$
where each v_k is one of the v_{jk} ($k \neq 0$), and vice versa, with
$$r = \sum_{j=1}^{m} n_j.$$

Derivation of (11.39), given (11.2), requires a series of pairwise comparisons of consequences of the form $(y_{jk}, y_{\alpha 0})$ versus $(y_{j0}, y_{\alpha \beta})$, $j \neq \alpha$; k, $\beta \neq 0$, where the two consequences have identical values of all variables other than Y_j and Y_α. If $(y_{jk}, y_{\alpha 0}) \gtrsim (y_{j0}, y_{\alpha \beta})$, then $v_{jk} + v_{\alpha 0} \geqslant v_{j0} + v_{\alpha \beta}$ or $v_{jk} \geqslant v_{\alpha \beta}$. If $(y_{j0}, y_{\alpha \beta}) \gtrsim (y_{jk}, y_{\alpha 0})$, then $v_{\alpha \beta} \geqslant v_{jk}$.

Let p_k denote the coefficient of v_k in (11.11), so that each p_k is one of the $p_{jk}^1 - p_{jk}^2$, and vice versa. Then
$$E(S_1) - E(S_2) = \sum_{k=1}^{r} p_k v_k = \sum_{k=1}^{r} \left(\sum_{j=1}^{k} p_j \right)(v_k - v_{k+1}) \tag{11.40}$$
on letting $v_{r+1} = 0$. This gives:

Theorem 11.3 Given (11.39) and no additional information on the v_{jk}, $E(S_1) \geqslant E(S_2)$ if $\sum_{j=1}^{k} p_j \geqslant 0$ for $k = 1, \ldots, r$; $E(S_2) \geqslant E(S_1)$ if

$\sum_{j=1}^{k} p_j \leqslant 0$ for $k = 1, \ldots, r$; otherwise, the sign of $E(S_1) - E(S_2)$ is indefinite.

Other Measures

Beginning with the mixed ordinal ranking (11.39), one may obtain a variety of subsequent relative value measures, such as a mixed ordered metric and various bounded interval measures. We shall indicate several of these briefly, leaving details of the discussion as exercises for the reader.

First, suppose we obtain the ordered metric ranking

$$v_1^{(1)} \geqslant v_2^{(1)} \geqslant \ldots \geqslant v_r^{(1)} \geqslant 0, \tag{11.41}$$

where each $v_j^{(1)}$ is one of the $v_k - v_{k+1}$ ($1 \leqslant j \leqslant r$), and vice versa. Letting $p_j^{(1)}$ be the coefficient of $v_j^{(1)}$ in (11.40), we may write

$$E(S_1) - E(S_2) = \sum_{j=1}^{r} p_j^{(1)} v_j^{(1)} = \sum_{j=1}^{r} \left(\sum_{k=1}^{j} p_k^{(1)} \right) (v_j^{(1)} - v_{j+1}^{(1)}), \tag{11.42}$$

with $v_{r+1}^{(1)} = 0$. The obvious theorem follows from (11.41) and (11.42).

Second, suppose we obtain a bounded interval measure

$$u_1 = 1, \qquad \alpha_j \leqslant u_j \leqslant \beta_j \quad \text{for} \quad j = 2, \ldots, r, \tag{11.43}$$

where

$$u_j = \frac{v_j}{v_{j-1}}, \qquad 0 \leqslant \alpha_j \leqslant \beta_j \leqslant 1, \qquad j = 2, \ldots, r.$$

Then

$$\frac{E(S_1) - E(S_2)}{v_1} = \sum_{k=1}^{r} p_k \prod_{j=1}^{k} u_j. \tag{11.44}$$

Minimizing and maximizing the right-hand side of (11.44), subject to (11.43), leads to results similar to those stated in theorem 11.1.

Finally, consider the bounded interval measure

$$a_j \leqslant L_j \leqslant a_j + b_j, \qquad j = 1, \ldots, r, \tag{11.45}$$

where

$$L_j = \frac{v_j - v_{j+1}}{v_1}, \qquad v_{r+1} = 0,$$

$$0 \leqslant a_j \leqslant a_j + b_j \leqslant 1,$$

$$\sum_{j=1}^{r} a_j \leqslant 1 \leqslant \sum_{j=1}^{r} (a_j + b_j),$$

$$\sum_{j=1}^{r} L_j = 1. \tag{11.46}$$

With this,

$$\frac{E(S_1) - E(S_2)}{v_1} = \sum_{j=1}^{r} \left(\sum_{k=1}^{j} p_k \right) L_j. \tag{11.47}$$

Minimization and maximization of the right-hand side of (11.47), subject to (11.45) and (11.46), leads to results similar to those stated in theorem 11.2.

In general, we would not recommend analysis by the above methods unless $r = \sum n_j$ is fairly small, of the order of about 12 or less. If r is larger and m is greater than 2, the methods of the last two sections appear to be more efficient (although the algebra may be slightly more tedious).

Numerical estimates of the v_j may be obtained from either bounded interval measure by methods similar to those illustrated in the last two sections.

11.5 AN ORDERED METRIC RANKING AND BOUNDED INTERVAL MEASURES

In this section, value measures of the type mentioned in Section 9.5 in (9.20) and immediately thereafter are considered. The basic items of concern in these measures are the adjacent relative value differences $v_{jk} - v_{j,k+1}$, $j = 1, \ldots, m$; $k = 1, \ldots, n_j$, with $v_{j,n_j+1} = v_{j0}$ for all j. Assume (11.2) as given.

Ordered Metric Ranking

In obtaining an ordered metric ranking of the $r = \sum_{j=1}^{m} n_j$ adjacent differences $v_{jk} - v_{j,k+1}$, one might first find it expedient to get rankings of the $n_j (v_{jk} - v_{j,k+1})$ for each j and then combine these (or "weave them together") to give the ordered metric ranking

$$v_1' \geqslant v_2' \geqslant \ldots \geqslant v_r' \geqslant 0, \tag{11.48}$$

in which each v_k' is one of the $v_{jk} - v_{j,k+1}$, and vice versa. The ordered metric ranking (11.48) is *not* the same ranking as (11.41). (11.41) was obtained from a mixed ordinal ranking, and many of the $v_k^{(1)}$ may be equal to a $v_{jk} - v_{\alpha\beta}$ with $j \neq \alpha$. In (11.48) each v_k' is one of the $v_{jk} - v_{j,k+1}$, the difference of adjacent relative values for the *same* variable Y_j. Hence, (11.48) will usually be easier to obtain than (11.41), although the two ordered metric rankings have the same number of terms (r).

In comparing $v_{jk} - v_{j,k+1}$ with $v_{\alpha\beta} - v_{\alpha,\beta+1}$, $\alpha \neq j$, it is only necessary to compare two consequences $(y_{jk}, y_{\alpha,\beta+1})$ and $(y_{j,k+1}, y_{\alpha\beta})$. If

$$(y_{jk}, y_{\alpha,\beta+1}) \gtrsim (y_{j,k+1}, y_{\alpha\beta}),$$

then $v_{jk} + v_{\alpha,\beta+1} \geqslant v_{j,k+1} + v_{\alpha\beta}$ or $v_{jk} - v_{j,k+1} \geqslant v_{\alpha\beta} - v_{\alpha,\beta+1}$. If

$$(y_{j,k+1}, y_{\alpha\beta}) \gtrsim (y_{jk}, y_{\alpha,\beta+1}),$$

then $v_{\alpha\beta} - v_{\alpha,\beta+1} \geqslant v_{jk} - v_{j,k+1}$. When $\alpha = j$ (and $\beta \neq k$) one may use direct judgment in comparing the difference in preference between y_{jk} and $y_{j,k+1}$ with the difference in preference between $y_{j\beta}$ and $y_{j,\beta+1}$, or use gambles similar to those described in Section 4.10. For example, in comparing $v_{j1} - v_{j2}$ with $v_{j2} - v_{j3}$ we could compare (y_{j2}) and $((y_{j1}), \frac{1}{2}, (y_{j3}))$. In comparing $v_{j1} - v_{j2}$ with $v_{j3} - v_{j4}$, we could compare $((y_{j1}), \frac{1}{2}, (y_{j4}))$ and $((y_{j2}), \frac{1}{2}, (y_{j3}))$.

Given (11.48), let q_k be the coefficient of v'_k in (11.12). Each q_k is one of the $\sum_{\nu=1}^{k} (p^1_{j\nu} - p^2_{j\nu})$, and vice versa. For example, if

$$v'_6 = v_{34} - v_{35}, \qquad \text{then} \qquad q_6 = \sum_{\nu=1}^{4} (p^1_{3\nu} - p^2_{3\nu}).$$

From (11.12) we then have, identical to (9.21),

$$E(S_1) - E(S_2) = \sum_{k=1}^{r} q_k v'_k, \tag{11.49}$$

which, on applying Abel's identity, becomes

$$E(S_1) - E(S_2) = \sum_{k=1}^{r} \left(\sum_{j=1}^{k} q_j \right)(v'_k - v'_{k+1}),$$

in which $v_{r+1} = 0$, giving:

Theorem 11.4 Given (11.48) and no additional information on the v_{jk}, $E(S_1) \geqslant E(S_2)$ if $\sum_{j=1}^{k} q_j \geqslant 0$ for $k = 1, \ldots, r$; $E(S_2) \geqslant E(S_1)$ if $\sum_{j=1}^{k} q_j \leqslant 0$ for $k = 1, \ldots, r$; otherwise, the sign of $E(S_1) - E(S_2)$ is indefinite.

Bounded Interval Measure

Next, consider the bounded interval measure

$$w_1 = 1, \qquad \alpha_j \leqslant w_j \leqslant \beta_j, \qquad j = 2, \ldots, r, \tag{11.50}$$

where $0 \leqslant \alpha_j \leqslant \beta_j \leqslant 1$ and

$$w_j = \frac{v'_j}{v'_{j-1}}, \qquad j = 2, \ldots, r. \tag{11.51}$$

In terms of the original v_{jk}, each w_j will be of the form

$$\frac{v_{jk} - v_{j,k+1}}{v_{\alpha\beta} - v_{\alpha,\beta+1}}.$$

To bound w_j, the individual may make either direct comparison of the numerator with the denominator or consider appropriate gambles.

From (11.49) and (11.51),

$$\frac{E(S_1) - E(S_2)}{v'_1} = \sum_{k=1}^{r} q_k \prod_{j=1}^{k} w_j. \tag{11.52}$$

The minimization and maximization of the right-hand side of (11.52), subject to (11.50), is carried out in the usual fashion. For example,

$$\max \sum_{k=1}^{r} q_k \prod_{j=1}^{k} w_j = q_1 + f_2,$$

where

$$f_{r+1} = 0,$$
$$f_k = \max_{\alpha_k \leqslant w_k \leqslant \beta_k} w_k(q_k + f_{k+1}), \qquad k = r, r-1, \ldots, 2.$$

As usual, if $\max \sum q_k \Pi w_j \leqslant 0$, then $E(S_2) \geqslant E(S_1)$, and if $\min \sum q_k \Pi w_j \geqslant 0$, then $E(S_1) \geqslant E(S_2)$.

Setting $v_1' = 1$ and letting $\bar{w}_j = (\alpha_j + \beta_j)/2$ gives an approximate numerical measure of the v_j', i.e.,

$$\bar{v}_j' = \bar{w}_2 \bar{w}_3 \ldots \bar{w}_j = \prod_{k=2}^{j} \frac{\alpha_k + \beta_k}{2}, \qquad j = 2, \ldots, r.$$

If in addition one sets $v_{10} = v_{20} = \ldots = v_{m0} = 0$, then from $\bar{v}_j'$ and $v_1' = 1$ we obtain an approximate numerical measure of the v_{jk}.

11.6 METHOD OF PARTITIONS WITH CONTINUOUS VARIABLES

In dealing with a continuous outcome variable, we have noted that it is often advantageous, from a practical standpoint, to partition the values of the variable into a small number of (exclusive and exhaustive) sets. The probability measures over the new values of the variable (i.e., the sets of the partition) are taken with respect to the defined sets. For value measurement purposes we usually assume that the probability measure in a set is centered at some representative point in the set and then use these points as the arguments of the value function for the variable. For example, given that Y_1 is a continuous variable, partition the values $y_1 \in Y_1$ into $n_1 + 1$ sets $Y_{10}, Y_{11}, Y_{12}, \ldots, Y_{1n_1}$. Then pick a point in each set, say $y_{1k} \in Y_{1k}$, $k = 0, 1, \ldots, n_1$, and use the $n_1 + 1$ points $y_{10}, y_{11}, \ldots, y_{1n_1}$ as the arguments of V_1. Letting

$$p_{1k}^i = \int_{y_1 \in Y_{1k}} dF_1(y_1 \mid S_i)$$

we then use the approximations $p_{1k}^i V_1(y_{1k})$ in place of the

$$\int_{y_1 \in Y_{1k}} V(y_1) \, dF_1(y_1 \mid S_i), \qquad k = 0, 1, \ldots, n_1,$$

or take

$$\sum_{k=0}^{n_1} p_{1k}^i V_1(y_{1k}) \cong \int_{y_1 \in Y_1} V(y_1) \, dF_1(y_1 \mid S_i).$$

Instead of proceeding in the above manner for Y_1, one can obtain bounds on the integral $\int V(y_1)\,dF(y_1 \mid S_i)$ in a fashion similar to the procedure in Section 8.3. Doing this for each continuous outcome variable (or discrete outcome variable with a large number of values), we may obtain bounds on the difference of the expected relative values of any two strategies. This procedure is illustrated by means of the following semispecific example.

Let S_1 and S_2 be two strategies under study with expected values $E(S_1)$ and $E(S_2)$. Suppose there are three relevant mutually valuewise independent variables Y_1, Y_2, and Y_3, where Y_1 and Y_2 are continuous outcome variables and Y_3 is a discrete variable (either action or outcome) with an appropriately small number of values. We then have

$$E(S_i) = \int_{y_1 \in Y_1} V_1(y_1)\,dF_1(y_1 \mid S_i) + \int_{y_2 \in Y_2} V_2(y_2)\,dF_2(y_2 \mid S_i)$$
$$+ \sum_{k=0}^{n_3} p_{3k}^i V_3(y_{3k}).$$

Next, partition Y_1 into the sets $Y_{10}, Y_{11}, \ldots, Y_{1n_1}$ and partition Y_2 into the sets $Y_{20}, Y_{21}, \ldots, Y_{2n_2}$. Let

$$p_{jk}^i = \int_{y_j \in Y_{jk}} dF_j(y_j \mid S_i), \qquad i = 1, 2;\ j = 1, 2;\ k = 0, \ldots, n_j,$$

and for each Y_{jk} let x_{jk} and z_{jk} be two points of Y_j such that

$$(x_{jk}) \gtrsim (y_{jk}) \gtrsim (z_{jk}) \qquad \text{for every } y_{jk} \in Y_{jk},$$

where (x_{jk}), (y_{jk}), (z_{jk}) are three consequences which have similar values for the two Y_j not explicitly mentioned. Then, since

$$p_{jk}^i V_j(z_{jk}) \leqslant \int_{y_j \in Y_{jk}} V_j(y_j)\,dF_j(y_j \mid S_i) \leqslant p_{jk}^i V_j(x_{jk}),$$
$$i, j = 1, 2;\ k = 0, \ldots, n_j,$$

we get

$$\sum_{j=1}^{2} \sum_{k=0}^{n_j} p_{jk}^i V_j(z_{jk}) + \sum_{k=0}^{n_3} p_{3k}^i V_3(y_{3k})$$
$$\leqslant E(S_i) \leqslant \sum_{j=1}^{2} \sum_{k=0}^{n_j} p_{jk}^i V_j(x_{jk}) + \sum_{k=0}^{n_3} p_{3k}^i V_3(y_{3k}).$$

Therefore,

$$E(S_1) - E(S_2) \leqslant \sum_{j=1}^{2} \sum_{k=0}^{n_j} [p_{jk}^1 V_j(x_{jk}) - p_{jk}^2 V_j(z_{jk})]$$
$$+ \sum_{k=0}^{n_3} (p_{3k}^1 - p_{3k}^2) V_3(y_{3k}), \qquad (11.53a)$$

$$E(S_1) - E(S_2) \geqslant \sum_{j=1}^{2} \sum_{k=0}^{n_j} [p_{jk}^1 V_j(z_{jk}) - p_{jk}^2 V_j(x_{jk})]$$

$$+ \sum_{k=0}^{n_3} (p_{3k}^1 - p_{3k}^2) V_3(y_{3k}), \qquad (11.53b)$$

giving bounds on $E(S_1) - E(S_2)$. If the right-hand side of (11.53a) can be shown to be nonpositive, then $E(S_2) \geqslant E(S_1)$, and if the right-hand side of (11.53b) can be shown to be nonnegative, then $E(S_1) \geqslant E(S_2)$.

It is quite possible that with given partitions one might not be able to determine the sign of $E(S_1) - E(S_2)$, even with numerical values for all the probabilities and relative values. In this case, one might wish to refine the partitions by breaking some of the Y_{jk} into two or more sets, increasing both the n_j, $j = 1, 2$, and the accuracy of the bounds on $E(S_1) - E(S_2)$.

11.7 BOUNDED PROBABILITY MEASURES

With $E(S_i)$ given by (11.6),

$$E(S_i) = \sum_{j=1}^{m} \sum_{k=1}^{n_j} p_{jk}^i v_{jk}, \qquad (11.6)$$

where

$$v_{j1} \geqslant v_{j2} \geqslant \ldots \geqslant v_{jn_j} \geqslant v_{j0} = 0, \qquad j = 1, \ldots, m, \qquad (11.54)$$

suppose that for each Y_j one obtains bounds on the p_{jk}^i of the form

$$\alpha_{jk}^i \leqslant p_{jk}^i \leqslant \alpha_{jk}^i + \beta_{jk}^i, \qquad k = 0, 1, \ldots, n_j \qquad (11.55)$$

with

$$0 \leqslant \alpha_{jk}^i \leqslant \alpha_{jk}^i + \beta_{jk}^i \leqslant 1, \qquad k = 0, 1, \ldots, n_j,$$

$$\sum_{k=0}^{n_j} \alpha_{jk}^i \leqslant 1 \leqslant \sum_{k=0}^{n_j} \alpha_{jk}^i + \sum_{k=0}^{n_j} \beta_{jk}^i.$$

For a fixed i and j, the bounds given by (11.55) may be obtained by methods similar to those in Section 5.9.

Given the ordinal value rankings (11.54), the right-hand side of (11.6) may be minimized and maximized with respect to the p_{jk}^i subject to (11.55) and

$$\sum_{k=0}^{n_j} p_{jk}^i = 1, \qquad i = 1, \ldots, t; \, j = 1, \ldots, m.$$

Treating the p_{jk}^i as variables, we wish to extremize

$$\sum_{j=1}^{m} \sum_{k=1}^{n_j} p_{jk}^i v_{jk} = \sum_{j=1}^{m} \sum_{k=1}^{n_j} (\alpha_{jk}^i + \epsilon_{jk}^i) v_{jk}$$

$$= \sum_{j=1}^{m} \sum_{k=1}^{n_j} \alpha_{jk}^i v_{jk} + \sum_{k=1}^{n_1} \epsilon_{1k}^i v_{1k} + \ldots + \sum_{k=1}^{n_m} \epsilon_{mk}^i v_{mk},$$

subject to

$$0 \leqslant \epsilon_{jk}^i \leqslant \beta_{jk}^i, \qquad j = 1, \ldots, m; \ k = 0, 1, \ldots, n_j,$$

$$\sum_{k=0}^{n_j} \epsilon_{jk}^i = c_j^i, \qquad j = 1, \ldots, m,$$

where

$$c_j^i = 1 - \sum_{k=0}^{n_j} \alpha_{jk}^i.$$

To do this, first extremize each $\sum_{k=1}^{n_j} \epsilon_{jk}^i v_{jk}$. By means of the ordinal value ranking (11.54),

$$\min_{\{\epsilon_{jk}^i\}} \sum_{k=1}^{n_j} \epsilon_{jk}^i v_{jk} = \sum_{k=1}^{n_j} \epsilon_{jk}^{i0} v_{jk},$$

where

$$\epsilon_{j0}^{i0} = \min \{\beta_{j0}^i; c_j^i\},$$

$$\epsilon_{jn_j}^{i0} = \min \{\beta_{jn_j}^i; c_j^i - \epsilon_{j0}^{i0}\},$$

$$\vdots$$

$$\epsilon_{jk}^{i0} = \min \left\{ \beta_{jk}^i; c_j^i - \epsilon_{j0}^{i0} - \sum_{v=k+1}^{n_j} \epsilon_{jv}^{i0} \right\}, \qquad k = n_j - 1, n_j - 2, \ldots, 1,$$

and

$$\max_{\{\epsilon_{jk}^i\}} \sum_{k=1}^{n_j} \epsilon_{jk}^i v_{jk} = \sum_{k=1}^{n_j} \epsilon_{jk}^{i*} v_{jk},$$

where

$$\epsilon_{j1}^{i*} = \min \{\beta_{j1}^i; c_j^i\},$$

$$\vdots$$

$$\epsilon_{jk}^{i*} = \min \left\{ \beta_{jk}^i; c_j^i - \sum_{v=1}^{k-1} \epsilon_{jv}^{i*} \right\}, \qquad k = 2, \ldots, n_j,$$

$$\epsilon_{j0}^{i*} = \min \left\{ \beta_{j0}^i; c_j^i - \sum_{v=1}^{n_j} \epsilon_{jv}^{i*} \right\}.$$

Letting

$$m(S_i) = \min_{\{p_{jk}^i\}} \sum_{j=1}^{m} \sum_{k=1}^{n_j} p_{jk}^i v_{jk},$$

$$M(S_i) = \max_{\{p_{jk}^i\}} \sum_{j=1}^{m} \sum_{k=1}^{n_j} p_{jk}^i v_{jk},$$

we have

$$m(S_i) = \sum_{j=1}^{m} \sum_{k=1}^{n_j} (\alpha_{jk}^i + \epsilon_{jk}^{i0}) v_{jk} = \sum_{j=1}^{m} \sum_{k=1}^{n_j} p_{jk}^{i0} v_{jk},$$

$$M(S_i) = \sum_{j=1}^{m} \sum_{k=1}^{n_j} (\alpha_{jk}^i + \epsilon_{jk}^{i*}) v_{jk} = \sum_{j=1}^{m} \sum_{k=1}^{n_j} p_{jk}^{i*} v_{jk},$$

with

$$p_{jk}^{i0} = \alpha_{jk}^i + \epsilon_{jk}^{i0},$$
$$p_{jk}^{i*} = \alpha_{jk}^i + \epsilon_{jk}^{i*}.$$

Obviously

$$m(S_i) \leqslant E(S_i) \leqslant M(S_i),$$

giving:

Theorem 11.5 Given (11.55) for $j = 1, \ldots, m$, $i = 1, 2$ and no additional information on the p_{jk}^1 and p_{jk}^2 excepting for $\sum_{k=0}^{n_j} p_{jk}^i = 1$,

$$E(S_1) \geqslant E(S_2) \quad \text{if } m(S_1) \geqslant M(S_2);$$
$$E(S_2) \geqslant E(S_1) \quad \text{if } m(S_2) \geqslant M(S_1);$$

otherwise the sign of $E(S_1) - E(S_2)$ is indeterminate.

It should be noted that the only data we required on the v_{jk} in order to find $m(S_i)$ and $M(S_i)$ were the ordinal rankings (11.54). Writing out

$$m(S_1) - M(S_2) = \sum_{j=1}^{m} \sum_{k=1}^{n_j} (p_{jk}^{10} - p_{jk}^{2*})v_{jk},$$

$$m(S_2) - M(S_1) = \sum_{j=1}^{m} \sum_{k=1}^{n_j} (p_{jk}^{20} - p_{jk}^{1*})v_{jk},$$

and comparing these with (11.11), it is clear that any of the measures of relative values discussed previously in this chapter may be used in trying to determine if $m(S_1) - M(S_2) \geqslant 0$ or if $m(S_2) - M(S_1) \geqslant 0$.

From (11.55), one set of numerical estimates of the p_{jk}^i is given by

$$\bar{p}_{jk}^i = \alpha_{jk}^i + c_j^i \frac{\beta_{jk}^i}{\sum_{k=0}^{n_j} \beta_{jk}^i}, \quad i = 1, \ldots, t; \ j = 1, \ldots, m; \ k = 0, \ldots, n_j, \tag{11.56}$$

which insure that

$$\alpha_{jk}^i \leqslant \bar{p}_{jk}^i \leqslant \alpha_{jk}^i + \beta_{jk}^i, \quad \sum_{k=0}^{n_j} \bar{p}_{jk}^i = 1.$$

11.8 SETS OF INEQUALITIES ON THE v_{jk}

As in Section 10.11 one may obtain sets of inequalities on the v_{jk} by simple preference comparisons between consequences. For example, beginning with (11.2), (11.3), and (11.4), if $(y_{11}, y_{20}, y_{30}) \gtrsim (y_{10}, y_{21}, y_{31})$, then

$$v_{11} - v_{21} - v_{31} \geqslant 0,$$

a piece of information not contained in the initial rankings. Since only simple preference comparisons are used to generate the inequalities, each inequality will have no more than two v_{jk} for a given j, and if a given inequality does contain two v_{jk} for a given j, these will be of opposite sign when the inequality is written $\geqslant 0$. For example, if $(y_{13}, y_{21}, y_{31}, y_{40})$ $\gtrsim (y_{11}, y_{22}, y_{32}, y_{41})$, then

$$v_{13} - v_{11} + v_{21} - v_{22} + v_{31} - v_{32} - v_{41} \geqslant 0.$$

The number of inequalities on the v_{jk} and their variety is subject only to the ingenuity of the research worker and the willingness and discrimination in judgment on the part of the individual. Suppose we label the $r = \sum n_j v_{jk}$ ($k \neq 0$) as $v_1, \ldots, v_r$ (the numbering perhaps reflecting a mixed ordinal ranking), and suppose, by simple comparisons, one obtains n inequalities on the v_{jk} ($n \geqslant r$), say,

$$\sum_{k=1}^{r} a_{1k}v_k \geqslant 0,$$

$$\sum_{k=1}^{r} a_{2k}v_k \geqslant 0,$$

$$\vdots$$

$$\sum_{k=1}^{r} a_{nk}v_k \geqslant 0,$$

where each a_{jk} is either -1, 0, or 1. One way of using such a system of inequalities in analyzing, say, $E(S_1) - E(S_2)$ for sign is to employ the method of equating coefficients and write, using (11.40),

$$E(S_1) - E(S_2) = \sum_{k=1}^{r} p_k v_k = \sum_{j=1}^{n} b_j \sum_{k=1}^{r} a_{jk}v_k = \sum_{k=1}^{r} \left(\sum_{j=1}^{n} a_{jk}b_j \right) v_k,$$

giving a system of r linear equations in n unknowns $(b_1, \ldots, b_n)$,

$$\sum_{j=1}^{n} a_{j1}b_j = p_1,$$

$$\sum_{j=1}^{n} a_{j2}b_j = p_2, \qquad (11.57)$$

$$\vdots$$

$$\sum_{j=1}^{n} a_{jr}b_j = p_r.$$

If (11.57) has a nonpositive **b** solution $(b_j \leqslant 0, \ j = 1, \ldots, n)$, then $E(S_1) - E(S_2) \leqslant 0$ since $\sum a_{jk}v_k \geqslant 0$ for $j = 1, \ldots, n$. Similarly, if (11.57) has a nonnegative **b** solution $(b_j \geqslant 0, \ j = 1, \ldots, n)$, then $E(S_1) - E(S_2) \geqslant 0$.

In trying to determine if (11.57) has a uniform sign **b** solution, with

$n \geqslant r$, solve for r of the b_j in terms of the other $n - r$. Solving for $b_1, \ldots, b_r$ in terms of $b_{r+1}, \ldots, b_n$ gives, say,

$$b_1 = f_1(b_{r+1}, \ldots, b_n),$$
$$b_2 = f_2(b_{r+1}, \ldots, b_n), \qquad \qquad (11.58)$$
$$\vdots$$
$$b_r = f_r(b_{r+1}, \ldots, b_n),$$

where f_j is a linear function in $b_{r+1}, \ldots, b_n$, $j = 1, \ldots, r$. Then, if one can find $b_{r+1} \geqslant 0, \ldots, b_n \geqslant 0$, that make

$$f_j(b_{r+1}, \ldots, b_n) \geqslant 0, \qquad j = 1, \ldots, r,$$

it follows from (11.58) that we have a nonnegative **b** solution to (11.57). Similarly, if there exist $b_{r+1} \leqslant 0, \ldots, b_n \leqslant 0$ that make

$$f_j(b_{r+1}, \ldots, b_n) \leqslant 0, \qquad j = 1, \ldots, r,$$

then there exists a nonpositive **b** solution to (11.57).

If r is large, this procedure becomes rather cumbersome and may not be too efficient. However, if r is small (on the order of about 20 or less) it may be quite useful and powerful. The most attractive feature of this method is that all information on the v_{jk} is derived by simple pairwise comparisons of consequences.

11.9 MISCELLANEOUS REMARKS

Setting the Origins

In many sections of this chapter we have adopted the convention of equating the relative values of the least desirable values of the variables as in (11.4), viz.,

$$v_{10} = v_{20} = \ldots = v_{m0} = 0.$$

The main reason for setting the v_{j0} equal to one another was to give a way of interconnecting the m value functions $V_1, V_2, \ldots, V_m$ that was not only conceptually simple but also quite useful in obtaining certain value measures. The only reason for choosing zero as the common value of the v_{j0} was one of convenience, effecting a simplification of many formulas. There would be absolutely no difference in our results if we set $v_{j0} = b$, $j = 1, \ldots, m$, with b an arbitrary constant, but in doing this we would have to carry along certain terms containing b in many of the formulas of this chapter. The most common change would be to write $v_{jk} - b$ in place of v_{jk} in many places, as for example, in (11.6), (11.11), (11.16), etc.

Although, in general, the convention of setting $v_{10} = v_{20} = \ldots = v_{m0}$ is quite useful, there may be some situations in which it is better not to connect the m value functions in this way. For example, in certain problems concerning the design and development of physical systems (a new jeep for the Army, a new power plant for a 5-ton truck, a fuselage for a new aircraft, etc.), it may be advantageous to define a standard system (either the present system or one capable of realization) and set the relative values of the values of the performance variables for this "standard" equal to one another. If this is done, changes may be required if the methods of this chapter are to be used. The primary changes would come in certain types of value measures such as the mixed ordinal ranking.

Mixed Dominance

Analyses for mixed dominance among strategies have been omitted from this chapter. For some types of value measures this is not very difficult, and, if the serious student is interested in such analyses, he should be able to formulate them once he has a good grasp of the material in Chapter 7. To include them here would cause undue repetition.

Possibility of Further Simplification

By means of the assumption of valuewise independence of variables, we have seen how one may be able to reduce a very large problem to manageable size. This remark applies primarily to the task of measuring an individual's relative values. Even with this assumption (or approximation) there may still be imposing problems in analysis owing to a potentially huge number of strategies that require comparison. If numerical estimates of the relative values are obtained and if the probability functions follow certain "nice" forms, other tools of mathematical analysis than discussed here may be useful in discriminating among the $E(S_i)$. However, if we consider the probability distributions as arbitrary, what can be done to simplify further our attempt to find a strategy that maximizes the decision maker's expected relative value? Since we have already effected a simplification by assuming valuewise independence among certain variables (or sets of variables)—which, we remind the reader, may be totally unwarranted in some situations—if further simplification is to come about, it must be accomplished in the area of the probability functions (or by a simplification of relative values short of independence[6]). If, for example, there is stochastic independence or causal independence between certain variables, or if the stochastic process operative in the decision situation is Markovian in nature, then it may be possible to simplify greatly the task of identifying good strategies or a "best" strategy. This possibility is discussed in the final chapter.

[6] See Section 12.7.

EXERCISES[7]

1. Given the value rankings (11.2) and (11.3), using (11.4) if you wish, and no other information on the v_{jk}, $j = 1, \ldots, m$; $k = 0, \ldots, n_j$, describe a procedure which will permit maximum use of this information in analyzing $E(S_1) - E(S_2)$ for sign. [*Hint:* Use the method of equating coefficients.]

2. Given $m = 4$, $(n_1, n_2, n_3, n_4) = (2, 3, 4, 5)$, suppose with (11.4) that $v_{j1} \geqslant v_{j2} \geqslant \ldots \geqslant v_{jn_j} \geqslant 0$ for each j and for S_1 and S_2 the probabilities p^i_{jk}, $i = 1, 2$ are given by

$$[p^1_{jk}] = \begin{bmatrix} .4 & .3 & & & \\ .2 & .3 & .4 & & \\ .4 & .3 & .1 & .1 & \\ .2 & .3 & 0 & .1 & .2 \end{bmatrix}$$

$$j = 1, \ldots, 4; \quad k = 1, \ldots, n_j.$$

$$[p^2_{jk}] = \begin{bmatrix} .2 & .5 & & & \\ .1 & .2 & .5 & & \\ .1 & .4 & .3 & .1 & \\ .2 & .2 & .1 & 0 & .2 \end{bmatrix}$$

Show that $E(S_1) \geqslant E(S_2)$. *Note:* The p^i_{j0} have been omitted from these matrices.

3. Prove that $h_j = p^1_{j1} - p^2_{j1} + g_{j2}$ as given above (11.18).

4. Show that $m(S_1, S_2)$ in (11.21) equals $h_1 + g_2$.

5. Verify (11.23).

6. Given the bounded interval measures for $m = 3$, $n_1 = 2$, $n_2 = 3$, and $n_3 = 4$ at the end of Section 11.2, and the probabilities for S_1 and S_2:

$$[p^1_{jk}] = \begin{bmatrix} .3 & | & .6 & .1 & & \\ .5 & | & .2 & .2 & .1 & \\ .6 & | & .2 & 0 & .1 & .1 \end{bmatrix}$$

$$j = 1, 2, 3; \quad k = 0, \ldots, n_j,$$

$$[p^2_{jk}] = \begin{bmatrix} .5 & | & .4 & .1 & & \\ .4 & | & .3 & .1 & .2 & \\ .4 & | & .4 & .1 & 0 & .1 \end{bmatrix}$$

determine $m(S_1, S_2)$ and $M(S_1, S_2)$ as defined by (11.21) and (11.22) respectively. Using theorem 11.1, what can you conclude about the sign of $E(S_1) - E(S_2)$, given only the above information?

Using the numerical estimates of the v_{jk} (i.e., the $\bar{v}_{jk}$) obtained from the bounded interval measures at the end of Section 11.2, find $\bar{f}(S_1, S_2)$. Compare this to the mid-point of $[m(S_1, S_2), M(S_1, S_2)]$.

7. According to the definitions of Section 11.2, suppose with $m = 5$,

---

[7] Model IV applies unless otherwise stated.

$n_1 = 4$, $n_2 = 3$, $n_3 = 5$, $n_4 = 1$, $n_5 = 3$ you obtain the bounded interval measures:

$$.8 \leqslant u_2 \leqslant 1.0, \qquad .6 \leqslant u_3 \leqslant .8, \qquad .4 \leqslant u_4 \leqslant .6, \qquad .2 \leqslant u_5 \leqslant .4,$$
$$.6 \leqslant u_{12} \leqslant .8, \qquad .7 \leqslant u_{13} \leqslant .8, \qquad .3 \leqslant u_{14} \leqslant .5,$$
$$.5 \leqslant u_{22} \leqslant .8, \qquad .6 \leqslant u_{23} \leqslant .8,$$
$$.8 \leqslant u_{32} \leqslant 1.0, \qquad .8 \leqslant u_{33} \leqslant 1.0, \qquad .3 \leqslant u_{34} \leqslant .4, \qquad .7 \leqslant u_{35} \leqslant .9,$$
$$.6 \leqslant u_{52} \leqslant .8, \qquad .1 \leqslant u_{53} \leqslant .3.$$

Obtain an approximate numerical measure of the $v_{jk}, j = 1, \ldots, 5; k = 0, \ldots, n_j$, by the method suggested at the end of Section 11.2. (It is to be assumed we are setting $v_{j0} = 0$ for all j, and $v_{11} = 1$.)

8. (*Continuation.*) From Exercise 7 obtain two more sets of numerical estimates for the v_{jk} by (1) using the upper bounds of the u_j and u_{jk} and (2) using the lower bounds of the u_j and u_{jk}. Compare these estimates to the estimates obtained in Exercise 7. In each case set $v_{11} = 1$ to give an explicit unit measurement.

9. For (11.36) and (11.37) respectively verify that (11.35) is satisfied and that $a_j \leqslant \overline{L}_j \leqslant a_j + b_j$ and $a_{jk} \leqslant \overline{L}_{jk} \leqslant a_{jk} + b_{jk}$. Can you suggest an alternative procedure for estimating the L_j and L_{jk} that satisfy (11.35) and the bounding conditions? If so, which procedure do you feel is more reasonable?

10. For a decision situation with $m = 4$, $n_1 = n_2 = n_3 = n_4 = 3$, suppose the following bounded interval measures, as defined in Section 11.3, are obtained:

$$.15 \leqslant L_1 \leqslant .25, \qquad .30 \leqslant L_2 \leqslant .40, \qquad .16 \leqslant L_3 \leqslant .32, \qquad .10 \leqslant L_4 \leqslant .18,$$
$$.42 \leqslant L_{11} \leqslant .48, \qquad .36 \leqslant L_{12} \leqslant .44, \qquad .14 \leqslant L_{13} \leqslant .20,$$
$$.08 \leqslant L_{21} \leqslant .15, \qquad .72 \leqslant L_{22} \leqslant .80, \qquad .10 \leqslant L_{23} \leqslant .16,$$
$$.32 \leqslant L_{31} \leqslant .40, \qquad .32 \leqslant L_{32} \leqslant .40, \qquad .18 \leqslant L_{33} \leqslant .28,$$
$$.02 \leqslant L_{41} \leqslant .06, \qquad .20 \leqslant L_{42} \leqslant .34, \qquad .54 \leqslant L_{43} \leqslant .66.$$

In addition, suppose for S_1 and S_2 the following probabilities have been estimated:

$$[p^1_{jk}] = \begin{bmatrix} 0 & 1 & 0 & 0 \\ .4 & .1 & .1 & .4 \\ .2 & 0 & .6 & .2 \\ .1 & .5 & .3 & .1 \end{bmatrix}$$

$$j = 1, 2, 3, 4; \quad k = 0, 1, 2, 3.$$

$$[p^2_{jk}] = \begin{bmatrix} 0 & 0 & 1 & 0 \\ .4 & .2 & .2 & .2 \\ .1 & .7 & .2 & 0 \\ .1 & .3 & .5 & .1 \end{bmatrix}$$

Compute $m'(S_1, S_2)$ and $M'(S_1, S_2)$, defined by (11.34a) and (11.34b). From theorem 11.2, given only the above information on relative values, what can you conclude about the sign of $E(S_1) - E(S_2)$?

11. (*Continuation.*) Using the bounded interval measures of Exercise 10, find the $\bar{L}_j$ and $\bar{L}_{jk}$, using (11.36) and (11.37); then set $v_{11} = 1$ and obtain point estimates of the v_{jk} by using (11.38a), (11.38b), and (11.38c). Use these estimates in $E(S_1) - E(S_2)$ to give $f'(S_1, S_2)$, and compare $f'(S_1, S_2)$ with $m'(S_1, S_2)$ and $M'(S_1, S_2)$ found in the previous exercise.

12. For $m = 3$, $n_1 = 2$, $n_2 = 3$, $n_3 = 6$, suppose a mixed ordinal ranking of the v_{jk} ($v_{j0} = 0$ for $j = 1, 2, 3$) is given by

$$v_{11} \geqslant v_{21} \geqslant v_{12} \geqslant v_{31} \geqslant v_{22}$$
$$\geqslant v_{32} \geqslant v_{33} \geqslant v_{23} \geqslant v_{34} \geqslant v_{35} \geqslant v_{36} \geqslant 0.$$

For strategies S_1 and S_2, the following probabilities have been estimated:

$$[p_{jk}^1] = \begin{bmatrix} .07 & .42 & .51 & & & & \\ .37 & .20 & .26 & .17 & & & \\ .42 & .08 & .05 & .14 & .21 & .02 & .08 \end{bmatrix}$$

$$[p_{jk}^2] = \begin{bmatrix} .70 & .12 & .18 & & & & \\ .16 & .30 & .42 & .12 & & & \\ .07 & .27 & .13 & .20 & .07 & .14 & .12 \end{bmatrix}$$

$$j = 1, 2, 3;$$
$$k = 0, 1, \ldots, n_j.$$

Show that $E(S_1) \geqslant E(S_2)$.

13. Develop a mixed ordinal ranking from the following pairwise comparisons. Take (11.2), (11.3), and (11.4) as given, with $m = 4$, $n_1 = 2$, $n_2 = 3$, $n_3 = 3$, $n_4 = 4$. [See the paragraph following (11.39).]

$(y_{12}, y_{20}) \gtrsim (y_{10}, y_{21})$, $\quad (y_{20}, y_{31}) \gtrsim (y_{22}, y_{30})$, $\quad (y_{22}, y_{30}) \gtrsim (y_{20}, y_{32})$,

$(y_{32}, y_{40}) \gtrsim (y_{30}, y_{41})$, $\quad (y_{30}, y_{41}) \gtrsim (y_{33}, y_{40})$, $\quad (y_{33}, y_{40}) \gtrsim (y_{30}, y_{42})$,

$(y_{20}, y_{42}) \gtrsim (y_{23}, y_{40})$, $\quad (y_{23}, y_{40}) \gtrsim (y_{20}, y_{43})$.

14. Describe a method for obtaining (or trying to obtain) the ordered metric ranking (11.41).

15. What "obvious theorem follows from (11.41) and (11.42)"?

16. Describe a method for obtaining the bounded interval measure (11.43).

17. Specify methods for finding the extrema of the right-hand sides of (a) (11.44) subject to (11.43), and (b) (11.47) subject to (11.45) and (11.46).

18. Specify procedures you feel are "reasonable" for obtaining point estimates of the v_{jk} given (a) (11.43), and (b) (11.45).

19. For $m = 5$, $n_1 = 4$, $n_2 = 6$, $n_3 = 2$, $n_4 = 1$, $n_5 = 5$, an ordered metric ranking, as in (11.48), is given as follows (assume $v_{j1} \geqslant v_{j2} \geqslant \ldots \geqslant v_{jn_j} \geqslant v_{j0}$ for each j):

$v_{12} - v_{13} \geqslant v_{24} - v_{25} \geqslant v_{31} - v_{32} \geqslant v_{14} - v_{10} \geqslant v_{41} - v_{40} \geqslant v_{52} - v_{53} \geqslant$
$v_{53} - v_{54} \geqslant v_{21} - v_{22} \geqslant v_{11} - v_{12} \geqslant v_{32} - v_{30} \geqslant v_{23} - v_{24} \geqslant v_{55} - v_{50} \geqslant$
$v_{26} - v_{20} \geqslant v_{13} - v_{14} \geqslant v_{51} - v_{52} \geqslant v_{25} - v_{26} \geqslant v_{54} - v_{55} \geqslant v_{22} - v_{23} \geqslant 0.$

For three strategies, S_1, S_2, and S_3, the p^i_{jk}, $i = 1, 2, 3$, are given as follows:

$$[p^1_{jk}] = \begin{bmatrix} .28 & .23 & .22 & .20 & .07 & & \\ .05 & .13 & .05 & .26 & .16 & .19 & .16 \\ .40 & .40 & .20 & & & & \\ .54 & .46 & & & & & \\ .21 & .13 & .23 & .07 & .26 & .10 & \end{bmatrix}$$

$$[p^2_{jk}] = \begin{bmatrix} .18 & .36 & .20 & .12 & .14 & & \\ .07 & .08 & .16 & .10 & .22 & .12 & .25 \\ .39 & .34 & .27 & & & & \\ .60 & .40 & & & & & \\ .23 & .20 & .11 & .18 & .20 & .08 & \end{bmatrix}$$

$$[p^3_{jk}] = \begin{bmatrix} .24 & .40 & .12 & .06 & .18 & & \\ .08 & .10 & .14 & .18 & .09 & .22 & .19 \\ .46 & .42 & .12 & & & & \\ .64 & .36 & & & & & \\ .23 & .24 & .03 & .30 & .10 & .10 & \end{bmatrix}$$

$$j = 1, \ldots, 5;$$
$$k = 0, 1, \ldots, n_j.$$

Can you determine which of the three strategies has the greatest expected relative value?

20. For $m = 3$, $n_1 = n_2 = n_3 = 2$, the following ordered metric ranking has been obtained:

$$v_{11} - v_{12} \geqslant v_{12} - v_{10} \geqslant v_{21} - v_{22}$$
$$\geqslant v_{32} - v_{30} \geqslant v_{31} - v_{32} \geqslant v_{22} - v_{20} \geqslant 0.$$

Using this the following bounded interval measure has been determined:

$$.7 \leqslant \frac{v_{12} - v_{10}}{v_{11} - v_{12}} \leqslant .9, \qquad .3 \leqslant \frac{v_{21} - v_{22}}{v_{12} - v_{10}} \leqslant .5, \qquad .5 \leqslant \frac{v_{32} - v_{30}}{v_{21} - v_{22}} \leqslant .7,$$

$$.8 \leqslant \frac{v_{31} - v_{32}}{v_{32} - v_{30}} \leqslant 1.0, \qquad .6 \leqslant \frac{v_{22} - v_{20}}{v_{31} - v_{32}} \leqslant .8.$$

Along with these measures of relative values, the following bounded probability measures have been obtained for S_1 and S_2:

$$[(\alpha^1_{jk}, \alpha^1_{jk} + \beta^1_{jk})] = \begin{bmatrix} [.20, .30] & [.44, .60] & [.18, .25] \\ [.08, .15] & [.50, .65] & [.32, .43] \\ [.26, .40] & [.22, .31] & [.36, .48] \end{bmatrix}$$

$$[(\alpha^2_{jk}, \alpha^2_{jk} + \beta^2_{jk})] = \begin{bmatrix} [.15, .30] & [.30, .40] & [.30, .40] \\ [.06, .18] & [.26, .38] & [.40, .54] \\ [.50, .62] & [.12, .20] & [.18, .28] \end{bmatrix}$$

$$j = 1, 2, 3;$$
$$k = 0, 1, 2.$$

Show that $E(S_1) \geqslant E(S_2)$.

21. (*Continuation.*)　Letting $v_{11} - v_{12} = 1$, obtain point estimates of the v_{jk} by using the bounded interval measures in Exercise 20 in the procedure specified at the end of Section 11.5.　Let $v_{10} = v_{20} = v_{30} = 0$.

22. (*Continuation.*)　Using (11.56), obtain point estimates for the p_{jk}^i in Exercise 20.　Combine these with the relative value estimates of Exercise 21 to obtain an approximation to $E(S_1) - E(S_2)$.　Compare this with min $[E(S_1) - E(S_2)]$ from Exercise 20.

Chapter 12

SEQUENTIAL DECISION PROCESSES AND DYNAMIC PROGRAMMING

12.1 INTRODUCTION

Since most decision situations of fair size will have a very large number of possible strategies, it is desirable, if not necessary, to consider ways (which may involve admitted approximations) that reduce the labor required to determine a good or best strategy. Traditional decision theory very often provides us with such means, usually by selecting a very small number of variables of interest that are measured on convenient scales (dollars, time, units of inventory to order, etc.), by assuming a relatively simple predictive model (sometimes deterministic), and by assuming simple forms for value functions (e.g., the relative value of money is linear in the amount). Examples of such means are found in Churchman, Ackoff, and Arnoff (1957), Sasieni, Yaspan, and Friedman (1959), the journals *Operations Research* and *Management Science*, and elsewhere. But as noted in Chapter 1, this is not a book in the spirit of traditional decision theory, and we have no particular desire to consider a listing of "problem formulations" which succumb to the computational algorithms that have been (and are being) developed to handle the mathematically tractable "problems" often formulated by traditional decision theorists. As the title of this chapter implies, we shall discuss (under the appropriate conditions) the role that dynamic programming plays in the type of decision and value theory considered herein. To many analysts, dynamic programming is just one more algorithmic gimmick; are we not therefore trapped by our own words in the last sentence of the prior paragraph? Not really. As we shall see, certain general assumptions will be required in the context of sequential decision processes in order to apply dynamic programming methods, but beyond these general conditions, we do not require very much of the probability functions or value functions. For the very special case where there is both a stationary transition mechanism and a stationary value mechanism assumed for the sequential decision process, several efficient computational algorithms have been developed,[1] but these will not be discussed here. The advantage of using dynamic programming where applicable is that of computational efficiency— instead of trying to find a best strategy all at once, we build up a best strategy piece by piece. The advantages of Bellman's (1957) piece-by-piece approach will be noted as we proceed.

Sequential decision processes to which the dynamic programming approach may be applied are called Markovian decision processes.[2] A number of types of Markovian decision processes will be discussed under two general headings—Type I and Type II Markovian decision processes (M.D.P.). Type I and Type II M.D.P.'s, in our development, differ only with respect to the treatment of the value function. Type I M.D.P.'s assume independence among successive stages or periods in the relative value sense. Type II M.D.P.'s assume a conditional form of valuewise independence, which is a weaker assumption than complete independence. Because we have developed the notion of valuewise independence, the simpler Type-I processes will be discussed first, in Sections 12.4, 12.5, and 12.6, followed by the Type-II processes in Section 12.7.

Before going into the Type I M.D.P. we shall consider one definition of "sequential decision process," and take a brief look at a sequential decision process *per se* in Section 12.3.

12.2 INDEPENDENT COMPONENTS IN A DECISION SITUATION

Before going on to the sequential decision process as such, we shall note how it may be possible to effect certain simplification in analyzing a decision situation in which several types of independence prevail. In this and the following sections, X_j is an action variable, and Y_j is an outcome variable. The type of decision situation studied in this chapter is characterized by a set of *action* variables,

$$\{X_1, X_2, \ldots, X_M\}$$

and a set of *outcome* variables,

$$\{Y_1, Y_2, \ldots, Y_N\}.$$

The total set of variables relevant in the situation will be denoted as T,

$$T = \{X_1, X_2, \ldots, X_M, Y_1, Y_2, \ldots, Y_N\},$$

[1] See, e.g., Howard (1960).
[2] After A. A. Markov (1856–1922), a pioneer in stochastic processes.

or

$$T = \{Z_j\},$$

where each Z_j is one of the relevant action or outcome variables.

Priority Between Variables

In discussing types of independence other than valuewise independence among variables or sets of variables, it is useful to introduce the notion of *priority* between variables.

Definition 12.1   The variable Z_j is *prior* to the variable Z_k if and only if $Z_j \neq Z_k$ and the value of Z_j is realized at or before the time at which the value of Z_k is realized.

In other words, if Z_j is prior to Z_k, the value of Z_j that does in fact obtain will be realized (or be determined, or occur) at or before the time at which the resultant value of Z_k is realized. Obviously, one may select or decide upon a particular value for an action variable that is to be implemented sometime in the future, but this value is not realized until the implementation actually takes place. Because we are interested here in building up to a particular definition of a sequential decision process (to be made explicit in the next section), it will be assumed that for any two distinct variables Z_j and Z_k, either Z_j is prior to Z_k or Z_k is prior to Z_j (or possibly both if the values of Z_j and Z_k are realized simultaneously). This is stated formally in assumption 12.1. Our next definition concerns the set of variables prior to a given variable.

Definition 12.2   The set of all $Z_j \in T$ that are prior to Z_k is called the *prior set* of Z_k, denoted Z_k^P. That is,

$$Z_{k,}^P = \text{set of all } Z_j \text{ in } T, \quad Z_j \neq Z_k, \quad \text{that are prior to } Z_k.$$

Assumption 12.1   For any two distinct variables in T, say Z_j and Z_k,

either $Z_j \in Z_k^P$ or $Z_k \in Z_j^P$ (or possibly both).

In many types of decision situations, this assumption may be violated by the way in which the variables are originally formulated. It may, however, be possible to redefine the variables so that the assumption holds. As noted above, the assumption implies that for any pair (Z_j, Z_k), $Z_j \neq Z_k$, either Z_j is prior to Z_k or vice versa. This further implies that it is meaningful to compare any two variables with respect to the priority relation.

In considering various types of independence between components in a decision situation, we shall begin with a two-part partition of T, into sets T_1 and T_2, such that each T_i contains at least one action variable and at least one outcome variable, with $T = T_1 \cup T_2$.[3] With no loss in generality, suppose that

$$T_1 = \{X_1, X_2, \ldots, X_m, Y_1, Y_2, \ldots, Y_n\},$$
$$T_2 = \{X_{m+1}, \ldots, X_M, Y_{n+1}, \ldots, Y_N\},$$

where $1 \leqslant m < M, 1 \leqslant n < N$.

According to this partition of T, we now define the prior sets of each Z_k with respect to the two components of the partition.

Definition 12.3   The prior set of Z_k with respect to T_i, denoted Z_{ki}^P, is the set of all $Z_j \in T_i$ that are prior to Z_k.

For each Z_k, there is a prior set with respect to T_1 (Z_{k1}^P) and a prior set with respect to T_2 (Z_{k2}^P). Either one or both of these prior sets may be null. For example, if no variable in T is prior to X_1, then X_{11}^P and X_{12}^P are null sets, and we write $X_{11}^P = \emptyset$. To illustrate further, suppose

$$T_1 = \{X_1, Y_1\},$$
$$T_2 = \{X_2, Y_2, Y_3\},$$

and all priorities are summarized by

$$X_1 \to X_2 \to Y_1 \to Y_2 \to Y_3, \qquad Y_3 \to Y_2, \qquad (12.1)$$

where "$\to$" means "is prior to." By assumption 12.1, $\to$ is postulated to be an ordering of T which is transitive and connected, but not reflexive. For this example,

$$
\begin{aligned}
X_{11}^P &= \emptyset, & Y_{12}^P &= \{X_2\}, \\
X_{12}^P &= \emptyset, & Y_{21}^P &= \{X_1, Y_1\} = T_1, \\
X_{21}^P &= \{X_1\}, & Y_{22}^P &= \{X_2, Y_3\}, \\
X_{22}^P &= \emptyset, & Y_{31}^P &= \{X_1, Y_1\} = T_1, \\
Y_{11}^P &= \{X_1\}, & Y_{32}^P &= \{X_2, Y_2\}.
\end{aligned}
$$

Also, by (12.1),

$$
\begin{aligned}
X_1^P &= X_{11}^P \cup X_{12}^P = \emptyset, \\
X_2^P &= X_{21}^P \cup X_{22}^P = \{X_1\}, \\
Y_1^P &= Y_{11}^P \cup Y_{12}^P = \{X_1, X_2\}, \\
Y_2^P &= Y_{21}^P \cup Y_{22}^P = \{X_1, X_2, Y_1, Y_3\}, \\
Y_3^P &= Y_{31}^P \cup Y_{32}^P = \{X_1, X_2, Y_1, Y_2\}.
\end{aligned}
$$

---

[3] $T_1 \cup T_2$ is the set of all variables in either T_1 or T_2.

Total Independence

This brings us to the definition of total independence in the context of assumption 12.1.

Definition 12.4 T_1 and T_2 are *totally independent* if and only if:

1*a*. For each $X_j \in T_1$, X_{j2}^P has no effect upon the availability of acts (or values) of X_j;

1*b*. for each $X_j \in T_2$, X_{j1}^P has no effect upon the availability of acts (or values) of X_j;

2*a*. for each $Y_j \in T_1$, Y_j is stochastically independent of Y_{j2}^P, i.e., $P(Y_j \mid Y_j^P) = P(Y_j \mid Y_{j1}^P)$;

2*b*. for each $Y_j \in T_2$, Y_j is stochastically independent of Y_{j1}^P, i.e., $P(Y_j \mid Y_j^P) = P(Y_j \mid Y_{j2}^P)$; and

3. $V(x_1, \ldots, x_m, x_{m+1}, \ldots, x_M, y_1, \ldots, y_n, y_{n+1}, \ldots, y_N) =$
$V_1(x_1, \ldots, x_m, y_1, \ldots, y_n) + V_2(x_{m+1}, \ldots, x_M, y_{n+1}, \ldots, y_N)$.

What definition 12.4 says, in effect, is that if T_1 and T_2 are totally independent, then the original decision problem may be separated into two parts which have no interactions or interconnections with one another, and the optimal overall strategy may be obtained by finding the optimal substrategy for each part separately. Part 1 of the definition, if satisfied, simply says that whatever happens in the component different from the component of X_j prior to the time that an act of X_j is implemented has no influence on the set of acts in X_j that are available for implementation by the decision maker. The values of variables prior to X_j in its own component may of course affect the acts available in X_j. Part 2 of definition 12.4, if satisfied, says that the probabilities of the various values of Y_j occurring are in no way influenced by the values taken by variables prior to Y_j in the component that does not contain Y_j. Part 3 of the definition asserts valuewise independence or almost independence between $X_1 \times X_2 \times \ldots \times X_m \times Y_1 \times Y_2 \times \ldots \times Y_n$ and $X_{m+1} \times \ldots \times X_M \times Y_{n+1} \times \ldots \times Y_N$ as defined in Chapter 9.

Definition 12.4, as it stands, is really incomplete because (1*a*) and (1*b*) require explication. That is, we need to be more explicit about the meaning of "X_{ji}^P has no effect upon the availability of acts of X_j." The following auxiliary definition is offered as explication for (1*a*).

Definition 12.4a   Suppose $X_j \in T_1$. Let $X_j^P = \{Z_1, Z_2, \ldots, Z_n\}$, and let $\{c_i\}$, $i = 1, 2, \ldots, m$ be the set of $(z_1, \ldots, z_n) \in Z_1 \times \ldots \times Z_n$ for which $P(z_1, \ldots, z_n) > 0$ under one or more ways in which acts from the action variables in X_j^P can be chosen.

Next, partition $\{c_i\}$ into r ($\leqslant m$) nonnull subsets $B_1, B_2, \ldots, B_r$ such that c_i and c_s are both in the same B_k if and only if, for each $Z_t \in X_j^P \cap T_1$, the values of Z_t in c_i and c_s are identical. Finally, let $X_j(c_i)$ denote the set of acts in X_j that are judged capable of being implemented given c_i. Then X_{j2}^P has no effect on the availability of acts in X_j if and only if

$$X_j(c_i) = X_j(c_s)$$

whenever $c_i, c_s \in B_k$; $k = 1, \ldots, r$.

Explication of (1*b*) is obtained by replacing T_1 with T_2 and X_{j2}^P with X_{j1}^P in definition 12.4*a*.

If T_1 and T_2 are totally independent, and if either of these components has at least two action variables and at least two outcome variables, then we may further partition such a component and inquire as to total independence between its subcomponents. For example, if T_1 can be partitioned into T_{11} and T_{12}, with each T_{1i} containing at least one action and at least one outcome variable, then the definition of total independence between T_{11} and T_{12} would proceed as above with T_1 our new universe of discourse since we can forget about T_2 if T_1 and T_2 are totally independent. In such a way, the original set T can be partitioned into, say, K mutually totally independent components,[4] which may be denoted as $T_1, T_2, \ldots, T_K$. Then, in order to find the best over-all strategy within T it suffices to determine the best substrategy in each of the T_i, $i = 1, \ldots, K$. In determining the best substrategy in T_i, we may completely ignore all T_j with $j \neq i$, since nothing in these other $K - 1$ components has anything to do with T_i.

Suboptimization

In most (if not all) decision situations $K = 1$. However, it may be possible to determine several components of T which for "practical purposes" may be treated as totally independent of one another. Just as valuewise independence between components (or subsets of variables) is usually recognized as an approximation to the "real" situation, one may find good reason to *assume* total independence (a much stronger kind of independence) between components in order to have an approximation which will permit an economical analysis of the total decision problem. One term used by operations research (systems research, management science) to describe this kind of approach is *suboptimization*. The strategies determined for each separate component are not the optimal substrategies (in view of the fact that total independence is an approximation), but are "close to the best" substrategies. When these suboptimal

---

[4] If T_1 and T_2 are totally independent, and then if T_{11} and T_{12} are totally independent with $T_1 = T_{11} \cup T_{12}$, it follows that T_{11} and T_2 are totally independent and T_{12} and T_2 are totally independent, making T_{11}, T_{12}, and T_2 three mutually totally independent components of T.

substrategies are put together to give a total strategy (suboptimal), some revision may be required in obtaining a total strategy, particularly if Part 1 of definition 12.4 is violated by the separated components. Methods are being developed to handle the problem of correcting for interactions among separated components after suboptimal strategies have been determined in the various components,[5] but we shall not discuss these here.

12.3 THE SEQUENTIAL DECISION PROCESS

In this section, we shall give one definition for the phrase "sequential decision process," illustrate how some situations which do not fit the form given by the definition may be reformulated so as to satisfy the definition, and discuss the general concept of "strategy" in this context. In the next section, valuewise independence will be combined with the Markovian property, exhibited by some sequential decision processes, to yield the typical dynamic programming approach in getting a best solution to this type of decision problem.

In this and the following sections, certain notational problems present themselves. Since our discussion has many items to be accounted for, there is, on the one hand, the danger of making the notation so cumbersome as to be frightening and, on the other hand, the danger of making the notation so streamlined that one must continually refer to the original definitions in order to find out what is going on. Our own preferences tend toward symbolic economy in this context so that we suggest the reader take a good look at (12.10) through (12.12)[6] before proceeding with the material that follows these notational definitions.

If the decision situation contains totally independent components (definition 12.4), the following discussions may apply to each one of these components considered separately. The definition of "sequential decision process" follows.

Definition 12.5 A given decision situation is a (finite) *sequential decision process* if the total set of variables, T, relevant in the situation may be written as

$$T = \{X_1, X_2, \ldots, X_N, Y_1, Y_2, \ldots, Y_{N+1}\}, \qquad (12.2)$$

such that

$$Y_{N+1} \to X_N \to Y_N \to X_{N-1} \to Y_{N-1} \to \ldots \to X_2 \to Y_2 \to X_1 \to Y_1 \qquad (12.3)$$

and $N \geq 2$. N is called the number of *stages*.

---

[5] See, for example, Sanders (1963).

[6] In the case of probabilities we use notation quite similar to Howard's (1960), and less similar but related to Feller's (1957) and Rosenblatt's (1962).

By the definition, the number of outcome variables in T exceeds the number of action variables by one. The outcome variable Y_{N+1} is called the *initial outcome variable*. A value of Y_{N+1} is called a set of initial conditions of the process. In cases where the initial conditions are uniquely specified, Y_{N+1} will have exactly one value. At the other end, Y_1 is called the *terminal outcome variable*. Following Y_1, there may be an "indefinite future." In fact, in some situations it may be advantageous to terminate the explicit formulation with an action variable X_1 and let Y_1 represent a set of "indefinite futures," although we shall assume that the values of Y_1 are well defined. The role of Y_1 is discussed further in Section 12.5.

The "backward" notation used in (12.3) with regard to the subscripting of the X's and Y's is typical and will be familiar to many readers. In words, (12.3) may be interpreted as follows: The decision maker first observes a value of Y_{N+1}, then selects and implements an act in X_N. This is followed by his observance of a value of Y_N. After observing this value of Y_N, the decision maker then selects and implements an act in X_{N-1} which is followed by the occurrence of a value in $Y_{N-1}\ldots$. Finally, after observing the resultant value from Y_2, the decision maker implements an act in X_1, which is followed by the occurrence of a value from Y_1. Thus, we are considering processes which proceed through all N stages. One could also consider processes which may terminate at any stage along the way, but we shall not do this here explicitly. (It could be included, however, by adding a null act to each X and a null "outcome" to each Y.) The novelty of the dynamic programming approach—as formulated by Bellman (1957)—is that, in determining a strategy for the decision maker to follow, we begin with the last action variable X_1 and work backward in time to X_N.

At first glance, definition 12.5 may seem quite restrictive, because of (12.2) and (12.3), but appearances can be deceiving. The crucial words in the definition are "may be written as." Letting X'_j, Y'_k be action and outcome variables as originally formulated, suppose

$$Y'_{k-1} \rightarrow X'_j \rightarrow X'_{j+1} \rightarrow X'_{j+2} \rightarrow Y'_k \rightarrow Y'_{k+1} \rightarrow X'_{j+3} \rightarrow Y'_{k+2}$$

$$(12.4)$$

describes the sequence of acts and results. Let

$$Y_3 = Y'_{k-1},$$
$$X_2 = X'_j \times X'_{j+1} \times X'_{j+2},$$
$$Y_2 = Y'_k \times Y'_{k+1},$$
$$X_1 = X'_{j+3},$$
$$Y_1 = Y'_{k+2}.$$

Then (12.4) may be written as $Y_3 \to X_2 \to Y_2 \to X_1 \to Y_1$, in the form of (12.3). As another example, suppose

$$Y'_0 \to X'_1 \to \{Y'_1, Y'_2\} \to \{X'_2, X'_3\} \to Y'_3, \qquad (12.5)$$

but there is no prior relation between Y'_1 and Y'_2 (it is not clear which variable will realize its resultant value first) nor between X'_2 and X'_3. Letting $Y_3 = Y'_0$, $X_2 = X'_1$, $Y_2 = Y'_1 \times Y'_2$, $X_1 = X'_2 \times X'_3$, and $Y_1 = Y'_3$, (12.5) may be put in the form $Y_3 \to X_2 \to Y_2 \to X_1 \to Y_1$.

Conceptual and Available Strategies

The acts or values of X_n $(1 \leqslant n \leqslant N)$ in (12.3) will generally be denoted as x_n $(x_n \in X_n)$ or as $x_{n0}, x_{n1}, \ldots, x_{nr_n}$ with

$$X_n = \{x_{n0}, x_{n1}, \ldots, x_{nr_n}\}, \qquad n = 1, \ldots, N.$$

Similarly,

$$Y_n = \{y_{n0}, y_{n1}, \ldots, y_{ns_n}\}, \qquad n = 1, \ldots, N + 1.$$

In this notation a *conceptual strategy*, say S'_i, may be formulated as follows: First, let f_N denote a function which assigns an $x_N \in X_N$ to each $y_{N+1} \in Y_{N+1}$. We may write $f_N(y_{N+1}) = x_N$. Next, let f_{N-1} denote a function which assigns an $x_{N-1} \in X_{N-1}$ to each $(y_{N+1}, x_N, y_N) = (y_{N+1}, f_N(y_{N+1}), y_N)$. Here we may write $f_{N-1}(y_{N+1}, x_N, y_N) = x_{N-1}$. Continue in this fashion letting f_n denote a function which assigns an $x_n \in X_n$ to each conceptual history of the process to that point, as indicated by the results of the outcome variables $Y_{N+1}, Y_N, \ldots, Y_{n+1}$ and the functions $f_N, f_{N-1}, \ldots, f_{n+1}$:

$$f_n(y_{N+1}, x_N, y_N, x_{N-1}, \ldots, x_{n+1}, y_{n+1})$$
$$= f_n[y_{N+1}, f_N(y_{N+1}), y_N, f_{N-1}(y_{N+1}, f_N(y_{N+1}), y_N),$$
$$\ldots, f_{n+1}(y_{N+1}, f_N(y_{N+1}), y_N, f_{N-1}(y_{N+1}, f_N(y_{N+1}), y_N),$$
$$\ldots, f_{n+2}(y_{N+1}, \ldots, y_{n+3}), y_{n+2}), y_{n+1}] = x_n. \qquad (12.6)$$

Then

$$S'_i = \{f_N, f_{N-1}, \ldots, f_2, f_1\}. \qquad (12.7)$$

To illustrate, suppose the sequential decision process is described by $Y_4 \to X_3 \to Y_3 \to X_2 \to Y_2 \to X_1 \to Y_1$ with $(s_4, r_3, s_3, r_2, s_2, r_1, s_1) = (0, 1, 1, 1, 1, 1, 1)$, where

$$r_j + 1 = \text{number of elements in } X_j,$$

$$s_j + 1 = \text{number of elements in } Y_j.$$

One conceptual strategy is given by

$$f_3(y_{40}) = x_{30},$$
$$f_2(y_{40}, x_{30}, y_{30}) = x_{20},$$
$$f_2(y_{40}, x_{30}, y_{31}) = x_{20},$$
$$f_1(y_{40}, x_{30}, y_{30}, x_{20}, y_{20}) = x_{11},$$
$$f_1(y_{40}, x_{30}, y_{30}, x_{20}, y_{21}) = x_{11},$$
$$f_1(y_{40}, x_{30}, y_{31}, x_{20}, y_{20}) = x_{11},$$
$$f_1(y_{40}, x_{30}, y_{31}, x_{20}, y_{21}) = x_{11},$$

in which f_n is a constant for $n = 1, 2, 3$ (e.g., f_1 takes on the value x_{11} for each conceptual history). Another conceptual strategy is given by

$$f_3(y_{40}) = x_{30},$$
$$f_2(y_{40}, x_{30}, y_{30}) = x_{20},$$
$$f_2(y_{40}, x_{30}, y_{31}) = x_{21},$$
$$f_1(y_{40}, x_{30}, y_{30}, x_{20}, y_{20}) = x_{10},$$
$$f_1(y_{40}, x_{30}, y_{30}, x_{20}, y_{21}) = x_{11},$$
$$f_1(y_{40}, x_{30}, y_{31}, x_{21}, y_{20}) = x_{10},$$
$$f_1(y_{40}, x_{30}, y_{31}, x_{21}, y_{21}) = x_{11}.$$

It should be clear that if the decision problem is of fair size, the total number of conceptual strategies will be huge. Even in the above 3-stage process, with each variable beyond Y_4 capable of assuming two values, there are $2^7 = 128$ conceptual strategies.

Obviously, we will get nowhere fast in larger problems if it is necessary to work with strategies of the most general type given above.[7] Therefore, short of assuming total independence, we shall consider the possibility of simplifying the sequential decision problem.

To differentiate between a conceptual strategy and an *available strategy*, the following definition is offered.

Definition 12.6 A conceptual strategy S_i' as given by (12.7) is an *available strategy* if and only if for each n, $n = N, N - 1, \ldots, 1$, $f_n(y_{N+1}, x_N, \ldots, x_{n+1}, y_{n+1})$ specifies an available act in X_n, given

[7] True unless the decision maker (or research worker, perhaps) is able to eliminate all but a small number of strategies before further analysis is performed. *This is very often done in practice.* Note the difference between the way "admissible strategy" was used in Chapter 2 and the way "available strategy" is used here. Every admissible strategy is an available strategy, but not vice versa. In the general discussion to follow, the set of available strategies will be used.

$(y_{N+1}, x_N, \ldots, x_{n+1}, y_{n+1})$ for each $(y_{N+1}, x_N, \ldots, x_{n+1}, y_{n+1})$ for which $P(y_{n+1} \mid y_{N+1}, x_N, \ldots, x_{n+1})$ is defined and positive with

$$\sum_{y_{n+1}} P(y_{n+1} \mid y_{N+1}, x_N, \ldots, x_{n+1}) = 1,$$

where $x_N, x_{N-1}, \ldots, x_{n+1}$ are given by f_m for $m = N, N-1, \ldots, n+1$, respectively.

Simply stated, an available strategy is a conceptual strategy which can be implemented by the decision maker. While the set **S** of available strategies may be much smaller than the set of conceptual strategies, this generally will not alleviate the problem of size to any appreciable degree. Henceforth, we will be concerned only with available strategies, and when we write $(y_{N+1}, x_N, \ldots, x_{n+1}, y_{n+1})$, it is to be understood that this vector of values has positive probability of occurrence with one or more available strategies, or that $(y_{N+1}, x_N, \ldots, x_{n+1})$ has positive probability of occurrence with one or more available strategies but

$$P(y_{n+1} \mid y_{N+1}, x_N, \ldots, x_{n+1}) = 0.$$

We shall now consider a simplified sequential decision process which is not as simple as a process in which all stages are totally independent of one another, but which may be thought of as being one step removed from total independence. This is called a Type I M.D.P. since it contains the usual conditions on the probability functions which define a Markov process as in (12.8).

12.4 MODEL V—TYPE I MARKOVIAN DECISION PROCESSES

Building upon the ideas thus far developed in this chapter, we have the following definition:

Definition 12.7 The sequential decision process (12.2) and (12.3) is a *Type I Markovian decision process* if and only if:

1. For each X_n, the subset of acts in X_n available for implementation by the decision maker is uniquely determined, given the resultant value of Y_{n+1};

2. for each Y_n, $n < N$,

$$P(y_n \mid y_{N+1}, x_N, \ldots, y_{n+1}, x_n) = P(y_n \mid y_{n+1}, x_n); \qquad (12.8)$$

3. $V(y_{N+1}, x_N, y_N, x_{N-1}, y_{N-1}, \ldots, x_1, y_1) = V_{N+1}(y_{N+1}) + V_N(x_N, y_N)$
$+ V_{N-1}(x_{N-1}, y_{N-1}) + \ldots + V_1(x_1, y_1).$ $\qquad (12.9)$

Thus, we have a Type I M.D.P. if the variables in the N stages and the initial outcome variable are valuewise independent of one another,[8] if the probabilities of occurrence of the values of the outcome variable in each stage past the first (in time) depend only on the act implemented in that stage and on the resultant value of the previous outcome variable, and if the availability of an act in each stage past the first is completely determinable from the resultant value of the previous outcome variable.

Determining an Optimal Strategy

If the conditions of definition 12.7 are satisfied, then we can use Bellman's (1957) principle of optimality[9] in trying to determine an optimal strategy. Notationally, let

$$v_j^k(n) = V_n(x_{nk}, y_{nj}), \qquad (12.10)$$

$$j = 0, 1, \ldots, s_n; \ k = 0, 1, \ldots, r_n; \ n = 1, \ldots, N;$$

$$p_{ij}^k(n) = P(y_{nj} \mid y_{n+1,i}, x_{nk}), \qquad (12.11)$$

$$i = 0, 1, \ldots, s_{n+1}; \ j = 0, 1, \ldots, s_n; \ k = 0, 1, \ldots, r_n;$$
$$n = 1, \ldots, N.$$

$u_i(n) = $ maximum expected relative value over stages $n, n - 1, \ldots, 1$ (the last n stages), given $\qquad (12.12)$

$$y_{n+1} = y_{n+1,i}, \qquad i = 0, 1, \ldots, s_{n+1}; \ n = 1, \ldots, N.$$

To follow the usual parlance, a strategy which yields the $u_i(1)$, $u_i(2)$, $\ldots$, $u_i(N - 1)$, $u_i(N)$ will be called an *optimal strategy*. Application of the principle of optimality in this context yields

$$u_i(1) = \max_k \sum_{j=0}^{s_1} p_{ij}^k(1)v_j^k(1), \qquad i = 0, \ldots, s_2; \ k = 0, \ldots, r_1,$$
$$(12.13)$$

$$u_i(n) = \max_k \sum_{j=0}^{s_n} p_{ij}^k(n)[v_j^k(n) + u_j(n - 1)], \qquad (12.14)$$

$$i = 0, \ldots, s_{n+1}; \ k = 0, \ldots, r_n; \ n = 2, \ldots, N.$$

At stage 1, for each $y_{2i} \in Y_2$ we seek an act in X_1 that is available given y_{2i} and maximizes the (conditional) expected relative value in stage 1 (i.e., deriving from V_1). Having obtained $u_0(1), u_1(1), \ldots, u_{s_2}(1)$, we then put these into (12.14) for $n = 2$ and attempt to determine, for each $y_{3i} \in Y_3$, an act in X_2 that is available given y_{3i} and maximizes the

[8] $V_{N+1}(y_{N+1})$ plays no part in determining a best strategy and will therefore not appear in the formulation that follows.

[9] See also Sasieni, Yaspan, and Friedman (1959, Chapter 10) for an elementary discussion of dynamic programming.

expected relative value over stages 2 and 1. Continuing in this fashion, we eventually determine $u_0(N), u_1(N), \ldots, u_{s_N+1}(N)$.

It will be noted that (12.14) may be written as

$$u_i(n) = \max_k \left[\sum_{j=0}^{s_n} p_{ij}^k(n)v_j^k(n) + \sum_{j=0}^{s_n} p_{ij}^k(n)u_j(n-1) \right]. \quad (12.15)$$

Thus, in finding the k (or the $x_{nk} \in X_n$) which yields $u_i(n)$ we are maximizing the expected relative value in the nth stage, given $y_{n+1,i}$, plus the expected maximum relative value in stages $n-1, \ldots, 1$, given $y_{n+1,i}$. In less profound words, our interest lies not only in getting something out of the next stage (n), but also in placing the decision maker in a favorable position with respect to the remaining $n-1$ stages. It should be realized of course that our immediate interest lies in determining the $x_{Nk} \in X_N$ that give $u_i(N)$, since X_N is the first action variable to have a value implemented in the passage of time. It may happen that, after one or two stages of the process have actually passed, one may wish to formulate a new problem and go through the above procedure again, perhaps introducing several new stages beyond stage 1 in the old formulation.

In finding the k (or $x_{nk} \in X_n$) that maximizes the sum in (12.13) or (12.14) for a given $y_{n+1,i}$, it is to be understood that we look only at the x_{nk} that are available given $y_{n+1,i}$. Indeed, if $x_{nk_1} \in X_n$ is not available given y_{n+1,i_1}, then the bracket term in (12.15) is not defined or need not be defined for $k = k_1$, $i = i_1$.[10]

In addition to the terms used above, it is convenient to introduce a notation which, for each n and i (or $y_{n+1,i} \in Y_{n+1}$), identifies an available act in X_n that yields $u_i(n)$.

Following typical notation for this sort of thing, let

$d_i(n)$ = an act in X_n that is available, given $y_{n+1,i}$, and yields $u_i(n)$.

An optimal strategy may then be written as

$$S_{\text{opt}} = [\{d_i(N)\}, \{d_i(N-1)\}, \ldots, \{d_i(1)\}]. \quad (12.16)$$

An optimal strategy tells one what is best to do at each stage given the result of the previous stage, whatever that may be. The reader will note that a strategy of the form given by (12.16) is much simpler in content than a general strategy as given by (12.7). This is, of course, because of the fact that we are dealing with a Type I M.D.P., a special case of the general sequential decision process. To give a better comparison to

---

[10] It is also understood that there is a positive probability of occurrence for each $y_{ni} \in Y_n$ $(i = 0, \ldots, s_n; n = 1, \ldots, N)$ under one or more available strategies.

(12.6) and (12.7) in the Markovian context, all strategies of interest here may be written as

$$[\{f_N(y_{N+1})\}, \{f_{N-1}(y_N)\}, \ldots, \{f_1(y_2)\}]. \tag{12.17}$$

In terms of (12.17), an optimal strategy (12.16) is identified by

$$f_n(y_{n+1,i}) = d_i(n) \qquad \text{for all } i, n.$$

In determining the $d_i(n)$ for the finite stage case being considered, we first determine the $d_i(1)$, $i = 0, \ldots, s_2$ from (12.13), then the $d_i(2)$, $i = 0, \ldots, s_3$ from (12.14) with $n = 2$, and so on back to $d_i(N)$ from (12.14) with $n = N$.

ILLUSTRATIVE EXAMPLE.   The following numerical example illustrates the previous ideas.   Take

$$N = 3, \ Y_4 \to X_3 \to Y_3 \to X_2 \to Y_2 \to X_1 \to Y_1,$$

with

$$
\begin{aligned}
Y_4 &= \{y_{40}\}, & s_4 &= 0; \\
X_3 &= \{x_{30}, x_{31}, x_{32}, x_{33}\}, & r_3 &= 3; \\
Y_3 &= \{y_{30}, y_{31}, y_{32}\}, & s_3 &= 2; \\
X_2 &= \{x_{20}, x_{21}\}, & r_2 &= 1; \\
Y_2 &= \{y_{20}, y_{21}\}, & s_2 &= 1; \\
X_1 &= \{x_{10}, x_{11}, x_{12}\}, & r_1 &= 2; \\
Y_1 &= \{y_{10}, y_{11}, y_{12}, y_{13}\}, & s_1 &= 3.
\end{aligned}
$$

For $n = 1$, the following arrays give $p_{ij}^k(1)$ and $v_j^k(1)$:

i	k	j 0	1	2	3	Row Sums
	0	.2	.3	.2	.3	1.0
0	1	.4	.5	.1	0	1.0
	2	\(x_{12} unavailable given y_{20}\)				
	0	.1	.3	.2	.4	1.0
1	1	0	.4	.5	.1	1.0
	2	.2	.5	.2	.1	1.0

$$p_{ij}^k(1) = P(y_{1j} \mid y_{2i}, x_{1k}),$$

$$j$$

	0	1	2	3
0	.1	1.0	.8	.5
k 1	.1	.9	.6	.3
2	0	.7	.4	.2

$$v_j^k(1) = V_1(x_{1k}, y_{1j}).$$

From these two arrays we make up the following table of $\sum_{j=0}^{3} p_{ij}^k(1)v_j^k(1)$:

$$k$$

	0	1	2
i 0	.63	.55	—
1	.67	.69	.45

giving

$$u_0(1) = .63, \quad d_0(1) = x_{10} \quad (k = 0),$$
$$u_1(1) = .69, \quad d_1(1) = x_{11} \quad (k = 1). \tag{12.18}$$

We now go on to stage 2. Suppose the $p_{ij}^k(2)$ and $v_j^k(2)$ are given by the following tables. For convenience, $v_j^k(2) + u_j(1)$ is also shown:

$$j$$

i	k	0	1	Row Sums
0	0	.2	.8	1.0
	1	.7	.3	1.0
1	0	.4	.6	1.0
	1	.5	.5	1.0
2	0	.8	.2	1.0
	1	.1	.9	1.0

$$p_{ij}^k(2) = P(y_{2j} \mid y_{3i}, x_{2k}),$$

$$j \qquad\qquad\qquad\qquad\qquad j$$

k		0	1		k		0	1
	0	0	.7			0	.63	1.39
	1	.2	1.0			1	.83	1.69

$$v_j^k(2) = V_2(x_{2k}, y_{2j}) \qquad\qquad v_j^k(2) + u_j(1).$$

The next table, constructed from the above two [and (12.18)] gives $\sum_{j=0}^{1} p_{ij}^k(2)[v_j^k(2) + u_j(1)]$.

		k	
		0	1
	0	1.238	1.088
i	1	1.086	1.260
	2	.782	1.604

and hence

$$u_0(2) = 1.238, \quad d_0(2) = x_{20} \quad (k = 0),$$
$$u_1(2) = 1.260, \quad d_1(2) = x_{21} \quad (k = 1),$$
$$u_2(2) = 1.604, \quad d_2(2) = x_{21} \quad (k = 1).$$

Finally, for stage 3, suppose the $p_{0j}^k(3)$, $v_j^k(3)$, and $v_j^k(3) + u_j(2)$ are given by

		j		
		0	1	2
	0	0	.5	.5
k	1	.3	.6	.1
	2	.1	.6	.3
	3	.2	.1	.7

$$p_{0j}^k(3) = P(y_{3j} \mid y_{40}, x_{3k}),$$

		j					0	1	2
		0	1	2					
	0	0	.2	.1		0	1.238	1.460	1.704
k	1	0	.2	.1		1	1.238	1.460	1.704
	2	0	.2	.1	$\longrightarrow$	2	1.238	1.460	1.704
	3	0	.2	.1		3	1.238	1.460	1.704

$$v_j^k(3) = V_3(x_{3k}, y_{3j}) \qquad\qquad v_j^k(3) + u_j(2).$$

Our final table shows, in the three columns reading left to right, the expected value in stage 3, the expected value in stages 2 and 1, and the total expected value over all three stages for each $x_{3k} \in X_3$, $k = 0, 1, 2, 3$, given the $d_i(1)$ and $d_i(2)$.

	$\displaystyle\sum_{j=0}^{2} p_{0j}^{k}(3)v_{j}^{k}(3)$	$\displaystyle\sum_{j=0}^{2} p_{0j}^{k}(3)u_{j}(2)$	$\displaystyle\sum_{j=0}^{2} p_{0j}^{k}(3)[v_{j}^{k}(3) + u_{j}(2)]$
0	.15	1.4320	1.5820
1	.13	1.2878	1.4178
2	.15	1.3610	1.5110
3	.09	1.4964	1.5864

From this table we conclude that

$$u_0(3) = 1.5864, \qquad d_0(3) = x_{33} \qquad (k = 3),$$

and note that, while x_{33} gives the least expected value of the x_{k3} in stage 3 (i.e., .09), it places us in the best position for the remaining two stages. This indicates that it is advantageous to make a small "sacrifice" in the third stage in order to gain a potential or expected advantage later on. One witnesses this type of thing quite often in practice; some examples are the graduate student, medical student, etc., who makes various "sacrifices" during his period of study in order to be in a better position later on (he hopes); the young and growing company which practically goes broke (and sometimes does) from large advertising expenditures in the hope of gaining a firm foothold in the market; the parents who scrimp and save in order to send their kids to college; and so forth.

The economy that may be gained by using the dynamic programming approach in a Type I M.D.P. is quite easy to demonstrate, particularly if point estimates of the $p_{ij}^{k}(n)$ and the $v_{j}^{k}(n)$ have been obtained. In the above example, we compared 2 quantities to find $d_0(1)$, 3 quantities to find $d_1(1)$, 2 quantities each to find $d_0(2)$, $d_1(2)$, and $d_2(2)$, and 4 quantities to find $d_0(3)$. After adding the numbers, we see that 15 quantities in 6 subsets were used to find the best strategy. If, instead of using the dynamic programming approach, we had proceeded by comparing available strategies of the form (12.17) directly, we would have had to compare 168 quantities (the expected relative values of the 168 available strategies), in one set. A much more forceful example is given by supposing that $N = 10$,

$$(s_{11} + 1, r_{10} + 1, s_{10} + 1, r_9 + 1, \ldots, r_1 + 1, s_1 + 1)$$
$$= (1, 4, 4, 4, 4, \ldots, 4, 4).$$

If all four x_{nk} are available regardless of which $y_{n+1,i}$ occurs, and if all four conditional probabilities, given $y_{n+1,i}$, x_{nk}, are positive, then in the dynamic programming method there are $9(16) + 4 = 148$ quantities in

$9(4) + 1 = 37$ subsets that will be used to find an optimal strategy. If whole strategies of the form (12.17) are used in an analysis, there will be

$$4 \times 4^4 \times 4^4 \times \ldots \times 4^4 = 4 \times (4^4)^9 = 2^{74}$$
$$= 18{,}889{,}465{,}931{,}478{,}580{,}854{,}784$$

quantities to compare. As everyone knows, this last number is pretty large, although not nearly as large as one googol. Of course, the possibility always remains that the decision maker can pick a small number of these 2^{74} available strategies which he believes to contain the best strategy. If, for example, he picks a dozen of the 2^{74} for further consideration as his admissible strategies, then it might be just as well (for his purposes) to compute the expected relative value of those dozen strategies directly.

12.5 FURTHER DISCUSSION OF MODEL V

When point estimates of the $v_j^k(n)$ for each stage have been obtained [see Chapter 11 for some methods of getting approximate numerical values of the $v_j^k(n)$], and point estimates of the $p_{ij}^k(n)$ have been obtained, there should be no difficulty in computing an optimal strategy by the methods of the previous section, whether done by hand for processes of modest size or by an electronic digital computer for larger problems. Any competent programmer should have little trouble in composing a general program to handle this type of problem.

Notes on Formulation

In setting up a sequential decision situation, one is usually faced with an initial decision on the number of stages (N) to explicitly include in the formulation. The problem facing the decision maker (and, perhaps, the research worker) is the typical horizon problem of just how far to go into the future (explicitly). In terms of size and complexity, it is advantageous to keep N small. In addition, the level of uncertainty concerning the probabilities (and perhaps the relative values) usually increases as we get further away from the present. On the other hand, a larger N is usually thought to give a better or more accurate appraisal of the "best" act in X_N (given y_{N+1}).

In any sequential decision situation the decision of how large to make N is a matter of personal judgment. It is, of course, possible to set up a decision problem for the selection of N ($N = 1, 2, 3, \ldots, N_{\max}$ are the courses of action) but this will be so intertwined with the resultant sequential formulation that it hardly seems worthwhile. In our opinion, after due cogitation and consideration, it will be possible to arrive at an N that is satisfactory in the eyes of the decision maker and analytically reasonable in the eyes of the research worker or analyst. This, of course, does not preclude the possibility of choosing several values for N and running an analysis for each value, perhaps to see how sensitive or insensitive the $d_i(N)$ are with respect to N. But if one places the most confidence in the $d_i(N)$ for the largest of these several N, it seems rather senseless even to bother going through an analysis for smaller values of N unless the problem is so simple that an analysis for still larger values of N can be run with very little effort—which is seldom the case. One major difficulty in trying to compare analyses for several different N emerges with respect to measures of relative values. There is some reason to expect that for two different N, the relative values in a stage common to both may vary widely. This possibility should be clarified by the discussion that follows.

Relative Value in the Terminal Stage and Elsewhere

To simplify things a bit, we shall reduce the notation of (12.10) by letting

$$\{v_{nv}\} = \{v_j^k(n)\}. \tag{12.19}$$

That is, each v_{nv} is one of the $v_j^k(n)$ or $V_n(x_{nk}, y_{nj})$, and vice versa. For the nth stage, the set of relative values for the realizable ordered pairs in $X_n \times Y_n$ will be

$$\{v_{n0}, v_{n1}, \ldots, v_{nm_n}\}, \qquad n = 1, 2, \ldots, N,$$

where $m_n + 1$ is the number of ordered pairs in $X_n \times Y_n$ that can occur with one or more available strategies. As in Chapter 11, we may set

$$v_{10} = v_{20} = \ldots = v_{N0} = 0$$

and suppose, with no loss in generality, that

$$v_{n1} \geqslant v_{n2} \geqslant \ldots \geqslant v_{nm_n} \geqslant 0, \qquad n = 1, \ldots, N.$$

After determining the ranking of the v_{n1} (or $v_{n1} - v_{n0}$) for $n = 1, \ldots, N$, one may obtain bounded interval measures of the v_{nv}, as discussed in Sections 11.2 and 11.3, or may employ any of the other measures mentioned in Chapter 11 (or some not mentioned there). Application of one of the bounded interval measures in the context of Model V will be discussed in the next subsection.

Under the assumption of valuewise independence, with the value function of the form

$$V(y_{N+1}, z_{Nv_N}, z_{N-1,v_{N-1}}, \ldots, z_{1v_1})$$
$$= V_{N+1}(y_{N+1}) + v_{Nv_N} + v_{N-1,v_{N-1}} + \ldots + v_{1v_1},$$

according to (12.9) and (12.19), on letting $Z_n = X_n \times Y_n$, $z_{nv} \in Z_n$, it will be recalled that emphasis has been placed on obtaining measures of the v_{nv} using comparisons between complete consequences,[11] even though the consequences in a given comparison may differ with respect to the values of a small number of the variables Z_n, $n = 1, \ldots, N$. In this scheme, the variable $Z_1 = X_1 \times Y_1$ for the terminal stage (stage 1) occupies an unusual position in the value measurement context with respect to the variables for the stages prior to stage 1. The reason for this derives from the fact that we do not normally expect the world to come to an end after a value of Y_1 is realized, and are aware of some "indefinite future" beyond Y_1. In general, we would expect that the decision maker, in his value judgments, incorporates feelings about this indefinite future that are reflected in the v_{1v}, the relative values for the terminal stage. Specifically, the different values of Y_1 [or X_1, if Y_1 itself refers to a set of indefinite futures] may indicate to the decision maker quite different futures beyond the explicit stages of the formulated sequence of N stages. While there will obviously be uncertainties as to what these futures may be, we would expect (and in fact desire) that the decision maker's relative values for the terminal stage account for his feelings about the future, insofar as it depends on the results of the terminal stage.

On the other hand (under the assumption of valuewise independence among stages), we do *not* want the relative values in previous stages (2 through N) to reflect the desirability of future possibilities resulting from each of these stages. These future possibilities are fully accounted for by the probability distributions from (12.11). For example, in comparing $v_{21} - v_{20} = v_{21}$ with $v_{31} - v_{30} = v_{31}$, it seems much more appropriate to compare two consequences having the forms

$$(y_{N+1}, z_{Nv_N}, \ldots, z_{4v_4}, z_{30}, z_{21}, z_{1v_1}), \tag{12.20a}$$

and

$$(y_{N+1}, z_{Nv_N}, \ldots, z_{4v_4}, z_{31}, z_{20}, z_{1v_1}), \tag{12.20b}$$

than to compare, for example, two partial consequences (z_{30}, z_{21}) and (z_{31}, z_{20}), in which nothing is said about the values of other variables $(Y_{N+1}, Z_N, \ldots, Z_4, Z_1)$. If in fact the variables $Y_{N+1}, Z_N, \ldots, Z_1$ are valuewise independent, then in comparing (12.20a) and (12.20b), it should make no difference to the decision maker what $(y_{N+1}, z_{Nv_N}, \ldots, z_{4v_4}, z_{1v_1})$ is taken to be so long as the two consequences "make sense" to him (e.g., are possible of attainment under one or more available strategies).

In many instances, one might find that $v_{11} - v_{10}$ is much greater than any of the other $v_{n1} - v_{n0}$, and this should not be surprising in the light of the previous discussions. One of the special cases of Model V (considered in the next section) assumes that the stages prior to the terminal stage have

---

[11] In this notation a complete consequence has the form $(y_{N+1}, z_{Nv_N}, z_{N-1,v_{N-1}}, \ldots z_{1v_1})$.

worth only insofar as they propel one toward the various values of Y_1. In this case, $v_{n1} = v_{n0}$ for $n = 2, \ldots, N$. In certain very special cases that have stationary transition mechanisms from stage to stage and a simple value mechanism, there are other ways to account for the future beyond Y_1.[12]

Bounded Measures in Dynamic Programming

To conclude this section, a small example is presented to illustrate the use of bounded probability measures and bounded value measures in the dynamic programming approach. Suppose with $N = 2$ that

$$Y_3 = \{y_{30}\},$$
$$X_2 = \{x_{20}, x_{21}\},$$
$$Y_2 = \{y_{20}, y_{21}\},$$
$$X_1 = \{x_{10}, x_{11}\},$$
$$Y_1 = \{y_{10}, y_{11}\},$$

that all acts in X_2 and X_1 are available regardless of what comes before, and that each of the two values of Y_n for $n = 1, 2$ has positive probability of occurrence with each value of X_n and Y_{n+1}.

For stage 1, using the notation of (12.10), suppose we have the value measures

$$v_1^1(1) \geqslant v_1^0(1) \geqslant v_0^1(1) \geqslant v_0^0(1) = 0,$$

$$\frac{v_0^0(1)}{v_1^1(1)} = 0, \quad .2 \leqslant \frac{v_0^1(1)}{v_1^1(1)} \leqslant .3, \quad .8 \leqslant \frac{v_1^0(1)}{v_1^1(1)} \leqslant .9, \quad \frac{v_1^1(1)}{v_1^1(1)} = 1. \quad (12.21a)$$

Then set

$$v_1^1(1) = 1,$$

so that (12.21a) becomes

$$v_0^0(1) = 0, \quad .2 \leqslant v_0^1(1) \leqslant .3, \quad .8 \leqslant v_1^0(1) \leqslant .9, \quad v_1^1(1) = 1. \quad (12.21b)$$

Also, suppose the probabilities for stage 1 are bounded as follows:

$$.1 \leqslant p_{00}^0(1) \leqslant .3, \quad .8 \leqslant p_{01}^0(1) \leqslant .9; \quad p_{00}^0(1) + p_{01}^0(1) = 1; \quad (12.22a)$$
$$.5 \leqslant p_{00}^1(1) \leqslant .7, \quad .3 \leqslant p_{01}^1(1) \leqslant .4; \quad p_{00}^1(1) + p_{01}^1(1) = 1; \quad (12.22b)$$
$$.3 \leqslant p_{10}^0(1) \leqslant .5, \quad .6 \leqslant p_{11}^0(1) \leqslant .7; \quad p_{10}^0(1) + p_{11}^0(1) = 1; \quad (12.23a)$$
$$.4 \leqslant p_{10}^1(1) \leqslant .6, \quad .5 \leqslant p_{11}^1(1) \leqslant .8; \quad p_{10}^1(1) + p_{11}^1(1) = 1. \quad (12.23b)$$

First, given y_{20}, we try to find $d_0(1)$. To do this, compare

$$w_0^k(1) = \sum_{j=0}^{1} p_{0j}^k(1) v_j^k(1) \qquad (12.24)$$

[12] See, e.g., Sasieni, et al. (1959, Chapter 10) or Howard (1960).

for $k = 0, 1$ (for x_{10}, x_{11}). For $k = 0$, (12.24) and (12.21b) give

$$w_0^0(1) = p_{01}^0(1)v_1^0(1),$$

which, according to (12.21b) and (12.22a) has the bounds

$$.64 \leqslant w_0^0(1) \leqslant .81. \tag{12.25}$$

Next, for $k = 1$,

$$w_0^1(1) = p_{00}^1(1)v_0^1(1) + p_{01}^1(1),$$

which, by (12.21b) and (12.22b) has the bounds

$$.44 \leqslant w_0^1(1) \leqslant .58. \tag{12.26}$$

Comparing (12.25) and (12.26), we are certain that $w_0^0(1) > w_0^1(1)$, and therefore

$$d_0(1) = x_{10},$$

with

$$u_0(1) = w_0^0(1),$$

$$.64 \leqslant u_0(1) \leqslant .81.$$

Second, given y_{21}, we try to determine $d_1(1)$. Letting

$$w_1^k(1) = \sum_{j=0}^{1} p_{1j}^k(1)v_j^k(1)$$

(12.21b), (12.23a), and (12.23b), give

$$.48 \leqslant w_1^0(1) \leqslant .63,$$
$$.60 \leqslant w_1^1(1) \leqslant .72. \tag{12.27}$$

Since (12.27) does not allow us to conclude either $w_1^0(1) \geqslant w_1^1(1)$ or $w_1^1(1) \geqslant w_1^0(1)$, we do not know whether $d_1(1) = x_{10}$ or $d_1(1) = x_{11}$. However, this does not prevent continuation of the analysis. Since $u_1(1) = \max [w_1^0(1); w_1^1(1)]$, (12.27) allows us to conclude that:

$$\text{if } d_1(1) = x_{10}, \text{ then } .60 \leqslant u_1(1) \leqslant .63,$$

for $d_1(1)$ cannot equal x_{10} unless $w_1^0(1) \geqslant .60$. Also,

$$\text{if } d_1(1) = x_{11}, \text{ then } .60 \leqslant u_1(1) \leqslant .72.$$

From this we conclude that

$$.60 \leqslant u_1(1) \leqslant .72.$$

To summarize the analysis of stage 1:

$$.64 \leqslant u_0(1) \leqslant .81,$$
$$.60 \leqslant u_1(1) \leqslant .72,$$
$$d_0(1) = x_{10}, \tag{12.28}$$
$$d_1(1) \text{ is undetermined.}$$

For stage 2, suppose

$$v_1^1(2) \geqslant v_1^0(2) \geqslant v_0^1(2) \geqslant v_0^0(2) = 0,$$

$$\frac{v_0^0(2)}{v_1^1(2)} = 0, \quad .4 \leqslant \frac{v_0^1(2)}{v_1^1(2)} \leqslant .5, \quad .6 \leqslant \frac{v_1^0(2)}{v_1^1(2)} \leqslant .7, \quad \frac{v_1^1(2)}{v_1^1(2)} = 1; \quad (12.29a)$$

with

$$.4 \leqslant p_{00}^0(2) \leqslant .7, \quad .4 \leqslant p_{01}^0(2) \leqslant .6; \quad p_{00}^0(2) + p_{01}^0(2) = 1; \quad (12.30a)$$

$$.5 \leqslant p_{00}^1(2) \leqslant .7, \quad .4 \leqslant p_{01}^1(2) \leqslant .5; \quad p_{00}^1(2) + p_{01}^1(2) = 1. \quad (12.30b)$$

We also require comparison of $v_1^1(1)$ and $v_1^1(2)$, so suppose that

$$.8 \leqslant \frac{v_1^1(2)}{v_1^1(1)} \leqslant .9 \quad \text{or} \quad .8 \leqslant v_1^1(2) \leqslant .9. \quad (12.31)$$

Combining (12.29a) and (12.31), we get

$$v_0^0(2) = 0, \quad .32 \leqslant v_0^1(2) \leqslant .45, \quad .48 \leqslant v_1^0(2) \leqslant .63, \quad .8 \leqslant v_1^1(2) \leqslant .9.$$
$$(12.29b)$$

In stage 2, $u_0(2) = \max [w_0^0(2), w_0^1(2)]$, where

$$w_0^k(2) = \sum_{j=0}^{1} p_{0j}^k(2)[v_j^k(2) + u_j(1)], \quad k = 0, 1.$$

According to (12.28), (12.29b), (12.30a), and (12.30b),

$$\min w_0^0(2) = .6(0 + .64) + .4(.48 + .60) = .816,$$
$$\max w_0^0(2) = .4(0 + .81) + .6(.63 + .72) = 1.134,$$
$$\min w_0^1(2) = .6(.32 + .64) + .4(.8 + .60) = 1.136,$$
$$\max w_0^1(2) = .5(.45 + .81) + .5(.9 + .72) = 1.440,$$

or

$$.816 \leqslant w_0^0(2) \leqslant 1.134,$$
$$1.136 \leqslant w_0^1(2) \leqslant 1.440.$$

Comparing these two inequalities we conclude that

$$d_0(2) = x_{21},$$
$$u_0(2) = w_0^1(2).$$

Hence, the best action to implement at stage 2 is $x_{21} \in X_2$, even though we have not been able to determine an entire optimal strategy. If x_{21} is implemented and y_{21} results, we might expect from (12.27) that the decision maker will then implement x_{11} rather than x_{10}. Further analysis might indeed show that $w_1^1(1) \geqslant w_1^0(1)$, but for the purpose of what to do "now" (i.e., in stage 2), this conclusion is unnecessary.

12.6 SPECIAL CASES OF MODEL V

There are many special cases of Model V, arising from simplification in the probability functions and value functions in the Type I M.D.P. Some of these, owing to their nice mathematical forms, have been analyzed in detail. Because of this, we shall give a few references that the reader may pursue at his pleasure.

For purposes of this discussion, Model V is characterized by

$$u_i(n) = \max_k \sum_{j=0}^{s_n} p_{ij}^k(n)[v_j^k(n) + u_j(n-1)] \qquad (12.32)$$

$$i = 0, \ldots, s_{n+1}; \; k = 0, \ldots, r_n; \; n = 1, \ldots, N.$$

There is a change in (12.32) as compared to (12.13); when $n = 1$, $u_j(0)$ did not appear in (12.13). In terms of (12.32), (12.13) for $n = 1$ is obtained if $u_j(0) = 0$, or, what amounts to the same thing, if $u_j(0) = c$ for all j. $u_j(0)$ may be thought of as the relative value attached to some future beyond the terminal stage, given $y_{1j}, j = 0, \ldots, s_1$. As explained in the previous section, the $u_j(0)$ as written in (12.32) for $n = 1$ were incorporated in the $v_j^k(1)$, the relative values of the $(x_{1k}, y_{1j}) \in X_1 \times Y_1$. Thus (12.32) for $n = 1$ represents a slight special case of (12.13) where the relative values of the "futures" are separated from the relative values of the realizations in stage 1.

Further Independence of Relative Values

The first set of special cases of (12.32) concerns the $v_j^k(n) = V_n(x_{nk}, y_{nj})$. If X_n and Y_n are valuewise independent, then we may write

$$v_j^k(n) = f_j(n) + g_k(n) \qquad (12.33)$$

where $f_j(n)$ and $g_k(n)$ are value functions defined on Y_n and X_n, respectively. With (12.33), (12.32) becomes

$$u_i(n) = \max_k \sum_{j=0}^{s_n} p_{ij}^k(n)[f_j(n) + g_k(n) + u_j(n-1)],$$

which simplifies to

$$u_i(n) = \max_k \left\{ g_k(n) + \sum_{j=0}^{s_n} p_{ij}^k(n)[f_j(n) + u_j(n-1)] \right\}. \qquad (12.34)$$

If the relative value in the nth stage depends only on the value of Y_n and not X_n (the probabilities not being considered in this), then for each k or $x_{nk} \in X_n$,

$$v_j^k(n) = v_j(n) \qquad (12.35)$$

and (12.32) becomes

$$u_i(n) = \max_k \sum_{j=0}^{s_n} p_{ij}^k(n)[v_j(n) + u_j(n-1)]. \qquad (12.36)$$

In (12.36) the only way X_n gets into the picture is through the probabilities $p_{ij}^k(n)$. In addition to the cases of (12.33) and (12.35), it may happen that Y_n (or X_n) is the product of several other variables which may be valuewise independent with respect to each other. For example, if $Y_n = Y_{n_1} \times Y_{n_2}$ and if $V_n(y_n) = V_{n_1}(y_{n_1}) + V_{n_2}(y_{n_2})$ with $y_n \in Y_n$, $y_{n_1} \in Y_{n_1}$, $y_{n_2} \in Y_{n_2}$, then (12.36) may be written as

$$u_i(n) = \max_k \left[\sum_{y_{n_1}} P(y_{n_1} \mid y_{n+1,i}, x_{nk}) V_{n_1}(y_{n_1}) \right.$$
$$\left. + \sum_{y_{n_2}} P(y_{n_2} \mid y_{n+1,i}, x_{nk}) V_{n_2}(y_{n_2}) + \sum_{j=0}^{s_n} p_{ij}^k(n) u_j(n-1) \right].$$

A special case of (12.36) arises when the only variable that has value to the decision maker is Y_1, the terminal outcome variable. Regressing to the original form of Model V as given by (12.13) for $n = 1$, we get

$$u_i(1) = \max_k \sum_{j=0}^{s_1} p_{ij}^k(1) v_j(1), \tag{12.37a}$$

$$u_i(n) = \max_k \sum_{j=0}^{s_n} p_{ij}^k(n) u_j(n-1), \qquad n > 1. \tag{12.37b}$$

After the $v_j(1)$ for the $y_{1j} \in Y_1$ have been determined (or estimated or bounded in some fashion), we travel back through the stages at the whim of the probability functions.

An Alternative Formulation

To go further in our consideration of special forms of Model V, suppose that the X_n, $n = 1, \ldots, N$ are the same for all n except for the time factor; that is, assume that there is a basic set of acts or alternatives, say X, where the act implemented in stage n is taken from X for $n = 1, \ldots, N$. Let the acts in X be denoted as $x_0, x_1, \ldots, x_r$:

$$X = \{x_0, x_1, \ldots, x_r\}$$

where $r + 1$ is the total number of distinct acts in X.

In a similar fashion, suppose the Y_n, $n = 1, \ldots, N + 1$ are the same for all n except for the time factor. Let the values in Y be denoted as $y_0, y_1, \ldots, y_s$:

$$Y = \{y_0, y_1, \ldots, y_s\}$$

where $s + 1$ is the total number of distinct values in (or elements of) Y. In terms more familiar to many readers, Y is called the *set of states of the system*. The $y_j \in Y$ are called *states* and may, of course, be multi-dimensional vectors if Y itself is the product of a number of *state variables*.

In each stage of the M.D.P. one and only one of the states occurs. Corresponding to (12.10) and (12.11), let

$$p_{ij}^k(n) = P(y_j \text{ in stage } n \mid y_i \text{ in stage } n + 1, x_k \text{ in stage } n) \quad (12.38)$$

$$v_j^k(n) = V_n(x_k, y_j), \quad n = 1, \ldots, N. \quad (12.39)$$

For each $x_k \in X$ that is available in stage n when $y_i \in Y$ has occurred in stage $n + 1$, the $p_{ij}^k(n)$ satisfy

$$\sum_{j=0}^{s} p_{ij}^k(n) = 1.$$

$p_{ij}^k(n)$ is called a (conditional) *transition probability*. It represents the probability that the system will make the transition from state y_i at stage $n + 1$ to state y_j at stage n, given that the system was in state y_i at $n + 1$, and x_k was implemented in stage n.

Along with the $p_{ij}^k(n)$ in (12.38) it is common to define a set of elements $\{a_0, a_1, \ldots, a_s\}$ with $\sum a_i = 1$, which represent the probabilities that the system will be in state y_i, $i = 0, \ldots, s$, just prior to the time at which an act is implemented in stage N. That is,

$$a_i = P(\text{the realized value of } Y_{N+1} \text{ is } y_i), \quad i = 0, \ldots, s. \quad (12.40)$$

Consideration of the a_i is not necessary in determining optimal strategies.

As defined in (12.39), $v_j^k(n)$ is the relative value of the pair (x_k, y_j) in stage n, $n = 1, \ldots, N$. The stage index "n" has been retained to allow for changes in the relative value of (x_k, y_j) in different stages.

The basic model for the case under consideration may be written as

$$u_i(n) = \max_k \sum_{j=0}^{s} p_{ij}^k(n)[v_j^k(n) + u_j(n - 1)], \quad (12.41)$$

$$i = 0, \ldots, s; \ k = 0, \ldots, r; \ n = 1, \ldots, N,$$

which is similar in form to (12.32) but results from a new formulation as described previously.

For (12.41) as it presently stands, no assumption is being made as to the homogeneity of available acts in each stage for each y_i at the previous stage. For example, it may happen that, given y_1 in stage N, $\{x_0, x_1, x_2\}$ constitutes the set of acts available in stage $N - 1$, but given y_1 in stage $N - 1$, $\{x_0, x_1, x_3, x_4\}$ constitutes the set of acts available in stage $N - 2$. It should be noted that this does not violate condition (1) in definition 12.7.

With respect to (12.41), we get a set of special cases similar to those given by (12.34), (12.36), and (12.37a, b) on replacing s_n by s; with $p_{ij}^k(n)$ and $v_j^k(n)$ as defined by (12.38) and (12.39). Additional cases arise when specific assumptions are made about the behavior of the $p_{ij}^k(n)$ and $v_j^k(n)$ with respect to n.

Stationary Value Mechanisms

First, consider $v_j^k(n)$. We say that we have a *stationary value mechanism* if

$$v_j^k(n) = v_j^k \qquad \text{for all } n, \tag{12.42}$$

i.e., if the relative value accrueing from the pair (x_k, y_j) in stage n does not depend on the stage number. If (12.42) is assumed to hold, then (12.41) becomes

$$u_i(n) = \max_k \sum_{j=0}^s p_{ij}^k(n)[v_j^k + u_j(n-1)], \qquad n = 1, \ldots, N. \tag{12.43}$$

Subcases of (12.43) arise from $v_j^k = f_j + g_k$ and $v_j^k = v_j$, similar to (12.33) and (12.35). Retaining the basic form (12.41) for $n = 1$, some further assumption or procedure is required in handling the $u_j(0), j = 0, \ldots, s$.

Discount Factor

One can complicate (12.42) by introducing a discounting factor, say β, where $0 \leqslant \beta < 1$. If we assign the least desirable (x_k, y_j) a relative value equal to zero, say $v_0 = 0$, then the v_j^k are the same as the relative value intervals $(v_j^k - v_0)$, and it is meaningful (in a value-theoretic sense) to consider the possibility that

$$v_j^k(n) = \beta v_j^k(n-1)$$

or that

$$v_j^k(n) = \beta^{N-n} v_j^k, \qquad n = 1, \ldots, N. \tag{12.44}$$

Our "reference point" for (12.44) may be taken as the imminent stage, stage N, which defines the v_j^k. That is, $v_j^k = v_j^k(N)$ on setting $n = N$ in (12.44). The effect of (12.44) on $u_i(n)$ is given by

$$u_i(n) = \max_k \sum_{j=0}^s p_{ij}^k(n)[v_j^k + \beta u_j(n-1)].$$

Stationary Transition Mechanisms

Next, consider the $p_{ij}^k(n)$. Consider a pair (y_i, x_k) with i, k fixed. Suppose that for each n for which y_i can occur at stage $n + 1$ (under one or more available strategies), and then x_k can be implemented at stage n, we have

$$p_{ij}^k(n) = p_{ij}^k, \qquad j = 0, \ldots, s, \tag{12.45}$$

$$\sum_{j=0}^s p_{ij}^k = 1.$$

If (12.45) holds for all pairs (y_i, x_k) that can occur at some time during the process (y_i at $n + 1$, x_k at n), then we have a *stationary transition mechanism*, since the probabilities do not depend on time (or stage number). For this case (12.41) reduces to

$$u_i(n) = \max_k \sum_{j=0}^s p_{ij}^k [v_j^k(n) + u_j(n - 1)]$$

and (12.43) reduces to

$$u_i(n) = \max_k \sum_{j=0}^s p_{ij}^k [v_j^k + u_j(n - 1)]. \tag{12.46}$$

Constancy of Available Acts

Some simplification in the mathematical analysis of (12.46) occurs if the set of acts from X available in stage n, given state y_i in stage $n + 1$, depends only on y_i and not on n for each y_i. In this case each $u_i(n)$ for fixed i and variable n is determined with the same set of $x_k \in X$ or the same k from $\{0, 1, \ldots, r\}$. Additional simplification is obtained if every $x_k \in X$ is available in each stage, regardless of what state occurred in the previous stage, and if each y_j has a positive probability of occurrence in each stage under at least one available strategy.

Howard (1960) has analyzed situations of this general type in some detail, accounting for cases where the process may go on indefinitely (i.e., $N \to \infty$), and has developed an efficient iterative procedure he calls the "policy-iteration method" for obtaining an optimal policy. He also considers a form like (12.46) with a discount factor β included and goes on to consider continuous-time sequential decision processes where the time between state transitions is a random variable. For details we refer the reader to Howard's book.

More About Time

It will be noted that in formulating our basic N-stage sequential process, no explicit assumption was made concerning the duration of each stage. In particular, it was not stated that the stages must cover equal intervals of time, for indeed they may not. In fact, there is nothing in the basic formulation of Model V which prevents the duration of each stage from being a random variable, but if this is the case, there may be trouble with respect to obtaining measures of relative values.

Derman (1962) has considered a discrete-time M.D.P. with stationary transition mechanism and stationary value mechanism and discusses the solution of two problems using linear programming technics. One of these problems concerns a process with a trapped state, in which the system, once it goes into the trapped state, stays there (for ever). For this case, the number of periods or stages in the process is a random variable.

12.7 TYPE II MARKOVIAN DECISION PROCESSES AND RELATIVE VALUES OF TRANSITIONS

The formulation given by Howard (1960) contains a feature (and a point of view) not included in the development presented previously. His approach in treating values is more in line with the thinking of traditional decision theory[13] than with the theory of this book, and speaks in terms of "rewards" (measured in dollars, units of sales, or the like) instead of relative values. Instead of separating the rewards in each stage, he considers the rewards accrueing from transitions from one state to another. In his notation, r_{ij}^k is the reward obtained in going from state i to state j in a single transition when alternative k is implemented following state i and preceding state j. The change this approach causes in (12.46) may be expressed as

$$u_i(n) = \max_k \sum_{j=0}^{s} p_{ij}^k [r_{ij}^k + u_j(n-1)].$$

The purpose of this section is to investigate, from a value-theoretic point of view, the notion of "the relative values of transitions" rather than "the relative values of variables." In doing this we shall have to revise our thinking somewhat, since a new approach is called for.

Model VI and a Type II M.D.P.

The basic formulation used here is similar to the formulation of Section 12.4, differing only in the treatment of relative values. In defining a Type II M.D.P., parts 1 and 2 of definition 12.7, concerning availability of acts and the probability functions, are essentially unchanged.

To summarize briefly the starting point, we are concerned with a sequential decision process

$$Y_{N+1} \to X_N \to Y_N \to \ldots \to Y_2 \to X_1 \to Y_1,$$

where Y_{N+1} is a variable whose values define the possible initial conditions, $\{X_N, \ldots, X_1\}$ is a set of action variables, and $\{Y_N, \ldots, Y_1\}$ is a set of outcome variables. With $x_n \in X_n$, $n = 1, \ldots, N$, and $y_n \in Y_n$, $n = 1, \ldots, N+1$, it is assumed that:

1. For each X_n, the subset of acts in X_n available for implementation by the decision maker is uniquely determined given the resultant value of Y_{n+1};

[13] See Section 1.2.

2. for each Y_n, $n \leqslant N$,

$$P(y_n | y_{N+1}, x_N, \ldots, y_{n+1}, x_n) = P(y_n | y_{n+1}, x_n).$$

Notationally, the difference between a Type I and Type II M.D.P. is obtained by replacing $v_j^k(n)$ with $v_{ij}^k(n)$ in (12.13) and (12.14), giving

$$u_i(1) = \max_k \sum_{j=0}^{s_1} p_{ij}^k(1)v_{ij}^k(1) \tag{12.47}$$

$$u_i(n) = \max_k \sum_{j=0}^{s_0} p_{ij}^k(n)[v_{ij}^k(n) + u_j(n-1)], \qquad n = 2, \ldots, N \tag{12.48}$$

where

$$p_{ij}^k(n) = P(y_{nj} | y_{n+1,i}, x_{nk}), \qquad i = 0, \ldots, s_{n+1};$$

$$j = 0, \ldots, s_n; \quad k = 0, \ldots, r_n; \quad n = 1, \ldots, N,$$

similar to (12.11), with $Y_n = \{y_{n0}, y_{n1}, \ldots, y_{ns_n}\}$, $X_n = \{x_{n0}, x_{n1}, \ldots, x_{nr_n}\}$.

(12.47) and (12.48) constitute *Model VI*. This Model has a variety of special cases, one of which is Model V, arising as a special case of Model VI when $v_{ij}^k(n) = v_j^k(n)$ for all i, $i = 0, \ldots, s_{n+1}$. After the discussion of the previous section, the reader should be able to generate his own list of special cases of Model VI. In the remainder of this section we shall consider the $v_{ij}^k(n)$.

Simple Conditional Independence

The concept of the relative values of transitions follows from the notion of conditional independence,[14] defined below.

Suppose a value function V is defined on a set X of ordered triples (y, z, w). Let Y be the set of all elements appearing in the first place of one or more $(y, z, w) \in X$, with Z and W similarly defined. Then $X \subset Y \times Z \times W$. Let $Y(z)$ be the set of all y in at least one $(y, z, w) \in X$ for the given $z \in Z$, and let $W(z)$ be the set of all w in one or more $(y, z, w) \in X$ for the given $z \in Z$. $Y(z)$ and $W(z)$ are defined for each $z \in Z$. Clearly $X \subset \bigcup_{z \in Z} [Y(z) \times \{z\} \times W(z)]$.

Suppose next that, for a given $z^0 \in Z$, $Y(z^0)$ and $W(z^0)$ are independent with respect to V, given z^0, i.e., that there exist functions η_1 on $Y(z^0) \times \{z^0\}$ and η_2 on $\{z^0\} \times W(z^0)$ such that

$$V(y, z^0, w) = \eta_1(y, z^0) + \eta_2(z^0, w)$$

for all $(y, z^0, w) \in X$, where $\eta_1(\cdot, z^0)$ and $\eta_2(z^0, \cdot)$ are unique up to the simultaneous transformations $\eta_1(y, z^0) + \alpha(z^0)$, $\eta_2(z^0, w) - \alpha(z^0)$, given V. $\alpha(z^0)$ is an arbitrary constant.

---

[14] See Exercises 8 and 9 in Chapter 9.

We shall say that Y and W are independent with respect to V, given Z, if and only if $Y(z)$ and $W(z)$ are independent with respect to V, given z for every $z \in Z$. Letting $YZ(X)$ be the set of all (y, z) appearing in one or more $(y, z, w) \in X$ and $ZW(X)$ be the set of all (z, w) in at least one $(y, z, w) \in X$, the following definition applies:

Definition 12.8 Y and W are independent with respect to V, given Z, if and only if (i) there exist functions η_1 on $YZ(X)$ and η_2 on $ZW(X)$ satisfying

$$V(y, z, w) = \eta_1(y, z) + \eta_2(z, w)$$

for all $(y, z, w) \in X$, and (ii) with V fixed in origin and scale unit, η_1' on $YZ(X)$ and η_2' on $ZW(X)$ satisfy

$$V(y, z, w) = \eta_1'(y, z) + \eta_2'(z, w)$$

for all $(y, z, w) \in X$ if and only if there exists a real-valued function α on Z, such that

$$\eta_1'(y, z) = \eta_1(y, z) + \alpha(z) \quad \text{for all } (y, z) \in YZ(X),$$

$$\eta_2'(z, w) = \eta_2(z, w) - \alpha(z) \quad \text{for all } (z, w) \in ZW(X).$$

Completing the Definition of a Type II M.D.P.

With definition 12.8 at hand, we are now prepared to complete the definition of a Type II M.D.P., and to see how the form of V given in definition 12.9 arises from definition 12.8.

Definition 12.9   A sequential decision process with N stages is a *Type II Markovian decision process* if and only if conditions (1) and (2) stated above (12.47) are satisfied and (3') there exist real-valued functions ϕ_n defined on the sets of transitions $\{(y_{n+1}, x_n, y_n)\}$, $n = 1, \ldots, N$, that can occur under at least one available strategy satisfying

$$\begin{aligned}
V(y_{N+1}, x_N, y_N, \ldots, x_2, y_2, x_1, y_1) &= \phi_N(y_{N+1}, x_N, y_N) \\
&+ \phi_{N-1}(y_N, x_{N-1}, y_{N-1}) + \cdots \\
&+ \phi_2(y_3, x_2, y_2) + \phi_1(y_2, x_1, y_1)
\end{aligned}$$

$$\text{(12.49)}$$

for all $(y_{N+1}, x_N, \ldots, x_1, y_1)$ that have positive probability of occurrence under at least one available strategy. Moreover, ψ_n on $\{(y_{n+1}, x_n, y_n)\}$, $n = 1, \ldots, N$ satisfy

$$V(y_{N+1}, \ldots, x_1, y_1) = \sum_{n=1}^{N} \psi_n(y_{n+1}, x_n, y_n)$$

if and only if there exist functions α_n over Y_n, $n = 2, \ldots, N$, such that

$$\psi_N(y_{N+1}, x_N, y_N) = \phi_N(y_{N+1}, x_N, y_N) + \alpha_N(y_N),$$

$$\psi_n(y_{n+1}, x_n, y_n) = \phi_n(y_{n+1}, x_n, y_n) - \alpha_{n+1}(y_{n+1}) + \alpha_n(y_n),$$

$$n = N - 1, N - 2, \ldots, 2, \quad (12.50)$$

$$\psi_1(y_2, x_1, y_1) = \phi_1(y_2, x_1, y_1) - \alpha_2(y_2).$$

To connect (12.47) and (12.48) with (12.49), let

$$\phi_n(y_{n+1,i}, x_{nk}, y_{nj}) = v_{ij}^k(n).$$

It is now shown how (12.49) and (12.50) arise from the definition of conditional independence. For this demonstration certain domains of definition are required, as follows:

Let X be the set of all $(y_{N+1}, \ldots, x_1, y_1)$ that have positive probability of occurrence under one or more available strategies. Let

$R_n^1 = $ set of all $(y_{N+1}, \ldots, y_{n+1}, x_n)$ appearing in one or more $x \in X$, $n = 2, \ldots, N$,

$R_n^2 = $ set of all (x_n, y_n) appearing in one or more $x \in X$, $n = 1, 2, \ldots, N$,

$R_n^3 = $ set of all $(y_{N+1}, \ldots, y_{n+1}, x_n, y_n)$ appearing in one or more $x \in X$, $n = 2, \ldots, N$,

$R_n^4 = $ set of all (y_{n+1}, x_n, y_n) appearing in one or more $x \in X$, $n = 1, 2, \ldots, N$.

It is assumed that Y_n is the set of all y_n appearing in one or more $x \in X$, $n = 2, \ldots, N$. With these definitions, note that

$$X \subset R_2^1 \times Y_2 \times R_1^2,$$

$$R_n^3 \subset R_{n+1}^1 \times Y_{n+1} \times R_n^2, \quad n = 2, \ldots, N - 1.$$

In developing (12.49) and (12.50), suppose first that R_2^1 and R_1^2 are independent with respect to V, given Y_2. Then there exist functions ζ_2 on R_2^3 and ϕ_1 on R_1^4 such that

$$V(y_{N+1}, \ldots, x_2, y_2, x_1, y_1) = \zeta_2(y_{N+1}, \ldots, x_2, y_2) + \phi_1(y_2, x_1, y_1)$$

for all $(y_{N+1}, \ldots, y_1) \in X$. Moreover, ζ_2 and ϕ_1 are unique up to the simultaneous transformations $\zeta_2(y_{N+1}, \ldots, x_2, y_2) + \alpha_2(y_2)$, $\phi_1(y_2, x_1, y_1) - \alpha_2(y_2)$, given V, where α_2 is an arbitrary real-valued function on Y_2.

Next, given ζ_2, suppose R_3^1 and R_2^2 are independent with respect to ζ_2, given Y_3. Then

$$\zeta_2(y_{N+1}, \ldots, x_3, y_3, x_2, y_2) = \zeta_3(y_{N+1}, \ldots, x_3, y_3) + \phi_2(y_3, x_2, y_2)$$

for all $(y_{N+1}, \ldots, y_2) \in R_2^3$, where ζ_3 on R_3^3 and ϕ_2 on R_2^4 are unique up to the transformations $\zeta_3(y_{N+1}, \ldots, x_3, y_3) + \alpha_3(y_3)$, $\phi_2(y_3, x_2, y_2) - \alpha_3(y_3)$, given ζ_2. Here α_3 is an arbitrary real-valued function on Y_3.

In general, given ζ_n ($2 \leqslant n < N$), if R_{n+1}^1 and R_n^2 are independent with respect to ζ_n, given Y_{n+1}, then

$$\zeta_n(y_{N+1}, \ldots, x_{n+1}, y_{n+1}, x_n, y_n) = \zeta_{n+1}(y_{N+1}, \ldots, x_{n+1}, y_{n+1})$$
$$+ \phi_n(y_{n+1}, x_n, y_n) \quad (12.51)$$

for all $(y_{N+1}, \ldots, y_n) \in R_n^3$, where ζ_{n+1} on R_{n+1}^3 and ϕ_n on R_n^4 are unique up to the transformations $\zeta_{n+1}(y_{N+1}, \ldots, x_{n+1}, y_{n+1}) + \alpha_{n+1}(y_{n+1})$, $\phi_n(y_{n+1}, x_n, y_n) - \alpha_{n+1}(y_{n+1})$.

Letting $\phi_N = \zeta_N$ when $n = N - 1$ in (12.51), this succession of steps leads to (12.49), or, in general, with V fixed in origin and scale unit, to

$$V(y_{N+1}, x_N, y_N, \ldots, x_1, y_1) = [\phi_N(y_{N+1}, x_N, y_N) + \alpha_N(y_N)]$$
$$+ [\phi_{N-1}(y_N, x_{N-1}, y_{N-1})$$
$$- \alpha_N(y_N) + \alpha_{N-1}(y_{N-1})]$$
$$\vdots$$
$$+ [\phi_2(y_3, x_2, y_2) - \alpha_3(y_3) + \alpha_2(y_2)]$$
$$+ [\phi_1(y_2, x_1, y_1) - \alpha_2(y_2)],$$

which accounts for (12.50).

It should be clear that, since

$$\sum_{n=1}^{N} \phi_n(y_{n+1}, x_n, y_n) = \sum_{n=1}^{N} \psi_n(y_{n+1}, x_n, y_n) = V(y_{N+1}, \ldots, x_1, y_1),$$

with ϕ_n and ψ_n as in definition 12.9, an optimal strategy determined on the basis of (12.47) and (12.48) will be the same, regardless of whether we take $v_{ij}^k(n) = \phi_n(y_{n+1,i}, x_{nk}, y_{nj})$ for all n or $v_{ij}^k(n) = \psi_n(y_{n+1,i}, x_{nk}, y_{nj})$ for all n.

EXERCISES

1. Give an example in which assumption 12.1 is violated.

2. In a decision situation, suppose $T_1 = \{X_1, Y_1, Y_2, Y_3\}$, $T_2 = \{X_2, Y_4, Y_5\}$ with $T_1 \cup T_2 = T$, $T_1 \cap T_2 = \emptyset$. Identify the prior sets of each variable with respect to T_1, T_2, and T, given

$$X_1 \rightarrow Y_1 \rightarrow Y_2 \rightarrow Y_3 \rightarrow Y_4 \rightarrow X_2 \rightarrow Y_5, \qquad Y_3 \rightarrow Y_2 \rightarrow Y_1.$$

3. Given $T_1 \cup T_2 \cup T_3 = T$, $T_i \cap T_j = \emptyset$, $i \neq j$, show that if T_1 and $T_2 \times T_3$ are totally independent, and if T_2 and $T_1 \times T_3$ are totally independent, then T_3 and $T_1 \times T_2$ are totally independent, and thus that T_1, T_2, and T_3 are mutually totally independent.

4. Let $Y_3 \rightarrow X_2 \rightarrow Y_2 \rightarrow X_1 \rightarrow Y_1$ denote a sequential decision process for $N = 2$, where Y_3 is a variable whose values represent possible initial

conditions. Suppose $Y_3 = \{y_{30}, y_{31}\}$, $X_2 = \{x_{20}, x_{21}\}$, $Y_2 = \{y_{20}, y_{21}\}$, $X_1 = \{x_{10}, x_{11}\}$. Show that there are $64 = 2^6$ conceptual strategies in this situation. List four of them.

5. With given initial conditions and a sequential decision process $X_N \to Y_N \to X_{N-1} \to Y_{N-1} \to \ldots \to Y_2 \to X_1 \to Y_1$, suppose X_n has a_n elements (or values), $n = 1, \ldots, N$, and Y_n has b_n elements (or values), $n = 1, \ldots, N$. Show that the total number of conceptual strategies, say c, is given by

$$c = a_1^{b_2 b_3 \cdots b_N} a_2^{b_3 b_4 \cdots b_N} \cdots a_{N-2}^{b_{N-1} b_N} a_{N-1}^{b_N} a_N.$$

6. (*Continuation.*) Instead of given initial conditions, suppose Y_{N+1} is a variable whose values represent possible initial conditions. If Y_{N+1} has b_{N+1} values, then the total number of conceptual strategies is given by

$$d = c^{b_{N+1}}.$$

7. (*Continuation.*) If the decision situation in Exercise 5 is a Type I or Type II M.D.P., the total number of conceptual strategies of interest equals c', where

$$c' = a_1^{b_2} a_2^{b_3} \cdots a_{N-1}^{b_N} a_N.$$

If the sequential decision process in Exercise 5 is a Type I or Type II M.D.P., the number of available strategies out of the c that have different expected relative values can be no greater than c'.

8. (*Continuation.*) If the process of Exercise 6 is a Type I or II M.D.P., the total number of conceptual strategies of interest equals d', where

$$d' = a_1^{b_2} a_2^{b_3} \cdots a_N^{b_{N+1}}.$$

9. (*Continuation.*) In the language of Section 12.4, if the situation of Exercise 6 is a Type I (or Type II) M.D.P. and the dynamic programming approach is used, there will be no more than

$$a_1 b_2 + a_2 b_3 + \ldots + a_N b_{N+1}$$

quantities in no more than $b_2 + b_3 + \ldots + b_{N+1}$ subsets used to find an optimal strategy.

10. Consider a 2-stage decision process with given initial conditions y_{30} and $X_2 = \{x_{20}, x_{21}\}$, $Y_2 = \{y_{20}, y_{21}, y_{22}\}$, $X_1 = \{x_{10}, x_{11}\}$, $Y_1 = \{y_{10}, y_{11}\}$. Let $[(0, k_2, j), (j, k_1, h)]$ be the two-step transition $[(y_{30}, x_{2k_2}, y_{2j}), (y_{2j}, x_{1k_1}, y_{1h})]$, and suppose the $V[(0, k_2, j), (j, k_1, h)] = V(x_{2k_2}, y_{2j}, x_{1k_1}, y_{1h})$ are given as follows:

$$V[(0, 0, 0), (0, 0, 0)] = 0, \qquad V[(0, 0, 1), (1, 0, 0)] = 2,$$
$$V[(0, 0, 0), (0, 0, 1)] = 4, \qquad V[(0, 0, 1), (1, 0, 1)] = 7,$$
$$V[(0, 0, 0), (0, 1, 0)] = 1, \qquad V[(0, 0, 1), (1, 1, 0)] = 1,$$
$$V[(0, 0, 0), (0, 1, 1)] = 5, \qquad V[(0, 0, 1), (1, 1, 1)] = 10,$$
$$V[(0, 1, 0), (0, 0, 0)] = 7, \qquad V[(0, 1, 1), (1, 0, 0)] = 12,$$
$$V[(0, 1, 0), (0, 0, 1)] = 11, \qquad V[(0, 1, 1), (1, 0, 1)] = 17,$$
$$V[(0, 1, 0), (0, 1, 0)] = 8, \qquad V[(0, 1, 1), (1, 1, 0)] = 11,$$
$$V[(0, 1, 0), (0, 1, 1)] = 12, \qquad V[(0, 1, 1), (1, 1, 1)] = 20,$$

$$V[(0, 0, 2), (2, 0, 0)] = 7,$$
$$V[(0, 0, 2), (2, 0, 1)] = 5,$$
$$V[(0, 0, 2), (2, 1, 0)] = 4,$$
$$V[(0, 0, 2), (2, 1, 1)] = 3,$$
$$V[(0, 1, 2), (2, 0, 0)] = 13,$$
$$V[(0, 1, 2), (2, 0, 1)] = 11,$$
$$V[(0, 1, 2), (2, 1, 0)] = 10,$$
$$V[(0, 1, 2), (2, 1, 1)] = 9.$$

(a) Determine a set of numbers for the $\phi_2(0, k_2, j)$ and $\phi_1(j, k_1, h)$ that result from writing $V[(0, k_2, j), (j, k_1, h)] = \phi_2(0, k_2, j) + \phi_1(j, k_1, h)$, that agree with the above assignments to $V[\ ]$.

(b) Set four of the $v_{ij}^k(n) = 0$ so that you get a set of numbers consistent with the $V[\ ]$ in which every $v_{ij}^k(n)$ is nonnegative. $v_{ij}^k(n) = \phi_n(i, k, j)$.

(c) If your (a) answer differs from (b), show that they satisfy (12.50).

11. For a Type II M.D.P., the probabilities *and* relative values in the nth stage depend (only) on the result of the $(n + 1)$st stage. For a Type I M.D.P., only the probabilities (and not the relative values) in the nth stage depend on the result of the $(n + 1)$st stage. Now define a Type III M.D.P. in which only the relative values (and not the probabilities—which are independent among the stages) in the nth stage depend on the result in the $(n + 1)$st stage. Structure your definition in the manner of definitions 12.7 and 12.9, and write the general dynamic programming model for a Type III M.D.P.

12. Find the optimal strategy for a 3-stage Type II M.D.P., where each variable (including Y_4) has two values (x_{n0} and x_{n1}, or y_{n0} and y_{n1}), when all relative values and transition probabilities are given as follows:

Values:

$v_{00}^0(3) = 0,$	$v_{00}^1(3) = 3,$	$v_{10}^0(3) = 12,$	$v_{10}^1(3) = 16,$
$v_{01}^0(3) = 0,$	$v_{01}^1(3) = 8,$	$v_{11}^0(3) = 20,$	$v_{11}^1(3) = 24,$
$v_{00}^0(2) = 0,$	$v_{00}^1(2) = 6,$		
$v_{01}^0(2) = 4,$	$v_{01}^1(2) = 14,$		
$v_{10}^0(2) = 2,$	$v_{10}^1(2) = 12,$		
$v_{11}^0(2) = 10,$	$v_{11}^1(2) = 30,$		
$v_{00}^0(1) = 0,$	$v_{00}^1(1) = 15,$	$v_{01}^0(1) = 78,$	$v_{01}^1(1) = 80,$
$v_{10}^0(1) = 0,$	$v_{10}^1(1) = 22,$	$v_{11}^0(1) = 96,$	$v_{11}^1(1) = 100.$

Corresponding probabilities:

$p_{00}^0(3) = .2,$	$p_{00}^1(3) = .8,$	$p_{10}^0(3) = .5,$	$p_{10}^1(3) = .5,$
$p_{01}^0(3) = .8,$	$p_{01}^1(3) = .2,$	$p_{11}^0(3) = .5,$	$p_{11}^1(3) = .5,$
$p_{00}^0(2) = .3,$	$p_{00}^1(2) = .5,$		
$p_{01}^0(2) = .7,$	$p_{01}^1(2) = .5,$		
$p_{10}^0(2) = .1,$	$p_{10}^1(2) = .4,$		
$p_{11}^0(2) = .9,$	$p_{11}^1(2) = .6,$		
$p_{00}^0(1) = .5,$	$p_{00}^1(1) = .6,$	$p_{01}^0(1) = .5,$	$p_{01}^1(1) = .4,$
$p_{10}^0(1) = .2,$	$p_{10}^1(1) = .4,$	$p_{11}^0(1) = .8,$	$p_{11}^1(1) = .6.$

13. (*Continuation.*) Show that the following relative values are equivalent to the values in Exercise 12. [*Hint:* Use definition 12.9(3′).]

Values:

$$v_{00}^0(3) = 10, \qquad v_{00}^1(3) = 13, \qquad v_{10}^0(3) = 22, \qquad v_{10}^1(3) = 26,$$
$$v_{01}^0(3) = 1000, \qquad v_{01}^1(3) = 1008, \qquad v_{11}^0(3) = 1020, \qquad v_{11}^1(3) = 1024,$$
$$v_{00}^0(2) = 40, \qquad v_{00}^1(2) = 46,$$
$$v_{01}^0(2) = -46, \qquad v_{01}^1(2) = -36,$$
$$v_{10}^0(2) = -948, \qquad v_{10}^1(2) = -938,$$
$$v_{11}^0(2) = -1030, \qquad v_{11}^1(2) = -1010,$$
$$v_{00}^0(1) = -50, \qquad v_{00}^1(1) = -35, \qquad v_{01}^0(1) = 28, \qquad v_{01}^1(1) = 30,$$
$$v_{10}^0(1) = 40, \qquad v_{10}^1(1) = 62, \qquad v_{11}^0(1) = 136, \qquad v_{11}^1(1) = 140.$$

14. (*Continuation.*) Verify numerically that the relative values given in Exercise 13, combined with the probabilities in Exercise 12, give the same optimal strategy as was obtained in Exercise 12.

REFERENCES

Bellman, R., *Dynamic Programming*, Princeton University Press, Princeton, New Jersey, 1957.

Churchman, C. W., R. L. Ackoff, and L. E. Arnoff, *Introduction to Operations Research*, John Wiley and Sons, New York, 1957.

Derman, C., "On Sequential Decisions and Markov Chains," *Management Science*, **9**, 16–24 (1962).

Feller, W., *An Introduction to Probability Theory and Its Applications*, Vol. 1, 2nd ed., John Wiley and Sons, New York, 1957.

Howard, R. A., *Dynamic Programming and Markov Processes*, The Technology Press and John Wiley and Sons, New York, 1960.

Rosenblatt, M., *Random Processes*, Oxford University Press, New York, 1962.

Sanders, J., *An Application of a Theory of Multilevel Systems to Optimization Problems*, Ph.D. Thesis, Case Institute of Technology, Cleveland, 1963.

Sasieni, M., A. Yaspan, and L. Friedman, *Operations Research—Methods and Problems*, John Wiley and Sons, New York, 1959.

AUTHOR INDEX

SUBJECT INDEX

443